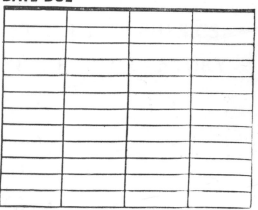

Berkeley Papers in History of Science

V

LITERATURE ON THE HISTORY OF PHYSICS IN THE 20TH CENTURY

J. L. Heilbron and Bruce R. Wheaton

with the assistance of

J. G. May, Robin Rider, and David Robinson

Office for History of Science and Technology
University of California, Berkeley

1981

The preparation of this volume was made possible in part by a grant from the Program for Research Tools and Reference Works of the National Endowment for the Humanities, an independent federal agency.

ISBN 0-918102-05-7

ISSN 0145-0379

Library of Congress catalog card no. 80-51580

Contents

Contents

Introduction

THE INTELLECTUAL and institutional growth of physics and the consequent transformation of science and society have influenced the character of our century. Historians and sociologists will be occupied in explaining the growth and the transformation for some time. To help them is a vast literature, composed mainly by physicists, which commemorates distinguished practitioners and celebrates the progress of the discipline. We have brought together both the historians' and the physicists' literature, subject to certain limits set out below. The resultant classified bibliography should assist those who wish to retrieve what has been done as well as those who seek topics that have not received due attention.

A glance will show that further work on Einstein or special relativity is not a high priority, whereas almost any branch of physics, save nuclear, that became prominent after 1930 needs and would repay thorough study. Our findings also make plain that too many papers are too often reprinted either verbatim or with trifling modifications. Another general trait of the literature that will surely depress the nonslavic reader is the quantity of work available only in Russian. Both in biography of physicists and history of scientific institutions, Russian scholars have outdistanced their Western colleagues.

We have other bibliographies in hand or in press to assist the student of the history of recent physics. *Literature* is one of three major publications of a survey of sources of 20th-century physics begun in 1976 with financial support from the National Endowment for the Humanities. The other publications are an *Inventory of published letters to and from physicists* and the massive *Inventory of sources for history of twentieth century physics*. The first of these lists letters to or from any of almost 6000 physicists active between 1895 and 1955 who published more than a few papers in the world's leading physics journals. (Criteria for admission and the list of 6000 are given in the *Inventory of sources*.) Almost every item recorded in *Literature* has been searched for letters; items we have been unable to examine are indicated by an asterisk before the author's name. *Literature* offers not only its classified lists but also the codes necessary to identify the sources of letters in the *Inventory of published letters*. In turn this *Inventory*, which gives each letter by correspondent and dateline, can serve as an index to *Literature*. The three bibliographies together make a research tool of unique range and power.

1. Scope

The core of the entries in *Literature* was gathered in a systematic search of, among others, the classified bibliographies in the journal *Isis*; the bibliographies to the articles on qualifying physicists in the *Dictionary of scientific biography* and in Poggendorff's *Handwörterbuch der exakten Naturwissenschaften*; the great Russian compendium, *Istoriya yestest-voznaniya: literatura, opublikovannaya i SSSR ot 1917 do 1961*; and other specialized lists mentioned below in section A.cb1. Additions were made from references in the works examined, book-sellers' lists, and antiquarian catalogs. A few journals have been searched systematically:

AHES, vols. 1-22 (1960-1980)
AIHS, nos. 50-104 (1960-1979)
AJP, vols. 1-47 (1933-1979)
Annals of science, vols. 16-36 (1960-1979)
Applied optics, vols. 1-19 (1962-1980)
Atlantide, vols. 1-7 (1963-1969)
BAS, vols. 1-35 (1945-1979)
BJHS, vols. 1-12 (1962-1979)
BJPS, vols. 1-30 (1950-1979)
BSPS, vols. 1-60 (1963-1980), save unpublished vols. (17, 30, 31, 40,
      41, 44, 45, 49)
Centaurus, vols. 1-23 (1950-1980)
Chymia, vols. 1-12 (1948-1967)
CP, vols. 1-20 (1959-1979)
Dialectica, vols. 1-34:1 (1947-1980)
Einheitswissenschaft, Hefte 1-7 (1933-1938)
Erkenntnis, vols. 1-13 (1930-1979)
History of science, vols. 1-17 (1962-1979)
HSPS, vols. 1-11 (1969-1981)
ICHS, *Actes*, Congresses 5, 7-15 (1947, 1953-1977)
IEUS, parts 1-20 (1938-1970)
Isis, vols. 36-70 (1945-1979)
JHI, nos. 1-40 (1940-1979)
JSHS, nos. 1-17 (1962-1978)
KHNT, vols. 9-22 (1964-1977)
Minerva, vols. 1-17 (1962-1979)
MSPS, vols. 1-9 (1956-1978)
NAS, *Biographical memoirs*, vols. 1-52 (1905-1980)
Natural philosopher, nos. 1-3 (1963-1964)
NTM, vols. 1-16 (1960-1979)
Organon, vols. 1-13 (1964-1977), save vol. 7
Osiris, vols. 1-15 (1936-1968)
PB, vols. 1-35 (1944-1979)

PE, vols. 1-14 (1966-1979)
Physis, vols. 1-21 (1959-1979)
PS, vols. 1-45 (1934-1978)
PT, vols. 1-32 (1948-1979)
PTeach, vols. 1-17 (1963-1979)
RHS, vols. 1-32 (1947-1979)
RS, *Notes and records*, vols. 1-34 (1938-1980)
RS, *Biographical memoirs*, vols. 1-26 (1955-1980)
RS, *Obituary notices*, vols. 1-9 (1932-1954)
RS, *Proceedings*, vols. 76A-132A (1905-1931)
Scientia, vols. 95-114 (1960-1979)
SHPS, vols. 1-10 (1970-1979)
SPU, vols. 1-21 (1958-1978)
SSS, vols. 1-9 (1971-1979)
Testi e contesti, nos. 1-4 (1979-1980)

Interpretation of abbreviated titles is given on page viii.

We have not thought it worth the space to include two large classes of literature frequently encountered in these sources: short obituary notices (four pages or less), which usually add little to the record, and Nobel lectures, which often have historical material. Obituaries can be retrieved from standard indexes, e.g., *The reader's guide to periodical literature,* the *Internationale Bibliographie der Zeitschriften-Literatur* and its predecessors, and from Poggendorff. The lectures can be found in the official annual of the Nobelstifting, *Les prix nobel*; in the reprints published in 1965 (A.pd1.no, np); and in such journals as *PB* and *Science.* To assist in locating obituaries and Nobel lectures, we give birth and death dates of all physicists listed separately in section B (Biography) and, where applicable, the date of their prize preceded by a dollar sign ($). The letter "C" following the year indicates that the prize was awarded in chemistry rather than physics.

Despite our ruthless policy toward short obituary notices, we have included in section B a genre often less informative: testimonials and tributes to physicists on a birthday or jubilee, or at an award ceremony. The rationale for inclusion is that these messages are not easily retrieved and represent an unusual and unexploited class of literature. But we have not tried to exhaust the class, which in the case of German and Russian physicists is extensive; a thorough search through general journals like *FF*, *Nwn*, and *UFN* would yield many items not noticed below. We have also systematically excluded the short, usually derivative, biographical sketches to be found in dictionaries of national biography and in most compendia of only honorific mention. A special sign (@) distinguishes physicists with entries in the *DSB*, which often contain information not easily available elsewhere. Only *DSB* articles that quote letters are listed explicitly.

Another excluded category is the general collections of *tezisy dokladov* (summaries of papers delivered at Soviet conferences). Titles may be retrieved from A.cb1.iv. We treat *avtoreferaty* (short summaries of dissertations) a little more generously; with perserverence many more than we cite might be located under the rubrics "Istoricheskiye nauki" and "Fiziko-matematicheskiye nauki" in the monthly supplement *Dopolnitsel'nyy vypusk* to the *Knizhnaya letopsis'*. Biographical and bibliographical information on Soviet and foreign scholars may also be extracted from the "zapiski ob uchenykh trudakh" in the AN. *Byulleten'*. We have made no effort to specify these entries.

To make section C (Institutions) manageable, we have omitted most university histories, many of which have slight accounts of physics departments or institutes. In the subject field categories (D-W) we have proceeded as follows. The sections devoted to the main fields of physics (D-O) are as complete as we could make them for the purer branches, that is, those furthest from practical application, chemistry, or the biological sciences. Coverage declines with purity. Review articles are not counted as historical literature unless they survey an unusually long span of time and treat at least some of the work historically. Chemistry (R) is limited to the most physical branches of physical, radio-, and electrochemistry; Nuclear Physics: Applications (I.t) excludes the nuclear-power industry beyond its earliest years and most literature on diplomacy and strategy. Physics and Society (U) is limited to historical sociology of physics and to biographies and letter collections of nonphysicists in which we have found correspondence with physicists. Writings on science and society, psychology, art, literature, etc., even by physicists, are excluded if their purpose is not historical analysis. Philosophy of Physics (W) has also been closely circumscribed: here choice was difficult because many philosophizing physicists find it convenient to begin with a little history. We have been more indulgent with the vast literature on the philosophical concerns of Albert Einstein and Ernst Mach.

We plan to provide control of some of the literature now excluded from U and W in our series of bibliographies of the nontechnical writings of distinguished physicists who acted as spokesmen for their science. Such bibliographies now exist for W. H. and W. L. Bragg (B.bs1.jh), M. Planck (B.pl1.ju), and E. Rutherford (B.ru1.jv). Representatives of other national scientific cultures will be subjects of later volumes.

We wish particularly to emphasize that admission to section B is reserved to persons active after 1895 and before the mid-1950s, and that material relevant to careers before 1895 is usually omitted. The earlier cutoff applies throughout the bibliography. The later cutoff, however, is peculiar to section B: elsewhere coverage comes as close to the present as sources permit. The literature has been searched systematically through 1979 and haphazardly through 1980. Pertinent 1981 imprints that have come to our attention are also included.

2. Codes

Each entry is identified by a six-character code of the form A.bc1.de. The capital letter gives the "category," e.g., biography, institutions, philosophy. The "classifier," two small letters and a number, specifies a person, an institution, a subfield of physics. The "accident," the two final lower case letters, is assigned so as to keep the classes in order, usually alphabetical by author. The breakdown will be plain from the table of contents for all sections except B. There the classifier designates a person whose last name begins with its first letter (e.g., B.bp1, Max Born); its second and third characters are assigned arbitrarily so as to maintain alphabetical order and to allow later additions. The first letter of the accident provides a rough subject breakdown:

- a. book length biography or autobiography
- b. general account of work
- c-d. short biographical study
- e. obituary (biography or memorial published within three years after death)
- g. testimonial, anniversary message, award presentation
- i. Festschrift
- j. bibliography, collected works, letters
- k. philosophy
- n. institutional connections
- p. pedagogy
- s. social concerns
- ι. international relations
- v. arts

The scheme has been altered slightly for Einstein and Mach to accommodate the very large literature. Einstein has six classifiers: biographical studies, B.ei1-2.; works, .ei3.; bibliography, correspondence, collected works, .ei5.; philosophy, .ei7.; miscellaneous, .ei9. Mach has two classifers: B.mb1., subdivided as a normal B entry; and .mb2., which refers to discussions of his work in physics and philosophy.

3. Cross-reference and indexing

In the B section compound names are filed under the final main part, usually that preceded by a clear space. The following representative names appear under the bold letter: d'Arsonval, de **Broglie**, **Des Coudres**, **Deslandres**, **Du**Mond, **É**hrenfest-Afanass'yeva, van't **Hoff**, Goeppert **Mayer**, Kamerlingh **Onnes**, Rausch von **Traubenberg**, Van **Vleck**. Honorific titles are disregarded: Lords Cherwell, Kelvin, and Rayleigh are found under their family names, Lindemann, Thomson, and Strutt. We follow general practice in filing umlauted letters under the unaccented letter as if followed by "e," and diverge from Library of Congress practice by filing Mc and Mac names as spelled. The use of computer data sorting in this and related publications dictates most of our conventions.

For consistency we have occasionally altered the spelling of the names of authors who published in several transliterated languges. We have used the English transliteration in all such cases. An example is B. M. Kedrov, spelled thus throughout our bibliography, whose articles in Polish are published under "Kiedrow."

The following rules of precedence are observed:

- Titles of the form "Pickwick and the quantum" go under L (quantum), with cross reference under B (Pickwick).

- Titles of the form "The Pickwick Club and the quantum" go under L (quantum), with cross reference under C (Pickwick Club).

- Titles of the form "Pickwick, the Pickwick Club, and the quantum" go under L (quantum), with cross references to B (Pickwick), and C (Pickwick Club).

- Titles of the form "Pickwick and Russian physics" go under B (Pickwick), usually without cross reference.

- Titles of the form "Fifty years of Russian physics" go under C (Soviet Union), no cross reference.

- Titles of the form "Fifty years of Russian acoustics" go under D.k (Mechanics: Acoustics), with cross reference under C (Soviet Union).

- Relevant articles in collections, as well as the collection itself, are usually cited separately in their proper places in the bibliography: "The Mudfog Association for the Advancement of Everything" in *A Festschrift for Charles Dickens* is listed in C, the *Festschrift* under B. When the collection contains only one pertinent article and both fall under the same classifier, only one entry is given.

- When more than one edition of a work is cited, the title given is either that of the original edition or that of the English edition. Brief bibliographic information about other editions, when known, appears in parentheses after the main entry. We made no systematic search for multiple editions.

- The main exception to the rule just given occurs for works containing letters. Each edition examined is given a separate code for unambiguous reference to the *Inventory of published letters*.

Since the internal structure of the bibliography and the cross-references serve as a subject index, the index of names at the end of the volume contains only authors and editors. Codes used in the cross-references and in the index may be abbreviated by omitting parts common to references in a sequence, e.g.: B.aa1.aa, B.aa1.bb, B.bb2.cc = B.aa1.aa, bb | bb2.cc.

4. Transliteration and diacriticals

We have transliterated from Cyrillic according to the scheme of the Library of Congress except for й (y), є and ё (ye is used initially, after vowels, and after short and hard signs; elsewhere it is e), ю (yu), and я (ya). These departures were dictated by the paucity of diacriticals in the phototypeset font available to us. For the same reason we render and alphabetize Polish 'Ł' without its slash, and Czech č without its cap. Style rather than ignorance has removed accents from uppercase French letters.

We have not sought but do report some work in languages that neither we nor many of our readers know. We do not include references to the pertinent literature in Japanese, but have tried to mitigate the loss by a systematic search of *JSPS*, which is published in Western language.

5. Acknowledgements

We are pleased to thank the National Endowment for the Humanities whose generous financial support made the creation of this bibliography possible. The compilation of sources and examination of most of them were the work of the staff of the Office for History of Science and Technology at the University of California, Berkeley. Our considerable demands on the inter-library loan facility at the University were always rewarded by prompt and courteous action. Most starred entries in the pages that follow are of books or periodicals not available in American libraries that subscribe to inter-facility loan.

Over the years we have employed the services of several research assistants in addition to those mentioned on the title page. We thank Rob Arasi, Dierk Groeneman, Alex Holzman, Henry Lowood, Rick Sonn, and Ken Uhlin. Judy Fox, John Brega, and Jacqueline Craig did the programming that produced the typeset copy. Ms. Craig also supervised the entry of bibliographic data by Karsten Benitz, Doug Fitzgerald, and Herb Quon, and arranged for final production of typeset copy. The editors set priorities for the search, established the organization of the material, ensured consistency and accuracy of bibliographic form, and did such library work as our collaborators left or allowed us.

No bibliography of this scope can be complete. We offer what we have in the hope that it will be useful enough to students of the development of modern physics that they will remove some of its failings by informing us of them. Later editions will incorporate corrections and amplifications sent to us.

J. L. Heilbron
Bruce R. Wheaton

Office for History of Science
and Technology
University of California, Berkeley

Symbols and abbreviations

* signifies an unexamined but bibliographically verified entry
$ signifies a Nobel laureate
@ signifies entry in *DSB*

AHES	*Archive for history of exact sciences.*	*ES*	*Eynshteynovskiy sbornik.*
AIHS	*Archives internationales d'histoire des sciences.*	*FF*	*Forschungen und Fortschritte.*
AJP	*American journal of physics.*	*HSPS*	*Historical studies in the physical sciences.*
AN	Akademiya Nauk S.S.S.R.	ICHS	International Congress of the History of Science.
APS	American Philosophical Society.	*IEUS*	*International encyclopedia of unified science.*
AS	Académie des Sciences, Paris.	IIYeT	AN. Institut Istorii Yestestvoznaniya i Tekhniki.
BAS	*Bulletin of the atomic scientists.*	*IMYeN*	*Istoriya i metodologiya yestestvennykh nauk.*
BJHS	*British journal for the history of science.*	*JCE*	*Journal of chemical education.*
BJPS	*British journal for the philosophy of science.*	*JHI*	*Journal for the history of ideas.*
BSPS	*Boston studies in philosophy of science.*	*JSHS*	*Japanese studies in the history of science.*
CSAC	Contemporary Scientific Archives Centre.	*KHNT*	*Kwartalnik historii nauki i techniki.*
CP	*Contemporary physics.*	*MSPS*	*Minnesota studies in the philosophy of science.*
DAI	*Dissertation abstracts international.*	*Mtly*	AN. *Materialy k bibliografii uchenykh SSR.*
DPG	Deutsche Physikalische Gesellschaft.	NAS	National Academy of Sciences, Washington, D.C.
DSB	*Dictionary of scientific biography.* 15 vols. NY, 1970-78.	*NR*	*Naturwissenschaftliche Rundschau.*

NTM	*Schriftenreihe für Geschichte der Naturwissenschaften, Technik und Medizin.*
Nwn	*Die Naturwissenschaften.*
NY	New York.
PE	*Physics education.*
PS	*Philosophy of science.*
PT	*Physics today.*
PTeach	*The physics teacher.*
PZ	*Physikalische Zeitschrift.*
RAS	Royal Astronomical Society.
RHS	*Revue d'histoire des sciences.*
RI	The Royal Institution of Great Britain.
RS	Royal Society of London.
SHPS	*Studies in history and philosophy of science.*
SIPS	Società Italiana per il Progresso delle Scienze.
SPU	*Soviet physics uspekhi.*
SSS	*Social studies of science.*
UFN	*Uspekhi fizicheskikh nauk.*
VIYeT	*Voprosy istorii yestestvoznaniya i tekhniki.*
ZGN	*Zeitschrift für die gesamte Naturwissenschaften.*
ZhETF	*Zhurnal eksperimental'noy i teoreticheskoy fiziki.*

A. GENERAL

Histories

aal.ab   Abbot, Charles G. *Adventures in the world of science.* Washington, D.C., 1958.

an   IIYeT. *Papers by Soviet scientists.* Moscow, 1977. (Distributed at ICHS, XIV (1977).)

be   Bernal, J. D. *Science in history.* NY, 1965.

bf   Bernstein, Jeremy. *A comprehensible world: On modern science and its origins.* NY, 1967.

cr   Crowther, J. G. *The progress of science. An account of recent fundamental researches in physics, chemistry and biology.* London, 1934.

da   Dampier, William Cecil. *A History of science and its relations with philosophy and religion.* Cambridge, 1971.

ha   Harré, Rom, ed. *Scientific thought 1900-1960. A selective survey.* Oxford, 1969.

ho   Holton, Gerald, ed. *The twentieth-century sciences: Studies in the biography of ideas.* NY, 1972.

ja   Jaffe, Bernard. *Outposts of science.* NY, 1935.

ne   Needham, Joseph, and Walter Pagel, eds. *Background to modern science.* Cambridge, 1938.

nf   Neyman, Jerzy, ed. *The heritage of Copernicus: Theories "more pleasing to the mind."* Cambridge, Mass., 1974.

pl   Pledge, H. T. *Science since 1500: A short history of mathematics, physics, chemistry, and biology.* NY, 1939.

pr   Price, Derek J. de Solla. *Science since Babylon.* New Haven, 1961; 2nd ed., revised, 1975.

st   Stuewer, Roger H., ed. *Historical perspectives of science.* Minneapolis, 1970. (*MSPS*, 5.)

ta   Taton, René, ed. *History of science, IV. Science in the twentieth century.* Tr. A. J. Pomerans. NY, 1966.

ur   Urbain, Georges, and Marcel Boll. *La science, ses progrés, ses applications.* 2 vols. Paris, 1933.

wi   Williams, Trevor I., ed. *A history of technology: The twentieth century.* 2 vols. NY, 1978.

See also: B.pd3.if

ab1.br Bromley, D. A., and V. W. Hughes, eds. *Facts of physics.* NY, 1970.

ca   Cajori, Florian. *A history of physics in its elementary branches including the evolution of physical laboratories.* NY, 1929.

cr   Crew, Henry. *The rise of modern physics.* Baltimore, 1935.

gr   Grigor'yan, A. T., and L. S. Polak, ed. *Ocherki razvitiya osnovnykh fizicheskikh idey.* Moscow, 1959.

hu   Hund, Friedrich. *Geschichte der physikalischen Begriffe.* Mannheim, 1972.

ku   Kuznetsov, B. G. *Puti fizicheskoy mysli.* Moscow, 1968.

la   Laue, Max von. *History of physics.* Tr. R. Oesper. NY, 1950. (German edn, 1946; French, 1953; Japanese, 1953; Russian, 1956.)

re   Reger, Karl, ed. *Meister der Physik.* Stuttgart, 1944.

sc   Scheel, Karl, ed. *Geschichte der Physik.* Berlin, 1926.

vo   *Voprosy istorii fiziko-matematicheskikh nauk.* Moscow, 1963.

wi   Wilson, William. *A hundred years of physics.* London, 1950.

ac1.ad Abro, A. d'. *The evolution of scientific thought from Newton to Einstein.* NY, 1950.

be   Bellone, Enrico. *I modelli e la concezione del mondo nella fisica moderna da Laplace a Bohr.* Milan, 1973.

el   Elkana, Yehuda. "The historical roots of modern physics." A.ad1.we, 199-265.

ha   Harrow, Benjamin. *From Newton to Einstein.* NY, 1920.

he   Heisenberg, Werner. "Zur Geschichte der physikalischen Naturerklärung." Akademie der Wissenschaften, Leipzig. Math.-Phys. Klasse. *Berichte, 85* (1933), 29-40.

ho   Holton, Gerald. *Thematic origins of scientific thought: Kepler to Einstein.* Cambridge, Mass., 1973.

je   Jeans, James. *The growth of physical science.* Cambridge, 1947.

ku   Kuznetsov, B. G. *Razvitiye fizicheskikh idey ot Galileya do Eynshteyna v svete sovremennoy nauki.* Moscow, 1963.

kv   Kuznetsov, B. G. *Razvitiye fizicheskikh idey ot Galileya do Eynshteyna v svete sovremennoy nauki.* Moscow, 1966.

la   *Laue, Max von. "Von Kopernikus bis Einstein." Göttingen. Max-Planck-Gesellschaft. *Jahrbuch,* 1956, 150-172.

sc   Schmidt, Egon. *Fra Arkimedes til Nils Bohr. Traek af fysikkens historie.* Copenhagen, 1968.

th   Thirring, Hans. "Der Weg der theoretischen Physik von Newton bis Schrödinger." *Acta physica austriaca, 14* (1961), 257-291.

un   Unsöld, Albrecht. "Die Evolution physikalischer Ideen seit der Renaissance." *NR, 30* (1977), 117-122.

wh   Whittaker, Edmund. *From Euclid to Eddington.* Cambridge, 1949.

ad1.ad Abro, A. d'. *The rise of the new physics. Its mathematical and physical theories.* 2 vols. NY, 1951.

bl   Blokhintsev, D. I. "Du developpement de la physique actuelle." *La nouvelle critique,* no. 113 (Feb. 1960), 64-70.

bo   Born, Max. "Physics in the last fifty years." *Nature, 168* (1951), 625-630. (Also in *Scientific American, 183* (Sep. 1950), 28-31.)

fe   Feather, Norman. "Twice thirty years of physics." *CP, 16* (1975), 489-497.

ga   Gamow, George. *Biography of physics.* NY, 1961.

he   *Heisenberg, Werner. "The development of concepts in physics of the 20th century." *Connaissance scientifique et philosophie.* Brussels, 1975. Pp. 161-174. (Académie Royale des Sciences, des Lettres, et des Beaux Arts, Brussels. *Publications du deuxième centennaire,* 4.)

hf   Hermann, Armin. *The new physics: The route into the atomic age.* Bonn, 1979.

hg   Herneck, Friedrich. *Bahnbrecher des Atomzeitalters. Grosse Naturforscher von Maxwell bis Heisenberg.* Berlin, 1970.

jo   Jordan, Pascual. "Physik im XX. Jahrhundert." A.aj1.ac, 15-37.

ju   Jungk, Robert. *Heller als tausend Sonnen.* Stuttgart, 1956.

jv   Jungk, Robert. *Brighter than a thousand suns.* Tr. James Cleugh. NY, 1958.

jw   Jungk, Robert. *Yarche tysyachi solnts: Povestvovaniye ob uchenykhatomnikakh.* Tr. V. N. Durnev. Moscow, 1961.

ku   Kuznetsov, B. G., ed. *Razvitiye sovremennoy fiziki.* Moscow, 1964.

me   Mehra, Jagdish, ed. *The physicist's conception of nature.* Dordrecht, 1973.

mf   Mendelssohn, Kurt. "Physical science in the twentieth century." *CP, 4* (1963), 422-434.

op   Oppenheimer, J. R. "The age of science 1900-1950." *Scientific American, 183* (Sep. 1950), 20-23.

ra   Rabi, Isidor Isaac. "Die Physik im 20. Jahrhundert." *PB, 7* (1951), 193-196.

sa   Satterly, John. "Reminiscences in physics from 1894 onwards." *AJP, 25* (1957), 288-300.

se   *Segrè, Emilio. "La fisica del secolo XX." Associazione Culturale Italiana. *Conferenze, 19* (1967), 1-19.

sf   Segrè, Emilio. *From X-rays to quarks. Modern physicists and their discoveries.* San Francisco, 1980. (Italian edn, Rome, 1976.)

un   University of California, Berkeley. *Symposium on the physical and earth sciences.* Berkeley, 1958.

we   Weiner, Charles, ed. *History of twentieth century physics.* NY, 1977. (Scuola Enrico Fermi. *Corso,* 57.)

wf   Weisskopf, Victor F. "Physics in the 20th century." *Science, 168* (1970), 923-930. (In German in *PB, 26* (1970), 64-72, 101-108.)

ae1.ca Cameron, Neil. "1900: The Cavendish physicists and the spirit of the age." B.ru1.ae, 124-139.

co   Colombo, Giuseppe. "Le scienze fisiche e le loro applicazioni nel cinquantennio 1865-1915." *Scientia, 19* (1916), 333-347.

fo   Forman, Paul, J. L. Heilbron, and Spencer Weart. "Physics *circa* 1900." *HSPS, 5* (1975), 1-185.

hi   Hirosige, Tetu, and Sigeko Nisio. "Rise and fall of various fields of physics at the turn of the century." *JSHS, 7* (1968), 93-113.

kl   Klein, Martin J. "Mechanical explanation at the end of the 19th century." *Centaurus, 17* (1972), 58-82.

os   Ostwald, Wilhelm. *Der energetische Imperativ.* Leipzig, 1912.

pi   Picard, Emile. *La science moderne et son état actuel.* Paris, 1914.

sc   Schuster, Arthur. *The progress of physics during 30 years, 1875-1908.* Cambridge, 1911.

ub   Ubbelohde, A. R. "Edwardian science and technology: Their interactions." *BJHS, 1* (1963), 217-226.

af1.ba Baracca, A., R. Livi, and S. Ruffo. "Ristrutturazione delle scienze tra le due guerre mondiali." U.aa1.fi, 271-277.

br   Broglie, Louis de. "Les progrès de la physique contemporaine." *Revue française de Prague, 14* (1935), 93-109.

ca   Carelli, Antonio. "La ricerca fisica nel primo trentennio del secolo XX." *Rivista di fisica, matematica, e scienze naturali, 3* (1932), 113-126.

cb   Casimir, H. B. G. "Als Demokrits Ideen Realität wurden: Die Entwicklung der Physik in den ersten Dezennien unseres Jahrhunderts." *PB, 35* (1979), 291-299.

de   Debye, Peter. "Physik." C.gal.hb, 46-56.

df   Dingler, Hugo. "Pascual Jordan, 'Die Physik des 20. Jahrhunderts'." *ZGN, 4* (1938/9), 389-393.

dg   Dingler, Hugo. "Die 'Physik des 20. Jahrhunderts'." *ZGN, 3* (1937/8), 321-335.

he   Heisenberg, Werner. "Wandlungen der Grundlagen der exakten Naturwissenschaft in jüngster Zeit." *Nwn, 22* (1934), 669-675.

io   Ioffe, A. F. "Novyye puti nauchnoy mysli v oblasti fiziki." *Nauchno-tekhnicheskiy vestnik, 1:3* (1921), 1-3.

jo   Jordan, Pascual. *Die Physik des 20. Jahrhunderts: Einführung in den Gedankeninhalt der modernen Physik.* Braunschweig, 1936. (English tr., NY, 1944.)

kh   Khvol'son, O. D. *Die Evolution des Geistes der Physik, 1873-1923.* Trans. V. R. Bursain. Brunswick, 1925.

ki   Khvol'son, O. D. *Die Physik 1914-1926.* Braunschweig, 1927.

la   *Langevin, Paul. *La physique depuis vingt ans.* Paris, 1923. (Russian tr., Leningrad, 1928.)

lo   Lodge, Oliver. *A century's progress in physics.* London, 1927.

mi   Millikan, Robert A. "The last fifteen years of physics." APS. *Proceedings, 65* (1926), 68-78. (Also in Smithonian Institution. *Annual report,* 1927, 191-199.)

pi   Picard, Emile. "Un coup d'oeil sur l'histoire des sciences et des théories physiques." *Revue scientifique, 68* (1930), 97-107, 129-139. (Also in AS. *Mémoires, 60* (1929).)

ru   Rutherford, Ernest. "Forty years of physics." A.aal.ne, 49-74. (Also in *Discovery, 1* (1938), 227-238; and in B.rul.jq, 479-492.)

st   Strutt, Robert John, Fourth Baron Rayleigh. "Some reminiscences of scientific workers of the past generation and their surroundings." Physical Society. *Proceedings, 48* (1936), 218-246.

te   Teillac, J. "From X-rays to neutrons." A.aal.ta, 203-213.

ag1.da   Darrow, Karl K. "The future of physics, past and present." *AJP, 12* (1944), 55-62

ho   Holton, Gerald. "On the recent past of physics." *AJP, 29* (1961), 805-810.

na   Nataf, Roger. "Après Einstein: Une science toujours en devenir." B.ei1.an, 161-204.

re   Rechenberg, Helmut. "Zur Physik der letzten 25 Jahre." *PB, 25* (1969), 481-487.

ro   Rollnik, Horst, et al. "Die physikalischen Fachbereiche in den vergangenen 25 Jahren." *PB, 34* (1978), 467-485.

se   Segrè, Emilio. "Physics in the last twenty years." *Science, 151* (1966), 1052-1055. (Also in *PB, 23* (1967), 62-68.)

sf   *Segrè, Emilio. *La fisica dell'ultimo trentennio.* Rome, 1977. (Accademia Nazionale dei Lincei. *Problemi attuali di scienza e cultura. Quaderni,* 228.)

ah1.bl   Bleuler, Konrad. "Die Entwicklung der theoretischen Physik in ihrer Beziehung zur mathematischen Forschung." *PB, 28* (1972), 145-152, 305-310.

ca   Caldirola, Piero. "I progressi della fisica teorica nell'ultimo cinquantennio." *Scientia, 92* (1957), 124-128.

di   Dingler, Hugo. "Zur Entstehung der sogenannten modernen theoretischen Physik." *Zeitschrift für die gesamte Naturwissenschaft, 4* (1938/9), 329-341.

dj   Dirac, P. A. M. "Methods in theoretical physics." A.aj1.fr, 21-28.

fi   Finzi, B. "I progresssi più significativi compiuti dalla fisica matematica negli ultimi cinquant'anni." *Scientia, 92* (1957), 88-94.

ku   Kuznetsov, B. G. "Geschichte der Physik und Geschichte der Mathematik." *NTM, 2:5* (1965), 17-23.

le   Levi-Città, Tullio. "Estensione ed evoluzione della fisica matematica (nell'ultimo ciquantennio, con speciale riguardo al contributo italiano.)" SIPS. *Atti, 5* (1912), 237-254. (Also in B.lk8.jl, *3*, 275-291; *Scientia, 11* (1912), 275-292.)

tu   Tuchkevich, V. M., ed. *Voprosy matematicheskoy fiziki.* Leningrad, 1976.

vi   Vizgin, V. P. "Stoletiye 'Erlangenskoy programmy' F. Kleyna." *VIYeT, 45* (1973), 34-38.

vj   Vizgin, V. P. "Vvedeniye 'Erlangenskoy programmy' v fiziku." ICHS, XIII (1971). Section 6, *Actes* (1974), 72-75.

vk   Vizgin, V. P. *"Erlangenskaya programma" i fizika.* Moscow, 1975.

vl   Vizgin, V. P. "Problemy vzaymosvyazi matematiki i fisiki." *Istoriko-matematicheskiye issledovaniya, 20* (1975), 28-50.

ai1.ch   Chalmers, T. W. *Historic researches.* London, 1949.

ra   Ramsauer, Carl. *Grundversuche der Physik in historischer Darstellung.* Berlin, 1953.

tq   Trigg, George L. *Crucial experiments in modern physics.* NY, 1971.

tr   Trigg, George L. *Landmark experiments in twentieth century physics.* NY, 1975.

aj1.bi   Birge, Raymond T. "Physics and physicists of the past fifty years." *PT, 9* (May 1956), 20-28.

br   Broglie, Louis de. *Savants et decouvertes.* Paris, 1951.

bu   Buckley, Paul, and F. David Peat, eds. *A question of physics: Conversations in physics and biology.* Toronto, 1979.

fp   Frenkel', V. Ya. "Wissenschaftliche Biographien." *Ideen des exakten Wissens,* 1971, 85-92.

fr   *From a life of physics.* n.p., [1968]. (International Atomic Energy Agency. *Bulletin,* Supplement.)

ho   Hoddeson, Lillian H. "The living history of physics and the human dimension of science." *PTeach, 12* (1974), 275 282.

io   Ioffe, A. F. *O fizike i fizikakh.* Leningrad, 1977.

ip   Ioffe, A. F. *Vstrechi s fizikami: Moi vospominaniya o zarubezhnykh fizikakh.* Moscow, 1960.

iq   Ioffe, A. F. *Begegnungen mit Physikern.* Tr. K. Werner. Leipzig, 1967.

ja   Jaffe, George. "Recollections of three great laboratories." *JCE, 29* (1952), 230-238.

jo   Jordan, Pascual. *Begegnungen: Albert Einstein, Karl Heim, Hermann Oberth, Wolfgang Pauli, Walter Heitler, Max Born, Werner Heisenberg, Max von Laue, Niels Bohr.* Oldenburg and Hamburg, 1971.

ko   Kovács, István. "Fizikusok fizikusokról." *Fizikai szemle, 26* (1976), 4-10.

li   Livanova, Anna. *Fiziki o fizikakh.* Moscow, 1968.

sc   Schwerte, Hans, and Wilhelm Spengler. *Forscher und Wissenschaftler im heutigen Europa, Weltall und Erde. Physiker, Chemiker, Erforscher des Weltalls, Erforscher der Erde, Mathematiker.* Oldenburg, 1955. (*Gestalter unserer Zeit,* 3.)

ak1.ba   Barr, E. Scott. "Anniversaries in 1957 of interest to physicists."
          AJP, 25 (1957), 370-379.

    bb   Barr, E. Scott. "Anniversaries in 1958 of interest to physicists."
          AJP, 26 (1958), 104-121.

    bc   Barr, E. Scott. "Anniversaries in 1959 of interest to physicists."
          AJP, 27 (1959), 209-233.

    bd   Barr, E. Scott. "Anniversaries in 1961 of interest to physicists."
          AJP, 29 (1961), 234-248.

    be   Barr, E. Scott. "Anniversaries in 1963 of interest to physicists."
          AJP, 31 (1963), 75-88.
    bf   Barr, E. Scott. "Anniversaries in 1971 of interest to physicists."
          AJP. 39 (1971). 859-867.
See also: K.fc1.cr

Characteristics

ba1.br   Broglie, Louis de. *Matter and light: The new physics.* Tr. W. H.
          Johnston. NY, 1939.

    bs   Broglie, Louis de. *Physics and microphysics.* Tr. Martin David-
          son. NY, 1955.

    bt   Broglie, Louis de. *Nouvelles perspectives en microphysique.* Paris,
          1956.

    bu   Broglie, Louis de. *New perspectives in physics. Where does physi-
          cal theory stand today?* Tr. A. J. Pomerans. NY, 1962.

    di   Dirac, P. A. M. "The evolution of the physicist's picture of na-
          ture." *Scientific American, 208* (May 1963), 45-53.

    dj   Dirac, P. A. M. "Development of the physicist's conception of
          nature." A.ad1.me, 1-14.

    ha   Haas, Arthur. *Das Naturbild der neuen Physik.* Berlin and
          Leipzig, 1920.

    he   Heisenberg, Werner. "Modern physics view of nature." *Science
          and culture, 31* (1965), 546-553.

    in   Ioffe, A. F. *Osnovnyye predstavleniya sovremennoy fiziki.* Len-
          ingrad and Moscow, 1949.

    jo   Jordan, Pascual. *Physik im Vordringen.* Braunschweig, 1949.

    jp   Jordan, Pascual. *Die weltanschauliche Bedeutung der modernen
          Physik.* Munich, 1971.

    jq   Jordan, Pascual. *Erkenntnis und Besinnung: Grenzbetrachtungen
          aus naturwissenschaftlichen Sicht.* Oldenburg, 1972.

    kl   Klein, Oskar. *Entretiens sur les idées fondamentales de la physique
          moderne.* Paris, 1938.

lo   Lodge, Oliver. *Atoms and rays: An introduction to modern views on atomic structure and radiation.* London, 1924.

mi   Millikan, Robert A. "Conceptions in physics changed in our generation." *Scientia, 41* (1927), 255-264.

pl   Planck, Max. *Das Weltbild der neuen Physik.* Leipzig, 1929.

pm   Planck, Max. *A survey of physical theory.* Tr. R. Jones and D. H. Williams. NY, 1960.

sc   Schmutzer, E. "Symmetrien in den physikalischen Naturgesetzen." *PB, 29* (1973), 213-219, 260-265.

we   Weizsäcker, C. F. von. *The world view of physics.* Chicago, 1952.

zi   Zimmer, Ernst. *Umsturz im Weltbild der Physik.* Munich, 1934.

bb1.bu   Buchwald, Eberhard. *Physik, Gleichung und Gleichnis. Vorträge und Aufsätze über Physik.* Mosbach in Baden, 1967.

fr   Frenkel', V. Ya. "Die Aufnahmebereitschaft für neue Ideen in der Physik." *Ideen des exakten Wissens,* 1969, 527-533.

ga   Gaston, Jerry. "Secretiveness and competition for priority of discovery in physics." *Minerva, 9* (1971), 472-492.

gu   Gutíerrez-Ríos, Enrique. "Factores personales en la génesis de la nueva física." *Atlantida, 6* (1968), 228-239.

ha   Haas, Arthur Erich. *Der Geist des Hellenentums in der modernen Physik.* Leipzig, 1914.

ho   Holton, Gerald. "The relevance of physics." *PT, 23* (Nov. 1970), 40-47.

hp   Holton, Gerald. *The scientific imagination: Case studies.* Cambridge, 1978.

kl   Kleinert, Andreas. "Vom Trieb zur theoretischen Physik." *PB, 34* (1978), 31-33.

kr   Kramers, H. A. "Physiker als Stilisten." *Nwn, 23* (1935), 297-301.

ku   Kuznetsov, B. G. "O stile fizicheskogo myshleniya XX veka." *ES,* 1967, 121-133.

sz   Szumilewicz, Irena. "Le problème de l'aliénation dans l'histoire de la physique." *Organon, 11* (1975), 79-96.

bc1.do   Dorfman, Ya. G. "L'evolution de la structure de la physique." *Organon, 5* (1968), 205-225.

ha   Hagenow, C. F. "Concerning the evolution of physics." *AJP, 8* (1940), 227-234.

hb   Halbwachs, Francis. "Structure de quelques révolutions scientifiques en physique." *Raison présente, 32* (1974), 85-101.

hs   Hsieh, Shih Hui. "Stages in the history of contemporary science and technology." *JSHS, 7* (1968), 115-128.

ku   Kudryavtsev, P. S. "Istoricheskoye razvitiye obshchikh tseley i zadach fiziki." AN. IIYeT. *Trudy, 34* (1960), 187-197.

kv   Kuhn, Thomas S. *The structure of scientific revolutions.* Chicago, 1970. (*IEUS,* 2:2.)

bg1.bl   Blüh, Otto. "L. W. Taylor's challenge to the teacher." *AJP, 17* (1949), 244-246.

gr   Gregory, J. M. "Physics teaching in the late 19th century: A case history." *PE, 8* (1973), 368-373.

ha   Halligey, P. "The evolution of MKS electrical units: Effects on the teaching of electricity." *CP, 7* (1966), 161-173.

hi   Higson, L. E. "Physics teaching in the early twentieth century." *PE, 3* (1968), 119-120.

ho   Höfler, Alois. "Zur physikalischen Didaktik und zur physikalischen Philosophie." *Zeitschrift für den physikalischen und chemischen Unterricht, 31* (1918), 1-9, 37-46.

ov   Overbeck, C. J. "Quarter century of progress in the college physics laboratory." *AJP, 25* (1957), 13-17.

pa   P[oske, F]. "Studien zur Didaktik des physikalischen Unterrichts." *Zeitschrift für den physikalischen und chemischen Unterricht, 31* (1918), 191-193.

pb   Parks, Kathleen E. "The teaching of physics in girls' schools." *PE, 3* (1968), 120-121.

ro   Rosen, Sidney. "A history of the physics laboratory in the American public high school (to 1910)." *AJP, 22* (1954), 194-204.

sc   Schofield, R., and D. Harding. "The teaching of physics over fifty years and more." *PE, 3* (1968), 115-119.

su   Sutton, Richard M. "The heritage of a physics teacher." *AJP, 21* (1953), 369-372.

th   Thomson, J. J. "The growth in opportunities for education and research in physics during the past fifty years." *Science, 74* (1931), 317-324.

we   Webster, D. L., and Frederic Palmer, Jr. "William Suddards Franklin, 1863-1930: First recipient of the Award for Notable Contributions to the Teaching of Physics." *AJP, 5* (1937), 31-34.

wi   Wilberforce, L. R. "The development of the teaching of physics." C.bc1.hi, 250-280.

wo   Woodall, A. J., and A. C. Hawkins. "Laboratory physics and its debt to G. F. C. Searle." *PE, 4* (1969), 283-285.

bh1.br   Brush, Stephen G. "The role of history in the teaching of physics." *PTeach, 7* (1969), 271-280.

hu   Hurwic, Jósef. "L'élément historique dans l'enseignement de la structure de la matière." ICHS, XI (1965). *Actes, 3* (1968), 309-311.

la   Langevin, Paul. *La valeur éducative de l'histoire des sciences.* Paris, 1960.

vo   * *Voprosy istorii fiziki i yeye prepodavaniya.* Tambov, 1961. (Tambov. Pedagogicheskiy institut. Sovetskoye natsionalnoye ob'yedineniye istorikov yestestvoznaniya i tekhniki. *Materialy Mezhvuzovskoy konferentsii po istorii fiziki.*)

wh   Whitaker, M. A. B. "History and quasi-history in physics education." *PE, 14* (1979), 108-112, 239-242.

bp1.ba   Barton, Henry A. "Twenty years of *Physics Today.*" *PT, 21* (May 1968), 66-71.

br   Brüche, Ernst. "Zur Rationalisierung im Zeitschriftenwesen." *PB, 7* (1951), 313-316.

mc   McCarthy, John J. "World trends in the publication of physical research, 1938-1948." *AJP, 19* (1951), 79-81.

Sources

ca1.ba   Barr, E. Scott. *An index to biographical fragments in unspecialized scientific journals.* University, Alabama, 1973.

cr   Crosland, Maurice P., ed. *The science of matter.* London, 1971.

do   Dorfman, Ya. G., and O. A. Lezhneva. "Istoriya fiziki." *VIYeT, 23* (1968), 32-36.

he   Hermann, Armin. *Lexicon, Geschichte der Physik A-Z. Biographien, Sachwörter, Originalschriften, und Sekundärliteratur.* Cologne, 1972.

hf   Hermann, Armin, ed. *Dokumente der Naturwissenschaft. Abteilung Physik.* 12 vols. Stuttgart, 1962-1969. (Volumes are separately catalogued.)

ka   Kapitsa, P. L. *Zhizn' nauki: Antologiya vstupleniy k klassike yestestvoznaniya.* Moscow, 1973.

me   Mezhrespublikanskoy konferentsii po istorii yestestvoznaniya i tekhniki v Pribaltike, VIII. *Mtly.* Ed. F. D. Klement, et al. Tartu, 1970.

mf   Mezhrespublikanskoy konferentsii po istorii yestestvoznaniya i tekhniki v Pribaltike, IX. *Mtly.* Ed. K. Aron, et al. Vilna, 1972.

ne   Newman, James R., ed. *The world of mathematics.* 4 vols. NY, 1956.

cb1.ba   Barr, E. Scott. "Biographical material in the first series of *The Physical Review."* *Isis, 58* (1967), 245-246.

bb   Barr, E. Scott. "Biographical material in the first one hundred volumes of *The Astrophysical Journal."* *Isis, 65* (1974), 513-515.

bi   Biermann, Kurt-R. "Attempt at a classification of unpublished sources in the more recent history of astronomy in German-speaking countries." *Vistas in astronomy, 9* (1967), 237-243.

br   Brush, Stephen G., ed. *Resources for the history of physics.* Hanover, New Hampshire, 1972.

bs   Brush, Stephen G. "Publications in the history of physics during 1973." *AJP, 43* (1975), 850-860.

he   Heilbron, J. L. "Quantum historiography and the Archive for History of Quantum Physics." *History of science, 7* (1968), 90-111.

hi   Higgins, Thomas James. "Book-length biographies of physicists and astronomers." *AJP, 12* (1944), 31-39.

iv   Ivanov, D. D., and N. A. Figurovskiy. *Istoriya yestestvoznaniya: Literatura, opublikovannaya v SSSR ot 1917 do 1961.* Moscow and Leningrad, 1949-1963.

kr   Kragh, Helge. *Bibliografisk vejledning til studiet af den moderne fysiks historie.* Roskilde, 1978. (Roskilde. Universitetscenter. IMFUFA. *Tekste,* 5.)

so   Sorkin, A. M. "Iz istorii bibliografii fiziko-matematicheskikh i yestestvennykh nauk v nachale XX v." *VIYeT, 11* (1961), 79-82.

cc1.an   AN. Arkhiv. *Avtografy uchenykh v Arkhiv Akademiy Nauk SSSR.* Leningrad, 1978.

he   Hermann, Armin. "Neue Quelle zur Quanten- und Relativitätstheorie." *PB, 23* (1967), 431-432.

kn   Körber, Hans-Günther. "Über die Korrespondenz des Chemikers Wilhelm Ostwald mit russischen und sowjetischen Gelehrten." *Deutschland-Sowjetunion.* Berlin, 1966.

ko Körber, Hans-Günther. "On the scientific correspondence of Wilhelm Ostwald with Polish scientists." ICHS, XI (1965). *Actes,* *4* (1968), 117-120.

kp Kolankowski, Z. "Pis'mennyye istochniki po istorii russkoy i sovetskoy nauki i tekhniki v Pol'she." *VIYeT, 38* (1972), 71-77.

kr Kolankowski, Zygmunt. "Twenty-five years of the operation of the archives of the Polish Academy of Sciences." Polska Akademia Nauk. *Review,* 1978:3, 65-71.

kt Krajewski, Wladyslaw. "Zasada korespondencji w fizyce a rozwój nauki." *KHNT, 18* (1973), 45-52.

ne Nevskaya, N. I. "Correspondence between astronomers." C.va4.an, 177-216.

st Streller, E. "Physikerbriefe in W. C. Röntgens Nachlass." *Röntgen-Blätter, 18* (1965), 220-235.

th Thiele, Joachim. "Aus der Korrespondenz Ernst Machs: Briefe deutscher und englischer Naturwissenschaftler." *NTM, 7:1* (1970), 66-75.

cd1.de Derzhavin, N., et al. "Fakty i dokumenty." *VIYeT, 51* (1975), 43.

go Gowing, Margaret. "The Contemporary Scientific Archives Centre." RS. *Notes and records, 34* (1979), 123-131.

he Hermann, Armin. "Sicherung von Physiker-Nachlässen." *PB, 29* (1973), 471-472.

ka Kallir, Rudolf F. *Autographensammler—Lebenslänglich.* Zurich, 1977.

vi Vinokurov, B. Z., et al. "Muzey istorii fiziki." *VIYeT, 45* (1973), 99-100.

ya Yasman, Z. D. "V Gosudarstvennom istoricheskom muzeye." *VIYeT, 38* (1972), 66-68.

ce1.fo Forman, Paul. "The Archive of Friedr. Vieweg & Sohn, Braunschweig: Correspondence of nineteenth-century physical scientists, especially German chemists." *Isis, 60* (1969), 384-386.

ga Gaysinskaya, L. I. "Dokumental'nyye materialy Obshchestva sodeystviya uspekham opytnykh nauki i ikh prakticheskikh primeniy." *Istoricheskiy arkhiv,* 1955:5, 194-195.

kn Knyazev, G. A., et al., ed. *Arkhiv Akademii Nauk SSSR: Obozreniye arkhivnykh materialov.* Leningrad, 1933, 1946, 1950, 1959, 1963. (AN. Arkhiv. *Trudy,* 1, 5, 9, 16, 19.)

ko Kolankowski, Zygmunt. *Przewodnik po zespotach i zbiorach archiwum P.A.N.* Warsaw, 1978.

ku Kuhn, Thomas S., J. L. Heilbron, Paul Forman, and Lini Allen. *Sources for history of quantum physics: An inventory and report.* Philadelphia, 1967. (American philosophical society. *Memoirs, 68.*)

le Levshin, B. V., et al. *Arkhiv AN SSSR: Obozreniye arkhivnykh materialov.* Vol. 6. Leningrad, 1971. (AN. Arkhiv. *Trudy,* 24.)

ni Nikulina, L. A., and N. F. Nikol'tseva. "V Leningradskom gosudarstvennom istoricheskom arkhive." *VIYeT, 38* (1972), 68-70.

nj Nikulina, L. A., and N. F. Nikol'tseva. "Materialy Leningradskogo gosudarstvennogo istoricheskogo arkhiva o russko-nemetskikh nauchnykh svyazyakh." *VIYeT, 43* (1973), 86-87.

sp Spalek, John M., et al. *Guide to the archival materials of the German-speaking emigration to the United States after 1933.* Charlottesville, Virginia, 1978.

vl Vladimirov, S. V., and V. A. Volkov. "Novyye arkhivnyye dokumenty ob akademikakh A. Ye. Arbuzove, V. I. Vernadskom, V. P. Vil'yamse, i drugikh uchenykh (1904-1911)." *VIYeT, 45* (1973), 62-69.

wa Warnow, Joan Nelson. *A Selection of manuscript collections at American repositories.* NY, 1969. (American Institute of Physics. Center for History of Physics. *Report,* 1.)

cf1.st Stargardt Antiquariat, Marburg. *Autographen, Katalog 591.* Marburg, 1969.

su Stargardt Antiquariat, Marburg. *Autographen, Katalog 593.* Marburg, 1970.

sv Stargardt Antiquariat, Marburg. *Autographen, Katalog 595.* Marburg, 1971.

sw Stargardt Antiquariat, Marburg. *Autographen, Katalog 599.* Marburg, 1972.

sx Stargardt Antiquariat, Marburg. *Autographen, Katalog 608.* Marburg, 1976.

sy Stargardt Antiquariat, Marburg. *Autographen, Katalog 612.* Marburg, 1977.

sz Stargardt Antiquariat, Marburg. *Autographen, Katalog 615.* Marburg, 1978.

ta Stargardt Antiquariat, Marburg. *Autographen, Katalog 617.* Marburg, 1979.

tb Stargardt Antiquariat, Marburg. *Autographen, Katalog 618.* Marburg, 1979.

Historiography

da1.ar   Arzamazov, V. P., et al. *Voprosy metodologii i istorii nauk.* Irkutsk, 1973.

do   Dorfman, Ya. G., and O. A. Lezhneva. "Istoriya fiziki." *VIYeT,* 23 (1968), 32-36.

gl   Glebov, L. A. "O metodike analiza fizicheskikh otkrytiy." *VI-YeT,* 22 (1967), 52-56.

ho   Holton, Gerald. "A new look at the historical analysis of modern physics." ICHS, XIII (1971). Plenary Sessions. *Actes* (1974), 88-144.

ke   Kedrov, B. M., and N. F. Ovchinnikov. *Problemy istorii i metodologii nauchnogo poznaniya.* Moscow, 1974.

ku   Kudryavtsev, P. S. "O vzaimootnoshenii fiziki i istorii fiziki." *VI-YeT, 33* (1971), 14-17.

ro   Rodnyy, N. I. *Ocherki po istorii i metodologii yestestvoznaniya.* Moscow, 1975.

un   Unsöld, Albrecht. "Physik und Historie." *PB, 15* (1959), 533-540.

db1.sp   Spasskiy, B. I., and L. V. Zarzhitskaya. "Nekotoryye rezul'taty kolichestvennogo analiza razvitiya fiziki." *VIYeT, 35* (1971), 40-43.

sq   Spasskiy, Boris I. "Zakonomernosti razvitiye fizicheskoy nauki." *IMYeN: Fizika, 12* (1972), 3-28.

su   Sullivan, Daniel, D. Hywell White, and Edward J. Barboni. "The state of a science: Indicators of the specialty of weak interactions." *SSS, 7* (1977), 167-200.

sv   Sullivan, Daniel, D. H. White, and E. J. Barboni. "Co-citation analysis of science: An evaluation." *SSS, 7* (1977), 223-240.

za   Zarzhitskaya, L. V., and B. I. Spasskiy. "Kolichestvennyye metody issledovaniya razvitiya otdel'nykh razdelov fiziki." *IMYeN: Fizika, 10* (1971), 10-14.

dc1.gr   Grigor'yan, A. T. "Z osiągnięć i zadań historii nauki i techniki w ZSRR." *KHNT, 9* (1964), 341-356.

gs   Grigor'yan, A. T. "O nekotorykh novykh problemakh i zadachakh istorii nauki: K itogam Sovetsko-amerikanskogo simpoziuma po istorii fiziko-matematicheskikh nauk i naukovedeniyu." *IMYeN: Fizika, 12* (1972), 197-202.

hi   Hirosige, Tetu. "Critical problems in the history of modern physics." ICHS, XIV (1974). *Proceedings, 1* (1974), 162-169.

ko   Kononkov, A. F. "K voprosu o razvitii sovetskoy istorii nauki." *IMYeN: Fizika, 12* (1972), 59-63.

ku   Kudryavtsev, P. S. "Razvitiye sovetskoy istorii fiziki." *VIYeT, 36* (1971), 31-37.

mc   McCormmach, Russell. "Commentary for the symposiun on critical problems in the history of modern physics." ICHS, XIV (1974). *Proceedings, 4* (1975), 223-231.

we   Weiner, Charles. "Prospects for research in the history of 20th century physics." ICHS, XII (1968). *Actes, 5* (1971), 111-115.

International meetings

ma1.bo   Bohr, Niels. "The Solvay meetings and the development of quantum physics." B.bo1.je, 79-100. (Also in *The quantum theory of fields.* NY, 1963. Pp. 13-36.)

bp   Bolle, Jacques. *Solvay: L'homme, la découverte, l'entreprise industrielle.* Brussels, 1968.

br   Broglie, Maurice de. *Les premiers congrès de physique Solvay.* Paris, 1951.

he   Héger, Paulo. *Vie d'Ernest Solvay.* Brussels, 1929.

hf   Hermann, Armin. "Das Jahr 1913 und der zweite Solvay-Kongress." *PB, 19* (1963), 453-462.

la   Langevin, André. "Paul Langevin et les congrès de physique Solvay." *La pensée,* no. 129 (Oct. 1966), 3-32; no. 130 (Dec. 1966), 89-104.

lb   Langevin, André. *Paul Lanvgevin et les congrès de physique Solvay.* Paris, [1966]. (Reprinted from A.ma1.la.)

lc   Langevin, André. "Pol' Lanzheven i sol'veyevskiye fizicheskiye kongressy." *VIYeT, 26* (1969), 3-26.

ld   Langevin, Paul, and Maurice de Broglie. "Obsuzhdeniye dokladov na sol'veyeskom kongresse 1911 g." *ES,* 1969-1970, 331-370.

me   Mehra, Jagdish. *The Solvay conferences on physics: Aspects of the development of physics since 1911.* Dordrecht, 1975.

pe   *Pelseneer, Jean. *Cinquantenaire des premiers conseils de physique Solvay, 1911-1961.* Brussels, 1961.

st   Starosel'skaya-Nikitina, O. A. "Iz istorii mezhdunarodnykh sol'veyevskikh fizicheskikh kongressov." IIYeT. *Trudy, 34* (1960), 9-63.

th   Thomson, J. J., et al. "Iz diskussii na sol'veyevskom kongresse 27-31 oktyabrya 1913 g. v Bryussele." *ES*, 1971, 323-348.

mb1.fr   Frenkel', Ya. I. "Mezhdunarodnyy fizicheskiy kongress v pamyat' A. Vol'ty v g. Komo." B.fr1.jf, 247-258.

mc1.ma   Marshak, Robert E. "The Rochester conferences: The rise of international cooperation in high energy physics." *BAS, 26* (Jun. 1970), 92-98. (Reprinted in U.gk5.le, 211-226.)

See also: T.ga1.go

Prizes

pa1.pa   Päsler, Max. "Orden pour le mérite für Wissenschaft und Künste (Friedensklasse)." *PB, 34* (1978), 536-539.

pb1.an   Anon. "Stalinskiye premii po fizike za 1947 g." *UFN, 36* (1948), 125-126.

ao   Anon. "Prisuzhdeniye Stalinskikh premiy za 1948 g." *UFN, 38* (1949), 128-132.

ap   Anon. *Laureaty Stalinskikh premiy za 1950 god.* Moscow, 1951.

ka   Kaftanov, S. V. *Laureaty Stalinskikh premiy: Novatory nauki i tekhniki.* Moscow, 1949.

sh   Shepel', V. V. "Laureaty Stalinskoy premii za 1949 god." *UFN, 41* (1950), 122-128.

va   Vasil'kov, I. *Stalinskiye premii v SSSR.* Moscow, 1947.

pc1.cu   Cuny, Hilaire. *Nobel de la dynamite et les prix Nobel.* Paris, 1970.

ha   *Hausen, Josef. *25 Nobel Preisträger.* Braunschweig, 1957.

iv   Ivezić, Stjepan. *Leksikon Nobelovaca, 1901-1964.* Pula, 1965.

ka   Kaplan, Flora. *Nobel prize winners; charts, indexes, sketches.* Chicago, 1939.

lu   Ludovici, Laurence J., ed. *Nobel prize winners.* London, 1957.

ma   *MacCallum, Thomas W., and Stephen Taylor. *The Nobel prize-winners and the Nobel Foundation, 1901-1937.* Zurich, 1938.

mo   Moulin, Léo. "The Nobel prizes for the sciences from 1901-1950. An essay in sociological analysis." *British journal of sociology, 6* (1955), 246-263.

no   Nobelstiftelsen, Stockholm. *Les prix Nobels.* Stockholm, 1904+.

np   Nobelstiftelsen, Stockholm. *Nobelprisen. 50 år.* Stockholm, 1950.

nq   Nobelstiftelsen, Stockholm. *Nobel: The man and his prizes.* Ed. W. Odelberg. NY, 1972. (Enlarged 3rd edn of A.pc1.sc.)

oh   Ohlmarks, Årke. *Nobel-pristågarna. En bokfilm.* Stockholm, 1969.

sc   Schück, H., et al. *Nobel, the man and his prizes.* Norman, Okl., 1950.

st   Stratton, F. J. M. "Nobel and his prizes." *Nature, 167* (1951), 422-425.

ve   Vészits, Ferencné. *A Nobel-díjasok Kislexikona.* Budapest, 1974.

wa   Walden, P. "Naturwissenschaften und Nobelstiftung." *PB, 5* (1949), 153-160.

zq   Zuckerman, Harriet. *Nobel laureates in the United States: A sociological study of scientific collaboration.* Ph.D. thesis. Columbia Univ., 1965. (*DAI, 28,* 4294A.)

zr   Zuckerman, Harriet. "The sociology of the Nobel prizes." *Scientific American, 217* (May 1967), 25-33.

zs   Zuckerman, Harriet. *Scientific elite: Nobel laureates in the United States.* NY, 1977.

pd1.an   Anon. "Der Nobelpreis für Physik, [1901-1950]." *PB, 7* (1951), 6-8, 71-75, 114-118, 170-174, 215-220, 265-269, 317-320, 362-365, 404-409, 460-464, 510-514, 559-562.

ba   Bagge, Erich. *Die Nobelpreisträger der Physik.* Munich, 1964.

er   Erckmann, Rudolf, ed. *Via regia: Nobelpreisträger auf dem Wege ins Atomzeitalter.* Munich, 1955.

fa   Farber, Eduard. *Nobel prize winners in chemistry 1901-1961.* London, 1963.

ha   Hartmann, Hans. "Die Physik-Nobelpreise als Spiegel der wissenschaftlichen Entwicklung im 20. Jahrhundert." *NR, 21* (1968), 245-251.

he   Heathcote, N. H. de V. *Nobel Prize winners in physics, 1901-1950.* NY, 1953.

hf   Hermann, Armin, ed. *German Nobel Prize winners.* Munich, 1968.

no   Nobelstiftelsen, Stockholm. *Physics [Nobel lectures].* 4 vols. Amsterdam, 1964-1972.

np   Nobelstiftelsen, Stockholm. *Chemistry [Nobel lectures].* 4 vols. Amsterdam, 1964-1972.

sc   Schneider, Erich. *Von Röntgen zu Einstein; von Planck zu Heisenberg: Nobelpreisträger der Physik und ihre Entdeckungen.* Berlin, 1953.

si   Siegbahn, Manne. "The physics prize." A.pc1.sc, 397-470. (Also in A.pc1.np, 123-185.)

we   Westgren, Arne. "The chemistry prize." A.pc1.sc, 317-396. (Also in A.pc1.np, 187-253.)

pe1.bo   Bolotovskiy, B. M. "Sovetskiye uchenyye: Laureaty Nobelevskoy premii po fizike 1958 goda." *UFN, 67* (1959), 163-169. (Also in P. A. Cherenkov et al., *Nobelevskiye lektsii.* Moscow, 1960. Pp. 64-74.)

bu   Buckel, Werner. "Supraleitung—Nobelpreise 1972 und 1973." *PB, 30* (1974), 204-214, 260-268.

dr   Dresden, Max. "The Nobel prizes in Physics, 1965." *PTeach, 4* (1966), 42-44.

ha   Haken, H. "Der Nobelpreis 1964 für den Maser." *PB, 21* (1965), 109-114.

io   Ioffe, A. F., et al. "Vydayushcheyesya nauchnoye otkrytiye." AN. *Vestnik,* 1958:12, 7-9.

kl   Klipping, G., and E. O. Schulz-DuBois. "Der Physik-Nobelpreis 1978." *PB, 35* (1979), 220-224.

kn   Knutsson, Folke. "Röntgen and the Nobel Prize: The discussion at the Royal Swedish Academy of Science in Stockholm in 1901." *Acta radiologica: Diagnosis, 15* (1974), 465-473.

re   Rechenberg, Helmut. "Nobelpreise für Physik und Chemie 1977." *PB, 33* (1977), 667-669.

ro   Rollnik, Horst. "Nobelpreis für Physik des Jahres 1979." *PB, 35* (1979), 666-669.

B. BIOGRAPHY

Abbe, Cleveland (1838-1916)

ab1.ch   Humphreys, W. J. "Cleveland Abbe." NAS. *BM, 8* (1919), 467-508.

Abbe, Ernst @ (1839-1905)

ab3.ag   Günther, Norbert. *Ernst Abbe, Schöpfer der Zeiss-Stiftung.* Stuttgart, 1951.

See also: C.gj2.br

Abraham, Henri (1868-1943)

ad1.cd   Paris. Ecole Normale. *Henri Abraham, commémoration du centenaire de sa naissance.* Paris, 1969.

Abraham, Max @ (1875-1922)

ae1.cd   Born, Max, and Max von Laue. "Max Abraham." *PZ, 24* (1923), 49-53. (Also in B.pb1.jb, *2*, 599-603.)

See also: E.ag1.go

Adam, Neil Kensington (1891-1973)

ae8.ec   Carrington, A., et al. "Neil Kensington Adam." RS. *BM, 20* (1974), 1-26.

Adams, Walter Sydney @ (1876-1956)

af1.eg   Joy, Alfred H. "Walter S. Adams." NAS. *BM, 31* (1958), 1-31.

    em   Stratton, F. J. M. "Walter Sydney Adams." RS. *BM, 2* (1956), 1-18.

Akulov, Nikolay Sergeyevich (1900-1976)

ag1.bd   Akulov, A. I. "Moya rabota u Lebedeva." IIYeT. *Trudy, 28* (1959), 121.

Alfvén, Hannes $70 (1908-   )

ah1.bf   Fünfer, E., and A. Schlüter. "Nobelpreis für Hannes Alfvén." *PB, 27* (1971), 266-267.

Alikhanov, Abram Isaakovich (1908-   )

ai1.cd   Anon. "Akademik Abram Isaakovich Alikhanov." *ZhETF, 27* (1954), 3-5.

Alikhanyan, Artemiy Isaakovich (1908-   )

ai3.gc   *"Artemiy Isaakovich Alikhanyan: K 50-letiyu so dnya rozhdeni-ya." AN Armyanskoy SSR. *Izvestiya,* ser. fiz.-mat. nauk, *11:4* (1958), 3-6.

Allen, Herbert Stanley (1873-1954)

ai5.ew   Wilson, William. "Herbert Stanley Allen." RS. *BM, 1* (1955), 5-9.

Allred, John C. (1926-   )

ai7.cb   Allred, John. "A scientific autobiography." *Adventures in experimental physics, 5* (1976), 72-73.

Alvarez, Luis W. $68 (1911-   )

aj1.cd   "Luis Alvarez: Nobelpreisträger für Physik 1968." *PB, 25* (1969), 175-177.

cg   Ashmore, A. "Luis W. Alvarez." *PE, 4* (1969), 88-89.

Amaldi, Edoardo (1908-   )

aj5.cd   Conversi, Marcello. "Foreword." B.aj5.id, xii-xiv.

gs   Segrè, Emilio. "To Edoardo Amaldi." B.aj5.id, xxi-xxii.

id   Conversi, Marcello, ed. *Evolution of particle physics. A volume dedicated to Edoardo Amaldi [on] his sixtieth birthday.* London, 1970.

jb   [Amaldi, Edoardo.] "List of papers." B.aj5.id, 335-342.

tp   Perrin, Francis. "Edoardo Amaldi et le CERN." B.aj5.id, xv-xviii.

Ambartsumyan, Viktor Amazaspovich (1908-   )

ak1.cd   Boyarchuk, A. A., et al. "Viktor Amazaspovich Ambartsumyan." *SPU, 21* (1978), 801-803.

jb   Ambartsumyan, V. A. *Nauchnyye trudy.* Ed. V V. Sobolev. 2 vols. Yerevan, 1960.

jm   *Viktor Amazaspovich Ambartsumyan.* Moscow, 1975. (*Mtly,* ser. fiz.-mat.)

See also: B.wf3.kl

Ames, Joseph Sweetman @ (1864-1943)

all.ac   Ames, J. S. "Recollections of a university professor." Rice Institute. *Pamphlets, 13* (1926), 209-225.

ed   Crew, Henry. "Joseph Sweetman Ames." NAS. *Biographical memoirs, 23* (1945), 181-201.

eg   Dorsay, N. Ernst. "Joseph Sweetman Ames: The man." *AJP, 12* (1944), 135-148.

Andrade, Edward Neville da Costa (1887-1971)

am1.ec Cottrell, Alan. "Edward Neville da Costa Andrade." RS. *BM, 18* (1972), 1-20.

See also: C.gh1.an

Andreyev, Nikolay Nikolayevich (1880-1970)

an1.ap Ostroumov, G. A., and G. N. Finashnaya, ed. *Nikolay Nikolayevich Andreyev.* Moscow, 1963. (*Mtly*, ser. fiziki, 14.)

gd   Anon. "N. N. Andreyev." *ZhETF, 29* (1955), 137-139. (Also in *Akusticheskiy zhurnal, 1* (1955), 195-199.)

gf   Chernov, L. A. "Nikolay Nikolayevich Andreyev." *UFN, 71* (1960), 525-528.

gh   Efrussi, [M.] "K semidesyatiletiyu so dnya rozhdeniya Nikolaya Nikolayevicha Andreyeva." *UFN, 44* (1951), 472-475.

jm   **Nikolay Nikolayevich Andreyev.* Moscow, 1963. (*Mtly*, ser. fiz.-mat.)

sb   Anon. "N. N. Andreyev—zasluzhenniy deyatel' nauki RSFSR." *Akusticheskiy zhurnal, 7* (1961), 109.

Andronov, Aleksandr Aleksandrovich @ (1901-1952)

ao1.bg Gorelik, G. S. "O nauchnykh rabotakh akademika A. A. Andronova." *Avtomatika i telemekhanika, 12* (1951), 195-200.

cb   *Anon. "Aleksandr Aleksandrovich Andronov." *Radiofizika,* 1961:3, 389-392.

ec   AN. *Pamyati Aleksandra Aleksandrovicha Andronova.* Moscow, 1955.

eg   Gorelik, G. S. "Pamyati A. A. Andronova." *UFN, 49* (1953), 449-468.

eh   Gorelik, G. S. "Zhizn' i trudy A. A. Andronova." B.ao1.ec, 3-19.

gc   Anon. "A. A. Andronov (K 60-letiyu so dnya rozhdeniya)." *Avtomatika i telemekhanika, 22* (1961), 1139-1142.

jd   Andronov, A. A. *Sobraniye trudov.* Ed. M. A. Leontovich et al. Moscow and Leningrad, 1956.

je   Anon. "Spisok rabot A. A. Andronova s annotatsiyami." B.ao1.ec, 33-44.

See also: D.td1.ay

Appell, Paul-Emile @ (1855-1930)

ap1.ab   Appell, Paul-Emile. *Souvenirs d'un Alsacien, 1858-1922.* Paris, 1923.

ed   Buhl, A. "Paul Appell." *L'enseignement mathématique, 30* (1931), 5-21; *33* (1934), 229-231.

eg   Poincaré, Raymond. "Paul Appell." Paris. University. *Annales, 5* (1930), 463-477.

gd   Buhl, A. "Le cinquantenaire scientifique de Paul Appell." *L'enseignement mathématique, 26* (1927), 5-11.

gs   Sarrailh, Jean, et al. "Centenaire de la naissance de Paul Appell." Paris. University. *Annales, 26:1* (1956), 13-31.

jl   Lebon, Ernest. *Biographie et bibliographie analytique des ecrits de Paul Appell.* Paris, 1910.

See also: B.lw3.js

Appleton, Edward Victor @ $47 (1892-1965)

ar1.ad   Clark, Ronald W. *Sir Edward Appleton*. Oxford, 1971.

er   Ratcliffe, J. A. "Edward Victor Appleton." RS. *BM, 12* (1966), 1-21.

jc   CSAC. *Sir Edward Appleton papers.* List in progress, 1981.

Arkad'yev, Vladimir Konstantovich @ (1884-1953)

as1.am   Miklashevskaya, Ye. I., et al., ed. *Vladimir Konstantinovich Arkad'yev.* Moscow and Leningrad, 1950. (*Mtly,* ser. fiziki, 5.)

bv   Vvedenskiy, B. A., and N. N. Malov. "O nauchnom znachenii rabot V. K. Arkad'yeva." B.as1.jc, 5-10.

cm   Malov, N. N. "Vladimir Konstantinovich Arkad'yev." *UFN, 62* (1954), 459-469.

ep   *Polivanov, K. M. "Vladimir Konstantinovich Arkad'yev." AN. *Izvestiya,* ser. fiz., 18 (1954), 307-311.

ge   Erastov, L. N. "Yubiley professora V. K. Arkad'yeva." Moscow. University. *Vestnik,* ser. fiz.-mat. i yestest. nauk, 1949:9, 185-186.

jc   Arkad'yev, V. K. *Izbrannye trudy.* Moscow, 1961.

pm   Miklashevskaya, Ye. I. "Kratkiy ocherk nauchnoy i pedagogi-
      cheskoy deyatel'nosti V. K. Arkad'yeva." B.as1.jc, 11-19.

Arrhenius, Svante @ $03C (1859-1927)

at1.ap   Reisenfeld, Ernst H. *Svante Arrhenius.* Leipzig, 1931.

  as   Solov'yev, Yu. I., and N. A. Figurovskiy. *Svante Arrenius, 1859-
        1959.* Moscow, 1959.

  cs   Solov'yev, Yu. I. "Neues Material über die wissenschaftlichen
        Beziehungen zwischen Svante Arrhenius und russischen
        Gelehrten." *NTM, 1:2* (1960/1), 104-118.

  ep   Reisenfeld, Ernst H. "Svante Arrhenius." Deutsche Chemische
        Gesellschaft. *Berichte, 63* (1930), 1-40.

  es   Sapozhnikov, A. P. "Svante Arrenius." *Mirovedeniye, 17* (1928),
        211-216.

  ew   Walker, J. "Arrhenius memorial lecture." Chemical Society.
        Journal, 131 (1928), 1380-1401.

  ex   W[alker], J. "Svante August Arrhenius." RS. *Proceedings, 119A*
        (1928), ix-xix.

  id   *Svante Arrhenius, till 100- årsminnet av hans födelse.* Uppsala,
        1959. (K. Svenska Vetenskapsakademien. *Årsbok,* 1959, bilaga.)

  jr   Solov'yev, Yu. I. "Pis'ma Svante Arreniusa P.I. Val'denu." *VI-
        YeT, 2* (1956), 259.

  js   Solov'yev, Yu. I. "Neopublikovannyye pis'ma S. Arreniusa, M.
        Leblana i G. Brediga V. A. Kistyakovskomu." IIYeT. *Trudy, 18*
        (1958), 412-417.

See also: B.ow1.ch

Arsonval, Arsène d' @ (1851-1940)

au1.ac   Chauvois, Louis. *D'Arsonval, 65 ans à travers la science.* Paris,
          1937.

  ag   *Chauvois, Louis. *D'Arsonval; une vie, une époque, 1851-1940.*
        Paris, [1941].

  bd   Blech, Gustavus M. "D'Arsonval's service to surgery." *Archives
        of physical therapy, 13* (1932), 775-779.

  ed   Belot, J. "D'Arsonval." *Journal de radiologie et d'électrologie, 24*
        (1941), 49-60.

  gb   Bourguidon, Georges. "Professor d'Arsonval." *Archives of physical
        therapy, 13* (1932), 717-726.

gd AS. "Cérémonie du centenaire de sa naissance." AS. *Notices et discours, 3* (1951), 286-307.

Artsimovich, Lev Andreyevich @ (1909-1973)

av1.gd Alikhanov, A. I. "Lev Andreyevich Artsimovich." *UFN, 67* (1959), 367-369.

gg Anon. "Akademik Lev Andreyevich Artsimovich." *ZhETF, 36* (1959), 649-651.

Astbury, William Thomas (1898-1971)

av7.eb Bernal, J. D. "William Thomas Astbury." RS. *BM, 9* (1963), 1-35.

Aston, Francis William @ $22 (1877-1945)

aw1.cg *Green, F. M. "The Chudleigh Mess." Great Britain. Royal Air Force. *News,* Jan. 1958, 4-7.

eh Hevesy, Georg von. "F. W. Aston." RS. *Obituary notices, 5* (1945-48), 635-651.

Austin, Louis Winslow @ (1867-1932)

See: E.tf1.ho

Ayrton, Hertha (1854-1923)

ax1.ap Sharp, Evelyn. *Hertha Ayrton.* London, 1926.

Ayrton, William Edward (1847-1908)

ax2.ep P[erry], J[ohn]. "William Edward Ayrton." RS. *Proceedings, 85A* (1911), i-viii.

Babcock, Harold Delos (1882-1968)

ba5.cb Bowen, Ira S. "Harold Delos Babcock." NAS. *BM, 45* (1974), 1-19.

Bachinskiy, Aleksey Iosifovich (1877-1944)

ba7.cp Putilov, K. A. "Aleksey Iosifovich Bachinskiy." B.ba7.jb, 5-16.

jb Bachinskiy, Aleksey I. *Izbrannyye trudy.* Moscow, 1960.

Bädecker, Karl (1877-1914)

See: O.bc1.ka

Bakh, Aleksey Nikolayevich (1857-1946)

See: P.ma1.or

Barkla, Charles Glover @ $17 (1877-1944)

bb1.cs   Stephenson, Reginald J. "The scientific career of Charles Glover Barkla." *AJP, 85* (1967), 140-152.

     eb   Allen, H. S. "Charles Glover Barkla (1877-1944)." RS. *Obituary notices, 5* (1947), 341-366.

See also: G.na1.wy, wz

Barnes, Howard Turner (1873-1950)

bb2.ef   Foster, J. S. "Howard Turner Barnes." RS. *Obituary notices, 8* (1952), 25-35.

Barshauskas, Kazimeras Matonich (1904-   )

bb4.em   *Martynaitis, M., ed. *Kazimeras Baršauskas.* Vil'nyus, 1969.

Barton, Edwin Henry (1858-1925)

bb5.ek   K., F. S. "Edwin Henry Barton." RS. *Proceedings, 111A* (1926), xl-xliii.

Barus, Carl @ (1856-1935)

bb7.el   Lindsay, R. Bruce. "Carl Barus." NAS. *BM, 22* (1943), 171-213.

Bateman, Harry @ (1882-1946)

bc1.ee   Erdelyi, Arthur. "Harry Bateman." RS. *Obituary notices, 5* (1948), 591-618.

     em   Murnaghan, F. D. "Harry Bateman." American Mathematical Society. *Bulletin, 54* (1948), 88-103.

     en   Murnaghan, F. D. "Harry Bateman." NAS. *BM, 25* (1949), 241-256.

See also: G.ba1.st

Bauer, Edmond @ (1880-1963)

bc4.ed   Letort, Maurice, et al. "Hommage à Edmond Bauer, 1880-1963." *Journal de chimie physique et de physico-chimie biologique, 61* (1964), 955-984.

Bauer, Louis Agricola @ (1865-1932)

bd1.bl   Littlehales, G. W. "Louis Agricola Bauer in the progress of science as exemplified by terrestrial magnetism." *Terrestrial magnetism and atmospheric electricity, 37* (1932), 209-211.

jh   Harradon, H. D. "Principal published papers of Louis A. Bauer." *Terrestrial magnetism and atmospheric electricity, 37* (1932), 220-224.

See also: P.ca1.ni, sv

Becker, Richard (1887-1955)

bd4.ek   Kersten, Martin. "Richard Becker." *PB, 34* (1978), 379-382.

Becquerel, Henri Antoine @ $03 (1852-1908)

be1.br   Ranc, Albert. *Henri Becquerel et la découverte de la radioactivité.* Paris, 1946.

ec   C[rookes], W[illiam]. "Antoine Henri Becquerel." RS. *Proceedings, 83A* (1909/10), xx-xxiii.

ed   Darboux, Gaston, et al. "Discours prononcés aux funérailles de M. Henri Becquerel." AS. *Comptes rendus, 147* (1908), 443-451.

See also: I.bb1.ba, bc

Becquerel, Jean (1878-1953)

be4.bb   Becquerel, Jean. *Notice sur les travaux scientifiques.* Paris, 1934.

eb   Broglie, Louis de. "Notice sur la vie et l'oeuvre de Jean Becquerel." AS. *Notices et discours, 5* (1963), 1-20.

Békésy, Georg von $ (1899-1972)

bf1.er   Ratliff, Floyd. "Georg von Békésy." NAS. *BM, 48* (1976), 25-49.

gk   Keidel, W. D. "Die Nobelpreisträger 1961: Georg von Békésy." *PB, 18* (1962), 57-60.

Belen'skiy, Semen Zakharovich (1916-1956)

bf4.cb   Anon. "Pamyati Semena Zakharovicha Belen'skogo." AN. Fizicheskiy Institut. *Trudy, 10* (1958), 3-4.

Belopol'skiy, Aristarkh Apollonovich @ (1854-1934)

bf5.bv   Vorob'yeva, Ye. Ya. "Nauchnyye svyazi A. A. Belopol'skogo s vydayushchimisya russkimi fizikami." *Istoriko-astronomicheskiye issledovaniya, 11* (1972), 287-302.

cm   Mel'nikov, O. A. "Aristarkh Apollonovich Belopol'skiy." B.bf5.jc, 7-58.

gp   *Pokrovskiy, K. D. "A. A. Belopol'skiy." *Astronomicheskiy kalendar*, 1928, 123-125.

jc   Belopol'skiy, A. A. *Astronomicheskiye trudy.* Moscow, 1954.

Benndorf, Hans (1870-1953)

bf7.gs   Székely, Angelika. "[Hans] Benndorf achtzig Jahre alt." *Acta physica austriaca, 4* (1950), 155-159.

Berkeley, Randal Thomas Mobray Rawdon (1865-1942)

bf9.eh   Hartley, Harold. "Randal Thomas Mowbray Rawdon Berkeley Earl of Berkeley." RS. *Obituary notices, 4* (1942), 167-182.

Berliner, Arnold (1862-1942)

bg1.el   Laue, Max von. "Arnold Berliner." *Nwn, 33* (1946), 257-258. (Also in B.lf6.jl, *3*, 198-199.)

ge   Einstein, Albert. "Zu Dr. Berliners siebzigsten Geburtstag." *Nwn, 20* (1933), 913.

gw   Windelband, Wolfgang. "Dem siebziger Arnold Berliner." *Nwn, 20* (1933), 914-915.

Bernal, John Desmond @ (1901-1971)

bg4.ch   Hodgkin, Dorothy M. C. "John Desmond Bernal." RS. *BM, 26* (1980), 17-84.

cr   Rozhanskiy, I. D. "Dzh.-D. Bernal." *UFN, 45* (1951), 169-194.

em   Mackay, A. "Dzhon Desmond Bernal." *VIYeT, 43* (1973), 21-34.

ty   Yevreynova, T. N. "Professor D. Bernal i yego lektsii v Moskovskom universitete." Moscow. University. *Vestnik: seriya biologii,* 1 (1957), 249-255.

See also: U.be1.go

Bethe, Hans Albrecht $67 (1906-   )

bh1.ab   Bernstein, Jeremy. *Hans Bethe: Prophet of energy.* NY, 1980.

cb   Bernstein, Jeremy. "Hans Bethe." *New Yorker, 55* (3 Dec. 1979), 50-107, (10 Dec. 1979), 52-108, (17 Dec. 1979), 48-99.

im   Marshak, Robert E., ed. *Perspectives in modern physics. Essays in honor of Hans A. Bethe.* NY, 1966.

sb   Bethe, Hans A. "Hans Bethe on science." *Center magazine, 1:3* (1968), 66-70.

Bhabha, Homi Jehangir @ (1909-1966)

bh4.ec   Cockcroft, John. "Homi Jehangir Bhabha." RI. *Proceedings, 41* (1967), 411-422.

em   Menon, N. G. K. "Homi Jehangir Bhabha." RI. *Proceedings, 41* (1967), 423-438.

ep   Penney, W. G. "Homi Jehangir Bhabha." RS. *BM, 13* (1967), 35-55.

See also: L.ed1.kr

Bialobrzeski, Czeslaw @ (1878-1953)

bi1.es   Scislowski, W. "Czeslaw Bialobrzeski." *Acta physica polonica, 13* (1954), 301-308.

Bijl, Hendrik Johannes van der (1887-1948)

bi3.es   Schonland, B. F. J. "Hendrik Johannes van der Bijl." RS. *Obituary notices, 7* (1950), 27-34.

Bitter, Francis (1902-1967)

bi4.ab   Bitter, Francis. *Magnets: The education of a physicist.* NY, 1959.

Bjerknes, Vilhelm Frimen Koren @ (1862-1951)

bj1.af   *Friedman, Robert Marc. *Vilhelm Bjerknes and the Bergen School of meteorology, 1918-1923: A study of the economic and military foundations for the transformation of atmospheric science.* Ph.D. thesis. Johns Hopkins Univ., 1979. (*DAI, 39*, 5684A.)

bf   Flohn, Hermann. "Vilhelm Bjerknes, die Wettervorhersage zur Wissenschaft erhoben." A.aj1.sc, 303-310.

cb   Bergeron, Tor, Olaf Devik, and Carl Ludvig Godske. "Vilhelm Bjerknes." *Geofysiske publikasjoner, geophysica norvegica, 24* (1962), 6-37.

cc   *Bergeron, Tor. "Vilhelm Bjerknes." Bergen. University. *Småskrifter*, no. 11 (1962), 7-30.

ed   Devik, Olaf. "Minnetale over Vilhelm Bjerknes." Norske Videnskaps-Akademi, Oslo. *Årbok*, 1951, 49-72.

eg   Gold, E. "Vilhelm Friman Koren Bjerknes." RS. *Obituary notices, 7* (1951), 303-317.

See also: P.fb1.ti

Bjerrum, Niels Janniksen @ (1879-1958)

bj4.ej   Jensen, Aksel T. "Niels Bjerrum." Danske Videnksabernes Sel-
           skab. *Oversigt,* 1958-59, 99-113.

Blackett, Patrick Maynard Stewart $48 (1897-1974)

bk1.eh   Hodgkin, Alan, Harrie Massey, et al. "Memorial meeting for
           Lord Blackett." RS. *Notes and records, 29* (1975), 135-162.

   el   Lovell, Bernard. "Patrick Maynard Stuart Blackett." RS. *BM, 21*
           (1975), 1-115. (Also separately published, London, 1976.)

   gp   Philipp, K. "P. M. S. Blackett, Nobelpreisträger 1948." *PB, 5*
           (1949), 28-30.

   jd   CSAC. *Lord Blackett papers at the Royal Society, London.* List
           63/1/79, 401 p.

Blaton, Jan (1907-1948)

bk4.er   Rubinowicz, Adalbert. "Jan Blaton." *Acta physica polonica, 10*
           (1950), 1-6.

Bleakney, Walker (1901-   )

bk7.cb   Bleakney, Walker, and Alfred Kastler. "Reminiscences from the
           youth of Walker Bleakney and Alfred Kastler." *AJP, 40* (1972),
           950-959.

Bloch, Felix $52 (1905-   )

See: O.da1.ro

Blondel, André Eugene @ (1863-1938)

bl4.cb   Broglie, Louis de. "La vie et l'oeuvre de André Blondel." AS.
           Memoires, 67 (1944), 29p.

Blondlot, Réné Prosper @ (1863-1938)

See: G.pa1.la

Bodenstein, Max @ (1871-1942)

bm1.el   Laue, Max von. "Gedächtnisrede auf Max Bodenstein." Akade-
           mie der Wissenschaften, Berlin. *Jahrbuch,* 1946-49, 127-138.

Bogolyubov, Nikolay Nikolayevich (1909-   )

bm4.cb   Anon. "Akademik Nikolay Nikolayevich Bogolyubov." *ZhETF,
           37* (1959), 333-335.

cm Mitropol'skiy, Yu. A., and S. V. Tyablikov. "Nikolay Nikolaye-vich Bogolyubov." *UFN, 69* (1959), 159-164. (Also in *SPU, 2* (1959), 765-770.)

cn Mitropol'skiy, Yu. A., and S. V. Tyablikov. *Biographical sketch of Nikolay Nikolayevich Bogolyubov.* Washington, D. C., 1960. (Translated from *Uspekhi matematicheskikh nauk, 14* (1959), 167-180.)

jm Mitropol'skiy, Yu. A., et al., ed. *Nikolay Nikolayevich Bogolyubov.* Moscow, 1959. (*Mtly,* ser. matematiki, 8.)

Boguslavskiy, Sergey Anatol'yevich (1883-1923)

bn1.cq Predvoditelev, A. S. "Sergey Anatol'yevich Boguslavskiy." C.vm1.pr, 180-184.

cs Semenchenko, V. K. "Sergey Anatol'yevich Boguslavskiy." B.bn1.jb, 9-17.

el Landsberg, G. S. "S. A. Boguslavskiy." *UFN, 4* (1924), 95-97.

jb Boguslavskiy, S. A. *Izbrannyye trudy po fizike.* Ed. V. K. Semen-chenko. Moscow, 1961.

Bohm, David Joseph (1917-   )

bn8.cc Bohm, David J. [Interview.] A.aj1.bu, 124-150.

Bohr, Niels Hendrik David @ $22 (1885-1962)

bo1.ad *Danin, Daniil S. *Nil's Bor.* Moscow, 1978.

ah Holst, Poul. *Niels Bohr, atomfysikkens organisator.* Copenhagen, 1972.

aj Klyaus, Ye. M., et al. *Nil's Bor.* Moscow, 1977.

ak Kuznetsov, B. G., ed. *Nils Bohr: Zhizn' i tvorchestvo, sbornik sta-tey.* Moscow, 1967.

am Moore, Ruth. *Niels Bohr: The man, his science, and the world they changed.* NY, 1966.

ar Rozental, Stefan, et al. *Niels Bohr: His life and work as seen by his friends and colleagues.* Amsterdam and NY, 1967.

aw Werner, Sven. *Niels Bohr, 1885-1955. En billedbiografi.* Copenhagen, 1955.

bd Dirac, P. A. M. "The versatility of Niels Bohr." B.bo1.ar, 306-309.

bk Klein, Oskar. "Om Niels Bohrs videnskabelige gerning." *Fysisk tidsskrift, 60* (1962), 3-25.

bm   Møller, Christian, and Mogens Pihl. "Review of Niels Bohr's
      research work." B.bo1.ar, 240-260.

br   Rozental, Stefan. "Niels Bohr at work." *Nuclear physics, 41*
      (1963), 13-16.

cb   Adler, David Jens. "Childhood and youth." B.bo1.ar, 11-37.

cc   Andersen, Mogens. "An impression." B.bo1.ar, 321-324.

cd   Andronikashvili, Elevter. "Tri dnya s Nil'som Borom." *Khimiya i
      zhizn'*, 1975:9, 22-30.

ce   Bohr, Hans. "My father." B.bo1.ar, 325-339.

cf   Bohr, Niels. "Selvbiografi." *Acta jutlandica, 28* (1956), 135-138.

cg   Courant, Richard. "Fifty years of friendship." B.bo1.ar, 301-305.

ch   Gamow, George. "Der junge Niels Bohr." *PB, 16* (1960),
      525-527.

cj   Grigor'yan, A. T. "Nils Bor." *VIYeT, 10* (1960), 193-194. (Also
      in *Fizika v shkole*, 1960:6, 28-29.)

ck   Kalckar, Jørgen. "Niels Bohr and his youngest disciples."
      B.bo1.ar, 227-239.

cl   Klein, Oskar. "Glimpses of Niels Bohr as scientist and thinker."
      B.bo1.ar, 74-93.

cn   Pais, Abraham. "Reminiscences from the post-war years."
      B.bo1.ar, 215-226.

co   Rosenfeld, Léon. "Nogle minder om Niels Bohr." *Fysisk tidsskrift,
      60* (1962), 65-75.

cp   Rosenfeld, Léon, and Erik Rüdinger. "The decisive years, 1911-
      1918." B.bo1.ar, 38-73.

cq   Rozental, Stefan. "Niels Bohr." *American Scandinavian review, 57*
      (1967-70), 352-360.

cr   Rozental, Stefan. "The forties and fifties." B.bo1.ar, 149-190.

cs   Scharff, William. "Memories of Tisvilde." B.bo1.ar, 315-320.

cv   Weizsäcker, Carl Friedrich von. "Niels Bohr, der Schöpfer des
      Atommodells." A.aj1.sc, 71-78.

cx   *Wheeler, John A. "Zum Andenken Niels Bohrs." *PB, 29*
      (1973), 531-534.

ec   Cockcroft, John. "Niels Henrik David Bohr." RS. *Biographical
      memoirs, 9* (1963), 37-53.

ee   Franck, James. "Niels Bohrs Persönlichkeit." *Nwn, 50* (1963),
      341-343.

eg   Jordan, Pascual. "Gedenken an Niels Bohr." *PB, 19* (1963), 60-63.

eh   Møller, Christian. "Niels Bohr." Danske Videnskabernes Selskab. *Oversigt,* 1962-63, 73-89.

ej   Nielsen, J. Rud, Felix Bloch, Aage Bohr, John A. Wheeler, Léon Rosenfeld, and V. F. Weisskopf. "Reminiscences." *PT, 16* (Oct. 1963), 21-64.

en   Oppenheimer, J. R. "Niels Henrik David Bohr." APS. *Yearbook,* 1963, 107-117.

ep   Peierls, R. E. "An appreciation of Niels Bohr." Physical Society of London. *Proceedings, 81* (1963), 793-799.

er   Rosenfeld, Léon. "Niels Bohr." *Nuclear Physics, 41* (1963), 1-12.

es   Rosenfeld, Léon. "Nil's Bor." *VIYeT, 17* (1964), 6-15.

et   Tamm, I. Ye., et al. "Pamyati Nil'sa Bora." *UFN, 80* (1963), 191-215, 251-254.

eu   Tamm, I. Ye. "Pamyati Nil'sa Bora." *VIYeT, 17* (1964), 3-5.

ev   Tamm, I. Ye. "Velikiy fizik dvadtsatogo veka." *Puti v neznayemoye, 5* (1965), 455-460.

ew   Thomson, George P. "Niels Bohr memorial lecture." Chemical Society. *Proceedings,* 1964, 351-354.

gh   Heisenberg, Werner. "Niels Bohr zum 50. Geburtstag." *Nwn, 23* (1935), 679.

gp   Pauli, Wolfgang. "Niels Bohr on his 60th birthday." *Review of modern physics, 17* (1945), 97-101. (Also in B.pd3.jb, 2, 1048-1052.)

gt   Rosenfeld, Léon. *Niels Bohr. An essay dedicated to him on the occasion of his sixtieth birthday.* Amsterdam, 1945. (Also in *BSPS, 21* (1979), 313-326.)

ih   Hansen, H. M., and K. G. Hansen, eds. *Festskrift til Nils Bohr.* Copenhagen, 1955.

ip   Pauli, Wolfgang, ed. *Niels Bohr and the development of physics.* NY, 1955. (Russian edn, Moscow, 1958.)

jb   Bohr, Niels. *Collected works.* Ed. Léon Rosenfeld, J. Rud Nielsen, and Erik Rüdinger. Amsterdam, 1972+.

jc   Bohr, Niels. *On the constitution of atoms and molecules.* Ed. Léon Rosenfeld. Copenhagen, 1963.

jd   Bohr, Niels. *Atomic theory and the description of nature.* Cambridge, 1934.

je   Bohr, Niels. *Essays 1958-1962 on atomic physics and human knowledge.* NY, 1963.

jf   Hoyer, Ulrich. "Work on volume II of the Bohr edition." ICHS, XIII (1971). *Actes, 6* (1974), 155-160.

jr   Ressia, Nicoletta. "Gli archivi Bohr a Copenhagen." *Scientia, 110* (1973), 251-258.

js   Schultz, Betty. "Niels Bohrs publikationer." *Fysisk tidsskrift, 60* (1962), 179-184.

kd   Danin, D. S. "Vozysheniye i odinochestvo. (Iz knigi o Nil'se Bore.)" *Puti v neznayemoye, 12* (1976), 300-352.

ke   Favrholdt, David. "Niels Bohr and Danish philosophy." *Danish yearbook of philosophy, 13* (1976), 206-220.

kf   Fok, Vladimir A. "Kritika vzglyadov Bora na kvantovuyu mekhaniku." *UFN, 45* (1951), 3-14.

kg   Fok, V. A. "Remarks on Bohr's article on his discussions with Einstein." *SPU, 1* (1958), 208-210.

kj   Klein, Oskar. "Blaise Pascal och Niels Bohr. Några reflexioner." *Lychnos,* 1942, 65-75.

kk   Koursanov, G. "Niels Bohr et la théorie de la connaissance." *Revue de synthèse, 93* (1972), 233-244.

kp   Petersen, Aage. "The philosophy of Niels Bohr." *BAS, 19* (Sep. 1963), 8-14.

kq   Petruccioli, Sandro. "Niels Bohr: gli atomi e la conoscenza: verso un nuovo modo di 'pensare' la realtà." *Scientia, 113* (1978), 1042-1052.

kr   Rosenfeld, Léon. "Niels Bohr's contribution to epistemology." *PT, 16* (Oct. 1963), 47-54. (Also in *BSPS, 21* (1979), 522-535; and in Danish in Danske Videnskabernes Selskab, *Oversigt,* 1962/63, 90-97.)

ks   Rosenfeld, Léon. "The epistemological conflict between Einstein and Bohr." *BSPS, 21* (1979), 517-521.

nb   Bjerge, T. "Professor Niels Bohr og den Danske Atomenergi-kommission." *Fysisk tidsskrift, 60* (1962), 173-178.

nk   Kampmann, Viggo. "Niels Bohr and the Danish atomic energy research establishment." B.bo1.ar, 281-289.

nn   Koch, Hans Henrik. "Science and administration." B.bo1.ar, 310-314.

np   Pedersen, Johannes. "Niels Bohr and the Royal Danish Academy of Sciences and Letters." B.bo1.ar, 266-280.

sp   Pihl, Mogens. "Niels Bohr and the Danish community." B.bo1.ar, 290-300.

tc   Alekseyev, I. S. "Deux exposés de Niels Bohr à Moscou." *La pensée,* no. 100 (1961), 18-23.

te   Anon. "Niels Bohr, symbol of international science." *PT, 25* (Sep. 1972), 30-31.

tf   Parkadze, V. D. "K vizitu N. Bora v SSSR." *VIYeT, 47-48* (1974), 133-134.

th   Trimble, R. F. "Niels Bohr's flight to Great Britian." *JCE, 54* (1977), 157-158.

tw   Weisskopf, Viktor F. "Niels Bohr and international scientific collaboration." B.bo1.ar, 261-265.

See also: B.cc1.ce |ei7.pb, pd; H.ce1.ch; I.db1.wg |dc1.wi |eb1.br; L.hd1.ta; L.i; U.kf1.sk; W.ce1.we

Boltwood, Bertram Borden @ (1870-1927)

bo3.ck   Kovarik, Alois F. "Bertram Borden Boltwood." NAS. *BM, 14* (1932), 67-96.

See also: B.ru1.jb; P.da1.ba

Boltzmann, Ludwig @ (1844-1906)

bo4.ab   Broda, Engelbert. *Ludwig Boltzmann; Mensch Physiker, Philosoph.* Vienna, 1955.

bk   Klein, Martin J. "The development of Boltzmann's statistical ideas." D.hf1.co, 53-106.

bl   Klein, Martin J. "Boltzmann, monocycles and mechanical explanation." *BSPS, 11* (1974), 155-175.

bs   Sommerfeld, Arnold. "Das Werk Boltzmanns." *Österreichische Chemiker-Zeitung, 47* (1944), 25-28.

cb   Broda, Engelbert. "Lyudvig Bol'tsman." *VIYeT, 4,* 47-54.

cc   Broda, Engelbert. "Philosophical biography of L. Boltzmann." D.hf1.co, 17-51.

cd   Bogolyubov, N. N., and Yu. U. Sanochkin. "Lyudvig Bol'tsman." *UFN, 61* (1957), 7-15.

cf   Flamm, Ludwig. "Pamyati Lyudviga Bol'tsmana." *UFN, 61* (1957), 3-5.

cg   Flamm, Ludwig. "Die Persönlichkeit Boltzmanns." *Österreichische Chemiker-Zeitung, 47* (1944), 28-30.

ch   Flamm, D. "Life and personality of Ludwig Boltzmann."
      D.hf1.co, 3-16.

cs   Thirring, Hans. "Ludwig Boltzmann in seiner Zeit." *NR, 10*
      (1957), 411-415.

ct   Thirring, Hans. "Ludwig Boltzmann." *Acta physica austriaca, 11*
      (1957), 1-10.

ee   Ehrenfest, Paul. "Ludwig Boltzmann." *Mathematisch-*
      Naturwissenschaftliche Blätter, no. 12 (1906), 1-5. (Also in
      B.ec1.je, 131-135.)

el   Lorentz, H. A. "Ludwig Boltzmann." DPG. *Verhandlungen, 9*
      (1907), 206-238.

ev   Voigt, Woldemar. "Ludwig Boltzmann." Gesellschaft der Wissen-
      schaften, Göttingen. *Nachrichten: Geschäftliche Mitteilungen,*
      1907, 69-82.

gd   Davydov, B. I. "Velikiy fizik: K 50-letiyu so dnya smerti Lyud-
      viga Bol'tsman." *UFN, 61* (1957), 17-22.

gf   Flamm, Ludwig. "Zum 50. Todestag von Ludwig Boltzmann."
      PB, 12 (1956), 408-411.

gl   Laue, Max von. "Zu Ludwig Boltzmanns 100. Geburtstage." *FF,*
      20 (1944), 46-47. (Also in B.lf6.jl, *3,* 187-188.)

kc   *Curd, Martin Vincent. *Ludwig Boltzmann's philosophy of science:*
      Theories, pictures and analogies. Ph.D. thesis. Univ. of Pittsburgh,
      1978. (*DAI, 39,* 1793A.)

kf   Elkana, Yehuda. "Boltzmann's scientific research program and
      its alternatives." W.aa1.el, 243-279.

See also: B.mb1.ke; D.ha1.du; H.ab1.jp; L.bd1.ba, be

Bon, Gustav Le (1841-1931)

See: G.pa1.nx

Bonner, Tom Wilkerson (1910-1961)

bo6.eh   Houston, W. V. "Tom Wilkerson Bonner." NAS. *BM, 38*
         (1965), 17-32.

Boot, Henry Albert Howard (1917-   )

bo7.jc   CSAC. *Henry A. H. Boot papers at the National Archive for Elec-*
         trical Science and Technology, London. List 68/6/79. 21 p.

Borgmann, Ivan Ivanovich (1849-1914)

bo9.cg Goloushkin, V. N. "Ivan Ivanovich Borgman." *UFN, 44* (1951), 255-263.

ck Krylov, A. N. "Pamyati Ivana Ivanovicha Borgmana." B.kt1.al, 448-452.

See also: B.rb7.jr

Born, Max $54 (1882-1970)

bp1.ab Born, Max. *Physik im Wandel meiner Zeit.* Braunschweig, 1957.

ac Born, Max. *My life and views.* NY, 1968.

ad Born, Max. *Physics in my generation.* NY, 1969. (Russian ed., Moscow, 1963.)

af Born, Hedwig, and Max Born. *Der Luxus des Gewissens: Erlebnisse und Einsichten im Atomzeitalter.* Ed. Armin Hermann. Munich, 1969.

ag Born, Max. *Mein Leben. Die Erinnerungen des Nobelpreisträgers.* Munich, 1975.

ah Born, Max. *My life. Recollections of a Nobel Laureate.* NY, 1978.

am Hermann, Armin. "Max Born, eine Biographie." Max Born. *Zur statistischen Deutung der Quantentheorie.* Stuttgart, 1962. Pp. 1-33. (Dokumente der Naturwissenschaft, Abteilung Physik, 1.)

bb Born, Max. "Über meine Arbeiten." B.bp1.jb, *1*, xiii-xxiv.

bf Frenkel', V. Ya. "Max Born." *Ideen des exakten Wissens,* 1972, 289-298.

bk Konno, Hiroyuki. "The historical roots of Born's probabilistic interpretation." *JSHS, 17* (1978), 129-145.

cb Born, Max. "Recollections." *BAS, 21* (Sep. 1965), 3-6, 9-13; *21* (Nov. 1965), 3-6.

ce Born, Max. "Erinnerungen und Gedanken eines Physikers." *Universitas, 23* (1968), 249-276.

cf Born, Max. "Aus 'Erinnerungen und Gedanken.'" *PB, 25* (1969), 289-295.

cg Born, Max. "Astronomical recollections." *Vistas in astronomy, 1* (1955), 41-44.

ch Hermann, Armin. "Max Born—Eine Biographie." L.ia1.bp, 1-33.

ck Koch, Erwin Erasmus. "Max Born zur Gegenwart: Aus einem Interview." *PB, 18* (1962), 484-487.

eh   Heisenberg, Werner. "Max Born zum Gedächtnis." *PB, 26* (1970), 49-54.

ek   Kemmer, N., and R. Schlapp. "Max Born." RS. *BM, 17* (1971), 17-52.

em   Matthew, J. A. D. "Max Born, 1882-1970." *PE, 13* (1978), 251-259.

gb   Franck, James. "Ein Geburtstagsgruss an Max Born." *PB, 18* (1962), 541-544.

ge   Fues, E. "Zum 80. Geburtstag von Max Born." *PB, 18* (1962), 545-551.

gh   Brüche, Ernst, and G. R. Schultze. "Max Born aus anderer Sicht: Eine Zusammenstellung zum 85sten Geburtstag." *PB, 23* (1967), 562-565.

gk   Grigor'yan, A. T., and P. S. Kudryavtsev. "Maks Born: K 90-letiyu so dnya rozhdeniya." *VIYeT, 15* (1963), 141-145.

is   *Scientific papers presented to Max Born.* NY, 1953.

jb   Born, Max. *Ausgewählte Abhandlungen.* 2 vols. Göttingen, 1963.

jh   Hockmann, G. "Max Borns öffentliches Wirken." *PB, 26* (1970), 55-57.

jk   Born, Max, and Albert Einstein. *The Born-Einstein letters.* Tr. Irene Born. NY, 1971. (German edn, Munich, 1969. B.ei6.eb.)

jm   Frenkel', V. Ya. "Maks Born: K perepiske s Eynshteynom." *ES,* 1969-1970, 55-66.

jo   **Politekhnik,* 3 Sep. 1945. [Letter of M. Born to Ya. I. Frenkel.]

kp   Puligandla, R. "Max Born and the problem of objectivity." *Scientia, 109* (1974), 499-508.

ks   Suvorov, S. G. "The epistemology of Max Born and of dialectical materialism." *SPU, 19* (1976), 317-336.

kv   Vogel, Heinrich. *Physik und Philosophie bei Max Born.* Berlin, 1968.

See also: B.ei6.eb, ed |ib1.bo, |kd1.ck; W.ad1.su

Borodovskiy, Vasily Andreyevich (1878-1914)

bp4.cf   Yakobson, L. I. "V.A. Borodovskiy i L. S. Kolovrat-Chervinskiy." *UFN, 47* (1952), 115-118.

cm   Zaytseva, L. L. "Novyye materialy o zhizni i nauchnoy deyatel'nosti V. A. Borodovskogo." *VIYeT, 4* (1960), 93-100.

ec   *Chugayev, L. A. "Vasiliy Andreyevich Borodovskiy." Leningrad. University. *Otchet o sostoyanii i deyatel'nosti Petrogradskogo universiteta za 1914 g.*

See also: I.ac1.za

Bose, Jagdish Chandra @ (1858-1937)

bq1.ag   Geddes, Patrick. *An Indian pioneer of science: The life and work of Sir Jagadis C. Bose.* London, 1920.

bl   Lebedinskiy, A. V. "Dzhegdish Chandra Bos kak biofizik." *VIYeT, 8* (1959), 18-25.

bv   Vvedenskiy, B. A. "Dzhegdish Chandra Bos i yego issledovaniya v oblasti fiziki." *VIYeT, 8* (1959), 6-17.

cl   Lezhneva, O. A. "Dzhagadis Chandra Boze." *UFN, 67* (1959), 171-176.

es   Saha, M. N. "Jagadis C. Bose." RS. *Obituary notices, 3* (1940), 2-12.

gm   Mitra, S. K. "Birth centenary of Sir Jagadish Chandra Bose, F.R.S." British Institution of Radio Engineers. *Journal, 18* (1958), 661.

gt   Topchiyev, A. V., et al. "K 100-letiyu so dnya rozhdeniya Dz. Ch. Bosa." *VIYeT, 8* (1959), 3-32.

jb   Bose, J. C. *Collected physical papers.* Bombay and London, 1927.

sn   Nandy, Ashis. "Defiance and conformity in science: The identity of Jagadis Chandra Bose." *SSS, 2:1* (1972), 31-85.

See also: E.tg1.bo

Bose, Satyendra Nath @ (1894-1974)

bq4.ab   Brown, Melvyn. *Satyen Bose: A life.* Calcutta, 1974.

ac   Chatterjee, Santimay, and Enakshi Chatterjee. *Satyendra Nath Bose.* New Delhi, 1976.

cb   Blanpied, William A. "Satyendranath Bose: Co-founder of quantum statistics." *AJP, 40* (1972), 1212-1220.

cm   Majumdar, R. C. "Introduction." B.bq4.im, vii-xxiii.

em   Mehra, Jagdish. "Satyendra Nath Bose." RS. *BM, 21* (1975), 117-154.

im   Majumdar, R. C., ed. *Bosons: Presented to Satyendra Nath Bose on the occasion of his seventieth birthday.* Dehli, 1964.

See also: L.fe1.th

Bothe, Walter Wilhelm Georg @ $54 (1891-1957)

br1.ef   Fleischmann, Rudolf. "Walter Bothe und sein Beitrag zur Atomkernforschung." *Nwn, 44* (1957), 457-460.

Bowden, Frank Philip (1903-1968)

br3.et   Tabor, D. "Frank Philip Bowden." RS. *BM, 15* (1969), 1-38.

Boys, Charles Vernon @ (1855-1944)

br4.al   *Lintern, John. *The life and work of C. V. Boys.* M.A. thesis. Univ. of Exeter, 1973.

bs   Satterly, John. "C. V. Boys' rainbow cup and experiments with thin films." *AJP, 19* (1951), 448-451.

es   Strutt, Robert John, Fourth Baron Rayleigh. "Charles Vernon Boys." RS. *Obituary notices, 4* (1944), 771-788.

Boys, Samuel Francis (1911-1972)

br6.ec   Coulson, C. A. "Samuel Francis Boys." RS. *BM, 19* (1973), 95-115.

Bradley, James Albert (1899-1972)

br8.el   Lipson, H. "James Albert Bradley." RS. *BM, 19* (1973), 117-128.

Bragg, William Henry @ $15 (1862-1942)

bs1.ac   Caroe, G. N. *William Henry Bragg, 1862-1942, man and scientist.* Cambridge, 1978.

ag   Grant, Kerr. *The life and work of Sir William Bragg.* Brisbane, 1952.

cb   Bragg, W. L. "William Henry Bragg." *The new scientist, 7* (1960), 718-720.

cc   Bragg, William Lawrence, and G. N. Caroe. "Sir William Bragg." RS. *Notes and records, 17* (1962), 169-182.

ch   Jenkin, John G. "William Bragg and lacrosse in Adelaide, 1885-1895." *The Australian physicist, 17* (Jun. 1980), 75-78.

ci   Jenkin, John G. "William Bragg in Adelaide: Tennis too!" *The Australian physicist, 18* (May 1981), 69-70.

ck   Khastgir, S. R. "Birth centenary series, 11. William Henry Bragg." *Science and culture, 28* (1962), 460-462.

ct   Tomlin, S. G. "Wm. Henry Bragg." *The Australian physicist, 1* (May 1976), 76-80; *2* (Jun. 1976), 97-99.

eb   Andrade, E. N. da C. "William Henry Bragg." RS. *Biographical notices, 4* (1943), 277-300.

ec   Andrade, E. N. da C., et al. "Sir William Bragg." *Nature, 149* (1942), 346-351.

es   *Siegbahn, Manne. "William Henry Bragg." *Kosmos, 20* (1942), 5-15.

jh   University of California, Berkeley. Office for History of Science and Technology. *William Henry Bragg and William Lawrence Bragg. A bibliography of their non-technical writings.* Berkeley, 1978.

jk   Bragg, W. L., and G. N. Caroe. "Sir William Bragg's manuscripts and papers and some memories of the Royal Institution in his time." RI. *Proceedings, 40* (1964), 203-206.

See also: B.bs4; G.qa1.su; O.fb1.ev

Bragg, William Lawrence @ $15 (1890-1971)

bs4.cb   Bragg, William Lawrence. "Reminiscences of fifty years research." RI. *Proceedings, 41* (1966), 92-100.

cd   Bragg, W. L. "Reminiscences of fifty years of research." Franklin Institute. *Journal, 284* (1967), 211-228.

ep   Phillips, David. "William Lawrence Bragg." RS. *BM, 25* (1979), 75-143.

See also: B.bs1

Branly, Edouard (1844-1940)

bt1.ap   Pelletier, Gabriel, and Jean Quinet. *Edouard Branly.* Paris, 1962.

eb   Broglie, Maurice de. "Discours...du centenaire de la naissance de Edouard Branly." AS. *Notices et discours, 2* (1944), 392-400.

Brattain, Walther Houser $56 (1902-)

bt3.cc   Brattain, Walter. "A scientific autobiography." *Adventures in experimental physics, 5* (1976), 29-31.

Braun, Charles-Ferdinand $09 (1850-1918)

bt5.ak   Kurylo, Friedrich, and Charles Süsskind. *Ferdinand Braun. A life of the Nobel prizewinner and inventor of the cathode ray oscilloscope.* Cambridge, Mass., 1981.

cs   Süsskind, Charles. "Ferdinand Braun: Forgotten forefather." *Advances in electronics and electron physics, 50* (1980), 241-260.

gm   Zenneck, Jonathan. "Zum 100. Geburtstag von Ferdinand Braun." *PB, 6* (1950), 269-273.

See also: T.ee1.si

Bridgman, Percy Williams $46 (1882-1961)

bt7.ab   Bridgman, Percy W. *Reflections of a physicist.* NY, 1955.

   ek   Kemble, E. C., and F. Birch. "Percy Williams Bridgman." NAS. *BM, 41* (1970), 23-67.

   en   Newitt, D. M. "Percy Williams Bridgman." RS. *BM, 8* (1962), 27-40.

   ks   Schlesinger, G. "P.W. Bridgman's operational analysis: The differential aspect." *BJPS, 9* (1959), 299-306.

See also: B.ei7.pk

Briggs, Lyman James (1874-1963)

bu1.ec   Condon, E. U. "Lyman James Briggs." APS. *Yearbook,* 1963, 117-121.

Brillouin, Léon Nicolas (1889-1969)

bu4.ab   Brillouin, Léon. *Vie, matière et observation.* Paris, 1959.

   ch   Harding, D. W. "A brief discussion of the life and work of Léon Brillouin." *PE, 4* (1969), 46-48.

   ck   Kastler, A. "Zhizn' i tvorchestvo Leona Brillyuena." *UFN, 106* (1972), 101-118. (In French in **L'onde électrique, 50:4* (1970), 1- .)

Britske, Ergard Viktorovich (1877-1953)

bu7.jm   **Ergard Viktorovich Britske.* Moscow, 1955. (*Mtly,* ser. khim.)

Broek, A.J. van den (1870-1926)

bv1.js   Snelders, H. A. M. "A bio-bibliography of the Dutch amateur physicist A.J. van den Broek." *Janus, 61* (1974), 59-72.

See also: H.be1.li

Broglie, Louis C. V. M. de $29 (1892-   )

bw1.ag   George, André, ed. *Louis de Broglie. Physicien et penseur.* Paris, 1953.

   bb   Broglie, Louis de. "Vue d'ensemble sur mes travaux scientifiques." B.bw1.ag, 457-493.

   bc   Broglie, Louis de. "Souvenirs personnels sur les débuts de la mécanique ondulatoire." *Revue de métaphysique et de morale, 48* (1941), 1-23.

   bm   March, Arthur. "Louis de Broglie, der Begründer der Wellenmechanik." A.aj1.sc, 79-86.

cb Broglie, Louis de. "Avant propos." B.bw1.jb, 7-16.

ce Broglie, Maurice de. "La jeunesse et les orientations intellec-
tuelles de Louis de Broglie." B.bw1.ag, 423-429.

ch Destouches, Jean-Louis. "Retour sur le passé." B.bw1.ag, 67-85.

ck Gabor, Dennis. "Louis de Broglie et les limites du monde visible." B.bw1.ag, 241-253.

cn George, André. "Esquisse pour un portrait." B.bw1.ag, 445-453.

cp Mauquin, Charles. "La thèse du doctorat de Louis de Broglie."
B.bw1.ag, 430-436.

ib Broglie, Louis de, et al. *Louis de Broglie: Sa conception du monde
physique: le passé et l'avenir de la méchnique ondulatoire.* Paris,
1973.

jb Broglie, Louis de. *Recherches d'un demi-siècle.* Paris, 1976.

nb Bord, Emil. "Louis de Broglie et L'Institut Henri Poincaré."
B.bw1.ag, 437-443.

See also: B.bw4.al |se1.ch |wf3.kl; G.qa1.pe; L.eb1 |ec1.ra

Broglie, Maurice de @ (1875-1960)

bw4.al Varende, Jean La. *Les Broglie.* Paris, 1950.

cp Pange, Jean de. "Comment j'ai vu 1900." *Revue des deux mondes,*
1962, 548-557.

ei Leprince-Ringuet, Louis. "Maurice de Brogie." AS. *Comptes
rendus, 251* (1961), 297-303.

el Lépine, Pierre. "Notice sur la vie et les travaux de Maurice de
Broglie." AS. *Notices et discours, 4* (1962), 625-656.

es Sudre, R. "Maurice de Broglie." *Revue des deux mondes,* July-
Aug. 1960, 577-582.

ew Wilson, William. "Maurice, le Duc de Broglie." RS. *BM, 7*
(1961), 31-36.

Brown, Benjamin H. (1866-1950)

bx1.cp Penrose, S. A. L. "Benj. H. Brown: A word portrait of a teacher
of physics." *AJP, 5* (1937), 161-166.

Buchwald, Eberhard (1886-1975)

bx4.ek Kersten, Martin. "Eberhard Buchwald." *PB, 32* (1976), 353-360.

Bumstead, Henry Andrews (1870-1920)

bx7.cp   Page, Leigh. "Henry Andrews Bumstead." NAS. *BM, 13* (1930), 103-124.

Burbury, Samuel Hawksley (1831-1911)

bx9.eb   B., G. H. "Samuel Hawksley Burbury." RS. *Proceedings, 88A* (1913), i-iv.

Burgers, Johannes Martinus (1895-   )

See: O.fd1.bu

Burgess, George Kimball (1874-1932)

by2.cb   Briggs, Lyman J., and Wallace R. Brode. "George Kimball Burgess." NAS. *BM, 30* (1957), 57-72.

Bush, Vannevar (1890-1974)

by4.ac   Bush, Vannevar. *Pieces of the action.* NY, 1970.

    cm   [McElroy, William D.] "A visit with Vannevar Bush." *Mosaic, 1:1* (1970), 9-13.

    ew   Wiesner, Jerome. "Vannevar Bush." NAS. *BM, 50* (1979), 89-117.

Callendar, Hugh Langbourne (1863-1930)

ca1.es   S., W. J. S. "Hugh Longbourne Callendar." RS. *Proceedings, 134A* (1932), xviii-xxvi.

Campbell, Norman R. (1880-1949)

cb4.kc   Buchdahl, Gerd. "Theory construction: The work of Norman Robert Campbell." *Isis, 55* (1964), 151-162.

See also: B.dp1.km

Casimir, Hendrik Bruygt Gerhard (1909-   )

cc1.cc   Casimir, H. B. G. "Recollections from the years 1929-1931." B.bo1.ar, 109-113.

    ce   Casimir, H. B. G. "Some recollections." A.ad1.we, 182-187.

Chadwick, James $35 (1891-1974)

cd1.em   Massey, Harrie, and Norman Feather. "James Chadwick." RS. *BM, 22* (1976), 11-70.

See also: K.ac1.ch

Chandrasekhar, Subrahmanyan (1910-   )

ce1.cc   Chandrasekhar, S. "The Richtmyer Memorial Lecture; some historical notes." *AJP, 37* (1969), 577-584.

Chaplygin, Sergey Alekseyevich @ (1869-1942)

ce4.ck   Krylov, A. N. "Sergey Alekseyevich Chaplygin." B.kt1.al, 485-492.

     ek   Krylov, A. N. "Sergey Alekseyevich Chaplygin." B.kt1.jj, *1:2*, 153-162.

     gd   Arzhanikov, N. S. "S. A. Chaplygin." *VIYeT, 10* (1960), 42-48.

See also: D.cb1.ft |eb1.gr, ss |ta1.kn, ko

Chapman, Sydney (1888-1970)

ce7.ec   Cowling, T. G. "Sydney Chapman." RS. *BM, 17* (1971), 53-89.

     jc   CSAC. *Sydney Chapman papers at the Bodleian Library, Oxford.* List 11/5/74, 4 p.

Cherenkov, Pavel A. $58 (1904-   )

cf1.gk   Kurchatov, I. V., et al. "Vydayushcheyesya nauchnoye otkrytiye." AN. *Vestnik,* 1958:12, 7-9.

Cherwell *see* Lindemann

Chew, Geoffrey F. (1924-   )

See: K.fb1.ga

Chree, Charles (1860-1928)

cf8.es   S., G. C. "Charles Chree." RS. *Proceedings, 122A* (1928/9), vii-xiv.

Chrystal, George @ (1851-1911)

cg1.ed   Black, J. Sutherland, and C. G. Knott. "Professor George Chrystal." Royal Society of Edinburgh. *Proceedings, 32* (1911-12), 477-503.

Chwolson *see* Khvol'son

Clay, Jacob @ (1882-1955)

ch1.er   Rathenau, G. W. "Levensbericht von Jacob Clay." Akademie van Wetenschappen, Amsterdam. *Jaarboek,* 1955/56, 209-212.

Coblentz, William Weber @ (1873-1962)

ci1.ac   Coblentz, W. W. *From the life of a researcher.* NY, 1951.

   cm   Meggers, William F. "William Weber Coblentz." NAS. *BM, 39* (1967), 55-101.

See also: G.fa2.jo, sa; P.ha1.st

Cochrane, William (1910-1972)

ci3.jc   CSAC. *William Cochrane papers at University of Glasgow Library.* List 26/3/75, 14 p.

Cockcroft, John Douglas $51 (1897-1967)

ci5.eo   Oliphant, M. L., and W. G. Penney. "John D. Cockcroft." RS. *BM, 14* (1968), 139-188.

Cohen, Ernst Julius @ (1869-1944)

cj1.bd   Browne, C. A. "Dr. Ernst Cohen as historian of science." *JCE, 25* (1948), 302-307.

   bm   Moesveld, A. L. T. "The scientific work of Ernst Cohen." *JCE, 25* (1948), 308-314.

   ed   Donnan, F. G. "Ernst Julius Cohen." RS. *Obituary notices, 5* (1948), 667-687.

Compton, Arthur Holly @ $27 (1892-1962)

ck1.ac   Blackwood, James R. *The house on College Avenue: The Comptons at Wooster, 1891-1913.* Cambridge, Mass., 1968.

   ag   Compton, Arthur Holly. *Atomic quest: A personal narrative.* NY and Oxford, 1956.

   ec   Allison, Samuel K. "Arthur Holly Compton, research physicist." *Science, 138* (1962), 794-799.

   ee   Allison, Samuel K. "Arthur Holly Compton." NAS. *BM, 38* (1965), 81-110.

   jc   Compton, Arthur Holly. *Scientific papers.* Ed. Robert S. Shankland. Chicago, 1973.

   jf   Compton, Arthur Holly. *The cosmos of Arthur Holly Compton.* Ed. Marjorie Johnston. NY, 1967.

   kc   Compton, Arthur Holly. *Man's destiny in eternity.* Boston, 1949.

   nw   Washington University, St. Louis. *Inauguration of Arthur Holly Compton as chancellor, Washington University.* Saint Louis, 1946.

See also: G.na1

Compton, Karl Taylor @ (1887-1954)

ck3.jd   Compton, K. T., and F. D. Roosevelt. "[Exchange of letters]." *Science, 84* (1936), 393-394.

   nh   Harrison, George Russell. "Karl Compton and American physics." *PT, 10* (1957), 19-22.

See also: B.ck1.ac

Conant, James Bryant (1893-1978)

cl1.ai   Conant, James B. *My several lives: Memoirs of a social inventor.* NY, 1970.

   ek   Kistiakowsky, George B., and F. H. Westheimer. "James Bryant Conant." RS. *BM, 25* (1979), 209-232.

Condon, Edward Uhler (1902-1974)

cl5.cc   Condon, E. U. "Reminiscences of a life in and out of quantum mechanics." International symposium on atomic, molecular, solid-state theory and quantum biology, VII. *Proceedings.* Ed. Per-Olov Löwdin. NY, 1973. Pp. 7-22.

   em   Morse, Philip M. "Edward Uhler Condon." NAS. *BM, 48* (1976), 125-151.

Conway, Arthur William (1875-1950)

cl7.ew   Whittaker, Edmund T. "Arthur William Conway." RS. *Obituary notices, 7* (1951), 329-340.

Coolidge, William David (1873-1975)

cm1.am   Miller, John Anderson. *William David Coolidge: Yankee scientist.* Schenectady, NY, 1963.

   cd   Coolidge, William David. [Reminiscences.] *PTeach, 3* (1965), 212-216.

Corbino, Orso Mario (1876-1937)

cm4.ef   Fermi, Enrico. "Un maestro: Orso Mario Corbino." *Nuova antologia, 72* (1937), 313-316. (Also in B.fg1.jj, *2,* 1017-1020.)

   el   Lombardi, Edoardo. "Orso Mario Corbino." *Ricerca scientifica, 8:1* (1937), 53-57.

See also: C.ia1.se

Coster, Dirk @ (1889-1950)

cn1.ek   Kramers, H. A. "Levensbericht van Dirk Coster." Akademie van wetenschappen, Amsterdam. *Jaarboek,* 1951/52, 198-201.

gk   Kramers, H. A. "D. Coster vijf en twintig jaren hoogleraar." *Nederlands tijdschrift voor natuurkunde, 15* (1949), 285-287.

Cotton, Aimé-Auguste (1869-1953)

co1.ad   Cotton, Eugénie. *Aimé Cotton.* Paris, 1967.

ed   Broglie, Louis de. "Notice sur la vie et l'oeuvre de Aimé Cotton." AS. *Notices et discours, 3* (1953), 448-477.

kr   Rosmorduc, Jean. "Aimé Cotton (1869-1951): Le rationalisme et l'expérience." *La pensée,* no. 165 (1972), 112-126.

Coudres, Theodor Des (1862-1926)

cp1.ew   Wien, Wilhelm. "Theodor Des Coudres." *PZ, 28* (1927), 129-135.

Coulson, Charles Alfred (1910-1974)

cp4.ed   Altmann, S. L., and E. J. Bowen. "Charles Alfred Coulson." RS. *BM, 20* (1974), 75-134.

jc   CSAC. *Charles Alfred Coulson papers at the Bodleian Library.* List 60/4/78. 364 p.

Courant, Richard (1888-1972)

cr1.ar   Reid, Constance. *Courant in Göttingen and New York. The story of an improbable mathematician.* NY, 1976.

eb   Aleksandrov, P. S., and O. A. Oleynik. "In memory of Richard Courant." *Russian mathematical surveys, 30:4* (1975), 157-178. (In Russian in *Uspekhi matematicheskikh nauk, 30:4* (1975), 205-226.)

is   *Studies and essays presented to Richard Courant on his 60th birthday.* NY, 1948.

Crehore, Albert Cushing (1868-1959)

cs1.ac   Crehore, Albert Cushing. *Autobiography.* Gates Mills, Ohio, 1944.

Crew, Henry (1859-1953)

ct1.em   Meggers, William F. "Henry Crew." NAS. *BM, 37* (1964), 33-54.

ps   Sutton, Richard M. "Henry Crew: Recipient of the 1941 Oersted medal." *AJP, 10* (1942), 28-31.

Crookes, William @ (1832-1919)

cu1.ac   Albe, E. E. Fournier d'. *The life of Sir William Crookes.* NY, 1924.

af   Dingwall, E. J. *The critic's dilemma.* Crowhurst, Sussex, 1966.

ah   Hall, Trevor H. *The spiritualists; the story of Florence Cook and William Crookes.* London, 1962.

bd   *DeKosky, Robert Keith. *The scientific work of Sir William Crookes.* Ph.D. thesis. Univ. of Wisconsin, 1972. (*DAI, 33,* 2281A.)

bg   Greenaway, Frank. "A Victorian scientist: The experimental researches of Sir William Crookes." Royal Institution. *Proceedings, 39* (1962), 172-198.

cl   Lodge, Oliver. "The life of Crookes." Society for Psychical Research. *Proceedings, 34* (1924), 310-323.

ed   Barret, W. T. "In memory of Sir William Crookes." Society for Psychical Research. *Proceedings, 31* (1921), 12-29.

ef   Tilden, A. "William Crookes." RS. *Proceedings, 96A* (1920), i-ix.

gw   Zeeman, Pieter. "Scientific worthies. Sir William Crookes." *Nature, 77* (1907/8), 1-3.

km   Medhurst, R. G., and K. M. Goldney. "William Crookes and the physical phenomena of mediumship." Society for Psychical Research. *Proceedings, 54* (1963-66), 25-157.

See also: B.lo8.ag; G.ea1.de; O.ba1.ch

Curie, Marie Sklodowska @ $03 $11C (1867-1934)

cv1.ab   *Cunningham, Marion. *Madame Curie (Sklodowska) and the story of radium.* London, 1918.

ac   Curie, Eve. *Madame Curie.* Tr. Vincent Sheean. NY and London, 1938.

ag   Hurwic, Józef. *Maria Sklodowska Curie.* Warsaw, 1967.

aj   Polska Akademia Nauk. Zaklad Historii Nauki i Techniki. *Studia poświecone Marii Skolodowskiej-Curie e Marianowi Smoluchowskiema.* Wroclaw, 1968. (*Monografie z dziejów nauki e techniki,* 51.)

am   Regaud, C. *Marie Sklodowska Curie.* Paris, 1934.

ap   Reid, Robert. *Marie Curie.* London and NY, 1974.

aw Wolczek, Olgierd. *Maria Sklodowska-Curie, her life and work.* Warsaw, 1967.

ax *Wolczek, Olgierd. *Maria Sklodowska-Curie.* Warsaw, 1975.

bf Hurwic, Jósef. "La voie scientifique de Marie Sklowdowska-Curie et l'importance de ses découvertes." *Journal de physique, 29:* supplément C:1 (1968), 5-6.

bg Hurwic, Jósef. "Rola Marii Sklodowskiej-Curie w nozwoju nauki." *KHNT, 12* (1967), 701-705.

bk Paneth, Friedrich A. "Marie Sklodowska-Curie, die Entdeckerin des Radiums." A.aj1.sc, 139-148.

bl Perrin, Francis. "L'oeuvre scientifique de Marie Sklodowska-Curie et son influence sur les grandes conquêtes de la physique moderne." B.cv1.gs, 13-23.

bn *Rumèbe, Gérard. *Maria Sklodowska Curie et la découverte du radium.* Paris, 1970. 15p.

bo Smeaton, William A. "Teorie pierwiastków chemicznych od Roberta Boyle do Marii Curie." Polska Akademia Nauk. Zaklad Historii Nauki i Techniki. *Studia,* 1968, 21-36.

bq Starosel'skaya-Nikitina, O. A., and Helena Starosel'skaya. "Rola Marii Sklodowskiej-Curie w rozwoju fizyki jadrowej." Polska Akademia Nauk. Zaklad Historii Nauk i Techniki. *Studia* (1968), 66-85.

bt Teske, Armin. "Szkic dzialalności Marii Sklodowskiej-Curie." Polska Akademia Nauk. Zaklad Historii Nauk i Techniki. *Studia* (1968), 7-13.

bw Wertenstein, L. "L'Oeuvre scientifique de Madame Marie Sklodowska-Curie." *Acta physica polonica, 4* (1935), xxi-xl.

bz Ziemecki, Stanislaw. "Sur l'oeuvre et la vie de Marie Sklodowska Curie." Lublin University. *Annales, 22AA* (1967), 21-50.

cb Baltá-Elías, José. "Maria Curie." *Atlantida, 6* (1968), 88-93.

cd Barr, E. Scott. "The incredible Marie Curie and her family." *PTeach, 2* (1964), 251-259.

ce *Bernardini, Gilberto. *Maria Sklodowska Curie nel centenario della nascità.* Rome, 1968. (Accademia Nazionale dei Lincei. *Celebrazioni lincee,* 8.)

cg Burdowicz-Nowicka, Maria. "Nieznane materialy do dziejów rodziny Marii Skladowskiej-Curie." *KHNT, 21* (1976), 485-496.

ci Cragg, Richard H. "Marie Curie." *New scientist, 36* (1967), 358-359.

ck Guillot, Marcel. "Marie Curie." *Nuclear physics, 103A* (1967), 1-8.

cm Hubicki, Wlodzimierz. "Marie Sklodowska Curie et le Congrès des Médicins et Naturalistes Polonais de 1900." Lublin. University. *Annales, 22AA* (1967), 73-80.

cn Hurwic, Jósef. "Maria Skladowska Curie—the woman and the scientist." Polska Akademia Nauk. *Review, 12:4* (1967), 25-31.

co Ioffe, A. F. "Mariya Sklodovskaya-Kyuri." A.aj1.io, 196-200.

cp Joliot-Curie, Irène. "La vie et l'oeuvre de Marie Sklodowska-Curie." *La pensée,* no. 58 (1954), 19-30. (Also in *VIYeT, 3,* 39-48.)

cq *Joliot-Curie, Irène. "Marie Curie: Ma mère." *Europe, 32* (Dec. 1954), 89-121.

cs Valadares, M. "[Reminiscences of Marie Curie]." *Journal de physique, 29*: supplément C:1 (1968), 11-13.

cw Wheeler, John A. "Maria Sklodowska-Curie as Copernicus of the world of the small." B.cv1.gs, 25-32.

gb *Anon. "Centenary of the birth of Marie Sklodowska Curie." Polska Akademia Nauk. *Review, 13:1* (1968), 12-28.

gf Foley, Hamilton. "Madame Curie, the nation's guest." Pan-American Union. *Bulletin* (Jul. 1921), 25-28.

gs Symposium celebrating the centenary of the birth of Maria Sklodowska-Curie. Warsaw, 1967. *Maria Sklodowska-Curie: Centenary lectures.* Vienna, 1968.

gy *Yakovlev, K. P. "K 60-letiyu M. Kyuri." *Nauchnoye slovo,* 1968:3, 176-179.

jb Curie, Marie. *Oeuvres.* Ed. Irène Joliot-Curie. Warsaw, 1954.

jc Curie, Marie, and Irène Curie. *Correspondance (1905-1934).* Ed. Gilette Ziegler. Paris, 1974.

jg Joliot, Frédéric. "Contamination radioactive de manuscrits de Pierre et Marie Curie, relatifs aux expériences ayant suivi la découverte du radium." AS. *Comptes rendus, 246* (1958), 1000-1003.

jk Klickstein, Herbert S. *Marie Sklodowska Curie: A bio-bibliographical study of Mme Curie's "Recherches sur les substances radioactives."* Mallincrodt Chemical Works, 1966.

jv Vrublevskaya, M. "Muzey Marii Skladovskoy Kyuri v Varshave." *VIYeT, 39* (1972), 109-110.

tc Curie, Marie. "Compte rendu d'un récent voyage aux Etats-Unis." Paris. University. *Annales, 5* (1930), 10-17.

tp Picone, Mauro, and Bronislaw Biliński. *Maria Sklodowska-Curie in Italia, nel centenario della nascità, 1867-1934.* Warsaw, 1969. (Polska Akademia Nauk. Stacja Naukowa w Rzymie. *Conferenze,* 41.)

See also: B.cv3; I.aa1.cp; I.bc

Curie, Pierre @ $03 (1859-1906)

cv3.ac Curie, Marie. *Pierre Curie.* Tr. Charlotte and Vernon Kellogg. NY, 1923. Reprinted NY, 1963.

ad Curie, Marie. *Pierre Curie.* Paris, 1924.

ae *Curie, Marie. *Pierre Curie.* Paris, 1955.

af Curie, Marie. *P'yer Kyuri.* Tr. M. P. Saskol'skaya; ed. I. M. Frank. Moscow, 1968.

bc *Broglie, Louis de. "Notice sur l'oeuvre de Pierre Curie." *Revue technique luxembourgeoise, 51* (1959), 1-3.

bf Gaysinskiy, M. "Nachal'nyy period issledovaniy v laboratorii Kyuri (1896-1918)." *VIYeT, 36-37* (1971), 123-126.

bi Joliot-Curie, Irène, and Frédéric Joliot. "P'yer Kyuri i puti razvitiya sovremennoy nauki." AN. *Vestnik,* 1956:5, 54-57. (Also in *VIYeT, 1,* 5-8.)

bj Joliot-Curie, Irène, and Frédéric Joliot. "Piotr Curie i dzisiejsze drogi rozwoju nauki. Wstepem poprzedzil Siemion Plotkin." *KHNT, 13* (1968), 609-617.

br Shpol'skiy, E. V. "Zhizn' i deyatel'nost' P'yera Kyuri." *UFN, 58* (1956), 581-598.

bt Starosel'skaya-Nikitina, O. A. "Zhizn' i tvorchestvo P'yera Kyuri." IIYeT. *Trudy, 19* (1957), 13-69.

cb Andreyev, N. N. "P'yer Kyuri." AN. *Vestnik,* 1959:5, 56-58.

cf Dejean, Maurice. "P'yer Kyuri. IIYeT. *Trudy, 19* (1957), 10-12.

ch Ioffe, A. F. "P'yer Kyuri—vydayushchiysya frantsuzskiy fizik." *Priroda,* 1956:5, 74-79. (Also in AN. *Vestnik,* 1956:5, 30-35; *UFN, 58* (1956), 571-579.)

cj Joliot, Frédéric, and Irène Joliot-Curie. "Pierre Curie." *La pensée,* no. 67 (1956), 11-14.

cp Nesmeyanov, A. N. "Pamyati P'yera Kyuri." IIYeT. *Trudy, 19* (1957), 7-9.

el Langevin, Paul. "Pierre Curie." *Revue de mois, 2* (1906), 5-36.

gb   Baranov, V. I. "K 50-letiyu so dnya smerti P'yera Kyuri." AN. Kommissiya po opredeleniyu absolyutnogo vozrasta geologicheskikh formatsii. *Byulleten', 2* (1957), 108-111.

gr   Starik, I. Ye. "P'yer Kyuri." AN. *Izvestiya,* ser. geol., 1956:4, 120-121.

gs   *Starosel'skaya-Nikitina, O. A. "P'yer Kyuri: K 100-letiyu so dnya rozhdeniya." *Kul'tura i zhizn'*, 1959:5, 61-62.

jj   *Joliot-Curie, Irène. "Carnets de laboratoire [de P. et M. Curie]." In B.cv3.ae. (Also in IIYeT. *Trudy, 19* (1957), 97-138.)

js   Stroński, Ignacy. "The collected papers of the Curie family." *AIHS*, no. 97 (1975), 309-313.

See also: B.cv1 |dp1.kc |lc3.cs; E.mc1.do; I.aa1.cp; I.bc; O.fa1.sh, su, wh

Curtis, Harvey Lincoln (1875-1956)

cw1.ac   Curtis, Harvey Lincoln. *Recollections of a scientist.* Bonn, 1958.

Curtis, William Edward (1889-1969)

cw3.er   Rochester, G. D. "William Edward Curtis." RS. *BM, 16* (1970), 63-76.

Daly, Reginald Aldworth @ (1871-1957)

db1.ed   Billings, Marland P. "Memorial to Reginald Aldworth Daly." Geological Society of America. *Proceeding*, 1958, 115-122.

eg   Birch, Francis. "Reginald A. Daly." NAS. *BM, 34* (1960), 31-64.

Danilov, Vitaliy Ivanovich (1902-1954)

dc1.cd   Anon. "Vitaliy Ivanovich Danilov." V. I. Danilov. *Stroyeniye i kristallizatsiya zhidkosti*. Kiev, 1956. Pp. 5-10. (Also in B.dc1.jd, 7-12, and *Problemy metallovedeniya i fiziki metallov* (Moscow, 1955), 7-12.)

jd   Danilov, V. I. *Vibrani pratsi.* Kiev, 1971.

Darrow, Karl Kelchner (1891-)

See: C.ua4.da

Darwin, Charles Galton @ (1887-1962)

de1.ar   Raverat, Gwen. *Period piece: A Cambridge childhood.* London, 1960.

eg   Taylor, G. I. "Sir Charles Darwin." APS. *Yearbook*, 1963, 135-140.

et Thomson, George P. "Charles Galton Darwin." RS. *BM, 9* (1963), 69-85.

Darwin, George Howard @ (1845-1912)

de2.eh H., S. S. "George Howard Darwin." RS. *Proceedings, 89A* (1913/14), i-xiii.

Davis, Bergen (1869-1958)

de5.ew Webb, Harold W. "Bergen Davis." NAS. *BM, 34* (1960), 65-82.

Davisson, Clinton Joseph @ $37 (1881-1958)

de7.ek Kelly, Mervin J., and Karl K. Darrow. "Clinton Joseph Davisson." NAS. *BM, 36* (1962), 51-84.

See also: E.bg1.ca, gf

Day, Arthur Louis (1869-1960)

de8.ca Abelson, Philip H. "Arthur Louis Day." NAS. *BM, 47* (1975), 27-47.

Debye, Peter Joseph Wilhelm @ $36C (1884-1966)

df1.ck Hückel, Erich. "Erinnerungen an Peter Debye und an meine Lehrjahre." *PB, 28* (1972), 53-57.

ed Davies, Mansel. "Peter J. W. Debye." *JCE, 45* (1968), 467-473.

ee Davies, Mansel. "Peter Joseph Wilhelm Debye." RS. *Biographical memoirs, 16* (1970), 175-232.

eh Hund, Friedrich. "Nachrufe auf verstorbene Mitglieder: Peter Debye." Akademie der Wissenschaften, Göttingen. *Jahrbuch,* 1966, 59-64.

ew Williams, J. W. "Peter Joseph Wilhelm Debye." NAS. *BM, 46* (1975), 23-68.

gl Laue, Max von. "Zu Peter Debyes 70. Geburtstag." *Zeitschrift für electrochemie, 58* (1954), 151-153.

gm Laue, Max von. "Peter Debye 75 Jahre alt." *Chemiker-Zeitung, 83* (1959), 217-218.

gs Sommerfeld, Arnold. "Überreichung der Planck-Medaille für Peter Debye." *PB, 6* (1950), 509-512.

jd Debye, Peter. *Collected papers.* NY, 1954.

Dempster, Arthur Jeffrey (1886-1950)

df6.ea Allison, Samuel K. "Arthur Jeffrey Dempster." NAS. *BM, 27* (1952), 319-333.

Denizot, Alfred (1873-1937)

dg1.ej Jablonski, A. "Alfred Denizot." *Acta physica polonica, 6* (1936), 95-102.

Dennison, David Mathias (1900-1976)

dh1.cd Dennison, David M. "Recollections of physics and physicists during the 1920's." *AJP, 42* (1974), 1051-1056.

  ec Crane, H. Richard. "David Mathias Dennison." NAS. *BM, 52* (1980), 139-159.

Deslandres, Henri Alexandre @ (1853-1948)

di1.ed Azambuja, L. d'. "Henri Deslandres." Société Astronomique de France. *Bulletin, 62* (1948), 179-184.

Dessauer, Friedrich (1881-1963)

di5.cr Regato, J. A. del. "Friedrich Dessauer." *International journal of radiation oncology and biological physics, 4* (1978), 225-332.

Deutsch, Martin (1917-   )

di9.cd Deutsch, Martin. "A scientific autobiography." *Adventures in experimental physics, 4* (1974), 125-127.

Dewar, James @ (1842-1923)

dj1.bd *Adwentowski, K., et al. "Dewar czy Olszewski?" *KHNT, 1* (1956), 539-561.

  cb *Armstrong, Henry E. *James Dewar.* London, 1924.

  cc Armstrong, Henry E. "Sir James Dewar." Chemical Society. *Journal, 131* (1928), 1066-1076.

  cf Findlay, Alexander. "James Dewar." Alexander Findlay and William Hobson, eds. *British Chemists.* London, 1947. Pp. 30-57.

  ea [Armstrong, H. E.] "James Dewar." RS. *Proceedings, 111A* (1926), xiii-xxiii.

  ec Crichton-Browne, James. "Sir James Dewar." Royal Society of Edinburgh. *Proceedings, 43* (1922-23), 255-260.

  jy Young, Henry. *A record of the scientific work of Sir James Dewar.* London, 1933.

nm   Mendelssohn, Kurt. "Dewar at the Royal Institution." RI. *Proceedings, 41* (1966), 212-233. (Also in *CP, 7* (1966), 331-342.)

Dingle, Herbert (1890-1978)

dj7.jd   Dingle, Herbert. *Science at the crossroads.* London, 1972.

Dirac, Paul Adrian Maurice $33 (1902-   )

dk1.bm   Mehra, Jagdish. "'The golden age of theoretical physics': P. A. M. Dirac's scientific work from 1924 to 1933." B.dk1.is, 17-59.

cd   Dirac, P. A. M. "Recollections of an exciting era." A.ad1.we, 109-146.

ce   Dirac, P. A. M. [Interview.] A.aj1.bu, 34-40.

cg   Eden, R. J., and J. C. Polkinghorne. "Dirac in Cambridge." B.dk1.is, 1-5.

cv   Vleck, John H. van. "Travels with Dirac in the Rockies." B.dk1.is, 7-16.

gl   Laue, Max von. "Max-Planck-Medaille an Paul Adrien Maurice Dirac." *PB, 8* (1952), 512-513.

gr   Rechenberg, Helmut. "Paul Dirac zum 70. Geburtstag." *PB, 28* (1972), 545-546.

gs   Snow, C. P., et al. "[Testimonials to Dirac]." A.ad1.me, 809-819.

is   Salam, Abdus, and E. P. Wigner, eds. *Aspects of quantum theory.* Cambridge, 1972.

kk   Kragh, Helge. *Methodology and philosophy of science in Paul Dirac's physics.* Roskilde, 1979. (Roskilde. Universitetscenter. IMFUFA. *Tekster,* 27.)

See also: E.bh1.br; L.hd1.br

Dobronravov, Nikolay Ivanovich (1891-1949)

dk7.es   Shimanskaya, N. S. "Pamyati Nikolaya Ivanovicha Dobronravova." Radiyevyy Institut im. Khlopina. *Trudy, 6* (1957), 20-23.

Dobson, Gordon Miller Bourne (1889-1976)

dk8.eh   Houghton, J. T., and C. D. Walshaw. "Gordon Miller Bourne Dobson." RS. *BM, 23* (1977), 41-57.

Dodge, Homer Levi (1887-)

dk9.pd Dodge, Homer Levi. "Response [to award of Oersted Medal]." *AJP, 13* (1945), 179-181.

pg Guernsey, Janet B. "Homer L. Dodge, first president of AAPT." *PTeach, 17* (1979), 84-95.

Donnan, Frederick George @ (1870-1956)

dl2.ef Freeth, F. A. "Donnan, Frederick G." RS. *BM, 3* (1957), 23-29.

Dorfman, Yakov Grigor'yevich (1898-1974)

dl8.ev Vonsovskiy, S. V. "Pamyati Yakova Grigor'yevicha Dorfmana." *UFN, 117* (1975), 705-710.

gk Kedrov, B. M., et al. "Ya. G. Dorfman (k 70-letiyu so dnya rozhdeniya)." *VIYeT, 31* (1970), 91-93.

Dorgelo, Hendrik Berend (1894-1961)

dm1.ed Druyveteyn, M. J. "In memoriam Professor Dr. H. B. Dorgelo." *Nederlands tijdschrift voor natuurkunde, 27:6* (1961), 181-184.

Drude, Paul Karl Ludwig @ (1863-1906)

dn1.ep Planck, Max. "Paul Drude." DPG. *Verhandlungen, 8* (1906), 599-630.

es *Richarz, Franz, and Walter König. *Zur Erinnerung an Paul Drude*. Giessen, 1906.

See also: B.rk7.cn

Dryden, Hugh Latimer (1898-1965)

dn5.eh Hunsaker, Jerome C., and Robert C. Seamans, Jr. "Hugh Latimer Dryden." NAS. *BM, 40* (1969), 35-68.

Duane, William @ (1872-1935)

do1.ed Bridgman, Percy W. "William Duane." NAS. *Bibliographical memoirs, 18* (1937), 23-41.

Duhem, Pierre Maurice Martin @ (1861-1916)

dp1.ad Pierre-Duhem, Hélène. *Un savant français: Pierre Duhem*. Paris, 1936.

ah Humbert, Pierre. *Pierre Duhem*. Paris, 1932.

bd Darbon, A. "L'histoire des sciences dans l'oeuvre de Pierre Duhem." B.dp1.bl, 499-548.

bf   Hadamard, Jacques. "L'oeuvre de Pierre Duhem dans son aspect mathématique." B.dp1.bl, 467-495.

bj   Jouquet, E. "L'oeuvre scientifique de Pierre Duhem." *Revue générale des sciences, 28* (1917), 40-49.

bl   *L'oeuvre scientifique de Pierre Duhem.* Bordeaux, 1927. (Also in Société des Sciences Physiques et Naturelles de Bordeaux. *Mémoires,* 1:2.)

bn   Loustauneau, Pierre. "Duhem physicien." *Etudes philosophiques, 22* (1967), 433-438.

bp   Manville, Octave. "La physique." B.dp1.bl, 3-464.

br   Paul, Harry W. "Pierre Duhem: Science and the historian's craft." *JHI, 33* (1972), 497-512.

cm   Miller, Donald G. "Pierre Duhem." *PT, 19* (Dec. 1966), 47-53.

cn   Miller, Donald G. "Pierre Duhem, un oublié." *Revue des questions scientifiques, 28* (1967), 445-470.

cr   Picard, Emile. "La vie et l'oeuvre de Pierre Duhem." AS. *Mémoires, 57* (1921), xcix-cxlii.

ej   Jordan, E. "Pierre Duhem." Société des Sciences Physiques et Naturelles, Bordeaux. *Mémoires, 1:1* (1917), 4-39.

ek   Jordan, Edouard. "Pierre Duhem." France. Ecole Normale Supérieure. Association Amicale de Secours des Anciens Elèves. *Reunion générale annuelle,* 1917, 158-173.

jd   Duhem, Pierre. "Liste des publications." Société des Sciences Physiques et Naturelles, Bordeaux. *Mémoires, 1:1* (1917), 41-70.

je   Duhem, Pierre. "Notice sur les titres et travaux scientifiques." Société des Sciences Physiques et Naturelles, Bordeaux. *Mémoires, 1:1* (1917), 71-169.

jm   Manville, Octave, et al. *L'oeuvre scientifique de Pierre Duhem.* Bordeaux, 1927.

kc   Brouzeng, Paul. "Magnétisme et énergétique. La méthode de Duhem." *RHS, 31* (1978), 333-344.

kg   Grünbaum, Adolf. "The Duhemian argument." *PS, 27* (1960), 75-87.

kl   Lowinger, Armand. *The methodology of Pierre Duhem.* NY, 1941.

km   Mellor, D. H. "Models and analogies in science: Duhem *versus* Campbell?" *Isis, 59* (1968), 282-290.

kr   Rey, Abel. "La philosophie scientifique de M. Duhem." *Revue de metaphysique et morale, 12* (1904), 699-744.

See also: B.lw3.js

DuMond, Jesse William Monroe (1892-1976)

dp5.ep   Panofsky, W. K. H. "Jesse W. M. DuMond." NAS. *BM, 52* (1980), 161-201.

Dyson, Frank Watson @ (1868-1939)

dq1.ee   Eddington, A. S. "Sir Frank Watson Dyson." RS. *Obituary notices, 3* (1940), 159-172.

Dyson, Freeman John (1923-   )

dq3.ad   Dyson, Freeman J. *Disturbing the universe.* NY, 1979.

Dziewulski, Waclaw (1882-1938)

dr1.ep   Patkowski, J., and S. Szczeniowski. "Wenceslaus Dziewulski." *Acta physica polonica, 7* (1938), 97-109.

Eccles, William Henry (1875-1966)

ea6.cr   Ratcliffe, J. A. "William Henry Eccles." RS. *BM, 17* (1971), 195-214.

Eckart, Carl Henry (1902-1973)

ea8.em   Munk, Walter H., and Rudolf W. Preisendorfer. "Carl Henry Eckart." NAS. *BM, 48* (1976), 195-219.

Eddington, Arthur Stanley @ (1882-1944)

eb1.ad   Douglas, A. V. *The life of Arthur Stanley Eddington.* London and NY, 1956.

aj   Jacks, Lawrence P. *Sir Arthur Eddington: Man of science and mystic.* Cambridge, 1949.

am   Kilmister, Clive W. *Men of physics: Sir Arthur Eddington.* Oxford and NY, 1966.

bd   Douglas, A. V. "Sir Arthur Eddington, der Entdecker der atomaren Zerstrahlung der Sterne in Licht." A.aj1.sc, 250-259.

eg   Greaves, W. M. H. "Arthur Stanley Eddington." Royal Society of Edinburgh. *Yearbook,* 1946, 22-30.

en   Plummer, H. C. "Arthur Stanley Eddington." RS. *Obituary notices, 5* (1945), 113-125.

er   Spencer-Jones, H., et al. "Sir Arthur Eddington." *Nature, 154* (1944), 757-760.

es Spencer-Jones, H., and E. T. Whittaker. "Arthur Stanley Eddington." RAS. *Monthly notices, 105* (1945), 68-79.

gv Thomson, J. J. "Sir A. Eddington honoured. Sir J. J. Thomson's tribute." *Times of London* (26 Sep. 1930), 10d.

kc Brown, G. Burniston. "The philosophies of science of Eddington and Milne." *AJP, 17* (1949), 553-558.

kd Dambska, Izydora. "Quelques remarques sur la philosophie de la science de A. S. Eddington." *Revue de synthèse, 77* (1956), 310-341.

ke Dingle, Herbert. *The sources of Eddington's philosophy.* Cambridge, 1954.

km Merleau-Ponty, Jacques. *Philosophie et théorie physique chez Eddington.* Paris, 1965. (Besançon. University. *Annales littéraires, 75.*)

kq Ritchie, A. D. *Reflections on the philosophy of Sir Arthur Eddington.* London, 1948.

ks Ullmo, Jean. *Les idées d'Eddington sur l'interaction électrique et le nombre 137.* Paris, 1934.

kt Whittaker, Edmund Taylor. "Some disputed questions in the philosophy of the physical sciences." Royal Society of Edinburgh. *Proceedings, 61* (1942), 160-175.

ku Whittaker, Edmund Taylor. *Eddington's principle in the philosophy of science.* Cambridge, 1951.

kv Witt-Hansen, J. *Exposition and critique of the conceptions of Eddington concerning the philosophy of physical science.* Copenhagen, 1958.

ky Yolton, John W. *The philosophy of science of A. S. Eddington.* The Hague, 1960.

Ehrenfest, Paul @ (1880-1933)

ec1.af Frenkel', V. Ya. *Pavel Erenfest.* Moscow, 1971.

ag Bolotovskiy, B., and Ya. A. Smorodinskiy. [Review of B.ec1.af.] *UFN, 107* (1972), 173-174.

ak Klein, Martin J. *Paul Ehrenfest. The making of a theoretical physicist.* NY, 1970.

cf Frenkel', V. Ya. "Paul' Erenfest: Uchenyy i chelovek." *UFN, 98* (1969), 537-568.

cg Frenkel', V. Ya. "Physik und Kritik: Paul Ehrenfest." *Ideen des exaktens Wissens,* 1974:9, 39-43.

ci   Ioffe, A. F. "Dopolneniye k 'Vospominaniyam o professore P. Erenfeste' G. Ye. Yulenbeka." A.aj1.io, 219-221.

cu   Uhlenbeck, G. E. "Reminiscences of Professor Paul Ehrenfest." *AJP, 24* (1956), 431-433. (In part in *UFN, 62* (1957), 371-372.)

je   Ehrenfest, Paul. *Collected scientific papers.* Ed. Martin J. Klein. Amsterdam, 1959.

jf   Ehrenfest, Paul, and A. F. Ioffe. *Nauchnaya perepiska.* Leningrad, 1973.

jw   Wheaton, Bruce R. *Catalog of the Ehrenfest Archive.* Leyden, 1977. (Museum Boerhaave, Leyden. *Communications,* 151.)

tf   Frenkel', V. Ya. "Paul' Erenfest v Rossii i v SSSR." *Priroda, 7* (1969), 85-95.

tg   Frenkel', V. Ya. "Paul' Erenfest v Rossii i v SSSR." *Priroda, 8* (1969), 83-91.

See also: L.cb1.kl |cd1.kl |fb1.kk |fd1.kl

Ehrenfest-Afanas'yeva, Tat'yana (1876-1964)
See: D.hf1.sv

Ehrenhaft, Felix (1879-1952)
See: E.be1.di, ho

Eichenwald *see* **Eykhenval'd**

Einstein, Albert @ $21 (1879-1955)

BIOGRAPHICAL BOOKS

ei1.ak   Akademiya na Naukite, Sofia. Otdelenie Za Matematicheski i Fizicheski Nauki. *Albert Aynshchayn.* Sofia, 1966.

1.an   Angelis, Gaston D', ed. *Einstein.* Paris, 1966.

1.be   Beckhard, Arthur. *Albert Einstein.* NY, 1959.

1.bn   Bernstein, Jeremy. *Einstein.* NY, 1973.

1.bt   Bertin, Antonio. *Einstein: La vita, il pensiero, I testi esemplari.* Milan, 1971. (*I memorabili,* 24.)

1.bz   *Broda, Engelbert. *Einstein und Österreich.* Vienna, 1980.

1.cb   Broglie, Louis de, et al. *Einstein.* NY, 1979.

1.cl   Clark, Ronald W. *Einstein: The life and times.* NY, 1971.

1.dc   Cuny, H. *Albert Einstein: The man and his theories.* London, 1963.

1.du   Dukas, Helen, and Banesh Hoffmann, eds. *Albert Einstein: The human side.* Princeton, 1979.

1.dw   Durić-Trbukhović, Desanka. *U senci Alberta Ajnstajna.* Kruševac, 1969.

1.ea   Einstein, Albert. *Out of my later years.* NY, 1950.

1.ef   Feuer, Lewis S. *Einstein and the generations of science.* NY, 1974.

1.eu   Flückiger, Max. *Albert Einstein in Bern.* Bern, 1974.

1.fe   Forsee, A. *Albert Einstein: Theoretical physicist.* NY, 1963.

1.fr   Frank, Philipp. *Einstein: His life and times.* Ed. S. Kusaka. Tr. G. Rosen. NY, 1974. (French tr., Paris, 1950.)

1.fs   Frank, Philipp. *Einstein. Sein Leben und seine Zeit.* Munich, 1949.

1.gd   Garbedian, H. Gordon. *Albert Einstein: Maker of universes.* NY and London, 1939.

1.gt   Hamilton, Peter N. *Albert Einstein.* Guilford, England, and Valley Forge, Pa., 1973.

1.he   Herneck, Friedrich. *Albert Einstein: Ein Leben für Wahrheit, Menschlichkeit und Frieden.* Berlin, 1963. (3rd ed. Berlin, 1967.)

1.hi   Herneck, Friedrich. *Albert Einstein.* 2nd ed. Leipzig, 1975.

1.hj   *Herneck, Friedrich. *Einstein privat: Herta W. erinnert sich an die Jahre 1927 bis 1933.* Berlin, 1978.

1.ho   Hoffmann, Banesh. *Albert Einstein creator and rebel.* NY, 1972.

1.if   Infeld, Leopold. *Albert Einstein: His work and its influence on our world.* NY, 1950.

1.in   *Infeld, Leopold. *Albert Einstein, jego dziela i rola w nauce.* Warsaw, 1956.

1.jp   Jordan, Pascual. *Albert Einstein. Sein Lebenswerk und die Zukunft der Physik.* Frauenfeld, 1969.

1.kl   Kuznetsov, Boris Grigor'yevich. *Eynshteyn.* Moscow, 1962.

1.km   Kuznetsov, Boris Grigor'yevich. *Eynshteyn.* Rev. ed. Moscow, 1967.

1.kn Kuznetsov, Boris Grigor'yevich. *Einstein.* Tr. V. Talmy. NY, 1970.

1.kp Kuznetsov, Boris Grigor'yevich. *Etyudy po Eynshteyne.* Moscow, 1965. (2nd ed. Moscow, 1970.)

1.ks Kuznetsov, Boris Grigor'yevich. *Eynshteyn: Zhizn', smert', bessmertiye.* Moscow, 1972. (French trn by Paul Krellstein, Paris, 1967.)

1.lc Lanczos, Cornelius. *Albert Einstein and the cosmic world order.* NY, 1965.

1.le Lanczos, Cornelius. *The Einstein decade, 1905-1915.* NY, 1974.

1.lt Leithäuser, Joachim G. *Albert Einstein.* Berlin, [1965].

1.ma L'vov, V. Ye. *Zhizn' Al'berta Eynshteyna.* Moscow, 1959. (*Zhizn' zamechatel'nykh lyudey, 8.*)

1.mr Marianoff, D., and P. Wayne. *Einstein: An intimate study of a great man.* Garden City, 1944.

1.ne *Melcher, Horst. *Albert Einstein wider Vorurteile und Denkgewohnheiten.* Berlin, 1978.

1.nm Michelmore, P. *Einstein, profile of the man.* NY, 1962.

1.og Reichinstein, O. *Albert Einstein: A picture of his life and of his conception of the world.* Tr. M. Juers and O. Sigmund. London, 1934.

1.or Reiser, Anton (Rudolf Kayser). *Albert Einstein: A biographical portrait.* NY, 1930.

1.ps Seelig, Carl. *Albert Einstein und die Schweiz.* Zurich, Stuttgart and Vienna, 1952.

1.pt Seelig, Carl. *Albert Einstein: Eine dokumentarische Biographie.* Zurich, Stuttgart and Vienna, 1954.

1.pu Seelig, Carl. *Albert Einstein, a documentary biography.* Tr. Mervyn Savill. London, 1956.

1.pw Seelig, Carl. *Albert Einstein: Leben und Werk eines Genies unser Zeit.* 2nd ed. Zurich, 1960. (Russian trn, Moscow, 1964.)

1.ta Vallentin, A. *The drama of Albert Einstein.* Tr. M. Budberg. Garden City, 1954. (German ed. Stuttgart, 1954.)

1.tm Whitrow, G. J., ed. *Einstein: The man and his achievement.* London, 1967.

HISTORICAL ARTICLES

ei2.am   Amaldi, Edoardo. "Influenza del pensiero di Albert Einstein sulla sviluppo della fisica moderna." *Cultura e scuola, 5:19* (1966), 5-12.

2.ar   Armand, Louis. "La grandeur d'Einstein." B.ei1.an, 281-286.

2.be   Bergia, Silvio. "Einstein nel centenario della nascità: Un itinerario essenziale attraverso l'opera e la critica." *Testi e contesti, 1* (1979), 69-90.

2.bn   Bernstein, Jeremy. "The secrets of the old one." *New Yorker,* 10 Mar. 1973, 44-101; 17 Mar. 1973, 44-91.

2.bo   Bernstein, Jeremy. [Contribution.] B.ei4.yb, 17-27.

2.br   Broglie, Louis de. "My meeting with Einstein at the Solvay Conference of 1927." B.ei4.yf, 14-17.

2.cb   Bronowski, Jacob. "Albert Einstein." A.pc1.lu, 151-164.

2.cd   Bronowski, Jacob. "Comment [on Einstein]." *Impact of science on society, 29* (1979), 3-9.

2.db   Brüche, Ernst. "Wurde Einstein zum Tode verurteilt?" *PB, 25* (1969), 126-129.

2.ec   Cranberg, Lawrence. "Einstein: Amateur scientist." *PT, 32* (Dec. 1979), 9-11.

2.ek   Cuny, Hilaire. "Tel que nous l'avons connu..." B.ei1.an, 261-280.

2.fd   Delorme, Albert. "Einstein et Solovine." *Revue de synthèse, 78* (1957), 539-541.

2.ge   Einstein, Albert. "Autobiographisches—autobiographical notes." B.ei4.zs, 2-95.

2.gh   Einstein, Albert. "Tvorcheskaya avtobiografiya." B.ei6.cb, 27-71. (Also in *UFN, 59* (1956), 71-105.)

2.gj   Einstein, Albert. "Avtobiograficheskiye nabroski." *UFN, 86* (1965), 407-411.

2.he   Feinberg, Gerald. [Contribution.] B.ei4.yb, 27-41.

2.hf   Fine, Arthur. "The young Einstein and the old Einstein." *Essays in memory of Imre Lakatos.* Ed. R. S. Cohen. Dordrecht, 1976. Pp. 145-179. (*BSPS, 39.*)

2.if   Finetti, Bruno de. "Einstein: Generalità e intuizione." *Scientia, 113* (1978), 115-122.

2.jf   Fok, Vladimir A. "Zamechaniya k tvorcheskoy avtobiografii Al'berta Eynshteyna." B.ei6.cb, 72-85.

2.jk   Frank, Philipp G. "Einstein." *Synthèse, 9* (1955), 435-437.

2.kf   French, A. P. "Einstein, a condensed biography." B.ei4.yf, 53-63.

2.lg   Geheniau, Jules. "Einstein: L'homme et son oeuvre vue dans l'actualité scientifique." Société des sciences, des arts et des lettres du Hainaut. *Mémoires et publications, 72* (1958), 13-23.

2.ls   Halsman, Philippe. "Einstein." B.ei4.yf, 27-28.

2.mf   Hoffmann, Banesh. "Albert Einstein." Leo Baeck Institut. *Yearbook, 21* (1976), 279-288.

2.mh   Hoffmann, Banesh. "Unexpected rewards." *AJP, 45* (1977), 787-794.

2.mj   Hoffmann, Banesh. "Einstein the catalyst." *PT, 32* (Mar. 1979), 36-40.

2.nh   Holton, Gerald. "Eynshteyn o fizicheskoy real'nosti." *ES,* 1969-70, 207-229.

2.nj   Holton, Gerald. "On trying to understand scientific genius." *American scholar, 41* (1971/2), 95-110.

2.nl   Holton, Gerald. "Finding favor with the angel of the Lord: Notes toward the psychobiographical study of scientific genius." W.aa1.el, 349-387.

2.oi   Illy, József. "Albert Einstein in Prague." *Isis, 70* (1979), 76-84.

2.ok   Illy, József. "Albert Einstein a Praha." *Dĕjiny vĕd a techniky, 12* (1979), 65-79.

2.pi   Ioffe, A. F. "Al'bert Eynshteyn " *UFN, 71* (1960), 3-7.

2.pk   Ioffe, A. F. "Al'bert Eynshteyn." A.aj1.io, 224-230.

2.qa   Kahan, Théo. "Avant Einstein." B.ei1.an, 67-106.

2.qk   Klein, Martin J. "Einstein and some civilized discontents." *PT, 18* (Jan. 1965), 38-44.

2.ql   Klein, Martin J. "Einstein, Albert." *DSB, 4* (1971), 312-333.

2.qm   Klein, Martin J. "Einstein, Boltzmann's principle, and the mechanical world view." ICHS, XIV (1974). *Proceedings, 1* (1974), 183-194.

2.qn   Klein, Martin J. "Einstein and the academic establishment." B.ei4.yf, 209-214.

2.rk   Körber, Hans-Günther. "Zur Biographie des jungen Albert Einstein." *FF, 38* (1964), 74-78.

2.sk   *Kuwaki, Ayao. [*Albert Einstein.* (In Japanese)]. Tokyo, 1934.

2.tk   Kuznetsov, B. G. "Eynshteyn i klassicheskaya nauka." B.ei7.ae, 75-116.

2.tm   Madaule, Jacques. "Un génie modeste." B.ei1.an, 21-66.

2.uk   Markov, M. A. "Reflections of a Soviet scientist on Einstein."
        BAS, 35 (Mar. 1979), 27-34.

2.um   Masriera, Miguel. "Prólogo." P. Michelmore. *Einstein: Perfil de
        un hombre.* Tr. Juan Godó Costa. Barcelona, 1968.

2.vm   McCrea, W. H. "Albert Einstein, physicist." *Interdisciplinary sci-
        ence reviews, 3* (1978), 275-293.

3.am   Meyenn, Karl von. "Einsteins Dialog mit den Kollegen."
        B.ei4.yn, 464-489.

3.bm   Muralt, Alexander v. "Albert Einstein und seine Zeit." *PB, 35*
        (1979), 554-568.

3.cn   Ne'eman, Yuval. "Coherence, abstraction, and personal involve-
        ment: Albert Einstein, physicist and humanist." *Impact of science
        on society, 29* (1979), 17-25.

3.do   Oppenheimer, J. Robert. "Prisutsviye Eynshteyna." *ES,* 1969-70,
        264-269.

3.dp   Oppenheimer, J. Robert. "On Albert Einstein." B.ei4.yf, 44-49.
        (Also in *BAS, 35* (Mar. 1979), 36-39.)

3.ep   Pauli, Wolfgang. "Albert Einstein in der Entwicklung der Phy-
        sik." *Universitas, 13* (1958), 593-598. (Also in *PB, 15* (1959),
        241-245, and B.pd3.jb, *2,* 1362-1367.)

3.fp   Pyenson, Lewis. "Einstein's early scientific collaboration." *HSPS,
        7* (1976), 83-123.

3.fr   Pyenson, Lewis. "L'education scientifique du jeune Albert Ein-
        stein." *Spectre, 8:3* (1979), 5-14. (Association des Professeurs de
        Sciences du Québec. *Bulletin pédagogique.*)

3.gr   Rosser, W. G. V. "Albert Einstein: His life." *PE, 14* (1979),
        220-223.

3.ir   Rothenberg, Albert. "Einstein's creative thinking and the general
        theory of relativity: A documented report." *American journal of
        psychiatry, 136:1* (1979), 38-43.

3.js   *Sanesi, Elena. "Einstein e Pavia." *Settanta, 3* (1972), 33- .

3.ks   Schofield, Roy. "Albert Einstein: Anniversary feature." *PE, 14*
        (1979), 206-208.

3.mc   Seaborg, Glenn T. "Albert Einstein—a reflection." *BAS, 35* (Mar.
        1979), 20.

3.ms   Sinaceur, Mohammed Allal. "The circle and the line." *Impact of
        science on society, 29* (1979), 27-35.

3.sn   Snow, C. P. "Albert Einstein." B.ei4.yf, 3-8.

3.sp   Speziali, P. "Einstein's friendship with Michele Besso." B.ei4.yf, 9-12.

3.st   Tonnelat, M. A. "Einstein, mythe et réalité." *Scientia, 114* (1979), 297-326.

3.ta   Tamm, I. Ye. "Albert Einstein and modern physics." *Culture and life,* 1960:5, 36-38.

3.tr   Treder, Hans-Jürgen. "The Einstein century in the history of physics." *Impact of science on society, 29* (1979), 37-43.

3.wh   Whitrow, G. J. "Einstein." *Observatory, 75* (1955), 166-170.

REMINISCENCES OF/BY

ei4.ab   Bergman, H. "Personal remembrances of Albert Einstein." *BSPS, 13* (1974), 388-594.

4.al   *Born, Max. "Erinnerungen an Albert Einstein." *Zeitschrift für den mathematischen und naturwissenschaftlichen Unterricht, 9* (1956), 97-105.

4.am   Born, Max. "Erinnerungen an Einstein." *PB, 21* (1965), 297-306.

4.bb   Born, Max, and Leopold Infeld. *Erinnerungen an Einstein.* Berlin, 1969.

4.bl   Brown, Harrison. "An early brief encounter [with Einstein]." *BAS, 35* (Mar. 1979), 17-19.

4.bp   Commins, Dorothy B. "A moment with Einstein: 1953." *Journal of historical studies, 1* (1967), 159-160.

4.co   Cohen, I. Bernard. "An interview with Einstein." *Scientific American, 193:1* (Jan. 1955), 68-73. (In Russian in *ES,* 1967, 45-56.)

4.cz   Czerny, Marianus. "Eine Erinnerung an Albert Einstein." *PB, 35* (1979), 270.

4.de   Einstein, Albert, and R. A. Millikan. "Einstein discusses revolution he caused in scientific thought." *Science news letter, 19* (1931), 51-52.

4.ds   Eisenhart, Churchill. "Albert Einstein as I remember him." Washington Academy of Science. *Journal, 54:8* (1964), 325-328.

4.dv   Frank, Philipp. "Anecdotes." B.ci4.yf, 23.

4.ea   Gamow, George. "Reminiscence." B.ei4.yf, 29-30.

4.eg   Gerlach, Walther. "Erinnerungen an Albert Einstein, 1908-1930." *PB, 35* (1979), 93-102. (In English in B.ei4.ya, 189-200.)

4.fi   Infeld, Leopold. "Moi vospominaniya ob Eynshteyne." *UFN, 59* (1956), 135-184.

4.fj   Infeld, Leopold. "Moi vospominaniya ob Eynshteyne." B.ei6.cb, 197-260.

4.fm   Infeld, Leopold. *Leben mit Einstein. Kontur einer Erinnerung.* Vienna, Frankfurt, and Zürich, 1969.

4.ge   Kemeny, John G. "An Einstein anecdote." B.ei4.yf, 34.

4.gk   Kollros, Louis. "Einstein en Suisse, souvenirs." F.ab1.me, 271-281.

4.gs   Salamon, Esther. "Memories of Einstein." *Encounter, 52* (May 1979), 18-23.

4.hs   Shankland, R. S. "Conversations with Albert Einstein." *AJP, 31* (1963), 47-57; *41* (1973), 895-901. (In Russian in *ES,* 1967, 57-79.)

4.ht   Shankland, R. S. "Conversations with Albert Einstein." B.ei4.yf, 38-39.

4.in   Snow, C. P., et al. "Reminiscences." B.ei4.yf, 3-49.

4.is   Solovine, Maurice. "Freundshaft mit Albert Einstein." *PB, 15* (1955), 97-103.

4.it   Solovine, Maurice. "Excerpts from a memoir." B.ei4.yf, 9-12.

4.iw   Straus, Ernst G. "Memoir." B.ei4.yf, 31-32.

4.jl   Talmey, Max. "Personal recollections of Einstein's boyhood and youth." *Scripta mathematica, 1* (1932), 68-71.

4.jt   Teller, Edward. "Memoir." B.ei4.yf, 24-26.

4.kv   Douglas, A. Vibert. "Forty minutes with Einstein." Royal Astronomical Society of Canada. *Journal, 50* (1956), 99-102.

4.le   Wheeler, John A. "Memoir." B.ei4.yf, 21-22.

4.lf   Wheeler, John A. "Mercer Street and other memories." B.ei4.ya, 201-230.

4.li   Wigner, Eugene P. "Memoir." B.ei4.yf, 33.

4.lm   Whyte, L. L. "Reminiscences of Einstein." B.ei4.yf, 18-20.

4.lz   Zaykov, R. G. "Vospominaniya ob Al'berte Eynshteyne." *VIYeT, 18* (1965), 16-19.

OBITUARIES

ei4.ma   *Andrade, E. N. da C. "Einstein: A tribute." *Discovery,* Jun. 1955, 230- .

4.mb   Broglie, Louis de. "Notice nécrologique sur Albert Einstein." AS. *Comptes rendus, 240* (1955), 1741-1745.

4.mh   Heisenberg, Werner. "Albert Einsteins wissenschaftliches Werk." *Universitas, 10* (1955), 897-902.

4.mi   Ioffe, A. F. "Pamyati Al'berta Eynshteyna." *UFN, 57* (1955), 187-192. (Also in AN. *Vestnik,* 1955:7, 98-101.)

4.mj   Ioffe, A. F. "Pamyati Al'berta Eynshteyna." B.ei6.cb, 20-26.

4.ml   Ivanenko, D. D., and B. G. Kuznetsov. "Pamyati Al'berta Eynshteyna." IIYeT. *Trudy, 5* (1955), 3-32.

4.ng   Rosenthal-Schneider, Ilse. "Albert Einstein, 14 March 1879-18 April 1955." *Australian journal of science, 18* (1955), 15-20.

4.ns   Seelig, Carl. *Helle Zeit—dunkle Zeit: In memoriam Albert Einstein.* Zürich, 1956.

4.of   Wheeler, John A. "Albert Einstein." NAS. *BM, 51* (1980), 97-117.

4.ow   Whittaker, Edmund Taylor. "Albert Einstein." RS. *BM, 1* (1955), 37-67.

TESTIMONIALS

ei4.pb   Bondi, H. "Einstein: A lecture on the centenary of his birth." *PE, 14* (1979), 208-212, 223.

4.pm   Born, Max. "In memory of Einstein." *Interdisciplinary science reviews, 3* (1978), 267-274.

4.pr   *Borzhanskiy, L. "Al'bert Eynshteyn: K 50-letiyu yego rozhdeniya." *Vestnik inzhenerov,* 1929:4, 156-158.

4.ps   Casals, Pablo. "A tribute." B.ei4.yf, 43.

4.pv   Hönl, Helmut. "Albert Einstein." *PB, 10* (1954), 119-122.

4.qc   Ioffe, A. F. "Albert Einstein (k 5-letiyu so dnya smerti)." *UFN, 71* (1960), 3-7.

4.qi   *Ivanenko, D. D., et al. "K 20-letiyu so dnya smerti A. Eynshteyna." *VIYeT, 52* (1976), 13-42.

4.ql   Laue, Max von. "Zu A. Einsteins 50. Geburtstag." *Nwn, 17* (1929), 173.

4.qn   Laue, Max von. "Zu Albert Einsteins 70-ten Geburtstag." *Reviews of modern physics, 21* (1949), 348-349.

4.qp   Laue, Max von. "Albert Einstein." B.lf6.jl, *3,* 221-229. (Also in A.aj1.sc, 47-55.)

4.rm   Millikan, R. A. "Albert Einstein on his seventieth birthday." *Reviews of modern physics, 21* (1949), 343-345.

4.ro   Oppenheimer, J. R. "Celebration of the sixtieth birthday of Albert Einstein." *Science, 89* (1939), 335-336.

4.rv   Schöpf, Hans-Georg. "Zum 100. Geburtstag von A. Einstein: Albert Einsteins annus mirabilis 1905." *NTM, 15:2* (1978), 1-17.

4.sd   Shpol'skiy, E. V. "Al'bert Eynshteyn (1879-1955)." B.ei6.cb, 7-19.

4.sm   Sommerfeld, Arnold. "To Albert Einstein's seventieth birthday." B.ei4.zs, 99-105.

4.sn   Sommerfeld, Arnold. "Albert Einstein 70 Jahre." *PB, 5* (1949), 127.

4.tk   Stockton, William. "Celebrating Einstein." *Applied optics, 18* (1979), 1300-1304.

4.tt   Tamm, I. Ye. "A Soviet view of Einstein." *Soviet review, 1* (Aug. 1960), 37-42.

4.ud   Welker, Heinrich. "Zum 100. Geburtstag von Albert Einstein, Max von Laue, Otto Hahn, und Lise Meitner." *PB, 35* (1979), 189-191.

4.ya   Aichelburg, P. C., and R. U. Sexl, eds. *Albert Einstein: His influence on physics, philosophy, and politics.* Braunschweig and Wiesbaden, 1979.

4.yb   Angoff, Charles, ed. *Science and the human imagination: Albert Einstein.*" Rutherford, N. J., 1978. (*Leverton Lectures, 5.*)

4.yd   *Finis, Francesco de, ed. *Albert Einstein, 1879-1979: Relativity, quanta, and cosmology in the development of the scientific thought of Albert Einstein.* 2 vols. NY, 1979.

4.yf   French, A. P., ed. *Einstein: A centenary volume.* Cambridge, Mass., 1979.

4.yn   Nelkowski, H., et al., eds. *Einstein Symposium Berlin.* Berlin, 1979. (*Lecture notes in physics, 100.*)

4.yw   *Woolf, Harry, ed. *Some strangeness in the proportion: A centennial symposium to celebrate the achievements of Albert Einstein.* Reading, Mass., 1980.

4.zs   Schilpp, Paul A., ed. *Albert Einstein: Philosopher-scientist.* Evanston, 1949.

4.zt   Einstein, Albert. "Remarks concerning the essays brought together in this co-operative volume." B.ei4.zs, 665-688.

4.zu UNESCO. *Science and synthesis: An international colloquium organized by UNESCO on the tenth anniversary of the death of Albert Einstein and Teilhard de Chardin.* Tr. Barbara M. Crook. NY, 1971.

WORKS, GENERAL

ei5.ad Bernstein, M. "A. Eynshteyn o nauchnom tvorchestve." *ES,* 1968, 187-218.

5.ak Born, Max. "Einstein's statistical theories." B.ei4.zs, 163-177.

5.ap Broglie, Louis de. "A general survey of the scientific work of Albert Einstein." B.ei4.zs, 109-127.

5.ar Broglie, Louis de. "La physique contemporaine et l'oeuvre d'Albert Einstein." AS. *Notices et discours, 3* (1949), 39-66. (Also in B.ei1.an, 7-19.)

5.at Broglie, Louis de. "L'oeuvre d'Einstein et la dualité des ondes et des corpuscules." *Reviews of modern physics, 21* (1949), 345-347.

5.av Broglie, Louis de. *Le dualisme des ondes et des corpuscules dans l'oeuvre de Albert Einstein.* Paris, 1955. (In Russian in *VIYeT, 18* (1965), 5-15.)

5.be Earman, John, and Clark Glymour. "Lost in the tensors: Einstein's struggles with covariance principles, 1912-1916." *SHPS, 9* (1978), 251-278.

5.bs Grigor'yan, A. T. *Eynshteyn i razvitiye fiziko-matematicheskov mysli: Shornik statey.* Moscow, 1962.

5.ch Heisenberg, Werner. "The scientific work of Albert Einstein." *Science and culture, 29* (1963), 392-395.

5.cl Holton, Gerald. "Constructing a theory: Einstein's model. *American scholar, 48* (1979), 309-340.

5.dj Jammer, Max. "Albert Einstein und das Quantenproblem." B.ei4.yn, 146-167.

5.dp Jordan, Pascual. "Einsteins physikalisches Lebenswerk." *PB, 11* (1955), 289-297.

5.ef Landé, Alfred. "Albert Einstein and the quantum riddle." *AJP, 42* (1974), 459-464.

5.eh Laue, Max von. "Albert Einstein, der Schöpfer der Relativitätstheorie und Entdecker der Lichtquanten." A.aj1.sc, 47-55.

5.el Lemaître, Georges. "L'oeuvre scientifique d'Albert Einstein." *Revue des questions scientifiques, 16* (1955), 475-487.

5.et Mehra, Jagdish. "Albert Einsteins erste wissenschafliche Arbeit." *PB, 27* (1971), 385-391.

5.fe McCormmach, Russell. "Editor's foreword." *HSPS, 2* (1970), ix-xx.

5.ff McCormmach, Russell. "Editor's foreword." *HSPS, 7* (1976), xi-xxxv.

5.fm McCrea, W. H. "On the objective of Einstein's work." *BJPS, 8* (1957). 18-29.

5.gf Rosenfeld, Léon. "Professor Einstein's dilemma." *The listener, 44* (1950), 823-824.

5.gr Rosenthal-Schneider, Ilse. "Presuppositions and anticipations in Einstein's physics." B.ei4.zs, 131-146.

5.hf Tamm, I. Ye. "A. Eynshteyn i sovremennaya fizika." B.ei6.cb, 86-92.

5.ht Teller, Edward. "Albert Einstein: Three successes, three failures: Unconventional thoughts about an unconventional man." *Interdisciplinary science reviews, 3* (1978), 265-266.

5.if *Wheeler, John A. *Einsteins Vision. Wie steht es heute mit Einsteins Vision, alles als Geometrie aufzufassen?* Berlin and NY, 1968.

5.ih Wheeler, John A. "Einstein und was er wollte." *PB, 35* (1979), 385-397.

ON RELATIVITY THEORY

ei5.kf Anon. *Bibliothèque publique d'information: Einstein=mc².* Paris, 1979.

5.kh Anon. "Dokumentenanhang." *Relativitätstheorie und Weltanschauung: Zur philosophischen und wissenschaftspolitischen Wirkung Albert Einsteins.* Berlin, 1967. Pp. 258-285.

5.ko Barnett, Lincoln. *The universe and Dr. Einstein.* NY, 1948.

5.ks Bergia, Silvio. *Einstein e la relatività.* Bari, 1978.

5.kw Brasch, Frederick E. "Einstein's appreciation of Simon Newcomb." *Science, 69* (1929), 248-249.

5.lf Chudinov, E. M. "A. Eynshteyn ob otnoshenii geometrii k real'nosti." *ES,* 1971, 302-316.

5.lm Cuny, Hilaire. *Albert Einstein et la relativié.* Paris, 1961.

5.ls Dingle, Herbert. "Was Einstein aware of the Michelson-Morley experiment?" *Observatory, 93* (1973), 33-34.

5.mf   Florentiis, Giuseppe de. *A. Einstein, lo scienziato della relatività.* Milan, 1971.

5.mn   Fokker, A. D. "Albert Einstein, inventor of chronogeometry." *Synthèse, 9* (1955), 442-444.

5.mv   Fernandez, Carlos Graef. "My tilt with Albert Einstein." *American scientist, 44* (1956), 204-211.

5.nf   Grandolfo, Martino. *Einstein e il problema dell'universo.* Rome, 1975.

5.nk   Grigor'yan, A. T. "Appraisal of Newton's mechanics and of Einstein's *Autobiography.*" *AIHS,* no. 54-55 (1961), 13-22. (In Russian in IIYeT. *Trudy, 34* (1960), 177-186. In French in *Scientia, 96* (1961), 356-363.)

5.np   Harder, Allen. "The Copernican character of Einstein's cosmology." *Annals of science, 29* (1972), 339-347.

5.od   Holton, Gerald. "Influences on Einstein's early work in relativity theory: A report based on archival materials." ICHS, XI (1965). *Actes, 1* (1968), 87-106. (Also in *Organon, 3* (1966), 225-244.)

5.oe   Holton, Gerald. "The metaphor of space-time events in science." *Eranos-Jahrbuch, 34* (1965), 33-78.

5.of   Holton, Gerald. "Einstein, Michelson, and the 'crucial experiment.'" *Isis, 60* (1969), 133-197.

5.oh   Holton, Gerald. "Einstein and the 'crucial' experiment." *AJP, 37* (1969), 968-982.

5.oj   Holton, Gerald. "Einstein and the 'crucial' experiment." ICHS, XII (1968). *Actes, 16* (1971), 165-186.

5.ol   Holton, Gerald. "Eynshteyn, Maykel'son i 'reshayushchiy' eksperiment." *ES,* 1972, 104-211.

5.pf   Joshi, V. J. "Was Einstein aware of the Michelson-Morley experiment?" *Observatory, 22* (1972), 102.

5.pi   Kuznetsov, B. G. "Einstein und das Machsche Prinzip." *Ideen des exakten Wissens,* 1970, 49-55.

5.pk   Lanczos, Cornelius. "Einstein's path from special to general relativity." *R pl1.dl,* 5 19.

5.pp   Laue, Max von. "Eynshteyn i teoriya otnositel'nosti." *ES,* 1968, 7-27.

5.qf   Lemaître, Georges. "Rencontres avec A. Einstein." *Revue des questions scientifiques, 129* (1958), 129-132.

5.qm   Madaule, Jacques. "Quand Einstein eut la vision de l'univers." *Revue de Paris, 73* (1966), 59-72.

5.rf   Maurides, Stamatia. "L'importance de la cosmologie dans la
        pensée et dans l'oeuvre d'Einstein." ICHS, XI (1965). *Actes, 3*
        (1968), 136-142.

5.rm   Moszkowski, Alexander. *Einstein: Einblicke in seine Gedank-
        enwelt; gemeinverständliche Betrachtungen... entwickelt aus
        Gesprächen mit Einstein.* Berlin, 1921-1922.

5.rn   Moszkowski, Alexander. *Einstein the searcher: His works ex-
        plained from dialogues with Einstein.* Tr. H. L. Brose. NY, 1921.
        (Reissued as *Conversations with Einstein.* NY, 1970.)

5.sn   Nordmann, Charles. *Einstein et l'univers. Une lueur dans le
        mystère des choses.* Paris, 1921.

5.sp   *Polvani, Giovanni. "Introduzione storica allo studio della
        relatività di Einstein." *Elettrotecnica, 16* (1929), 360-366,
        385-390.

5.tf   Rohden, Huberto. *Einstein: O enigma da matemática.* Sao Paulo,
        1972.

5.tk   Schurmann, Paul F. "La obra de Einstein y la evolución de la
        ciencia." *Dia medico Uruguay, 23* (1955), 731-740.

5.ts   Strauss, Martin. "Einstein's theories and the critics of Newton."
        Synthèse, 18 (1968), 251-284.

5.we   Wheeler, John A. "The black hole: An imaginary conversation
        with Albert Einstein." B.ei4.ya, 51-56.

BIBLIOGRAPHY AND COLLECTED PAPERS

ei6.af Arzeliés, N. "Istoricheskiye i bibliograficheskiye zametki." *ES,*
        1973, 267-360.

6.ak   Boni, Nell, Monique Russ, and Dan H. Lawrence. *A bibliograph-
        ical checklist and index to the published writings of Albert Einstein.*
        Paterson, N. J., 1960.

6.as   Cassidy, David C. "Biographies of Einstein." B.ei4.yn, 490-500.

6.ax   Ginzburg, V. L. "Al'bert Eynshteyn: Sobraniye nauchnykh tru-
        dov." *ES,* 1969-70, 390-404.

6.bc   Klein, Martin J., and Allan Needell. "Some unnoticed publica-
        tions by Einstein." *Isis, 68* (1977), 601-604.

6.bl   Shields, Margaret C. "Bibliography of the writings of Albert Ein-
        stein to October 1949." B.ei4.zs, 691-756.

6.cb   *Eynshteyn i sovremennaya fizika: Sbornik pamyati A. Eynshteyna.*
        Moscow, 1956.

6.cd   Einstein, Albert. *Fizika i real'nost': Sbornik statey.* Moscow, 1965.

6.cf   Einstein, Albert. *Sobraniye nauchnykh trudov.* Ed. I. Ye. Tamm et al. 4 vols. Moscow, 1965-67.

CORRESPONDENCE AND TALKS

ei6.dg   Raskin, N. M. "Pis'ma Eynshteyna v Akademiyu Nauk SSSR." *VIYeT, 20* (1966), 86-87.

6.dr   Einstein, Albert. *Albert Einstein—Michele Besso: Correspondance 1903-1955.* Ed. and tr. P. Speziali. Paris, 1972.

6.dt   Einstein, Albert. "Perepiska A. Eynshteyna i M. Besso, 1903-1955." *ES,* 1974, 5-112.

6.du   Frank, A. M. "K perepiske Eynshteyn-Besso." *ES,* 1974, 113-114.

6.eb   Einstein, Albert, Hedwig Born, and Max Born. *Albert Einstein—Hedwig und Max Born: Briefwechsel 1916-1955.* Munich, 1969. (English trn, NY, 1971. B.bp1.jk.)

6.ed   Einstein, Albert. "Perepiska A. Eynshteyna i M. Borna." *ES,* 1971, 7-54.

6.ee   Einstein, Albert. "Perepiska A. Eynshteyna i M. Borna." *ES,* 1972, 7-103.

6.fc   Cartan, Elie, and Albert Einstein. *Letters on absolute parallelism, 1929-1932.* Ed. Robert Debeaver, tr. Jules Le Roy and Jim Ritter. Princeton, 1979.

6.gf   Einstein, Albert, and Sigmund Freud. *Lettres de Einstein et Freud échangées sur la guerre.* Liège, 1972.

6.gi   Frenkel', V. Ya. "Novyye materialy o diskussii Eynshteyna i Fridmana po relyativistskoy kosmologii." *ES,* 1973, 5-18.

6.ha   Bernstein, . "O pis'me Eynshteyna Zhaku Adamaru." *ES,* 1967, 30-44.

6.ik   Proosdij, B. A. van. "Some letters from Albert Einstein to Heike Kamerlingh Onnes." *Janus, 48* (1959), 133-137.

6.jl   Kraus, Oskar. *Offene Briefe an Albert Einstein und Max von Laue über die gedanklichen Grundlagen der speziellen und allgemeinen Relativitätstheorie.* Vienna and Leipzig, 1925.

6.km   Herneck, Friedrich. "Zu einem Brief Albert Einsteins an Ernst Mach." *PB, 15* (1959), 563-564.

6.ko   Herneck, Friedrich. "Zum Briefwechsel Albert Einsteins mit Ernst Mach." *FF, 37* (1963), 239-243.

6.lh   Hönl, Helmut. "Ein Brief Albert Einstein an Ernst Mach." *PB, 16* (1960), 571-580.

6.mp   Thiele, Joachim. "Briefe Albert Einsteins an Joseph Petzold." *NTM, 8:1* (1971), 70-74.

6.ns   Kahn, Carla, and Franz Kahn. "Letters from Einstein to de Sitter on the nature of the universe." *Nature, 257* (1975), 451-454.

6.os   Einstein, Albert. "Iz prazhskikh pisem A. Eynshteyna." *VIYeT, 18* (1965), 20-22. (Letters to M. Smoluchowski.)

6.pf   Einstein, Albert. *Lettres à Maurice Solovine.* Ed. and tr. M. Solovine. Paris, 1956.

6.ps   Einstein, Albert, and Arnold Sommerfeld. *Briefwechsel.* Ed. Armin Hermann. Basel and Stuttgart, 1968.

6.qf   Hermann, Armin. "Albert Einstein und Johannes Stark. Briefwechsel und Verhältnis der beiden Nobelpreisträger." *Sudhoffs Archiv, 50* (1966), 267-285.

6.rc   Einstein, Albert. "Iz perepiski Eynshteyna." *ES,* 1967, 7.

6.rg   Anon. "Pis'ma Eynshteyna moravskomy konditeru Kolachnomu." *Puti v neznayemoye, 5* (1965), 490-491.

6.sb   Beijing. University. *Gazette.* [Letter of Albert Einstein.] 26 Dec. 1922 and 4 Jan. 1923.

6.sr   Salzer, Herbert. "Two letters from Einstein concerning his distant parallelism field theory." *AHES, 12* (1974), 89-96.

6.sv   Sanesi, Elena. "Three letters from Albert Einstein and some information on Einstein's stay in Pavia." *Physics, 18* (1976), 174-178.

6.th   Herneck, Friedrich. *Einstein und sein Weltbild: Aufsätze und Vorträge.* Berlin, 1976.

6.tj   *Ishiwara, Jun. *Einstein Kyôzyu Kôen-roko.* Tokyo, 1923.

DOCUMENTS

ei6.vf Forman, Paul, and Paul Hanle. *Einstein: A centenary exhibition.* Washington, D. C., 1979.

6.vh   Herneck, Friedrich. "Die Einstein-Dokumente im Archiv der Humboldt-Universität zu Berlin." *NTM, 10:2* (1973), 32-38.

6.vj   Kahan, Théo. "Un document historique de l'Académie des Sciences de Berlin sur l'activité scientifique d'Albert Einstein (1913)." *AIHS,* no. 60-61 (1962), 337-342.

6.vk Kirsten, Christa, and Hans-Jürgen Treder, eds. *Albert Einstein in Berlin, 1913-1933.* Teil I: *Darstellung und Dokumente.* Teil II: *Spezialinventar.* Berlin, 1979.

6.vp Lewis, Albert C. *Albert Einstein, 1879-1955.* Austin, 1979.

6.vr Rasmussen, Paul C. "Einstein and the Library of Living Philosophers." *ICarbS, 2:2* (1975), 95-100.

6.vz Zurich. Eidgenössische Technische Hochschule. *Die Einstein-Sammlung der ETH-Bibliothek in Zürich.* Zurich, 1970. (ETH. Bibliothek. *Schriftenreihe,* 13.)

6.xh Hermann, Steffi, and Armin Hermann. *Einstein anekdotisch. Ein Genie — Zum Lachen.* Munich, 1970.

6.xi Hermann, Armin. "Albert Einstein anekdotisch." *PB, 26* (1970), 502-504.

6.xk Hoffmann, Banesh, and Joan Warnow. "Glimpses of Einstein: A photo essay." *PTeach, 12* (1974), 200-204.

6.xp Warnow, Joan N. *Images of Einstein. A catalog.* NY, 1979.

6.xw Wickert, Johannes. *Albert Einstein in Selbstzeugnissen und Bilddokumenten.* Reibeck bei Hamburg, 1972.

6.yp Kursunoglu, Behram, Arnold Perlmutter, and Linda F. Scotts, eds. *On the path of Albert Einstein.* NY and London, 1979.

PHILOSOPHY, GENERAL

ei7.ae *Eynshteyn i filosofskiye problemy fiziki XX veka.* Moscow, 1979.

7.af Frank, Philipp. "Einstein's philosophy of science." *Reviews of modern physics, 21* (1949), 349-355.

7.aj Frenkel', V. Ya. "Perechityvaya nauchnuyu prozu Eynshteyna." *ES,* 1974, 385- .

7.al Gribanov, D. P. "Filosofskoye mirovozzreniye Eynshteyna." B.ei7.ae, 7-45.

7.an Griffin, N. "Einstein's philosophy of science." *Scientia, 106* (1971), 25-37.

7.bj Janich, Peter. "Die erkenntnistheoretischen Quellen Einsteins." B.ei4.yn, 412-427

7.bt Metz, André. "Einstein et la philosophie des sciences." *AIHS,* no. 80 (1967), 225-234.

7.cf Northrop, F. S. C. "Einstein's conception of science." B.ei4.zs, 387-408.

7.cr Palter, Robert M. "Philosophic principles and scientific theory." *PS, 23* (1956), 111-135.

7.ct   *Relativitätstheorie und Weltanschauung. Zu philosophischen und wissenschaftspolitischen Wirkung Albert Einsteins.* Berlin, 1967.

7.cv   Russo, François. "Le 'philosophe-savant'." B.ei1.an, 227-260.

7.dc   *Steinburg, Heiner. "Grundzüge der philosophischen Auffassungen Albert Einsteins." B.ei7.ct.

7.df   Suvorov, S. G. "Einstein's philosophical views and their relation to his physical opinions." *SPU, 8:4* (1966), 578-609.

7.dm   Ushenko, Andrew Paul. "Einstein's influence on contemporary philosophy." B.ei4.zs, 609-645.

7.dw   Weizsäcker, C. F. von. "Einstein and the philosophy of physics." *Measure, 2* (1951), 231-240.

7.dz   Weizsäcker, C. F. von. "Einstein's importance to physics, philosophy and politics." B.ei4.ya, 159-168.

PHILOSOPHY, PARTICULAR

ei7.gb Ballentine, L. E. "Einstein's interpretation of quantum mechanics." *AJP, 40* (1972), 1763-1771.

7.gg   Bowman, Peter A. "Einstein's second treatment of simultaneity." Philosophy of Science Association. *Proceedings,* 1976:1, 71-81.

7.gm   Feyerabend, Paul K. "Zahar on Einstein." *BJPS, 25* (1974), 25-28.

7.hg   Griffin, N. "Einstein's simplicism." *Scientia, 106* (1971), 1029-1054.

7.hk   *Herneck, Friedrich. "Einstein und die Willensfreiheit." *Physik in der Schule,* 1969:4, 145-149.

7.if   Holton, Gerald. "On being caught between Dionysians and Apollonians." *Daedalus, 103* (1974), 65-81.

7.ih   Holton, Gerald. "Einstein's model for constructing a scientific theory." B.ei4.ya, 109-136.

7.ij   Holton, Gerald. "What, precisely, is 'thinking'? . . . Einstein's answer." *PTeach, 17* (1979), 157-164. (Also in B.ei4.yf, 153-166.)

7.kb   Illy, József. "Einstein eltávolodása a pozitivizmustól." *Magyar filzófiai szemle, 19* (1975), 151-160.

7.kk   Kuznetsov, Boris Grigor'yevich. "Eynshteyn i printsip Makha." *ES,* 1967, 134-174.

7.le   Lenzen, Victor F. "Einstein's theory of knowledge." B.ei4.zs, 357-384.

7.lm Müller-Markus, Siegfried. *Einstein und die Sowjetphilosophie. Krisis einer Lehre.* 2 vols. Dordrecht, 1960-66.

7.lo Omel'yanovskiy, M. E. "Eynshteyn, osnovaniya sovremennoy fiziki i materialisticheskaya dialektika." B.ei7.ae, 46-74.

7.lp Neidorf, Robert. "Is Einstein a positivist?" *PS, 30* (1963), 173-188.

7.ls Paty, Michel. "Sur le réalisme d'Albert Einstein." *La pensée,* no. 204 (1979), 18-37.

7.mb Schey, Harry M. "Einstein's rejection of quantum theory: A personal motive." *American imago, 28* (1971), 187-190.

7.mp Wertheimer, Michael. "Relativity and Gestalt: A note on Albert Einstein." *Journal of the history of the behavioral sciences, 1* (1965), 86-87.

7.nf Wickert, Johannes. "Zum produktiven Denken bei Einstein. Ein Beitrag zur Erkenntnispsychologie." B.ei4.yn, 443-463.

7.nm Zahar, Elie G. "Einstein's debt to Lorentz: A reply to Feyerabend and Miller." *BJPS, 29* (1978), 49-60.

PHILOSOPHICAL COMPARISONS

ei7.pb Kuznetsov, Boris Grigor'yevich. "Einstein et Bohr." *Organon, 2* (1965), 105-121.

7.pd Bernstein, Jeremy. "Einstein and Bohr: A debate." *PTeach, 4* (1966), 258-265.

7.pk Chudinov, E. M. "Eynshteyn i Bridzhmen: O dvukh podkhodakh k probleme empiricheskogo obosnovaniya fizicheskoy teorii." *ES,* 1974, 335-350.

7.pp Lionnais, F. Le. "Descartes et Einstein." *RHS, 5* (1952), 139-154.

7.pv Kuznetsov, Boris Grigor'yevich. *Einstein and Dostoevsky.* Tr. V. Talmy. London, 1972.

7.qb Bühler, Karl. "Christian von Ehrenfels und Albert Einstein." *Gestalthaftes Sehen.* Ed. F. Weinhandl. Darmstadt, 1960. Pp. 86-91.

7.qh Kuznetsov, Boris Grigor'yevich. "Einstein and Epicurus." *Diogenes, 81* (1973), 44-69.

7.qm Kuznetsov, Boris Grigor'yevich. "Galilée et Einstein: Prologue et épilogue de la science classique." ICHS, XII (1968). *Actes, 5* (1971), 59-63.

7.qp   Elsbach, Alfred Coppel. *Kant und Einstein; Untersuchungen über das Verhältnis der modernen Erkenntnistheorie zur Relativitätstheorie.* Berlin, 1924.

7.qq   Friedlander, S. *Kant gegen Einstein.* Berlin, 1932.

7.qt   Sambursky, Schmuel. "Von Kepler bis Einstein: Das Genie in der Naturwissenschaft." *Eranos-Jahrbuch, 40* (1970), 201-238.

7.rd   Brauner, Bohuslav. "Einstein and Mach." *Nature, 113* (1924), 927.

7.rj   Frank, Philipp. "Einstein, Mach, and logical positivism." B.ei4.zs, 271-286.

7.ro   Herneck, Friedrich. "Nochmals über Einstein und Mach." *PB, 17* (1961), 275-276.

7.rq   Herneck, Friedrich. "Die Beziehungen zwischen Einstein und Mach, dokumentarisch dargestellt." *Wissenschafliche Zeitschrift, mathematisch-naturphilosophische Reihe, 15* (1966), 1-14.

7.rv   Hönl, Helmut. "Albert Einstein und Ernst Mach: Das machsche Prinzip und die Krise des logischen Positivismus: Walter Gerlach zum Gedächtnis." *PB, 35* (1979), 485-494.

7.rx   Kuznetsov, Boris Grigor'yevich "Einstein und Mozart." *Ideen des exakten Wissens,* 1972, 783-788.

7.sa   Cohen, I. Bernard. "Einstein and Newton." B.ei4.yf, 40-42.

7.sb   Pais, Abraham. "Einstein, Newton, and success." B.ei4.yf, 35-37.

7.sc   Unsöld, Albrecht. "Ptolemäus—Kopernikus—Einstein." *PB, 20* (1964), 204-211.

7.th   Herneck, Friedrich. "Eine bisher unbeachtete Quelle von Einsteins Ablehnung der statistischen Quantenmechanik: Einstein und Schopenhauer." ICHS, XII (1968). *Actes, 5* (1971), 41-44.

7.uk   Kuznetsov, Boris Grigor'yevich. "Spinoza et Einstein." *Revue de synthèse, 88* (1967), 31-52.

7.ul   Kuznetsov, Boris Grigor'yevich. "Spinoza i Eynshteyn." *ES,* 1968, 28-49.

SOCIAL CONCERNS

ei9.ac Cocho, Flavio, Germinal Cocho, and Raul Rechtman. "Aspetti della correlazione scienza-società nell'opera scientifica di Einstein." *Testi e contesti,* no. 4 (1980), 63-71.

9.bc   Einstein, Albert. "Letter to Royal Society on occasion of the Newton bicentenary." *Nature, 119* (1927), 467.

9.be Einstein, Albert. *The world as I see it.* Tr. Alan Harris. London, 1935.

9.bf Einstein, Albert. *The world as I see it.* Tr. Alan Harris. NY, 1949.

9.bh Einstein, Albert. *Einstein on peace.* Ed. Otto Nathan and Heinz Norden. NY, 1960.

9.bk Einstein, Albert. *Ideas and opinions.* Ed. Sonja Bargmann. NY, 1954.

9.cb Feld, Bernard T. "Einstein and the politics of nuclear weapons." *BAS, 35* (Mar. 1979), 5-16.

9.cd French, A. P. "Einstein and world affairs." B.ei4.yf, 185-198.

9.cf Frankfurt, U. I., and A. M. Frank. "Eynshteyn kak istorik nauki." *ES,* 1966, 298-338.

9.cm Garvy, George. "Albert Einstein and the Nobel Peace Prize for Karl Kautsky." *International review of social history, 18* (1973), 107-109.

9.ct Grundmann, Siegfried. "Der deutsche Imperialismus, Einstein und die Relativitätstheorie (1914-1933)." B.ei7.ct, 155-285.

9.df Herneck, Friedrich. "Albert Einstein und das politische Schicksal seines Sommerhauses in Caputh bei Potsdam (mit Erstveröffentlichung von vier Einstein-Briefen)." *NTM, 11:1* (1974), 32-39.

9.dm Hinshaw, Virgil G., Jr. "Einstein's social philosophy." B.ci4.zs, 649-661.

9.do Hoffmann, Banesh. "Einstein and Zionism." B.ei4.ya, 169-176.

9.dt Israel, H., ed. *Hundert Autoren gegen Einstein.* Leipzig, 1931.

9.ek Klein, Martin J. "Einstein on scientific revolutions." *Vistas in astronomy, 17* (1975), 113-120.

9.em Kuznetsov, Boris Grigor'yevich. "Einstein, science and culture." B.ei4.yf, 167-184.

9.ep Lynch, Arthur. *The case against Einstein.* London, 1932.

9.ew Mannoury, G. "The cultural phenomenon Albert Einstein." *Synthèse, 9* (1955), 438-441.

9.fk Olszewski, Eugeniusz. "Einstein's social and political view." ICHS, XI. (1965). *Actes, 1* (1968), 153-156.

9.fp Rotblat, Joseph. "Einstein the pacifist warrior." *BAS, 35* (Mar. 1979), 21-26.

9.fs   *Severi, Francesco. "Uno sforzo di chiarificazione della dottrina di Einstein ricordando l'uomo." Associazione Culturale Italiana. *Conferenze, 20* (1967), -.

9.ft   Simon, Pierre Henri. "Du pacifisme à la bombe." B.ei1.an, 205-226.

9.fu   Tauber, Gerald E. "Einstein and Zionism." B.ei4.yf, 199-208.

9.fv   Thüring, B. "Albert Einsteins Umsturzversuch in der Physik und seine inneren Möglichkeiten und Ursachen." *Forschungen und Judenfrage, 4* (1940), 134-162.

9.fw   Wagner, Jozef. *Was Einstein wirklich sagte.* Vienna, 1970.

9.gy   Yourgrau, Wolfgang. "Einstein—and the vanity of academia." B.ei4.ya, 213-220.

INSTITUTIONS AND NATIONALITIES

ei9.ha   Anon. "Professor Dr. Albert Einstein and the Leiden University, 1920-1956." *Janus, 46* (1957), 77-78.

9.hg   Grundmann, Siegfried. "Die Auslandsreisen Albert Einsteins und die Aussenpolitik der deutschen Monopolbourgeoisie nach dem ersten Weltkrieg." *NTM, 2:6* (1965), 1-9.

9.hm   Hermann, Armin. "Einstein und die deutschen Physiker: Zitate aus Briefen Einsteins." *PB, 25* (1969), 99-100.

9.ho   Hermann, Armin. "Einstein auf der Salzburger Naturforscherversammlung 1909." *PB, 25* (1969), 433-436.

9.hq   Hermann, Armin. "Einstein und Deutschland." B.ei4.yn, 537-550.

9.ib   Herneck, Friedrich. "Über die deutsche Reichsangehörigkeit Albert Einsteins." *FF, 37* (1963), 137-140.

9.id   Herneck, Friedrich. "Einstein und die Humboldt-Universität." Berlin University. *Wissenschaftliche Zeitschrift, mathematisch-naturphilosophische Reihe, 15* (1966), 797-801.

9.ik   Kollros, Louis. "Alberto Einstein in Svizzera." *Filosofia, 9* (1958), 3-12.

9.ip   Proosdij, B. A. van. "Einstein and the University of Utrecht." *Janus, 47* (1958), 131-132.

9.jf   Rooseboom, Maria. "Matériaux pour l'histoire des sciences du temps moderne, viii. Albert Einstein und die niederlandischen Universitäten." *Janus, 47* (1958), 198-201.

9.jt   Treder, Hans-Jürgen, and Christa Kirsten. "Albert Einstein an der Berliner Akademie der Wissenschaften, 1913-1933." Akademie der Wissenschaften, Berlin. *Archivmitteilungen, 28* (1978), 141-144.

ei9.mf   Finlay-Freundlich, Erwin. "Wie es dazu kam, dass ich den Einsteinturm errichtete." *PB, 25* (1969), 538-541.

9.mi   Greither, Aloys. "Albert Einstein's friendship with the painter Josef Scharl." *CIBA Symposium, 16* (1968), 57-68.

9.nf   Herneck, Friedrich. "Einsteins freundschaft mit Ärzten." *NTM, 8:2* (1971), 24-34.

9.nh   Loria, Arturo. "Einstein and education." B.ei4.yf, 215-228.

9.nk   Mercier, André. "Birth and role of the GRG—Organization and the cultivation of international relations among scientists in the field." B.ei4.ya, 177-188.

9.nm   Michaelis, A. R. "Albert Einstein as seen by artists." *Interdisciplinary science reviews, 3* (1978), 263-264.

9.nt   Zubiri, Xavier. *Naturaleza, historia, dios.* 3rd edn, Madrid, 1955.

See also: B.bo1.ks | ih1.bo | la6.ck | lc3.je | lj3.jk | mb2.ec, ec, ei, ej, ek, ey | mk1.ds | pll.cc, kh | so1.je; C.ap1.kl; D.bd1.ak | cf1.he | hb1.me | hh1.te; E.ae1.mc | mb1 fr; F; G.ba1.wo | ca1.fm | qa1.be, bo, bp; L.cb1.kk, kl, km, le, pa, pb | fb1.kk, kl | fe1.ez; L.i; R.dd1.kl; U.gg1.gr, kl | ka1.ej

Elsasser, Walter Maurice (1904-   )

ell.ae   Elsasser, Walter M. *Memoirs of a physicist in the atomic age.* NY, 1978.

Elster, J. P. L. Julius @ (1854-1920)

em1.ew   Wiechert, Emil. "Julius Elster: Gedächtnisrede." Akademie der Wissenschaften, Göttingen. *Nachrichten*, 1921, 53-60.

See also: I.rc1.ba

El'yashevich see Yel'yashevich

Emden, Robert @ (1862-1940)

en1.gs   Sommerfeld, Arnold, and M. Wolf. "Zu Robert Emdens 70. Geburtstag." *Nwn, 20* (1932), 161.

Eötvös, Roland von @ (1848-1919)

eo1.cn   Novobátzky, K. "Appreciation of Roland Eötvös." Budapest
          University. *Annales: Sectio geologica, 7* (1964), 3-7.

cv   Vassails, Gérard. "Lóránd Eötvös." *RHS, 6* (1953), 22-41.

jb   Anon. "Irodalom. Báró Eötvös Loránd." *Matematikai és physikai
          lapok, 27* (1918), 284-297.

je   Eötvös, Roland. *Gesammelte Arbeiten.* P. Selényi, ed. Budapest,
          1953.

See also: D.bg1; F.dg1.ki; P.bg1.ku, pe |ca1.ha

Epstein, Paul Sophus (1883-1966)

eo5.cd   DuMond, Jesse W. M. "Paul Sophus Epstein." NAS. *BM, 45*
          (1974), 127-152.

Esclangon, Ernest Benjamin @ (1876-1954)

ep1.bp   Pérard, Albert. "Quelques mots de l'oeuvre scientifique d'Ernest
          Esclangon." Société Astronomique de France. *Bulletin, 68*
          (1954), 201-204.

Eucken, Arnold Thomas @ (1884-1950)

er1.bp   Planck, R. "Arnold Eucken und die Verfahrenstechnik." *Nwn,
          32* (1944), 103-104.

gp   Patat, F. "Arnold Eucken zum 60. Geburtstag." *Nwn, 32* (1944),
          101-102.

Eve, Arthur Stewart (1862-1948)

er7.ef   Foster, J. S. "Arthur Stewart Eve." RS. *Obituary notices, 6*
          (1949), 397-407.

Ewald, Peter Paul (1888-   )

es1.ce   Ewald, Peter Paul. "Physicists I have known." *PT, 27* (Sep.
          1974), 42-47.

gh   Hosemann, Rolf. "Max-Planck-Medaille 1978 für Paul Ewald."
          PB, 34 (1978), 715-718.

Ewing, James Alfred @ (1855-1935)

ew1.ab   Bates, L. F. *Sir Alfred Ewing.* London, 1946.

eg   Glazebrook, R. T. "James Alfred Ewing." RS. *Obituary notices, 1*
          (1935), 475-492.

See also: U.kb1.jq

Ewing, William Maurice (1906-1974)

ew3.eb   Bullard, Edward. "William Maurice Ewing." RS. *BM, 21* (1975), 269-311.

Exner, Franz (1849-1926)

ex1.eb   Benndorf, Hans. "Zur Erinnerung an Franz Exner." *Physikalische Zeitschrift, 28* (1927), 397-409.

es   *Schweidler, Egon von. "[Franz Exner.]" Akademie der Wissenschaften, Vienna. *Almanach, 77 (1928), -* .

Eykhenval'd, Aleksandr Aleksandrovich (1864-1944)

ey1.ck   Kaptsov, N. A. "Aleksandr Aleksandrovich Eykhenval'd." C.vm1.pr, 116-171.

cm   Mlodzeyevskiy, A. B. "A. A. Eykhenval'd." C.vb1.ti, 170-185.

cn   Mlodzeyevskiy, A. B. "Aleksandr Aleksandrovich Eykhenval'd." B.ey1.je, 253-261.

je   Eykhenval'd, A. A. *Izbrannyye raboty.* Moscow, 1956.

Fabry, Charles @ (1867-1945)

fb1.cl   Lecomte, Jean, Albert Arnulf, and E. Vassy. "Charles Fabry." *Applied optics, 12* (1973), 1117-1129.

ec   Broglie, Louis de. "Notice sur la vie et l'oeuvre de Charles Fabry." AS. *Mémoires, 67* (1946), 27.

ed   Broglie, Maurice de. "Charles Fabry." RS. *Obituary notices, 5* (1945-48), 445-450.

Fage, Arthur (1890-1977)

fb7.ec   Collar, A. R. "Arthur Fage." RS. *BM, 24* (1978), 33-53.

Fajans, Kasimir (1887-1975)

fc1.gd   Anon. "Kasimir Fajans." *Journal of nuclear medicine, 7* (1966), 402-404. (Also *UFN, 99* (1969), 342-345.)

Falkenhagen, Hans (1895-1971)

fd1.gd   Debye, Peter. "Hans Falkenhagen zum 70. Geburtstag am 13 Mai 1965." *Zeitschrift für physikalische chemie* (Leipzig), 1965, 289-291.

Farr, Clinton Coleridge (1866-1943)

fd5.eg   Grant, Kerr. "Clinton Coleridge Farr." RS. *Obituary notices, 4* (1944), 503-506.

Feddersen, Berend Wilhelm (1832-1918)

fe1.eo   Oettingen, A. von. "Nachruf für B. W. Feddersen." Akademie der Wissenschaften, Leipzig. Math.-Phys. Klasse. *Berichte, 70* (1918), 353-361.

Fedorov, Yevgraf Stepanovich (1853-1919)

ff1.as   Shafranovskiy, I. I. *Ye. S. Fedorov.* Moscow and Leningrad, 1963.

bd   Delone, B. N. "Ye. S. Fedorov kak geometr." IIYeT. *Trudy, 10* (1956), 5-12.

cb   Ansheles, S. M., and I. I. Shafranovskiy. "Yevgraf Stepanovich Fedorov." Leningrad. University. *Uchenyye zapiski,* ser. geologo-pochvennykh nauk, *8* (1941), 5-15.

jc   Bokiy, G. B., and I. I. Shafranovskiy. "Iz perepiski Ye. S. Fedorova s A. Shenflisom." *Nauchnoye nasledstvo, 2* (1951), 314-343.

jd   Bokiy, G. B., and I. I. Shafranovskiy. "Iz perepiski Ye. S. Fedorova s Yu. V. Vul'fom." *Nauchnoye nasledstvo, 2* (1951), 349-354.

jf   Burckhardt, J. J. "Der Briefwechsel von E. S. von Federow und A. Schoenflies, 1889-1908." *AHES, 7* (1971), 91-141.

js   Shafranovskiy, I. I., and N. M. Raskin. *Rukopisnyye materialy Ye. S. Fedorova v Arkhive Akademii Nauk AN SSSR: Nauchnoye opisaniye, teksty.* Moscow and Leningrad, 1957. (AN. Arkhiv. *Trudy, 14.*)

ns   Shafranovskiy, I. I. "Ye. S. Fedorova i Akademiya Nauk." IIYeT. *Trudy, 10* (1956), 28-65.

See also: O.ac1.ko |fa1.an, bo, ye

Fermi, Enrico @ $38 (1901-1954)

fg1.af   Fermi, Laura. *Atoms in the family: My life with Enrico Fermi.* Chicago, 1954.

al   Latil, Pierre de. *Enrico Fermi: The man and his theories.* Tr. Len Ortzen. London, 1965.

an   *Pontecorvo, Bruno. *Enriko Fermi.* Moscow, 1971.

ao   Pontecorvo, Bruno. *Fermi e la fisica moderna.* Rome, 1972.

ap   Pontecorvo, Bruno. *Enrico Fermi v vospominaniyakh uchenikov i druzey.* Moscow, 1972.

as   *Rasetti, Franco. *Enrico Fermi.* Rome, 1968. (Accademia Nazionale dei Lincei. *Celebrazioni lincee, 12.*)

au   Segrè, Emilio. *Enrico Fermi: Physicist.* Chicago, 1970.

bd   Anderson, Herbert L. "The legacy of Fermi and Szilard." *BAS, 30* (Sept. 1974), 56-62.

bf   Biermann, Ludwig. "Enrico Fermi, der Erbauer des ersten Atomreaktors." A.aj1.sc, 87-93.

bs   Segrè, Emilio. "Enrico Fermi: Physicist." *BAS, 26* (Nov. 1970), 32, 37-39.

cc   Chandrasekhar, S. "Remarks on Enrico Fermi" A.ad1.me, 800-802.

cl   Lafferty, P. E. "Enrico Fermi." *PE, 6* (1971), 216-217.

co   Paldy, Lester G. "A master teacher [A. Amidei]." *PTeach, 7* (1969), 39-44.

cr   Pontecorvo, Bruno. "Enriko Fermi." B.fg1.jk, *1*, 9-45.

cs   Pontecorvo, Bruno. "Enrico Fermi." *Ideen des exakten Wissens,* 1972, 403-418.

cu   Segrè, Emilio. "Biographical introduction." B.fg1.jj, *1*, xvii-xlii.

ea   Arangio-Ruiz, Vincenzo. "Enrico Fermi." Accademia Nazionale dei Lincei. *Problemi attuali di scienza e cultura. Quaderno, 35* (1955), 3-7.

ec   Allison, Samuel K. "Enrico Fermi." NAS. *BM, 30* (1957), 125-155.

ed   Allison, Samuel K., et al. "Enrico Fermi." *PT, 8* (Jan. 1955), 9-13.

ef   Amaldi, Edoardo. "Enrico Fermi." Accademia Nazionale dei Lincei. *Problemi attuali di scienza e cultura. Quaderno, 35* (1955), 8-22.

eh   Bretcher, E., and John Cockcroft. "Enrico Fermi." RS. *BM, 1* (1955), 69-78.

ep   Persico, Enrico. "Souvenir de Enrico Fermi." *Scientia, 90* (1955), 316-324.

eq   Pontecorvo, Bruno. "Enrico Fermi." *UFN, 57* (1955), 349-359.

gb   Bethe, Hans A. "Memorial symposium held in honor of Enrico Fermi." *Review of modern physics, 27* (1955), 249-275.

gg   Goudsmit, S. A. "Nobel Prize goes to Enrico Fermi." *Journal of applied physics, 10* (1939), 14-15.

jb   Amaldi, Edoardo. "The Fermi manuscripts at the Domus Galilaeana." *Physis, 1* (1959), 69-72.

jd   Anderson, H. L., and Samuel K. Allison. "From Professor Fermi's notebooks." *Reviews of modern physics, 27* (1955), 273-275.

jg   Derenzini, Tullio. "Analisi dei manoscritti di Enrico Fermi conservati presso la 'Domus Galilaeana' di Pisa." *Physis, 6* (1964), 75-85.

jj   Fermi, Enrico. *Note e memorie. Collected papers.* 2 vols. Ed. Emilio Segrè. Chicago and Rome, 1962-65.

jk   Fermi, Enrico. *Nauchnyye trudy.* 2 vols. Ed. Bruno Pontecorvo. Moscow, 1972.

nf   Fermi, Laura. "The Fermis' path to Los Alamos." I.tb1.ba, 89-103.

See also: H.ea1.tu; I.ta1.wa | tb1.bc | tc1.an; K.ac1.se | ad1.wi | ae1.an; L.ff1.be; T.ei1.zi

Fesenkov, Vasiliy Grigor'yevich (1889-1972)

fg4.jm   **Vasiliy Grigor'yevich Fesenkov.* Moscow, 1961. (*Mtly*, ser. fiz.-mat.)

Fessenden, Reginald Aubrey (1866-1932)

fh1.af   **Fessenden, Helen May. *Fessenden, builder of tomorrows.* NY, 1940.

Fischer-Schaetti, Fritz (1898-1947)

fh4.cb   Balmer, Heinz. "Fritz Fischer: Ein Meister der technischen Physik, 1898-1947." *Gesnerus, 35* (1978), 107-131.

Fitzgerald, George Francis @ (1851-1901)

fi1.jf   FitzGerald, G. F. *Scientific writings.* Joseph Larmor, ed. Dublin, 1902.

Flamm, Ludwig (1885-1964)

fj1.et   Thirring, Hans. "Ludwig Flamm." *Acta physica austriaca, 24* (1966), 1-50.

Fleming, John Adam (1877-1956)

fj3.ct   Tuve, Merle A. "John Adam Fleming." NAS. *BM, 39* (1967), 103-140.

Fleming, John Ambrose @ (1849-1945)

fj4.af *Fleming, John Ambrose. *Fifty years of electricity: The memoires of an electrical engineer.* London, 1921.

ag Fleming, John Ambrose. *Memories of a scientific life.* London and Grand Rapids, 1934.

cm MacGregor-Morris, J. T. "Sir Ambrose Fleming (Jubilee of the valve)." RS. *Notes and records, 11* (1955), 134-144.

ee Eccles, W. H. "John Ambrose Fleming." RS. *Obituary notices, 5* (1945), 231-242.

Flerov, Georgiy Nikolayevich (1913-   )

fj6.ab Bondarenko, M. A., et al. *Georgiy Nikolayevich Flerov.* Dubna, 1973.

Flint, Henry T. (1890-1971)

fj8.jc CSAC. *Henry Flint papers at University of London Library and the Imperial War Museum.* List 27/4/75, 14 p.

Fok, Vladimir Aleksandrovich (1898-1974)

fk1.gb Anon. "Vybory v Akademiyu Nauk SSSR." *UFN, 21* (1939), 239-242.

gc Anon. "Akademik Vladimir Aleksandrovich Fok." *ZhETF, 35* (1958), 1321 1324.

gd Anon. "Vladimir Aleksandrovich Fok." Leningrad. University. *Vestnik,* ser. fiz. i khimii, 1958:22, 5-13.

ge Anon. "Chestvovaniye akademika V. A. Foka." AN. *Vestnik,* 1959:3, 113-114.

gv Vcselov, M. G. "Vladimir Aleksandrovich Fock." *SPU, 1* (1958), 321-325.

jm Smirnov, V. I., and T. O. Vreden-Kobetskaya, ed. *Vladimir Aleksandrovich Fok.* Moscow, 1956. (*Mtly,* ser. fiziki, 7.)

Föppl, August @ (1854-1924)

fl1.af Föppl, August. *Lebenserrinerungen.* Munich and Berlin, 1925.

id *Beiträge zur technischen Mechanik und technischen Physik. August Föppl zum 70. Geburtstag.* Berlin, 1924.

Foote, Paul Darwin (1888-1971)

fm1.cf   Foote, Paul D. "Physics then and now." *PT, 9* (Sep. 1956), 21-22.

   ed   Astin, Allen V. "Paul Darwin Foote." NAS. *BM, 50* (1979), 175-194.

Forsyth, Andrew Russell @ (1858-1942)

fn1.ew   Whittaker, E. T. "Andrew Russell Forsyth." RS. *Obituary notices, 4* (1942), 209-227.

Foster, John Stuart (1850-1964)

fn5.eb   Bell, R. E. "John Stuart Foster." RS. *BM, 12* (1966), 147-161.

Fowler, Alfred @ (1868-1940)

fo1.ed   Dingle, Herbert. "Alfred Fowler." RS. *Obituary notices, 3* (1941), 48-497.

Fowler, Ralph Howard @ (1889-1944)

fo4.em   Milne, E. A. "Ralph Howard Fowler." RS. *Obituary notices, 5* (1945), 61-78.

Franck, James @ $25 (1882-1964)

fp1.co   Oldenberg, O. "James Franck at Göttingen." *AJP, 39* (1971), 41-43.

   cr   Pohl, Robert W. "Von den Studien- und Assistentenjahren James Francks: Errinerungen an das Physikalische Institut der Berliner Universität." *PB, 28* (1972), 542-544.

   ed   Born, Max. "James Franck." *PB, 20* (1964), 324-327.

   ek   Kuhn, H. G. "James Franck." RS. *BM, 11* (1965), 53-74.

   er   Rabinowitch, Eugene. "James Franck, 1882-1964, Leo Szilard, 1898-1964." *BAS, 20* (Oct. 1964), 16-20.

   gp   Pohl, Robert, and Max von Laue. "James Franck zum 70. Geburtstag." *Zeitschrift für Physik, 133* (1952), 1.

   gw   Westphal, Wilhelm H. "James Franck 80 Jahre." *PB, 18* (1962), 370-371.

Frank, Il'ya Mikhaylovich $58 (1908-   )

fq1.gd   Barit, I. Ya., et al. "Il'ya Mikhailovich Frank." *SPU, 21* (1978), 887-890.

See also: B.cf1.gk

Frank, Philipp @ (1884-1966)

fq4.eh Holton, Gerald, et al. "In memory of Philipp Frank." *PS, 35* (1968), 1-5.

gd Bergmann, Peter G., et al. "Greetings to Philipp Frank." *BSPS, 2* (1965), ix-xxx.

ic Cohen, Robert S., and M. W. Wartofsky, ed. *Feschrift for Philipp Frank.* Dordrecht and NY, 1965. (*BSPS, 2.*)

kf *Gligorijević, Miroslav. "Filosofija nauke Filipa Franka." *Dijalektika, 8:3* (1973), 87-97.

kj *Inglis, Brian D. *Philipp Frank's philosophy of scientific knowing.* Ph.D thesis. Marquette Univ., 1970. (*DAI, 31,* 4838A.)

Frenkel', Yakov Il'ich @ (1894-1952)

frl.af Frenkel', V. Ya. *Yakov Il'ich Frenkel'.* Moscow and Leningrad, 1966.

ak Tuchkevich, V. M., ed. *Vospominaniya o Ya. I. Frenkele.* Leningrad, 1976.

bf Frenkel', V. Ya. "O stile nauchnogo tvorchestva Ya. I. Frenkelya." *UFN, 113* (1974), 535-547. (Also in *SPU, 17,* (1975), 577-583.)

bg Frenkel', V. Ya. "Yakov (James) Il'ich Frenkel (1894-1952): Materials for his scientific biography." *AHES, 13* (1974), 1-26.

bk Ioffe, A. F. "O nauchnom nasledii Ya. I. Frenkelya." B.frl.jd, 17-18.

cf Frenkel', V. Ya. "K biografii Ya. I. Frenkelya." B.frl.jf, 5-26.

ci Ioffe, A. F. "Yakov Il'ich Frenkel'." A.ajl.io, 208-11.

ct Tamm, I. Ye. "Yakov Il'ich Frenkel'." *UFN, 76* (1962), 397-430.

cu Tamm, I. Ye. "Yakov Il'ich Frenkel." *SPU, 5:2* (1962), 173-193.

cy *Yeremeyeva, S. I. "Yakov Il'ich Frenkel'." Moscow. Publichnaya biblioteka. *Vydayushchiyesya fiziki mira.* Ed. B. G. Kuznetsov. Moscow, 1958.

ec Ansel'm, A. I. "Yakov Il'ich Frenkel'." *UFN, 47* (1952), 470-476.

ee Anon. "Yakov Il'ich Frenkel'." *ZhETF, 23* (1952), 613-618.

eg Dorfman, Ya. G. "Yakov Il'ich Frenkel." B.frl.jd, *1*, 3-15.

jd Frenkel', Ya. I. *Sobraniye izbrannykh trudov.* 3 vols. Moscow, 1956-59.

jf   Frenkel', Ya. I. *Na zare novoy fiziki: Sbornik izbrannykh nauchno-populyarnykh rabot.* Leningrad, 1970.

jk   Frenkel', V. Ya. "Iz istorii fiziki 30-x godov (pis'ma Ya. I. Frenkelya professoru E. Khillu)." *VIYeT,* 1980:1, 136-143.

jt   Tamm, I. Ye. "Yakov Il'ich Frenkel': Pis'ma k rodnym." *Puti v neznayemoye, 4* (1964), 549-599.

See also: E.bd1.sm; I.dd1.sm; O.da1.vo; P.aa1.ba; R.ba1.br

Fridman, Aleksandr Aleksandrovich @ (1888-1925)

fs1.at   *Trostnikov, V. N. *Vydayushchiysya sovetskiy uchenyy A. A. Fridman.* Moscow, 1963.

bl   Loskutov, K. N. "Otzyv akademika V. A. Steklova o trudakh A. A. Fridmana." D.ab1.ii, 228-231.

cl   *Loytsyanskiy, L. G., and A. I. Lur'ye. "Aleksandr Aleksandrovich Fridman." Leningrad. Politekhnicheskiy institut. *Trudy, 1* (1949), 83-86.

gp   Polubarinova-Kochina, P. Ya. "Aleksandr Aleksandrovich Fridman (k 75-letiyu so dnya rozhdeniya)." *UFN, 80* (1963), 345-352. (Also in *SPU* (1964), 467-472.)

jf   Fridman, A. A. *Izbrannyye trudy.* L. S. Polak, ed. Moscow, 1966.

jg   Gavrilov, A. F. "Vospominaniya o Fridmane: K perepiske A. A. Fridmana." IIYeT. *Trudy, 22* (1959), 389-400.

ji   *Gyunter, N. M. "Nauchnyye trudy A. A. Fridmana." Leningradskoye fiziko-matematicheskoye obshchestvo. *Zhurnal, 1:1* (1926), 5-11.

See also: B.ei6.gi |go1.jp; D.eb1.me; F.bh1.lo |de1.fo; P.aa1.iz |kc1.ze

Friedrich, Walter (1883-1968)

ft1.af   **Walter Friedrich, Leben und Wirken.* Berlin, 1963.

gl   Laue, Max von. "Walter Friedrich 70. Jahre." *PB, 9* (1953), 561-562.

Frisch, Otto Robert (1904-1979)

fu1.af   Frisch, Otto R. *What little I remember.* Cambridge, 1979.

jc   CSAC. *Otto Frisch papers.* List in progress, 1981.

Frost, Edwin Brant (1866-1935)

fu6.es   Struve, Otto. "Edwin Brant Frost." NAS. *BM, 19* (1938), 25-51.

Frumkin, Aleksandr Naumovich (1895-1976)

fv1.jm   *Aleksandr Naumovich Frumkin.* Moscow, 1955; 2nd ed., 1970. (*Mtly*, ser. khim., 21, 44.)

Gabor, Dennis $71 (1900-1979)

ga3.eb   Allibone, T. E. "Dennis Gabor." RS. *BM, 26* (1980), 107-147.

Gaede, Wolfgang (1878-1945)

gb1.ag   Gaede, Hannah. *Wolfgang Gaede: Der Schöpfer des Hochvakuums.* Karlsruhe, 1954.

cd   Dunkel, Manfred. "Gedenken an Wolfgang Gaede." *PB, 34* (1978), 228-232.

Gamow, George @ (1904-1968)

gc1.ag   Gamow, George. *My world line: An informal autobiography.* NY, 1970.

ky   Yourgrau, Wolfgang. "The cosmos of George Gamow." *New scientist, 48* (1970), 38-39.

See also: I.da1.rp

Garbasso, Antonio (1871-1933)

gd1.ec   Bernardini, Gilberto. "Antonio Garbasso." *La ricerca scientifica, 7* (1933), 441-446.

ep   Puccianti, Luigi. "Commemorazione del presidente dell'Accademia Antonio Garbasso." Accademia Nazionale dei Lincei. Classe di Scienze Fisiche. *Atti, 17* (1933), 988-995.

es   *Ronchi, Vasco. "Antonio Garbasso." *Luce e immagini, 7* (1933), 1-13.

Geiger, Hans Johannes W. @ (1882-1945)

ge1.el   Laue, Max von. "Nachruf auf Hans Geiger." Akademie der Wissenschaften, Berlin. *Jahrbuch*, 1946-49, 150-158. (Also in B.lf6.jl, *3*, 204-212.)

See also: C.gb3.cb; H.bf1.tr; T.gb1.tr

Geitel, Hans F. K. @ (1855-1923)

See: B.em1

Gell-Mann, Murray $69 (1929-   )

See: K.aa1.pf

Gentile, Giovanni, Jr. (1906-1942)

gf4.eg   Polvani, Giovanni. "Giovanni Gentile junior." *Nuovo cimento, 1* (1943), 155-160.

ep   Polvani, Giovanni. "Commemorazione di Giovanni Gentile junior." Istituto Lombardo di Scienze e Lettere. *Rendiconti, 75: Parte generale* (1941-42), 146-154.

jg   Gentile, Giovanni, Jr. *Scritti minori di scienza, filosofia, e littera-tura.* Florence, 1943.

Gerlach, Walther (1889-1979)

gg1.gr   Rechenberg, Helmut. "Walther Gerlach zum neunzigsten." *PB, 35* (1979), 370-374.

kw   Wagner, Kurt. *Naturwissenschaft und Humanismus. Zur weltan-schaulichen Position Walther Gerlachs.* Berlin, 1969.

Gershun, Aleksandr L'vovich (1868-1915)

gg4.ci   Ivanov, N. I. "Aleksandr L'vovich Gershun." *UFN, 42* (1950), 476-484.

Gibbs, Josiah Willard @ (1839-1903)

gh1.ar   Rukeyser, Muriel. *Willard Gibbs.* NY, 1942.

aw   Wheeler, Lynde Phelps. *Josiah Willard Gibbs, the history of a great mind.* New Haven, 1951.

bd   Donnan, F. G., and Arthur E. Haas, eds. *A commentary on the scientific writings of J. Willard Gibbs.* 2 vols. New Haven, 1936.

bs   *Semenchenko, V. K. "Dzhosia Villard Gibbs: Yego zhiznennyi put' i osnovnyye nauchnyye raboty." B.gh1.ji, 9-23.

bw   Wheeler, Lynde Phelps. *The only work of Willard Gibbs in applied mechanics, comprising the text of his hitherto unpublished Ph.D. thesis and accounts of mechanical innovations.* NY, 1947.

cc   Crowther, J. G. "Josiah Willard Gibbs." C.ua1.cr, 227-297.

ch   Hastings, Charles S. "Josiah Willard Gibbs." NAS. *BM, 6* (1909), 373-393.

ck   Klein, Martin J. "Gibbs, Josiah Willard." *DSB, 5* (1972), 386-393.

jg   Gibbs, J. Willard. *The collected works of J. Willard Gibbs.* 2 vols. NY, 1928.

ji   *Gibbs, J. Willard. *Termodinamicheskiye raboty.* Tr. B. V. Semenchenko. Moscow and Leningrad, 1950.

Gibbs, Oliver Wolcott @ (1822-1908)

gh2.ec   Clarke, F. W. "Wolcott Gibbs." NAS. *BM, 7* (1910), 1-22.

See also: R.db1.he, hi

Giesel, Friedrich Oskar @ (1852-1927)

gh4.ct   Trenn, Thaddeus J. "Giesel, Friedrich Oskar." *DSB, 5* (1972, 394-395.

Ginzburg, Vitaliy Lazarevich (1916-)

gi1.gk   Keldysh, L. V., et al. "Vitalii Lazarevich Ginzburg." *SPU, 19* (1976), 872-887.

Giorgi, Giovanni (1871-1950)

gi5.cf   *Focaccia, Basilio. "Giovanni Giorgi." *Elettrotecnica, 38* (1951), 214-218.

Glazebrook, Richard Tetley @ (1854-1935)

gj1.ef   F., A. "Sir Richard Tetley Glazebrook." Physical Society of London. *Proceedings, 48* (1936), 929-933.

es   Strutt, Robert John, Fourth Baron Rayleigh, and F. J. Selby. "Richard T. Glazebrook." RS. *Obituary notices, 2* (1936-38), 29-56.

Gobrecht, Heinrich (1909-)

gk1.gn   Nelkowski, Horst. "Heinrich Gobrecht: 70 Jahre." *PB, 35* (1979), 411-413.

Goddard, Robert Hutchings @ (1882-1945)

gk4.al   Lehman, Milton. *This high man: The life of Robert Goddard.* NY, 1963.

jg   Goddard, R. H. *The papers of Robert H. Goddard.* Ed. Esther C. Goddard and G. Edward Pendry. 3 vols. NY, 1970.

Gogoberidze, Dmitriy Borisovich (1906-1957)

gll.ef Frank-Kamenetskiy, V. A., and V. B. Sakhov. "Pamyati Dmitri-ya Borisovicha Gogoberidze." *UFN, 53* (1954), 109-120.

Gol'dgammer, Dmitriy Aleksandrovich (1860-1922)

See: B.mpl.cp; E.mbl.ve

Goldhaber, Gerson (1924-)

gm4.cg Goldhaber, Gerson. "A scientific autobiography." *Adventures in experimental physics, 5* (1976), 160-162.

Goldstein, Eugen @ (1850-1930)

gnl.br Ramsauer, Carl. "Eugen Goldstein, ein extremer Experimenta-tor." *PB, 10* (1954), 543-548.

gw Westphal, Wilhelm H. "Zu Eugen Goldsteins 100. Geburtstag." *PB, 6* (1950), 410-412.

See also: K.ddl.ge

Golitsyn, Boris Borisovich @ (1862-1916)

gol.bp Predvoditelev, A. S. "O fizicheskikh rabotakh B. B. Golitsyna." B.gol.jg, *1*, 217-240.

bv *Zyukov, P. I. "Fizicheskie issledovaniya B. B. Golitsyna i ikh rol' v istorii fiziki na rubezhe XX veka." C.vbl.vo, 91-103.

bw Zyukov, P. I. "Vklad B. B. Golitsyna v razrabotku novykh ot-krytiy v fizike na rubezhe XX veka." IIYeT. *Trudy, 43* (1961), 140-150.

bx Zyukov, P. I. "K diskussiyam po rabotam B. B. Golitsyna." *Voprosy istorii fiziko-matematicheskikh nauk.* Moscow, 1963. Pp. 400-409.

ck Krylov, A. N. "Pamyati knyazya B. B. Golitsyna." B.ktl.al, 452-461. (Also in B.ktl.jj, *1:2*, 165-178, and *Priroda*, 1918:2, 171-180.)

cp Predvoditelev, A. S., and N. V. Veshnyakov. "Zhizn' i nauch-naya deyatel'nost akademika B. B. Golitsyna." B.gol.jg, *1*, 5-12.

cs Savarenskiy, Ye. F. "B. B. Golitsyn." C.vbl.pr, *1*, 308-316.

es S[chuster], A[rthur], and G. W. W. "Boris Galitzin." RS. *Proceedings, 94A* (1917/18), xxv-xxxi.

gl Lezhneva, O. A. "B. B. Golitsyn: K 100-letiyu so dnya rozhdeni-ya." *VIYeT, 14* (1963), 128-130.

jb   Blok, G. P., and M. V. Krutkov. *Rukopisi B. B. Golitsyna v Arkhive Akademii Nauk SSSR.* Moscow and Leningrad, 1952. (AN. Arkhiv. *Trudy, 10.*)

jg   Golitsyn, B. B. *Izbrannyye trudy.* 2 vols. Moscow, 1960.

jp   Polak, L. S. "Pis'ma A. A. Fridmana B. B. Golitsynu i V. A. Steklovu." IIYeT. *Trudy, 22* (1959), 324-388.

See also: B.lh3.al, jz; C.vml.zy; O.db1.il; P.bal.go, ky, zy

Gombás, Paul (1909-1971)

go4.eu   Urban, Paul. "Nachruf auf Professor Dr. Paul Gombás." *Acta physica austriaca, 34* (1971), 387-395.

Gorelik, Gabriel' Semenovich (1906-1957)

gpl.er   Rytov, S. M. "Pamyati G. S. Gorelika." *UFN, 62* (1957), 485-496.

Gorter, Cornelius Jacobus (1907-   )

gql.cg   Gorter, C. J. "Bad luck in attempts to make scientific discoveries." *PT, 20* (Jan. 1967), 76-81.

Gouy, George Louis @ (1854-1926)

See: B.vh4.ep

Graaff, Robert J. van de @ (1901-1967)

grl.bd   Burrill, E. Alfred. "Van de Graaff, the man and his accelerators." *PT, 20* (Feb. 1967), 49-52.

Gray, Andrew (1847-1925)

gr5.er   R., A. "Andrew Gray." RS. *Proceedings, 110A* (1926), xvi-xix.

Gray, Joseph Alexander (1884-1966)

gr6.el   Lewis, W. B. "Joseph Alexander Gray." RS, *BM, 13* (1967), 89-106

Gray, Louis Harold (1905-1965)

gr7.el   Loutit, J. F., and O. C. A. Scott. "Louis Harold Gray." RS. *BM, 12* (1966), 195-217.

Grebenshchikov, Il'ya Vasil'yevich (1887-1953)

gr8.jm   **Il'ya Vasil'yevich Grebenshchikov.* Moscow, 1947. (*Mtly,* ser. khim.)

Greenhill, Alfred George (1847-1927)

gr9.eb   B., H. F. "Alfred George Greenhill." RS. *Proceedings, 119A* (1928), i-iv.

Greinacher, Heinrich (1880-1974)

gs1.gb   Balmer, Heinz. "Heinrich Greinacher zum 90. Geburtstag." *PB, 26* (1970), 220-221.

Griffith, Alan Arnold (1893-1963)

gs6.er   Rubbra, A. A. "Alan Arnold Griffith." RS. *BM, 10* (1964), 117-136.

Griffiths, Griffiths, Ernest Howard (1851-1932)

gs8.ed   D., W. C. D. "Ernest Howard Griffiths." RS. *Obituary notices, 1* (1932), 15-18.

Griffiths, Ezer (1888-1962)

gs9.ed   Darwin, C. G. "Ezer Griffiths." RS. *BM, 8* (1962), 41-48.

Grimsehl, C. Ernst H. (1861-1914)

gt1.gh   Hahn, Karl. "Ernst Grimsehl." *PB, 17* (1961), 372-374.

Grinberg, Georgiy Abramovich (1900-   )

gu1.cf   Frenkel', V. Ya. "Georgiy Abramovich Grinberg." A.ah1.tu, 5-20.

Gross, Yevgeniy Fedorovich (1897-1972)

gv1.gc   Anon. "Yevgeniy Fedorovich Gross." Leningrad. University. *Vestnik,* ser. fiz. i khimii, 1957:22, 5-7.

    gd   Anon. "Ye. F. Gross." *Optika i spektroskopiya, 3* (1957), 674.

Guggenheim, Edward Armand (1901-1970)

gv8.et   Tompkins, F. C., and C. F. Goodeve. "Edward Armand Guggenheim." RS. *BM, 17* (1971), 303-326.

Guldberg, Cato Maximilian @ (1836-1902)

gw1.ch Haraldsen, Haakon. "Cato Maximilian Guldberg and Peter Waage." R.ac1.la, 19-35.

eg Goldschmidt, H. "Mindetale over Prof. Dr. Cato Maximilian Guldberg." Norske Videnskapsakademi. *Forhandlinger,* 1903:1, 1-12.

Haas, Arthur Erich @ (1884-1941)

· ha4.ah *Hermann, Armin. *Arthur Erich Haas; Eine bibliographie.* Munich, 1967. (Deutsches Museum. *Kleine Mitteilungen.* Reihe A, no. 24.)

See also: E.mb1.fr; H.bg1.ha, he, hf

Haber, Fritz @ $18C (1868-1934)

ha7.ad Goran, Morris. *The story of Fritz Haber.* Norman, Okl., 1967.

ag Günther, Paul. *Fritz Haber, ein Mann der Jahrhundertwende.* Munich, 1969.

ah Haber, Charlotte. *Mein Leben mit Fritz Haber.* Düsseldorf, 1970.

bh Haber, L. F. "Fritz Haber and the nitrogen problem." *Endeavour, 27* (1968), 150-153.

bt Terres, Ernst. "Die Bedeuntung Fritz Habers für die technische Chemie und die chemische Technik." *Nwn, 16* (1928), 1068-1070.

bw Wrangell, M. von. "Fritz Habers Bedeutung für die Landwirtschaft." *Nwn, 16* (1928), 1071-1075.

ch Laue, Max von. "Fritz Haber." B.lf6.jl, *3,* 219-220. (*Zeitschrift für Elektrochemie, 57* (1953), 1-2.)

cl Lohs, Karlheinz. "Fritz Haber, ein Exponent der burgerlichen Wissenschaft." *NTM, 1:4* [1963], 37-44.

cn Miles, Wyndham D. "Fritz Haber, father of chemical warfare." *Armed forces chemical journal, 14* (1960), 28-30.

cs Sachsse, Hans. "Fritz Haber, 1868-1934." *Chemie in unserer Zeit,* 1968:2, 144-148.

gh Harteck, P. "Zu Fritz Habers 100. Geburtstag." *PB, 24* (1968), 550-553.

gw Willstätter, Richard. "Fritz Haber zum 60. Geburtstag." *Nwn, 16* (1928), 1053-1060.

jh Haber, Fritz. *Aus Leben und Beruf: Aufsätze, Reden, Vorträge.* Berlin, 1927.

nf   Freundlich, H. "Fritz Haber im Karlsruher und Dahlemer La-
      boratorium." *Nwn, 16* (1928), 1060-1062.

See also: R.ag1.he |bb1.fr

Hahn, Otto @ $44C (1921-1968)

hb1.ab   Baumer, Fritz. *Otto Hahn.* Berlin, 1974.

ac   Berninger, Ernst. *Otto Hahn—Eine Bilddokumentation: Persön-
      lichkeit, wissenschaftliche Leistung, öffentliches Wirken.* Munich,
      1969.

ad   Berninger, Ernst. *Otto Hahn.* Bonn, 1970.

ae   Berninger, Ernst. *Otto Hahn in Selbstzeugnissen und Bilddokumen-
      ten.* Reinbech bei Hamburg, 1974.

ag   *Hahn, Dietrich, ed. *Otto Hahn, Begründer des Atomzeitalters:
      Eine Biographie in Bildern und Dokumenten.* Munich, 1979.

ah   Hahn, Otto. *New atoms, progress, and some memories.* NY, 1950.

aj   Hahn, Otto. *Vom Radiothor zur Uranspaltung. Eine wissenschaft-
      liche Selbstbiographie.* Braunschweig, 1962.

ak   Hahn, Otto. *A scientific biography.* Tr. and ed. W. Ley. NY,
      1966.

am   Hahn, Otto. *Mein Leben.* Munich, 1968.

an   Hahn, Otto. *My life: The autobiography of a scientist.* Tr. Ernst
      Kaiser and Eithne Wilkins. NY, 1970.

ap   Hahn, Otto. *Erlebnisse und Erkentnisse.* Ed. Dietrich Hahn.
      Düsseldorf and Wien, 1975.

as   *Hoffmann, Klaus. *Otto Hahn. Stationen aus dem Leben eines
      Atomforschers.* Berlin, 1978.

bh   Herneck, Friedrich. "Zum wissenschaftlichen Wirken von Otto
      Hahn und Lise Meitner im Chemischen Institut der Berliner
      Universität." Berlin. University. *Wissenschaftliche Zeitung,
      math.-natur. Reihe, 16* (1967), 833-837.

cf   Fajans, Kasimir. "Otto Hahn." *Journal of nuclear medicine, 7*
      (1966), 397-401. (Also *UFN, 99* (1969), 337-342.)

ch   Hahn, Otto. "Personal reminiscences of a radiochemist." Chemi-
      cal Society. *Journal* (1956), 3997-4003.

cj   Hahn, Otto. "Erinnerungen an einige Arbeiten anders geplant
      als verlaufen." *NR, 18* (1965), 86-91.

cl   *Hahn, Otto. "Begegnungen und Erlebnisse eines alten Ra-
      diochemikers." *Pharmazeutische Zeitung, 107* (1962), 1509-1512.

cn   Hahn, Otto. "Otto Hahn in Berlin. Vor 60 Jahren begann die Zusammenarbeit mit Lise Meitner." *PB, 23* (1967), 387-389.

cp   Hahn, Otto. "Autobiographical notes." *BAS, 23* (Mar. 1967), 19-24; *23* (Apr. 1967), 22-28.

cr   Meitner, Lise. "Otto Hahn, der Entdecker der Uranspaltung." A.aj1.sc, 149-157.

eg   Gerlach, Walther. "Otto Hahn." Akademie der Wissenschaften, Göttingen. *Jahrbuch,* 1968, 74-82.

ei   Gerlach, Walther. "Otto Hahn zum Gedächtnis." *PB, 24* (1968), 337-338.

ek   Gerlach, Walther. "Otto Hahn." Akademie der Wissenschaften, Munich. *Jahrbuch,* 1969, 255-261.

em   Gerlach, Walther. "Otto Hahn, ein Forscherleben unserer Zeit." *Akademische Gedenkfeier zu Ehren von Otto Hahn und Lise Meitner.* Munich, 1969. (Also in Deutsches Museum. *Abhandlungen und Berichte, 37:3.*)

eo   Hartmann, Hans. "Otto Hahn als Mensch und Forscher." *PB, 24* (1968), 442-450.

ep   Karlik, Berta. "Otto Hahn." *Acta physica austriaca, 29* (1969), 387-390.

es   Spence, R. "Otto Hahn." RS. *BM, 16* (1970), 279-313.

gc   Gerlach, Walther. "Otto Hahn 85 Jahre alt." *NR, 17* (1964), 85-87.

ge   Laue, Max von. "Otto Hahn zum 60. Geburtstag." *Nwn, 27* (1939), 153.

gf   *Laue, Max von. "Max-Planck Medaille, 1949." *PB, 5* (1949), 471- .

gg   Laue, Max von, Lise Meitner, et al. "Otto Hahn zum 8. März 1959." Max-Planck Gesellschaft. *Mitteilungen,* 1959, 3-90.

gi   Laue, Max von. "Zu Otto Hahns 75. Geburtstag." *B.lf6.jl, 3,* 263-265.

gm   Meitner, Lise. "Otto Hahn zum 8. März 1949." *Zeitschrift für Naturforschung, 4a* (1949), 81.

go   Meitner, Lise. "Otto Hahn zum 85. Geburtstag." *Nwn, 51* (1964), 97.

gp   Philipp, K. "Otto Hahn 70 Jahre." *PB, 5* (1949), 129-131.

See also: B.ei4.ud |kd1.ck |mk1.ds, if; I.c

Hale, George Ellery @ (1868-1938)

hc1.ac   Noyes, Alfred. *Watchers of the sky.* NW, 1923.

ag   Wilson, Carol Green. *California Yankee.* Claremont, Calif., 1946.

aw   Wright, Helen. *Explorer of the universe. A biography of George Ellery Hale.* NY, 1966.

ax   Wright, Helen, Joan Warnow, and Charles Weiner, ed. *The legacy of George Ellery Hale.* Cambridge, Mass., 1972.

bf   Andrews, L. B. "The works of George Ellery Hale — A survey of the career of a great living scientist". *Telescope, 3* (1936), 64-71, 95-100, 117-120, 127.

bp   Newcomb, Simon. *Reminiscences of an astronomer.* NY, 1903.

by   Yerkes, Robert M., ed. *The new world of science.* NY, 1920.

ca   Abetti, Giorgio. "Recollections of George Ellery Hale." Astronomical Society of the Pacific. *Leaflet,* no. 387 (1961), 8p.

cc   Cleminshaw, C. H. "George Ellery Hale." *Griffith observer, 32* (1968), 74-82.

cn   Newall, H. F. "Scientific worthies, XLVII: George Ellery Hale." *Nature, 132* (1933), 1-5.

cw   Wright, Helen. "Hale, George Ellery." *DSB, 6* (1972), 26-34.

eb   Adams, Walter S. "George Ellery Hale." *Astrophysical journal, 87* (1938), 369-388.

ec   Adams, Walter S. "George Ellery Hale." NAS. *BM, 21* (1940), 181-241.

ee   Babcock, Harold D. "George Ellery Hale." Astronomical Society of the Pacific. *Publications, 50* (Jun. 1938), 156-165.

eg   Dunham, Theodore, Jr. "Obituary notice of George Ellery Hale." RAS. *Monthly notices, 99* (1939), 322-328.

ei   Fox, Philip. "George Ellery Hale." *Popular astronomy, 46* (1938), 423-430.

en   Newall, H. F. "George Ellery Hale." RS. *Obituary notices, 2* (1939), 523-529.

gt   Turner, H. H. "Address on George Ellery Hale given at the time of the award of the gold medal of the RAS." RAS. *Monthly notices, 64* (1904), 388-401.

sk   Kevles, Daniel J. "George Ellery Hale, the First World War, and the advancement of science in America." *Isis, 59* (1968), 427-437.

ss   Seares, F. H. "The scientist afield." *Isis, 30* (1939), 241-267.

See also: P.ie1.ku, st

Hall, Edwin Herbert @ (1855-1938)

hc6.eb   Bridgman, Percy W. "Edwin Herbert Hall." NAS. *BM, 21* (1939-49), 73-94.

pm   Moyer, Albert E. "Edwin Hall and the emergence of the laboratory in teaching physics." *PTeach, 14* (1976), 96-103.

pw   Webster, David L. "Contributions of Edwin Herbert Hall to the teaching of physics." *AJP, 6* (1938), 14-16.

Hallwachs, Wilhelm Ludwig @ (1859-1922)

hd3.ew   Wiener, Otto. "Wilhelm Hallwachs." Akademie der Wissenschaften, Leipzig. Math.-Phys. Klasse. *Berichte über die Verhandlungen, 74* (1922), 293-316. (Also in *PZ, 23* (1922), 457-462.)

Hansen, William Webster @ (1909-1949)

he1.eb   Bloch, Felix. "William Webster Hansen." NAS. *Biographical Memoirs, 27* (1952), 121-137.

Harker, John Allen (1870-1923)

he2.eg   G[lazebrook], R. T. "John Allen Harker." RS. *Proceedings, 105A* (1924), xi-xiii.

Harkins, William Draper @ (1873-1951)

he3.cm   Mulliken, Robert S. "William Draper Harkins." NAS. *BM, 47* (1975), 49-81.

Hartley, Walter Noel (1864-1913)

he5.eb   B., J. Y. "Walter Noel Hartley." RS. *Proceedings, 90A* (1914), vi-xiii.

Hartree, Douglas Rayner @ (1897-1958)

he6.ed   Darwin, Charles Galton. "Douglas Hartree." RS. *BM, 4* (1958), 103-116.

jc   CSAC. *D. R. Hartree papers at Christ's College Library, Cambridge.* List 45/9/76, 4 p.

Hasenöhrl, Friedrich @ (1874-1915)

hf1.cl   Lenard, Philipp. "Friedrich Hasenöhrl." Lenard. *Great men of science.* Tr. H.S. Hatfield. NY, 1933. Pp. 371-382.

em   Meyer, Stefan. "Friedrich Hasenöhrl." *PZ, 16* (1915), 429-433.

Havelock, Thomas Henry (1877-1968)

hf5.ec   Binnie, A. M. "Thomas Henry Havelock." RS. *BM, 17* (1971), 327-377.

Heaviside, Oliver @ (1850-1925)

hg1.bl   Lee, George. *Oliver Heaviside and the mathematical theory of electronical communications.* London, 1947.

cg   Gossick, B. R. "Heaviside and Kelvin: A study in contrasts." *Annals of science, 33* (1976), 275-287.

cp   Wagner, Karl W. "Oliver Heaviside: Zur hundertsten Wiederkehr seines Geburtstages." *PB, 6* (1950), 460-462.

cv   Whittaker, Edmund Taylor. "Oliver Heaviside." Calcutta Mathematical Society. *Bulletin, 20* (1928/9), 199-220.

eg   Gill, F. "Oliver Heaviside." *Bell System technical journal, 4* (1925), 349-354.

er   R., A. "Oliver Heaviside." RS. *Proceedings, 110A* (1962), xiv-xv.

jg   Gossick, B. R. "Where is Heaviside's manuscript for volume 4 of his *Electromagnetic Theory*?" *Annals of science, 34* (1977), 601-606.

Heisenberg, Werner $32 (1901-1976)

hh1.ac   Cuny, Hilaire. *Heisenberg.* Paris, 1966.

ad   Heisenberg, Elisabeth. *Das politische Leben eines Unpolitischen. Errinerungen an Werner Heisenberg.* Munich, 1980.

ae   Heisenberg, Werner. *Der Teil und das Ganze: Gespräche im Umkreis der Atomphysik.* Munich, 1969.

ag   Heisenberg, Werner. *Schritte über Grenzen: Gesammelte Reden und Aufsätze.* Munich, [1971]. (English ed.: *Across the frontiers.* NY, 1974.)

ai   Heisenberg, Werner. *Physics and beyond: Encounters and conversations.* Tr. Arnold J. Pomerans. NY, [1971].

ak   Hermann, Armin. *Werner Heisenberg in Selbstzeugnissen und Bilddokumenten.* Reinbeck bei Hamburg, 1976.

am Hermann, Armin. *Werner Heisenberg, 1901-1976.* Tr. T. Nevill. Bonn, 1976.

ao Hermann, Armin. *Die Jahrhundertwissenschaft: Werner Heisenberg und die Physik seiner Zeit.* Stuttgart, 1977.

aq Leithäuser, Joachim G. *Werner Heisenberg.* Berlin, 1957.

aw Weizsäcker, Carl Friedrich von, and B. L. van der Waerden. *Werner Heisenberg.* Munich, 1977.

bb Bohm, David. "Heisenberg's contribution to physics." L.ie1.pr, 559-563.

bc Cassidy, David C. "Heisenberg's first paper." *PT, 31* (Jul. 1978), 23-28.

bd Cassidy, David C. "Heisenberg's first core model of the atom: The formation of a professional style." *HSPS, 10* (1979), 187-224.

br Rasche, Günther. "Werner Heisenberg und die moderne Physik." *NR, 30* (1977), 1-9.

cd Dolch, Heimo. "Werner Heisenberg, das Ringen um ein vertieftes Verständnis der Welt." A.aj1.sc, 94-102.

ch Heelan, Patrick A. "Heisenberg and radical theoretic change." *Zeitschrift für allgemeine Wissenschaftstheorie, 6* (1975), 113-136.

cj Heisenberg, Werner. [Interview.] A.aj1.bu, 3-16.

ed Dürr, Hans Peter, and Armin Hermann. "Abschied von Werner Heisenberg." *PB, 32* (1976), 97-104.

ej Jammer, Max. "Werner Heisenberg." *Zeitschrift für allgemeine Wissenschaftstheorie, 7* (1976), 1-10.

el Lederer, Erich, and W. Lohmann. "Zwei Erinnerungen an Heisenberg." *PB, 33* (1977), 89.

em Montaldi, Emilio. "Werner Heisenberg: 5 Dicembre 1901—1° Febbraio 1976." *Scientia, 110* (1975), 599-603.

eo Mott, Nevill, and Rudolf Peierls. "Werner Heisenberg." RS. *BM, 23* (1977), 213-251.

ev Verde, Mario. "Werner Heisenberg e la fisica del XX secolo." *Scientia, 111* (1976), 305-309.

gj Jordan, Pascual. "Werner Heisenberg 70 Jahre." *PB, 27* (1971), 559-562.

ib Bopp, Fritz, ed. *Werner Heisenberg und die Physik unserer Zeit.* Braunschweig, 1961.

jb   Burckhardt, Carl J. "Briefe aus den Jahren 1971-1973."
      Universität: Zeitschrift für Wissenschaft, Kunst und Literatur, 32
      (1977), 145-154.

kg   Heelan, Patrick A. *Quantum mechanics and objectivity: A study of*
      the physical philosophy of Werner Heisenberg. The Hague, 1965.

ki   Hörz, Herbert. *Werner Heisenberg und die Philosophie.* Berlin,
      1968.

kj   Kuznetsov, I. V. "V chem prav i chem oshibayetsya Verner
      Geyzenberg." *Voprosy filosofii,* 1958:11, 70-80.

See also: I.eb1.br, bs; L.af1.bl; L.d

Henderson, George Hugh (1892-1949)

hh5.el Lewis, W. B. "George Hugh Henderson." RS. *Obituary notices, 7*
        (1950), 155-166.

Herring, William Conyers (1914-   )

See: O.da1.he

Hertz, Gustav Ludwig $25 (1887-1975)

hi1.cr Rompe, R., and M. Steenbeck. "Gustav Hertz in der Entwick-
        lung der modernen Physik." B.hi1.jh, 9-13.

gg   Gerlach, Walther. "Geburtstagsgruss an Gustav Hertz." *PB, 28*
        (1972), 321-322.

gh   Hahn, Otto. "Ein Geburtstagsgruss an Gustav Hertz." *PB, 18*
        (1962), 324-325.

gi   Hartmann, W. "Gustav Hertz 80 Jahre." B.hi1.jh, 5-8.

ih   *Gustav Hertz in der Entwicklung der modernen Physik. Festschrift.*
        Berlin, 1967. (Akademie der Wissenschaften, Berlin. Math.-
        Phys.- Techn. Klasse. *Abhandlungen,* 1967:1.)

See also: C.gb3.cb

Hertzsprung, Ejnar @ (1873-1967)

hi6.cs Strand, Kaj Aage. "Ejnar Hertzsprung, neue Fundamente zum
        Bau des Weltalls." A.aj1.sc, 240-249.

See also: P.hb1

Herzberg, Gerhard $71C (1904-   )

hj1.gs Stoicheff, B. P. "Zum 70. Geburtstag von Gerhard Herzberg."
        PB, 31 (1975), 121-124.

Hess, Victor Franz @ $36 (1883-1964)

hk1.cs   Steinmaurer, Rudolf. "Nobelpreisträger Victor F. Hess." *Beiträge zur Technikgeschichte Tirols, 2* (1970), 3-6.

es   Steinmaurer, Rudolf. "Victor Franz Hess." Akademie der Wissenschaften, Vienna. *Almanach, 116* (1966), 317-328.

gq   Steinmaurer, Rudolf. "Victor F. Hess." *Acta physica austriaca, 7* (1953), 209-215.

gr   Steinmaurer, Rudolf. "Victor F. Hess." *Acta physica austriaca, 12* (1959), 121-122.

gs   Steinmaurer, Rudolf. "Victor F. Hess, der Entdecker der kosmischen Strahlung, 80 Jahre alt." *Acta physica austriaca, 17* (1964), 113-120.

Hevesy, Georg von @ $43C (1885-1966)

hl1.ch   Hevesy, Georg von. "Gamle dage." *Fysisk tidskrift, 60* (1962), 26-30.

ed   Cockcroft, J. D. "George de Hevesy." RS. *BM, 13* (1967), 125-166.

el   Levy, Hilde. "Gyorgy Hevesy." *Nuclear physics, 98* (1967), 1-24.

es   Spence, R. "George Charles de Hevesy." *Chemistry in Britain, 3* (1967), 527-532.

et   Szabadváry, F. "George Hevesy." *Journal of radioanalytical chemistry, 1* (1968), 97-102.

gb   Aten, A. H. W., E. Broda, et al. "Greetings to Professor Hevesy." *International journal of applied radiation and isotopes, 16* (1965), 505-519.

jh   Hevesy, Georg von. *Adventures in radioisotope research: The collected papers of George Hevesy.* 2 vols. Oxford and NY, 1962.

ji   Hevesy, Georg von. *Selected papers.* Oxford and NY, 1967.

Hicks, William Mitchinson (1850-1934)

hl4.em   Milner, S. R. "William Mitchinson Hicks." RS. *Obituary notices, 1* (1935), 393-399.

Hilbert, David @ (1862-1943)

hml.ar   Reid, Constance. *Hilbert.* Berlin and NY, 1970.

bc   Courant, Richard. "Hilbert als Analytiker." *Nwn, 10* (1922), 83-88.

be Dehn, M. "Hilberts geometrisches Werk." *Nwn, 10* (1922), 77-82.

bl Levi, Friedrich W. "David Hilbert, die Vollendung der klassischen und der Beginen der modern Mathematik." A.ajl.sc, 337-347.

bt Toeplitz, D. "Der Algebraiker Hilbert." *Nwn, 10* (1922), 73-77.

bw Weyl, Hermann. "David Hilbert and his mathematical work." American Mathematical Society. *Bulletin, 50* (1944), 612-654.

cb Born, Max. "Hilbert und die Physik." *Nwn, 10* (1922), 88-93.

em Sommerfeld, Arnold. "David Hilbert." Akademie der Wissenschaften, Göttingen. *Jahrbuch,* 1943/4, 87-92.

eo Sommerfeld, Arnold, and C. Carathéodory. "Zum Andenken David Hilbert." *Nwn, 31* (1943), 213-214.

ew Weyl, Hermann. "David Hilbert." RS. *Obituary notices, 4* (1944), 547-553.

gb Blumenthal, Otto. "David Hilbert." *Nwn, 10* (1922), 67-72.

ir Reidemeister, E., ed. *Hilbert: Gedenkband.* Berlin, 1971.

jh Hilbert, David. *Gesammelte Abhandlungen.* 3 vols. Berlin, 1935.

jm Minkowski, Hermann. *Briefe an David Hilbert.* Ed. L. Rüdenberg and H. Zassenhaus. Berlin, Heidelberg, and NY, 1973.

js Siegel, Karl. "Verzeichnis der bisherigen Publikationen von David Hilbert." *Nwn, 10* (1922), 99-103.

kb Bernays, Paul. "Die Bedeutung Hilberts für die Philosophie der Mathematik." *Nwn, 10* (1922), 93-99.

kd Chevalley, Claude, and Arnaud Dandieu. "Logique hilbertienne et psychologie." *Revue philosophique de la France et de l'étranger, 113* (1932), 99-111.

nb Biermann, Kurt-R. "David Hilbert und die Berliner Akademie." *Mathematische Nachrichten, 27* (1964), 377-384.

See also: F.dc1.ea |de1.me, mf; T.aa1.hr

Hildebrand, Joel Henry (1881-   )

hm6.ch Hildebrand, Joel. "Joel Hildebrand described by himself." *Perspectives in biology and medicine, 16* (1972), 88-111.

Hinshelwood, Cyril Norman @ $56C (1897-1967)

hm8.ct   Thompson, Harold. "Cyril Norman Hinshelwood." RS. *BM, 19* (1973), 375-431.

jc   CSAC. *Sir Cyril Hinshelwood papers at the Royal Society, London.* List 17/11/74, 7 p.

Hittorf, Johann Wilhelm @ (1824-1914)

hn1.as   Schmidt, Gerhardt Karl. *Wilhelm Hittorf.* Münster, 1924. (Gesellschaft zur Förderung der westfälischen Wilhelms Universität zu Münster. *Schriften, 4.*)

cs   Schimank, H. "Johann Wilhelm Hittorf zum Gedächtnis der 50. Wiederkehr seines Todestages am 28. Nov. 1914." *PB, 20* (1964), 571-577.

ct   Schmidt, G. C. "Wilhelm Hittorf." *PB, 4* (1948), 64-68.

Hönl, Helmut (1903-1981)

ho1.gg   Giannarás, Anastasios, ed. *Convivium cosmologicum: Helmut Hönl zum 70. Geburtstag.* Basel, 1973.

Hoff, Jacobus Henricus van't @ $01C (1852-1911)

hp1.ab   Ans, Jean d'. "Jacobus Henricus van't Hoff." *PB, 8* (1952), 510-512.

ac   Cohen, Ernst. *Jacobus Henricus van't Hoff. Sein Leben und Werken.* Leipzig, 1912.

ad   Dobrotin, R. B., and Yu. I. Solov'yev. *Vant-Goff.* Moscow, 1977.

ch   Hermans, P. H. "Has Van't Hoff been well read and understood by the profession?" *JCE, 53* (1976), 153-154.

ed   Donnan, F. G. "J. H. van't Hoff." RS. *Proceedings, 86A* (1912), xxxix-xliii.

ej   Jones, H. C. "J. H. van't Hoff." APS. *Proceedings, 50* (1911), iii-xii.

co   Ostwald, Wilhelm. "J. H. van't Hoff." Deutsche Chemische Gesellschaft. *Berichte, 44* (1911), 2219-2252.

ew   Walker, J. "J. H. van't Hoff." Chemical Society. *Journal, 103* (1913), 1127-1143.

jr   Riesenfeld, Ernst. "Arrhenius om van't Hoff och Ehrlich: Två brev från Ernst Riesenfeld." *Lychnos,* 1975/76, 85-100.

See also: B.ow1.ch

Hofstadter, Robert $61 (1915-   )

hq1.cs   Schopper, H. "Die Nobelpreisträger 1961: Robert Hofstadter."
          PB, 18 (1962), 55-57.

Holborn, Ludwig Christian F. @ (1860-1926)

hr1.eh   Henning, F. "Ludwig Holborn." *PZ, 28* (1927), 157-170.

Honda, Kōtarō @ (1870-1954)

hr6.ih   *Anniversary volume dedicated to Professor Kōtarō Honda on the
          completion of twenty-five years of his professorship by his friends and
          pupils.* Sendai, 1936.

See also: O.ba1.ka

Hopkinson, Bertram (1874-1913)

hs1.ce   E., J. A. "Bertram Hopkinson." RS. *Proceedings, 95A* (1918/19),
          xxvi-xxxvi.

     ec   Charlton, T. M. "Professor Bertram Hopkinson." RS. *Notes and
          records, 29* (1974), 101-109.

Horton, Frank (1878-1957)

hs5.ew   Whiddington, R. "Frank Horton." RS. *BM, 4* (1958), 117-127.

Houston, William Vermillion (1900-1968)

ht1.cp   Pitzer, Kenneth S., and Harold E. Rorschach, Jr. "William Ver-
          million Houston." NAS. *BM, 44* (1974), 127-137.

See also: O.da1.ro

Huggins, William @ (1824-1910)

hu1.ed   D[yson], F[rank] W[atson]. "William Huggins." RS. *Proceed-
          ings, 86A* (1911/12), i-xix.

     en   N., H. F. "William Huggins." RAS. *Monthly notices, 71* (1911),
          261-270.

     jh   *Huggins, William. *The scientific papers.* London, 1909.

Hull, Albert Wallace @ (1880-1966)

hv1.es   Suits, C. G., and J. M. Lafferty. "Albert Wallace Hull." NAS.
          BM, 41 (1970), 215-233.

Hull, Gordon Ferrie (1870-1956)

hv4.ch   Hull, Gordon Ferrie. "Reminiscences of a scientific comrade-ship." *AJP, 4* (1936), 61-65.

Hume-Rothery, William @ (1899-1968)

hv8.er   Raynor, G. V. "William Hume-Rothery." RS. *BM, 15* (1969), 109-139.

Hund, Friedrich (1896-)

See: L.dc1.hu

Hylleraas, Egil Andersen @ (1898-1965)

hy1.eg   Gjøtterud, O. K. "Egil Anderson Hylleraas." *Nuclear physics, 89* (1966), 1-10.

    ew   *Wergeland, H. "Egil A. Hylleraas." *Fra fysikkens verden, 28* (1966), 1-10.

    jh   Hylleraas, Egil Anderson. *Selected scientific papers.* Ed. J. Midtdal et al. Trondheim, 1968.

See also: H.ea1.hy

Infeld, Leopold @ (1898-1968)

if1.ai   Infeld, Leopold. *Quest: The evolution of a scientist.* NY, 1941.

    ak   Infeld, Leopold. *Szkice z przeszlosci.* Warsaw, 1965.

    al   Infeld, Leopold. *Kordian, fizyka i ja; wspomnienia.* Warsaw, 1967.

    am   *Infeld, Leopold. *Why I left Canada.* Ed. Lewis Pyenson. Montreal, 1978.

    bk   Kuznetsov, Boris Grigor'yevich. "Leopold Infeld a historia nauki." *KHNT, 13* (1968), 619-622.

    ci   Infeld, Leopold. "As I see it." *BAS, 21* (Feb. 1965), 7-14.

Ioffe, Abram Fedorovich @ (1880-1960)

io1.af   Frenkel', Ya. I. *Abram Fedorovich Ioffe.* Leningrad, 1968.

    ai   *Ioffe, A. F. *Moya zhizn' i rabota.* Moscow and Leningrad, 1933.

    as   Sominskiy, M. S. *Abram Fedorovich Ioffe.* Leningrad, 1964.

    bi   Ioffe, A. F. "Usloviya moyey nauchnoy raboty." AN *Izvestiya*, ser. fiz., 1936:1-2, 7-33.

br   *Regel', A. R., and V. P. Zhuze. "O rabotakh akademika A. F. Ioffe." Moscow. Publichnaya biblioteka. *Laureaty Leninskikh premiy.* Moscow, 1961. Pp. 9-17.

cf   Frenkel', V. Ya. "Abram Fedorovich Ioffe (Biograficheskiy ocherk)." *UFN, 132* (1980), 11-45.

cg   Grigor'yan, A. T. "Abram Fedorovich Ioffe." *VIYeT,* 1980:4, 49-53.

ci   Ioffe, A. F. "Mid-century thoughts." *News,* 1956:1, 15-16.

ck   Krylov, A. N. "Bol'shoy uchenyy." B.kt1.al, 492-497.

cx   Zhuze, V. P., ed. *Vospominaniya ob A. F. Ioffe.* Leningrad, 1973.

eg   Grigor'yan, A. T. "Abram Fedorovich Ioffe." *VIYeT, 10* (1960), 49-54.

ek   Kikoin, I. K., and M. S. Sominskiy. "Abram Fedorovich Ioffe." *SPU, 3* (1961), 798-809.

ga   *Anon. "Akademik A. F. Ioffe." *ZhETF, 10* (1940), 955-960.

gb   Anon. "Abram Fedorovich Ioffe." *ZhETF, 30* (1956), 3-6.

gd   Ansel'm, A. I., and V. P. Zhuze. "Abram Fedorovich Ioffe." *Zhurnal tekhnicheskoy fiziki, 25* (1955), 2013-2021.

gf   Frenkel', Ya. I. "Akademik Abram Fedorovich Ioffe." AN. *Vestnik,* 1940: 10, 72-77.

gk   Kikoin, I. K. "A. F. Ioffe." *UFN, 24* (1940), 3-10.

gr   *Regel', A. R., and L. S. Stil'bans. "Abram Fedorovich Ioffe." *Fizika tverdogo tela,* 1950, 2671-2676.

il   *Lukirskiy, P. I., et al., eds. *Sbornik, posvyashchennyy 70-letiyu akademika A. F. Ioffe.* Moscow, 1950.

ji   Ioffe, A. F. *Izbrannyye trudy.* 2 vols. Leningrad, 1974-75.

jm   Ansel'm, A. I., et al., eds. *Abram Fedorovich Ioffe.* Moscow, 1960. (*Mtly,* ser. fiz., 12.)

See also: B.ec1.jf; I.dd1.an

Ives, Hubert Eugene @ (1882-1953)

iv1.eb   Buckley, Oliver E., and Karl K. Darrow. "Hubert Eugene Ives." NAS. *BM, 29* (1953), 145-189.

Jackson, Willis (1904-1970)

jb1.eg   Gabor, Dennis, and J. Brown. "Willis Jackson Baron Jackson of Burnley." RS. *BM, 17* (1971), 379-398.

Jaeger, Frans Maurits @ (1877-1945)

jc1.bd   Dijkstra, D. W. "Jaeger als historicus." *Chemisch weekblad, 31* (1934), 203-205.

bl   Lifshits, Ye. "F. M. Jaeger als anorganicus en physicochemicus, 1909-1934." *Chemisch weekblad, 31* (1934), 187-191.

gj   Jorissen, W. P. "Frans Maurits Jaeger." *Chemisch weekblad, 31* (1934), 182-186.

jb   Beintema, J. "Bibliographie van Prof. Dr. F. M. Jaeger." *Chemisch weekblad, 31* (1934), 205-212.

See also: O.fb1.te; R.dh1.si |ds1.si

Jahn, Hans Max @ (1853-1906)

jd1.el   Landolt, H. "Hans Jahn." Deutsche Chemische Gesellschaft. *Berichte, 39* (1906), 4463-4470.

James, Reginald William (1891-1964)

jd5.ec   Bragg, W. L. "Reginald William James." RS. *BM, 11* (1965), 115-125.

Jeans, James Hopwood @ (1877-1946)

je1.am   Milne, E. A. *Sir James Jeans: A biography.* Cambridge, 1962.

em   Milne, E. A. "James Hopwood Jeans." RS. *Obituary notices, 5* (1947), 573-589.

Joffe *see* **Ioffe**

Joliot, Frédéric @ $35C (1900-1958)

jj1.ab   Biquard, Pierre. *Frédéric Joliot-Curie: The man and his theories.* Tr. G. Strachan. Greenwich, Conn., 1965.

ae   *Ehrenburg, I. G. *Frederik Zholio-Kyuri.* Moscow, 1958.

af   *Faynboym, I. V. *Iren i Frederik Zholio-Kyuri.* Moscow, 1964.

ag   Goldsmith, Maurice. *Frédéric Joliot-Curie: A biography.* London, 1976.

aj   *Kedrov, F. B. *Frederik Zholio-Kyuri.* Moscow, 1960.

ak   Kuznetsov, Boris Grigor'yevich. *Frederik Zholio-Kyuri: Uchenyy i borets za mir.* Moscow, 1952.

ap   Rouzé, Michel. *Frédéric Joliot-Curie.* Paris, 1950.

as   Shaskol'skaya, M. P. *Frederik Zholio-Kyuri.* Moscow, 1966. (French trn, Moscow, 1968.)

bb   Biquard, Pierre. *Frédéric Joliot-Curie et l'énergie atomique.* Paris, 1961.

bo   Savel, Pierre. "Vingt-sept années de collaboration scientifique avec Frédéric Joliot." *La pensée,* no. 87 (1959), 80-83.

br   *Skobel'tsyn, D. V. "K izdaniyu trudov Frederika Zholio-Kyuri na russkom yazyke." B.jj1.jo, 3-8.

bs   Skobel'tsyn, D. V. "Frédéric Joliot-Curie et les découvertes fondamentales du XXe siècle." *La pensée,* no. 87 (1959), 43-51.

bt   Teillac, Jean. "L'oeuvre et la pensée scientifiques de Frédéric Joliot-Curie." *La pensée,* no. 87, (1959), 6-13.

cb   *Anon. "Zholio-Kyuri pyat'desyat let." *Storonniki mira,* 1950:9, 78-79.

cf   Figurovskiy, N. A. "Frederik Zholio-Kyuri." *Khimiya v shkole,* 1956:5, 3-13.

ci   Ioffe, A. F. "Suprugi Zholio." A.aj1.io, 200-203.

cj   *Joliot, Frédéric. "Trudy Frederika Zholio-Kyuri (Avtoreferat)." B.jj1.jo, 11-29. (Also in *UFN, 67* (1959), 17-35.)

ck   Joliot-Curie, Irène. "Laboratornyye zapisnyye knizhki perioda otkrytiya poloniya i radiya." Trans. O. A. Starosel'skaya-Nikitina. IIYeT. *Trudy, 19* (1957), 97-138. (From intro. to B.cv3.ae.)

cl   *Kuznetsov, B. G. "O zhizni F. Zholio-Kyuri i o kharaktere nauki XX veka." *VIYET,* 1980:1, 38-43.

cm   *Mono, M. "Frederik Zholio-Kyuri." *Mir,* 1951:22, 33-49.

co   Orcel, Jean. "La pensée et l'action de Frédéric Joliot-Curie." *La pensée,* no. 87 (1959), 14-29.

cp   [Special number on Frédéric Joliot.] *La pensée,* no. 87 (1959).

ea   Barrabé, Louis. "Quelques souvenirs sur Frédéric Joliot-Curie." *La pensée,* no. 87 (1959), 58-62.

eb   Bernal, J. D. "Un grand homme, un homme profondément humain." *La pensée,* no. 81 (1958), 46-50.

ec   Biquard, Pierre. "Mon ami Frédéric Joliot-Curie." *La pensée,* no. 87 (1959), 71-79.

ed   Blackett, P. M. S. "Frédéric Joliot." RS. *BM, 6* (1960), 87-105.

eg   Broglie, Louis de. "Notice nécrologique sur Jean-Frédéric Joliot." AN. *Comptes rendus, 247* (1958), 697-702. (Also in *Revue général des sciences, 65* (1958), 265-270; *La pensée,* no. 87 (1959), 30-34.)

eh   Broglie, Louis de. "Notice sur la vie et l'oeuvre de Frédéric Joliot." AS. *Notices et discours, 4* (1959), 222-248.

ej   Cotton, Eugénie. "Souvenirs." *La pensée,* no. 87 (1959), 65-68.

ek   Figurovskiy, N. A. "Pamyati Frederika Zholio-Kyuri: K godovshchine so dnya smerti." *VIYeT, 9* (1960), 28-37.

en   Nesmeyanov, A. N., D. V. Skobel'tsyn, and J. D. Bernal. "Vystupleniya na vstreche uchennykh s uchastnikami Sessii Byuro Vsemirnogo Soveta Mira, posvyashchennoy pamyati Frederika Zholio-Kyuri." *VIYeT, 9* (1960), 18-27.

eo   Orcel, Jean. "Frédéric Joliot-Curie." *La pensée,* no. 81 (1958), 51-60.

ep   Perrin, Francis. "Allocution... [aux] funerailles nationales de Frédéric Joliot." AS. *Notices et discours, 4* (1958), 81-88.

eq   Powell, C. F. "La place de Frédéric Joliot-Curie dans la physique atomique." *La pensée,* no. 87 (1959), 35-42.

es   Shaskol'skaya, M. P. "Frederik Zholio-Kyuri." *UFN, 67* (1959), 3-15.

gc   Anon. "Frederik Zholio-Kyuri: Vydayushchiysya uchenyy, plamennyy borets za mir." *UFN, 41* (1950), 293-310.

gp   Prenant, Marcel. "Discours pour le cinquantenaire de Frédéric Joliot-Curie." *La pensée,* no. 30 (1950), 11-14.

gs   Skobel'tsyn, D. V. "Un chercheur et un combattant." *La pensée,* no. 30 (1950), 9-11.

ji   Joliot, Frédéric. "Quelques textes de Frédéric Joliot-Curie." *La pensée,* no. 87 (1959), 91-104.

jj   Joliot, Frédéric. *Textes choisis.* Paris, 1959.

jn   Joliot, Frédéric, and Irène Joliot-Curie. *Oeuvres scientifiques complètes.* Paris, 1961. (Russian edition, Moscow, 1957.)

jo   *Joliot, Frédéric, and Irène Joliot-Curie. *Izbrannyye trudy: Sovmestnyye trudy.* Moscow, 1957.

nr   Radvanyi, Pierre. "Frédéric Joliot au Collège de France dans les années d'après guerre." *La pensée,* no. 87 (1959), 84-88.

See also: B.cv1.jc; B.jk1 |kw1.cg |lc3.jj; I.ca1.io; U.be1.go

Joliot-Curie, Irène @ $35 (1897-1956)

jk1.bk   Kedrov, Fedor Borisovich. *Iren i Frederik Zholio-Kyuri: Vzglyady, idei, eksperimenty, ot proshlogo k budushchemu.* Moscow, 1973.

cs   Savich, P. "Moye sotrudnichestvo s Iren Kyuri." *VIYeT, 50* (1975), 67-76.

ec   Cotton, Eugénie. "Irène Joliot-Curie." *La pensée*, no. 67 (1956), 4-10.

eo   Orcel, Jean. "Irène Joliot-Curie." *La pensée*, no. 80 (1958), 79-102.

See also: B.jj1

Jones, Harry Clary @ (1865-1916)

jm1.er   Reid, E. Emmett. "Biographical sketch." *Harry Clary Jones. The nature of solution.* NY, 1917. vii-xiii.

Jordan, Pascual (1902-1980)

jo1.bb   Bagge, Erich. "Pascual Jordan und die Quantenphysik." *PB, 34* (1978), 224-228.

ge   Ehlers, Jürgen. "Pascual Jordan zum 70. Geburtstag." *PB, 28* (1972), 468-469.

Kapitsa, Petr Leonidovich $78 (1894-   )

kc1.ak   *Kedrov, Fedor B. *Kapitsa: Zhizn' i otkrytiya.* Moscow, 1979.

cd   Anon. "Vybory v Akademiyu Nauk." *UFN, 21* (1939), 238-239.

gc   Alekseyevskiy, N. Ye. "Petr Leonidovich Kapitsa." *SPU, 7* (1965), 629-635.

ge   Anon. "Akademik Petr Leonidovich Kapitsa." *ZhETF, 27* (1954), 265-268.

gf   Fainbaum, Iosif. "Pjotr Kapiza." *Ideen des exakten Wissens,* 1972, 743-749.

gi   *Ioffe, A. F. "Petr Leonidovich Kapitsa: K 50-letiyu so dnya rozhdeniya." *Elektrichestvo,* 1944:8-9, 18-20.

gp   Shpol'skiy, E. V. "Petr Leonidovich Kapitsa." *UFN, 54* (1954), 505-512.

gs   Spruch, Grace Marmor. "Pyotr Kapitza, octogenarian dissident." *PT, 32* (Sep. 1979), 34-41.

jk   Kapitsa, P. L. *Collected papers.* Ed. Dirk ter Haar. 3 vols. Oxford and NY, 1964-67.

jl   Kapitsa, P. L. *Eksperiment teoriya praktika: Stat'i vystupleniya.* Moscow, 1977. (1st. edn , Moscow, 1974.)

jm   Kapitsa, P. L. *Experiment, theory, practice: Articles and addresses.* Dordrecht, 1980. (*BSPS, 46.*)

jp   Parry, Albert, ed. *Peter Kapitsa on life and science.* NY, 1968.

See also: B.fk1.gb; O.hc1.lj

Kaptsov, Nikolay Aleksandrovich (1883-1966)

kc4.gs   *Sokolov, A. A. "25 let raboty professora N. A. Kaptsova v Moskovskom universitete." Moscow. University. *Vestnik,* 1948:4, 158.

Kármán, Theodor von @ (1881-1963)

kd1.ak   Kármán, Theodor von, and Lee Edson. *The wind and beyond: Theodore von Kármán, pioneer in aviation and pathfinder in space.* Boston, 1967.

bd   Dryden, H. L. "Contributions of Theodore von Kármán to applied mechanics." *Applied mechanics reviews, 16* (1963), 589-595.

be   Dryden, H. L. "The contributions of Theodore von Kármán." *Astronautics and aerospace engineering, 1* (1963), 12-17.

bj   Jones, E. T. "Theodore von Kármán and AGARD." Royal Aeronautical Society. *Journal, 69* (1963), 614.

cj   Kármán, Theodor von. "A few von Karmanisms." *Aerospace engineering, 18* (Jun. 1959), 22-23.

ck   Kármán, Theodor von, Max Born, Otto Hahn, and Wilhelm Westphal. "Vor fünfzig Jahren: Persönliche Erinnerungen." *PB, 16* (1960), 22-27.

ed   Dryden, Hugh L. "Theodore von Kármán." APS. *Yearbook,* 1963, 159-167.

ee   Dryden, Hugh L. "Theodore von Kármán." NAS. *BM, 38* (1965), 345-384.

eg   Goldstein, S. "Theodore von Kármán." RS. *BM, 12* (1966), 335-365.

em   Millikan, Clark B. "Theodore von Kármán—his American period." Royal Aeronautical Society. *Journal, 67* (1963), 615-617.

jg   Goodstein, Judith R., and Carolyn Kopp, ed. *The Theodore von Kármán collection at the California Institute of Technology.* Pasadena, 1981.

Karpinskiy, Aleksandr Petrovich @ (1846-1936)

kd4.ck   Krylov, A. N. "Pamyati Aleksandra Petrovicha Karpinskogo." *B.kt1.al,* 481-485.

See also: P.fa1.ko

Kaye, George William Clarkson (1880-1941)

kd8.eg   Griffiths, Ezer. "George William Clarkson Kaye." RS. *Obituary notices, 3* (1941), 881-895.

Kayser, Heinrich Gustav Johannes @ (1853-1940)

ke1.ak   Kayser, Heinrich G. J. "Erinnerungen aus meinem Leben." Typescript, 1936. (APS Library.)

ch   Herzberg, G. "Heinrich Kayser." RS. *BM, 1* (1955), 135-143.

ec   Crew, Henry. "Heinrich Gustav Johannes Kayser." *Astrophysical journal, 94* (1941), 5-11.

ep   Paschen, Friedrich. "Heinrich Kayser." *PZ, 41* (1941), 429-433.

Kazanskiy, Boris Aleksandrovich (1891-   )

ke4.jm   *Boris Aleksandrovich Kazsanskiy.* Moscow, 1952; 2nd ed., 1973. (*Mtly*, ser. khim., 51.)

Keesom, Willem Hendrik @ (1876-1956)

kf1.eg   Gorter, C. J. "Levensbericht van Wilhelmus Hendrikus Keesom." Akademie van Wetenschappen, Amsterdam. *Jaarboek*, 1956/7, 225-230.

Kelly, Mervin Joe (1894-1971)

kf5.ep   Pierce, John R. "Mervin Joe Kelly." NAS. *BM, 46* (1975), 191-219.

Kelvin *see* **Thomson, W.**

Kerr, John @ (1824-1907)

kg1.eg   Gray, Andrew. "John Kerr." RS. *Proceedings, 82* (1909), i-v.

Khlopin, Vitaliy Grigor'yevich (1890-1950)

kg4.jm   *Vitaliy Grigor'yevich Khlopin.* Moscow and Leningrad, 1947. (*Mtly*, ser. khim., 4.)

Khvol'son, Orest Danilovich (1852-1934)

kg8.ck   *Krylov, A. N. "Rech' na otkrytii s'yezda fizikov 4 fevralya 1919 g." Russkoye fiziko-khimicheskoye obshchestvo. *Zhurnal*, otd. fiziki, *51* (1919), 315-316.

gd   Dobiash, A. A. "Orest Danilovich Khvol'son: K poluvekovomu yubileyu yego nauchnoy raboty." Russkoye fiziko-khimicheskoye obshchestvo. *Zhurnal*, chast' fiz., *58* (1926), 87-104.

Kikoin, Isaak Konstantinovich (1908-)

kh1.gc   Anon. "Akademik Isaak Konstantinovich Kikoin." *ZhETF, 34* (1958), 537-540.

Kimball, George Elbert (1906-1967)

ki5.cm   Morse, Philip M. "George Elbert Kimball." NAS. *BM, 43* (1973), 129-146.

King, Louis Vessot (1886-1956)

ki7.ef   Foster, J. S. "Louis Vessot King." RS. *BM, 3* (1957), 101-108.

Kistiakowsky, George (1900-)

ki9.ak   Kistiakowsky, George B. *A scientist at the White House: The private diary of President Eisenhower's Special Assistant for Science and Technology.* Cambridge, Mass., 1976.

Klein, Oskar Benjamin (1894-1977)

kj1.ck   Klein, Oskar. "From my life of physics." A.aj1.fr, 60-68.

cl   *Klein, Oskar. "Ur mitt liv i fysiken." Sweden. Statens Naturvetenskapliga Forskningsråd. *Svensk naturvetenskap, 26* (1973), 159-172.

Klopsteg, Paul Ernest (1889-)

kk1.pp   Phillips, Melba. "Paul E. Klopsteg, founder of AAPT." *PTeach, 15* (1977), 212-214.

Knowlton, A. A. (1875-1957)

kl1.pr   Roller, Duane. "The Oersted Medal and the significance of its award to Professor A. A. Knowlton." *AJP, 20* (1952), 267-270.

Knudsen, Martin Hans Christian @ (1871-1949)

kl4.bp   Pihl, Mogens. *Betydningsfulde danske bidrag til den klassiske fysik.* Copenhagen, 1972.

ed   Bohr, Niels, and F. R. H. Rasmussen. "Martin Knudsen." *Fysisk tidsskrift, 47* (1949), 145-164.

ej   Jacobsen, J. C., and Niels Bohr. "Martin Knudsen." Danske Videnskabernes Selskab. *Oversigt,* 1949/50, 55-65.

Kochin, Nikolay Yevgrafovich @ (1901-1944)

kl8.ap   *Polubarinova-Kochina, P. Ya. *Zhizn' i deyatel'nost' N. Ye. Kochina.* Leningrad, 1950.

jm   Dorodnitsyn, A. A., et al., ed. *Nikolay Yevgrafovich Kochin.* Moscow and Leningrad, 1948. (*Mtly*, ser. matematiki, [4].)

Kohlrausch, Friedrich Wilhelm G. @ (1840-1910)

km1.er   Rubens, Heinrich. "Gedächtnisrede auf Friedrich Kohlrausch." Akademie der Wissenschaften, Berlin. Phys.-Math. Klasse. *Abhandlungen*, 1910: Gedächnisreden 1, 11p.

ew   Wien, Wilhelm. "Friedrich Kohlrausch." *Annalen der Physik, 31* (1910), 449-454.

Kondrat'yev, Viktor Nikolayevich (1902-1979)

km4.jm   Voyevodskiy, V. V., et al., ed. *Viktor Nikolayevich Kondrat'yev.* Moscow, 1964. (*Mtly*, ser. khim., 33.)

Konobeyevskiy, Sergey Tikhonovich (1890-1970)

kn1.gx   Zhdanov, G. S. "Sergey Tikhonovich Konobeyevskiy." *UFN, 71* (1960), 161-165.

Konstantinov, Boris Pavlovich (1910-1969)

kn4.ct   Tuchkevich, V. M., et al. "Boris Pavlovich Konstantinov." B.kn4.it, 7-13.

it   Tuchkevich, V. M., ed. *Problemy sovremennoy fiziki: Sbornik pamyati akad. B. P. Konstantinova.* Leningrad, 1974.

See also: D.kb1.ri

Kossel, Walther Ludwig @ (1888-1956)

ko1.gb   Buchwald, Eberhard. "Walther Kossel 60 Jahre." *PB, 4* (1948), 29-30.

gl   Laue, Max von. [Zu Walther Kossels 60. Geburtstag.] *Optik, 3* (1948), 1.

gs   Sommerfeld, Arnold. "Zum 60. Geburtstage von Walther Kossel." *Zeitschrift für Naturforschung, 2a* (1947), 595.

See also: A.bb1.bu; E.bg1.mo

Kowarski, Lew (1907-1979)

kp1.ak   Kowarski, Lew. *Réflexions sur la science.* Geneva, 1978.

Kramers, Hendrik Anthony @ (1894-1952)

kq1.bc   Casimir, H. B. G. "The scientific work of H. A. Kramers." *Nederlands tijdschrift voor natuurkunde, 18* (1952), 167-172. (Also in *Fysisk tidsskrift, 52* (1954), 9-16.)

eb   Bohr, Niels. "Hendrik Anthony Kramers." *Nederlands tijdschrift voor natuurkunde, 18* (1952), 161-166. (Also in *Fysisk tidsskrift, 52* (1954), 1-8.)

er   Romein, J. "[H. A. Kramers]". Maatschappij der Nederlandse Letterkunde, Leyden. *Jaarboek,* 1951-53, 82-91.

ew   Wheeler, John A. "Hendrik Antoon Kramers." APS. *Yearbook,* 1953, 355-360.

jk   Kramers, H. A. *Collected scientific papers.* Ed. H. B. G. Casimir et al. Amsterdam, 1956.

Kravets, Torichan Pavlovich (1876-1955)

kq4.as   Savost'yanova, M. V., and V. Yu. Roginskiy. *Torichan Pavlovich Kravets.* Leningrad, 1979.

bd   Anon. "Torichan Pavlovich Kravets." *Zhurnal tekhnicheskoy fiziki, 21* (1951), 385-388.

bs   Savost'yanova, M. V. "O rabotakh T. P. Kravtsa i yego uchenikov po skrytomu fotograficheskomu izobrazheniyu." B.kq4.jk, 320-332.

cf   Fayerman, G. P. "Torichan Pavlovich Kravets." B.kq4.jk, 5-29.

cv   Vavilov, S. I. "O vstrechakh s T. P. Kravtsem." IIYeT. *Trudy, 17* (1957), 96-99.

eg   *Gorokhovskiy, Yu. N. "T. P. Kravets." *Uspekhi nauchnoy fotografii, 5* (1957), 200-205.

gg   Gorokhovskiy, Yu. N., et al. "K 75-letiyu so dnya rozhdeniya T. P. Kravtsa." *UFN, 44* (1951), 301-310. (Also in *Zhurnal tekhnicheskoy fiziki, 4* (1951), 385-388.)

gr   *Radovskiy, M. I. "K 70-letiyu T. P. Kravtsa." *UFN, 29* (1946), 212-213.

jk   Kravets, T. P. *Trudy po fizike.* Moscow and Leningrad, 1959.

jl   Kravets, T. P. *Ot N'yutona do Vavilova: Ocherki i vospominaniya.* Leningrad, 1967.

See also: G.da3.go, sa |ha1.ne

Krishnan, Kariamanikkam Srinivasa (1898-1961)

kq8.cl   Lonsdale, Kathleen, and H. J. Bhabha. "Kariamanikkam Srinivasa Krishnan." RS. *BM, 13* (1967), 245-255.

Kronig, Ralph de Laer (1904-   )
See: E.bf1.kr

Krutkov, Yuriy Aleksandrovich (1890-1952)

ks1.cf   Frenkel', V. Ya. "Yuriy Aleksandrovich Krutkov." *UFN, 102* (1970), 634-654.

cg   Frenkel', V. Ya. "Yuriy Aleksandrovich Krutkov." *SPU, 13* (1970), 816-825.

Krylov, Aleksey Nikolayevich @ (1863-1945)

kt1.ai   Khanovich, I. G. *Akademik Aleksey Nikolayevich Krylov.* Leningrad, 1967.

aj   Krylov, A. N. *Moi vospominaniya.* Moscow and Leningrad, 1945.

ak   *Krylov, A. N. *Vospominaniya i ocherki.* Ed. I. S. Isakov and S. Ya. Streich. Moscow, 1956.

al   Krylov, A. N. *Moi vospominaniya.* Moscow, 1963.

ap   *Pisarzhevskiy, Oleg Nikolayevich. *Admiral korabel'noy nauki.* Moscow and Leningrad, 1945.

as   AN. *Pamyati Alekseya Nikolayevicha Krylova.* Ed. Yu. A. Shimanskiy. Moscow, 1958.

at   *Streich, S. Ya. *Aleksey Nikolayevich Krylov: Yego zhizn' i deyatel'nost'.* Moscow, 1950.

bc   Chaplygin, S. A. "Nauchnaya deyatel'nost' A. N. Krylova." AN. Fiziko-matematicheskiy institut. *Trudy,* otdel mat., 1934:5, 6-12.

bd   Chaplygin, S. A. "Nauchnaya deyatel'nost' Alekseya Nikolayevicha Krylova." B.kt1.aj, 533-542.

bi   Idel'son, N. I. "Raboty A. N. Krylova po astronomii." IIYeT. *Trudy, 15* (1956), 24-31.

bl   Lunts, Ye. B. "Kratkiy ocherk nauchnoy i inzhenernoy deyatel'nosti akademika Alekseya Nikolayevicha Krylova." *Vestnik mashinostroyeniya, 19:4* (1939), 6-10.

bm   Mandel'shtam, L. I. "O nauchnykh rabotakh A. N. Krylova." AN. *Obshcheye sobraniye Akademii Nauk SSSR, 25-30 sentyabrya 1943 goda.* Moscow and Leningrad, 1944. Pp. 61-76.

bn   Mandel'shtam, L. I. "O nauchnykh rabotakh A. N. Krylova." B.kt1.as, 7-21.

bp   Mandel'shtam, L. I. "O nauchnykh rabotakh A. N. Krylova." B.me1.ia, 283-301.

br *Novitskiy, D. I. "Obzor nauchnykh trudov i deyatel'nosti akad. A. N. Krylova." *K 50-letiyu nauchnoy deyatel'nosti akademika A. N. Krylova.* Moscow and Leningrad, 1936. Pp. 7-33.

bs Smirnov, V. I. "Matematicheskiye raboty A. N. Krylova." IIYeT, *Trudy, 15* (1956), 13-23.

bt Smirnov, V. I. "Raboty A. N. Krylova po matematicheskoy fizike i mekhanike." B.kt1.as, 36-46.

cb *Anon. "Kratkaya biografiya i chastichnyy perechen' nauchnykh trudov akad. A. N. Krylova." *Sudostroyeniye,* 1934:1, 25-27.

ch Ioffe, A. F. "A. N. Krylov v Akademii nauk." IIYeT. *Trudy, 15* (1956), 6-12.

ck Kravets, T. P. "Pamyati A. N. Krylova." IIYeT. *Trudy, 15* (1956), 32-39.

cl *Krylov, A. N. "Moy put' v nauke." *Morskoy sbornik,* 1939:2, 7-10.

cm Krylov, A. N. "Moi vospominaniya." B.kt1.jj, *1:1,* 43-264.

cr *Sadovskiy, A., and D. Slaventantor. "Akademik Krylov." *Literaturnyy sovremennik,* 1941:7-8, 99-111.

cs Shatelen, M. A. "Iz vospominaniy o vstrechakh s Alekseyem Nikolayevich Krylovym." IIYeT. *Trudy, 15* (1956), 40-45.

ct Shimanskiy, Yu. A. "Aleksey Nikolayevich Krylov." B.kt1.jk, 734-743.

cu Smirnov, V. I., et al. "Ocherk zhizni i deyatel'nosti A. N. Krylova." B.kt1.jj, *1:1,* 7-39.

cv Vavilov, S. I. "Pamyati A. N. Krylova." IIYeT. *Trudy, 15* (1956), 3-4. (Also in B.va4.jv, *3,* 589-590.)

ec Anon. "Aleksey Nikolayevich Krylov." AN. *Vestnik,* 1945: 12, 5-9.

gb *Anon. "Akademik A. N. Krylov: K 45-letiyu nauchnoy i pedagogicheskoy deyatel'nosti." *Morskoy sbornik,* 1935:5, 139-142.

gc *Anon. "Akademik Aleksey Nikolayevich Krylov." *Sudostroyeniye,* 1938:8-9, 461-462.

gi *Ioffe, A. F. "80-letiye akademika A. N. Krylova." *Priroda,* 1943:6, 81-82.

gs Shimanskiy, Yu. A. "Akademik Aleksey Nikolayevich Krylov." AN. *Vestnik,* 1943:7-8, 85-90.

jg *Kryzhanovskaya, N. A. *Akademik A. N. Krylov: Bibliograficheskiy ukazatel'.* Ed. S. T. Luchininov. Leningrad, 1952.

jh Krasotkina, T. A. "Iz perepiski A. N. Krylova s S. O. Maka-rovym, i P. de-Kolongom, N. Ye. Zhukovskim i drugimi." IIYeT. *Trudy, 15* (1956), 54-168.

jj Krylov, A. N. *Sobraniye trudov.* Ed. V. I. Smirnov et al. 12 vols. Moscow, 1936-1956.

jk Krylov, A. N. *Izbrannyye trudy.* Ed. Yu. A. Shimanskiy. Moscow, 1958.

jm Dinze, O. V., ed. *Aleksey Nikolayevich Krylov.* Moscow, 1945. (*Mtly*, ser. matematiki, 1.)

jp Khanovich, I. G. "*Sobraniye trudov* akademika A. N. Krylova." B.kt1.as, 149-168.

jr Shilov, N. I. "Neizdannoye pis'mo akademika A. N. Krylova V. V. Vitkovskomu." IIYeT. *Trudy, 5* (1955), 381-384.

jt Smirnov, V. I. *Rukopisnoye naslediye akademika Alekseya Niko-layevicha Krylova: Nauchnoye opisaniye.* Leningrad, 1969. (AN. Arkhiv. *Trudy, 23.*)

ni Ioffe, A. F. "A. N. Krylov v Akademii nauk." A.ajl.io, 203-208. *O fizike,* 1977. Pp. 203-208.

nk Kol'tsov, A. V. "Organizatsionnaya deyatel'nost' A. N. Krylov v Akademii nauk v 1918-1920 gg." IIYeT. *Trudy, 15* (1956), 46-53.

ps Skrynskiy, N. G. "Pedagogicheskoye naslediye A. N. Krylova." B.kt1.as, 124-134.

si Isachenkov, N. V. "Aleksey Nikolayevich Krylov i Voyenno-Morskoy Flot." AN. *Obshcheye sobraniye Akademii Nauk SSSR, 25-30 sentyabrya 1943 goda.* Moscow and Leningrad, 1944.

xg Grigor'yan, A. T. "N'yutonovedcheskiye issledovaniya A. N. Krylova." VIYeT, *13* (1962), 79-83.

See also: D.hb1.mi |tc1.fi, sh |te1.si; E.mt1.ry; G.da1.bb; P.ib1.id; U.kh1.fe

Krylov, Nikolay Mitrofanovich @ (1879-1955)

kt3.cb Bogolyubov, N. N. "Nikolay Mitrofanovich Krylov." B.kt3.jk, *1*, 7-13.

jk Krylov, N. M. *Izbrannyye trudy.* 3 vols. Kiev, 1961.

jm Isakov, O. V., and N. N. Bogolyubov, ed. *Nikolay Mitrofanovich Krylov.* Moscow, 1945. (*Mtly*, ser. matematiki, 2.)

Kuenen, Johannes Petrus @ (1866-1922)

ku1.bl Lorentz, Hendrik Antoon. "Kuenen als natuurkundige." *De gids, 86* (1922), 209-215.

eh   Haas, W. J. de. "Prof. Dr. J. P. Kuenen." *Physica, 2* (1922), 281-287.

jb   Bouman, J., and W. J. de Haas. "Lijst van verhandelingen van Professor Dr. J. P. Kuenen." *Physica, 2* (1922), 342-344.

Kuhn, Werner @ (1899-1963)

kvl.ek   Kuhn, Hans J. "Werner Kuhn." Naturforschende Gesellschaft, Basel. *Verhandlungen, 74* (1963), 239-258.

Kunze, Paul (1897-)

See: K.ael.gu

Kurchatov, Igor' Vasil'yevich @ (1903-1960)

kwl.ab   Astashenkov, Petr Timofeyevich. *Kurchatov*. Moscow, 1967.

ac   *Astashenkov, Petr Timofeyevich. *Akademik L. V. Kurchatov*. Moscow, 1971.

ag   Golovin, Igor N. *I. V. Kurchatov. A socialist-realist. Biography of the Soviet nuclear scientist*. Tr. W. H. Dougherty. Bloomington, 1968. (Russian ed., Moscow, 1967.)

bc   Badal'yan, R. G. "Pervyye nauchnyye issledovaniya I. V. Kurchatova." *IMYeN: Fizika, 10* (1971), 164-170.

bi   Ioffe, A. F. "I. V. Kurchatov: Issledovatel' dielektrikov." *UFN, 73* (1961), 611-614. (In English in *SPU, 4* (1961), 279-281.)

cg   Golovin, I. N. "I. V. Kurchatov i Frederik Zholio-Kyuri." *IMYeN: Fizika, 6* (1968), 8-14.

cr   Rabinowitch, Eugene. "Igor Kurchatov, 1903-1960: An introduction." *BAS, 23* (Dec. 1967), 8-18.

ec   Anon. "Igor' Vasil'yevich Kurchatov." *UFN, 73* (1961), 593-604. (In English in *SPU, 4* (1961), 380-387.)

See also: O.bbl.io

Kurdyumov, Georgiy Vyacheslavovich (1902-)

kxl.gc   Anon. "K pyatidesyatiletiyu G. V. Kurdyumova." *Problemy metallovedeniya i fiziki metallov*. Moscow, 1952. Pp. 3-8.

Kurlbaum, Ferdinand @ (1857-1927)

kx4.eh   Henning, F. "Ferdinand Kurlbaum." *PZ, 29* (1928), 97-104.

Kurnakov, Nikolay Semenovich @ (1860-1941)

ky1.cs   Shchukarev, S. A. "Iz vospominaniy o N. S. Kurnakove." *VI-YeT, 13* (1962), 105-106.

jm   *Nikolay Semenovich Kurnakov.* Moscow, 1961. (*Mtly*, ser. khim., 30.)

See also: O.ac1.ko

Kuznetsov, Vladimir Dmitriyevich @ (1887-1963)

kz1.bb   *Bol'shanina, M. A., and N. F. Kunin. "Nauchnaya i obshchestvennaya deyatel'nost' V. D. Kuznetsova." Tomsk. University. Sibirskiy fiziko-tekhnicheskiy institut. *Trudy,* 5:3 (1939), 1-14.

ib   *Bol'shanina, M. A., ed. *Issledovaniya po fizike tverdogo tela.* Moscow, 1957.

Laby, Thomas Howell (1880-1946)

la1.ep   Picken, D. K., and M. L. Oliphant. "Thomas Howell Laby." RS. *Obituary notices, 5* (1948), 733-755.

Lamb, Horace @ (1849-1934)

la3.eg   Glazebrook, R. T. "Sir Horace Lamb." RS. *Obituary notices, 1* (1935), 375-392.

Lampa, Anton (1868-1938)

la6.ak   Kleinert, Andreas. *Anton Lampa, 1868-1938.* Berlin, 1976. (Deutscher Bibliotheksverband. *Bibliographien, 4.*)

ck   Kleinert, Andreas. "Anton Lampa und Albert Einstein." *Gesnerus, 32* (1975), 285-292.

See also: C.ap1.kl

Landau, Lev Davidovich @ $62 (1908-1968)

la8.ab   Abrikosov, A. A. *Akademik L. D. Landau: Kratkaya biografiya i obzor nauchnykh rabot.* Moscow, 1965.

af   Bessarab, Maiya Gakovlevna. *Stranitsy zhizni Landau.* Moscow, 1971.

ak   Dorozynski, Alexander. *The man they wouldn't let die.* NY, 1965.

al   Livanova, Anna. *L. D. Landau.* Moscow, 1978. (English trn, Oxford and NY, 1980.)

am Haar, Dirk ter, ed. *Men of physics: L. D. Landau.* 2 vols. Oxford and NY, 1965-69.

bg Ginzburg, V. L. "Fundamental'nyy trud po teoreticheskoy fizike." B.la8.il, 17-23.

cb Abrikosov, A. A. "My years with Landau." *PT, 26* (Jan. 1973), 56-60.

ce Anon. "Ob akademike L. D. Landau." B.la8.il, 29-30.

cp Pellam, J. "Lev Davydovich Landau." *PT, 14* (Mar. 1961), 42-46.

cr Rumer, Georg. "Zum Gedenken an L. D. Landau." *PB, 29* (1973), 147-152.

eg Ginzburg, V. L. "Lev Davidovich Landau (k shestidesyatiletiyu so dnya rozhdeniya)." *UFN, 94* (1968), 181-184.

ej Lifshits, Ye. M. "Lev Davidovich Landau." *UFN, 97* (1969), 169-186. (Also in B.la8.jl, *2,* 427-448; in English in *SPU, 12* (1970), 135-145; B.la8.jm, *2,* 427-447.)

ek Lifshits, Ye. M. "Lev Davydovitch Landau." RS. *BM, 15* (1969), 141-158.

el Lifshits, Ye. M. "Landau, great scientist and teacher." A.aj1.fr, 71-77.

gb Anon. "Akademik Lev Davidovich Landau." *ZhETF, 34* (1958), 3-6.

gd Berestetskiy, V. B. "Lev Davidovich Landau: K pyatidesyatiletiyu so dnya rozhdeniya." *UFN, 64* (1958), 615-623.

gk Kofink, W. "Nobelpreis für Physik 1962 an L. D. Landau." *PB, 18* (1962), 568-571.

il Landau, L. D. *Nauchnoye tvorchestvo: Sbornik.* Ed. A. I. Chernov. Moscow, 1963.

jl Landau, L. D. *Collected papers.* Oxford and NY, 1965.

jm Landau, L. D. *Sobraniye trudov.* 2 vols. Moscow, 1969.

sl Lifshits, Ye. M. "L. D. Landau's plain talk to students of physics." *AJP, 45* (1977), 415-422.

See also: K.aa1.be; O.hc1.lj

Landé, Alfred (1888-1975)

lb3.iy Yourgrau, Wolfgang, and Alwyn van der Merwe, eds. *Perspectives in quantum theory: Essays in honor of Alfred Landé.* Cambridge, Mass., 1971.

See also: H.dc1.fo

Landsberg, Grigoriy Samuilovich @ (1890-1957)

lb6.el   Mandel'shtam, S. L. "Kratkiy ocherk zhizni i deyatel'nosti aka-
          demika G. S. Landsberga." *UFN, 63* (1957), 289-299.

en   Mandel'shtam, S. L., and I. L. Fabelinskiy. "Grigoriy Samuilo-
          vich Landsberg." B.lb6.jl, 5-40.

gb   Anon. "K shestidesyatiletiyu so dnya rozhdeniya akademika G.
          S. Landsberga." *UFN, 41* (1950), 128-130.

gd   Anon. "Akademik G. S. Landsberg." *ZhETF, 20* (1950),
          289-291.

ge   *Anon. "Grigoriy Samuilovich Landsberg." *Zavodskaya labora-
          toriya*, 1950:4, 511-512.

jl   Landsberg, G. S. *Izbrannyye trudy.* Ed. I. L. Fabelinskiy. Mos-
          cow, 1958.

jm   Mandel'shtam, S. L., et al., ed. *Grigoriy Samuilovich Landsberg.*
          Moscow, 1953. (*Mtly*, ser. fiziki, 6.)

pf   Fabrikant, V. A. "G. S. Landsberg kak avtor i redaktor uchebni-
          kov po fizike." *UFN, 63* (1957), 455-460.

See also: G.fa6.ba |ha1.mo

Langevin, Paul @ (1872-1946)

lc3.ag   Geyvish, Yu. G. *Pol' Lanzheven: Uchenyy, borets za mir i
          demokratiyu.* Moscow, 1955.

ah   *Ghimesan, S. *Paul Langevin.* Bucharest, 1964.

aj   Langevin, André. *Paul Langevin, mon père: L' homme et
          l'oeuvre.* Paris, 1971.

al   Langevin, Paul. *La pensée et l'action.* Ed. Paul Laberenne. Paris,
          1955.

as   Starosel'skaya-Nikitina, O. A. *Pol' Lanzheven.* Moscow, 1962.

bb   Anon. "Pamyati Polya Lanzhevena." AN. *Vestnik*, 1947: 5,
          39-47.

bs   Starosel'skaya-Nikitina, O. A. "La contribution de Paul
          Langevin à la théorie relativiste et sa portée historique." ICHS,
          VIII (1956). *Actes, 1* (1958), 178-182.

cb   Anon. "85 let so dnya rozhdeniya Polya Lanzhevena." AN. *Vest-
          nik*, 1957:3, 140-141.

cc   Anon. "Le retour de Paul Langevin en France (1941-1944)." *La
          pensée*, no. 12 (1947), 77-78.

ce   Cogniot, Georges. "Hommage à Paul Langevin." *La pensée*, no.
          53 (1954), 11-13.

cf   Cogniot, Georges. "Paul Langevin: Une vie au service de la sciences et de la paix." *La pensée*, no. 191 (1977), 62-69.

cg   Dorfman, Ya. G. "Pol' Lanzheven." B.lc3.jm, 721-746.

ch   Dupuy, Paul. "Souvenirs." *La pensée*, no. 12 (1947), 63-64.

ci   Gratiot-Alphandéry, Hélène. "Le contenu scientifique de l'oeuvre de Paul Langevin." *La pensée*, no. 165 (1972), 6-11.

ck   Joliot, Frédéric. "Le professeur Langevin et l'effort scientifique de guerre." *La pensée* (1944), 32-37.

cm   Kapitsa, P. L. "Iz vospominaniy o P. Lanzhevene." *VIYeT, 18* (1965), 23-28.

co   Kedrov, B. M. "Pol' Lanzheven: K 100-letiyu so dnya rozhdeniya." *VIYeT, 41* (1972), 56-58.

cq   Labérenne, Paul. "A la mémoire de Paul Langevin." *La pensée*, no. 40 (1952), 65-67.

cr   Labérenne, Paul. "Les sciences de la nature, *La pensée* et Paul Langevin." *La pensée*, no. 191 (1977), 70-76.

cs   Langevin, André. "Paul Langevin et Pierre Curie." *La pensée*, no. 160 (1971), 1-19.

cu   Oreel, Jean. "Hommage á Paul Langevin." *La pensée*, no. 53 (1954), 9-11.

cv   Vassart, Robert. "Paul Langevin à Troyes (1941-1944)." *La pensée*, no. 12 (1947), 68-76.

cw   Wallon, Henri, and Jean Orcel. "A la mémoire de Paul Langevin." *La pensée*, no. 34 (1951), 7-13.

eb   Broglie, Louis de. "Notice sur la vie et l'oeuvre de Paul Langevin." AS. *Mémoires, 67* (1947), 34p.

ed   Cogniot, Georges. "Paul Langevin." *La pensée*, no. 21 (1948), 3-15.

ef   Cotton, Aimé. "L'oeuvre scientifique de Paul Langevin." *La pensée*, no. 12 (1947), 21-30.

eg   Cotton, Eugénie. "Hommage à Paul Langevin." *La pensée*, no. 77 (1958), 13-16.

ei   Einstein, Albert. "Paul Langevin." *La pensée*, no. 12 (1947), 13-14.

ek   Ioffe, A. F. "A la mémoire d'un maître et ami." *La pensée*, no. 12 (1947), 15-16.

em   Joliot, Frédéric. "Paul Langevin." *Experientia, 3* (1947), 167.

en   Joliot, Frédéric. "Paul Langevin rationaliste." *La pensée,* no. 12 (1947), 57-58.

eo   Joliot, Frédéric. "Paul Langevin." RS. *Obituary notices, 7* (1952), 405-419.

eq   Landsberg, G. S. "Pol' Lanzheven (1872-1946)." *UFN, 31* (1947), 290-296.

es   Rolland, Paul Le. "L'unité de sa vie et de sa pensée." *La pensée,* no. 12 (1947), 34-40.

gj   Joliot, Frédéric. "Discours prononcé à la cérémonie en l'honneur de Paul Langevin." *Experientia,* 1947, 167-168.

il   *Hommage à Paul Langevin.* Paris, 1945.

jb   Biquard, Pierre. *Langevin: Présentation, choix de textes, bibliographie, illustrations.* Paris, 1969.

je   Langevin, Luce. "Paul Langevin et Albert Einstein, d'après une correspondence et des documents inédits." *La pensée,* no. 161 (1972), 3-40.

jj   Langevin, Paul. "Quatre lettres de Paul Langevin à Frédéric Joliot-Curie." *La pensée,* no. 87 (1959), 105-112.

jl   Langevin, Paul. *Oeuvres scientifiques.* Paris, 1950.

jm   Langevin, Paul. *Izbrannyye trudy.* Ed. A. B. Shekhter and O. A. Starosel'skaya-Nikitina. Moscow, 1960.

jp   Langevin, Paul. "Pis'mo P. Lanzhevena k sovetskim uchenym." *Ogonek,* 1956: 51, 31.

kg   Geyvish, Yu. G. "Pol' Lanzheven: Vydayushchiysya frantsuzkiy fizik-materialist." *UFN, 42* (1950), 462-475.

kh   *Geyvish, Yu. G. "Pol' Lanzheven—vydayushchiysya fizik-materialist." *Filosofskiye zapiski, 3* (1950), 160-179.

kj   Huard, Raymond. "Essai sur les premières démarches de la pensée philosophique de Paul Langevin." *La pensée,* no. 109 (1963), 64-81.

kl   Labérenne, Paul. "Itinéraire philosophique de Paul Langevin." *La pensée,* no. 175 (1974), 24-37.

km   Maiocchi, Roberto. "Le considerazioni epistemologiche di Paul Langevin sulla meccanica quantistica ed i loro riflessi nella cultura francese anteguerra." *Scientia, 110* (1975), 493-518.

kp   Montel, E., M. Paty, et al. "Langevin et il rationalismo." *Scientia, 108* (1973), 171-220.

nc   Cotton, Eugénie. "Paul Langevin maître de conférences à l'Ecole normale de Sèvres." *La pensée,* no. 12 (1947), 41-44.

nh Hadamard, Jacques. "Paul Langevin au Collège de France." *La pensée*, no. 12 (1947), 31-33.

nl Langevin, Jean. "Paul Langevin et le 'Journal de physique'." *La pensée*, no. 165 (1972), 127-134.

pc Cogniot, Georges. "Qu'est-il advenu des propositions de Langevin en politique scolaire?" *La pensée*, no. 165 (1972), 60-69.

pg Kahane, Ernest. "Paul Langevin et la méthode historique dans l'enseignement des sciences." *Organon, 3* (1966), 161-167. (Also in ICHS, XI (1965). *Actes, 2* (1967), 104-108.)

pl Langevin, Luce. "L'importance de l'histoire des sciences dans l'éducation." *La pensée*, no. 165 (1972), 12-19.

pm *Livshits, Ye. S. "Bor'ba Lanzhevena za demokratizatsiyu shkoly vo Frantsii." *Sovetskaya pedagogika*, 1952:5, 103-108.

po Ranc, Albert. "Paul Langevin et l'histoire des sciences." *La nef, 4* (May 1947), 136-138.

pr Séclet-Riou, Mme. F. "Paul Langevin éducateur." *La pensée*, no. 12 (1947), 45-56.

pt Snyders, Georges. "Quelques lignes de force essentielles." *La pensée*, no. 165 (1972), 45-49.

pv Starosel'skaya-Nikitina, O. A. "Pol' Lanzheven kak istorik yestestvoznaniya." IIYeT. *Trudy, 1* (1954), 267-308.

sb Bayet, Albert. "Paul Langevin et la défense des droits de l'homme." *La pensée*, no. 12 (1947), 59-62.

sd Beauvais, Jacques. "Le contenu civique et démocratique de l'oeuvre de Paul Langevin." *La pensée*, no. 165 (1972), 42-45.

sg Jourdain, Francis. "Paul Langevin le militant." *La pensée*, no. 12 (1947), 65-67.

sk Montel, E. "Le savant hors de la tour d'ivoire." *Scientia, 108* (1973), 175-204.

sn Paty, M. "Science et humanisme." *Scientia, 108* (1973), 205-220.

ss Schatzman, E. "La méthode de la liberté." *Scientia, 108* (1973), 173-174.

sw Wallon, Henri. "Paul Langevin et la Résistance." *La pensée*, no. 46 (1953), 3-5.

tc Langevin, André. "O stycich Paula Langevina a jeho kolegů s ceskoslovenskými fyziky." *Dejiny ved a techniky, 10* (1977), 1-7.

te Bernal, J. D. "Langevin et l'Angleterre." *La pensée*, no. 12 (1947), 17-20.

tr   Radovskiy, M. I. "Nauchnyye svyazi Lanzhevena s sovetskimi uchenymi." *Priroda*, 1962:11, 96-98.

tt   Starosel'skaya-Nikitina, O. A. "Pol' Lanzheven i franko-sovetskiye kul'turnyye svyazi." AN. *Vestnik*, 1956: 1, 66-70.

See also: A.ma1.la, lb, lc; B.mb2.pn | ru1.al; C.fa5.la; F.be1.cv | bh1.cu | fd1.ku; O.bb1.st

Langley, Samuel Pierpont @ (1834-1906)

lc6.ab   Adler, Cyrus. *I have remembered the days.* Philadelphia, 1941.

eb   Abbot, Charles Greeley. "Samuel Pierpont Langley." *Astrophysical journal, 23* (1906), 271-283.

ed   Adler, Cyrus. "Samuel Pierpont Langley." Philosophical Society of Washington. *Bulletin, 15* (1907), 1-26.

er   Walcott, C. D. "Samuel Pierpont Langley." NAS. *BM, 7* (1917), 247-268.

ew   White, A. D., E. C. Pickering, and Octave Chanute. "Samuel Pierpont Langley." *Smithsonian miscellaneous collections, 49*: 1720, (1907), 49p.

Langmuir, Irving @ $32C (1881-1957)

ld3.ar   Rosenfeld, Albert. *The quintessence of Irving Langmuir: A biography.* NY, 1960.

aw   Westervelt, Virginia Veeder. *Incredible man of science.* NY, 1968.

bc   Bridgman, Percy W. "Some of the physical aspects of the work of Langmuir." B.ld3.jl, *1*, xxxi-lv; *12*, 433-457.

bh   Hull, Albert W. "Dr. Irving Langmuir's contributions to physics." *Nature, 181* (1958), 148-149.

br   Rideal, Eric. "Some of the chemical aspects of the work of Langmuir." B.ld3.jl, *1*, xvii-xxx; *12*, 419-432.

cb   Blodgett, Katherine B. "Irving Langmuir." *JCE, 10* (1933), 396-399.

ch   Hildebrand, Joel H. "The humanism of Irving Langmuir." B.ld3.jl, *12*, 233-240.

cs   Suits, C. Guy. "Foreword." B.ld3.jl, *1*, vii-xi; *12*, vii-xi.

ct   Suits, C. Guy, and Miles J. Martin. "Irving Langmuir." NAS. *BM, 45* (1974), 215-247.

et   Taylor, Hugh. "Irving Langmuir." RS. *BM, 4* (1958), 167-184.

ew   Whitney, W. R. "Irving Langmuir." Philosophical Society. *Yearbook,* 1957, 129-133.

jl   Langmuir, Irving. *The collected works of Irving Langmuir.* 12
      vols. Ed. C. Guy Suits and Harold E. Way. NY, 1960-62.

See also: D.da1.ey, ha; E.bi1.be, co, ro | tt1.je; K.ea1.co; P.fc1.by, sc |
      mb1.so; R.ah1.ab, ve, zi | bd1.ko, kp | dh1.ec

Laporte, M. L. A. Marcel (1889-   )

ld6.al   Laporte, Marcel. *Les joies de la recherche: la vie scientifique d'un
          physicien français, pionnier de l'électronique moderne.* Paris, 1977.

Laporte, Otto (1902-1971)

le3.ec   Crane, H. R., and D. M. Dennison. "Otto Laporte." NAS. *BM,
          50* (1979), 269-285.

Lark-Horovitz, Karl (1892-1958)

le6.aj   Johnson, Vivian A. *Men of physics: Karl Lark-Horovitz, pioneer
          of solid state physics.* Oxford, 1969.

Larmor, Joseph @ (1857-1942)

lf3.cb   Birkhoff, George D. "Sir Joseph Larmor and modern mathemat-
          ical physics." *Science, 97* (1943), 77-79.

ee   Eddington, A. S. "Joseph Larmor." RS. *Obituary notices, 4*
          (1942/3), 197-207.

em   Morton, W. B. "Sir Joseph Larmor." Belfast Natural History and
          Philosophical Society. *Proceedings and reports, 2:3* (1942/3),
          82-90.

gf   Fleming, John Ambrose, et al. "Sir Joseph Larmor." Physical
          Society of London. *Proceedings, 53* (1941), 54-65.

jl   Larmor, Joseph. *Mathematical and physical papers.* 2 vols. Cam-
          bridge, 1929.

See also: E.ad1; P.fc1.ap

Latimer, Wendell Mitchell @ (1893-1955)

lf4.eh   Hildebrand, Joel H. "Wendell Mitchell Latimer." NAS. *BM, 32*
          (1958), 221-237.

Laue, Max von @ $14 (1879-1960)

lf6.ah   Herneck, Friedrich. *Max von Laue.* Berlin, 1979.

bl   Leibfried, Günther. "Max von Laue, der Beweis von der Wel-
          lennatur der Röntgenstrahlen und der atomistischen Struktur der
          Materie." A.aj1.sc, 56-62.

cd   Borrmann, G. "Max von Laue und das Fritz-Haber-Institut."
       PB, 15 (1959), 453-456.

ce   Ewald, Peter Paul. "Max von Laue—Mensch und Werk." *PB,*
       35, (1979), 337-349.

cg   Hermann, Armin. "Laue, Max von." *DSB, 8* (1973), 50-53.

ch   Herneck, Friedrich. "Max von Laue als Forscher und Humanist."
       NTM, 16: 2 (1979), 14-21.

ck   Krugmann, R. "Aus einer Unterhaltung mit M. von Laue." *PB, 5*
       (1949), 447-448.

cl   Laue, Max von. "Mein physikalischer Werdegang." *PB, 16*
       (1960), 260-266. (Also in B.lf6.jl, *3,* v-xxiv; and in Russian in
       UFN, 72 (1960), 831-840.)

co   Päsler, Max. "Leben und wissenschaftliches Werk Max von
       Laues." *PB, 16* (1960), 552-567.

cp   Päsler, Max. "Gedanken an Max von Laue." *PB, 25* (1969),
       449-450.

ee   Ewald, Peter Paul. "Max von Laue." RS. *BM, 6* (1960), 135-156.

ef   Franck, James. "Max van Laue." APS. *Yearbook* (1960), 155-
       159.

em   Meissner, Walther. "Max von Laue als Wissenschaftler und
       Mensch." Akademie der Wissenschaften, Munich. Math.-
       Naturw. Klasse. *Sitzungsberichte,* 1960, 101-121.

ew   Westphal, Wilhelm H. "Der Mensch Max von Laue." *PB, 16*
       (1960), 549-551.

gb   Beck, F. "Max von Laue zum 80. Geburtstag." *PB, 15* (1959),
       446-452.

gc   Belov, N. V. "Maks Laue." *Kristallografiya, 4* (1959), 639-640.

gd   Brill, R., and Otto Hahn, et al. "Feierstunde zu Ehren von Max
       von Laue an seinem 80. Geburtstag." Max-Planck Gesellschaft.
       Mitteilungen, 1959, 323-366.

gh   Hiller, J. E. "Prof. von Laue 80 Jahre alt." *NR, 12* (1959), 363.

gm   Planck, Max. "Max von Laue." *Nwn, 17* (1929), 787-788.

gn   Planck, Max. "Max von Laue." *Nwn, 27* (1939), 665-666.

gs   Sommerfeld, Arnold. "Max von Laue zum 70. Geburtstag." *PB,*
       5 (1949), 443.

jl   Laue, Max von. *Gesammelte Schriften und Vorträge.* 3 vols.
       Braunschweig, 1961.

jm   Laue, Max von. *Stat'i i rechi.* Moscow, 1969.

sb   Br[üche, Ernst]. "Champion of freedom [Max von Laue]." *PB, 5*
      (1949), 448-449.

See also: B.ei4.ud |ei6.jl |mk1.ds, if; C.gb5.bo |gm1.ge

Lauritsen, Charles Christian (1892-1968)

lf8.cf   Fowler, William A. "Charles Christian Lauritsen." NAS. *BM, 46*
          (1975), 221-239.

Lawrence, Ernest Orlando @ $39 (1901-1958)

lg3.ac   Childs, Herbert. *An American genius: The life of Ernest Orlando
          Lawrence.* NY, 1968.

ad   Davis, Nuel Pharr. *Lawrence and Oppenheimer.* NY, 1968.

cw   Wilkes, Daniel. "200 man-years of life: The story of Ernest Or-
          lando Lawrence." *PTeach, 3* (1965), 247-255, 266.

eb   Alvarez, Luis W. "Ernest Orlando Lawrence." NAS. *BM, 41*
          (1970), 251-294.

gh   Houston, W. V. "The progress of science: Nobel prize award in
          physics for 1939 to E. O. Lawrence." *Scientific monthly, 50*
          (1940), 277-278.

Lazarev, Petr Petrovich @ (1878-1942)

lg6.as   Shuleykin, V. V. *Akademik Petr Petrovich Lazarev.* Moscow,
          1960. (Moscow. University. *Zamechatel'nyye uchenyye.*)

bv   Vavilov, S. I. "Fotokhimicheskiye issledovaniya akademika P. P.
          Lazareva." AN. *Izvestiya,* ser. fiz., 7 (1943), 193-199.

cc   Deryagin, B. V. "Petr Petrovich Lazarev." *SPU, 21* (1978),
          378-380.

cd   Deryagin, B. V., and M. P. Volarovich. "Petr Petrovich Lazarev:
          Kratkaya biografiya." B.lg6.jl, *1,* 13-40.

cg   Getman, F. D., and L. K. Kuvanova. "O P. P. Lazareve (iz ne-
          opublikovannykh pisem)." AN. *Vestnik,* 1952:4, 70-74.

ci   Il'ina, O. A., et al. "Iz perepiski akademika P. P. Lazareva."
          IMYeN. Fizika, 8 (1970), 223-249.

ck   Kononkov, A. F. "Akademik Petr Petrovich Lazarev." *IMYeN:
          Fizika, 12* (1972), 125-135.

cm   Kravkov, S. V. "Petr Petrovich Lazarev." *UFN, 46* (1952),
          441-449.

cv   Vavilov, S. I. "Pamyati akademika P. P. Lazareva." B.va4.jv, *3,*
          202-208.

cz   Zelinskiy, N. D., and G. S. Landsberg. "Petr Petrovich Lazarev."
      AN. *Vestnik*, 1952: 4, 67-69.

ek   Kravets, T. P. "Tvorcheskiy put' akademika P. P. Lazareva."
      AN. *Izvestiya*, ser. fiz., *7* (1943), 185-192. (Also in *UFN, 27*
      (1945), 13-21.)

es   Shpol'skiy, E. V. "Petr Petrovich Lazarev." *UFN, 27* (1945),
      1-12.

ev   *Vavilov, S. I. "Pamyati akad. P. P. Lazareva." AN. *Vestnik*,
      1942:7-8, 97-102.

jl   Lazarev, P. P. *Sochineniya.* 3 vols. Moscow and Leningrad,
      1950-57.

jm   Volarovich, M. P., and N. M. Nesterova, ed. *Petr Petrovich La-
      zarev.* Moscow, 1958. (*Mtly*, ser. fiz., 10.)

sm   Mendelevich, G. A. "Akademik P. P. Lazarev o printsipakh or-
      ganizatsii Muzeya istorii yestestvoznaniya i tekhniki. (Po arkhiv-
      nym materialam)." *UFN, 53* (1954), 137-140.

See also: P.mb1.de

Lebedev, Aleksandr Alekseyevich (1893-1969)

lh1.cb Anon. "Akademik Aleksandr Alekseyevich Lebedev." *ZhETF,*
        25 (1953), 623-625.

gb   Baumgart, K. K. "Laureat Stalinskoy premii 1947 g., professor
      Leningradskogo universiteta, akad. A. A. Lebedev." Leningrad.
      University. *Vestnik*, 1947: 8, 117-118.

gv   *Vafiadi, V. G. "Geroy Sotsialisticheskogo Truda akademik
      Aleksandr Alekseyevich Lebedev." *Optiko-mekhanicheskaya pro-
      myshlennost'*, 1957:3, 3-4.

jm   Vafiadi, V. G., and N. M. Nesterova, ed. *Aleksandr Alekseyevich
      Lebedev.* Moscow, 1957. (*Mtly*, ser. fiz., 18.) Moscow, 1957.

Lebedev, Petr Nikolayevich @ (1866-1912)

lh3.ae Dukov, Victor. *Pyotr Nikolayevich Lebedev.* Tr. D. Skvirsky.
        Moscow, 1956. (Russian edition, Moscow, 1951; 2nd ed.,
        1956.)

ak   Kaptsov, N. A. *Petr Nikolayevich Lebedev, 1866-1912.* Moscow,
      1950. (Moscow. University. *Zamechatel'nyye uchenyye.*)

al   *Lazarev, P. P. *A. G. Stoletov, N. A. Umov, P. N. Lebedev, B. B.
      Golitsyn.* Leningrad, 1927.

as   Shugaylin, A. V. *Vydayushchiysya fizik-materialist P. N. Lebedev.*
      Kiev, 1957.

at   Timiryazev, A. K. *Klassiki russkoy fiziki: Lomonosov, Stoletov, Lebedev.* Moscow, 1949.

bb   Andreyev, K. "Chelovek, vsvesivshiy svet." *Ogonek,* 1950:46, 17-18.

bk   Kravets, T. P. "Petr Nikolayevich Lebedev i yego tvorchestvo." B.lh3.jo, 11-32.

bp   Serdyukov, A. R. "K istorii otechestvennoy reaktivnoy tekhniki: Proekty dvigateley dlya vozdukhoplavaniya P. N. Lebedeva." *UFN, 50* (1953), 309-313.

br   *Tereshchenko, A. I. "P. N. Lebedev i znacheniye yego rabot dlya razvitiya radiofiziki." Kharkov. University. *Uchenyye zapiski, 102* (1959), 7-13.

bt   Timiryazev, A. K. "Nauchnyye raboty P. N. Lebedeva." IIYeT. *Trudy, 28* (1959), 79-90.

cb   Amfiteatrova-Levitskaya, A. N. "Pamyati druga." IIYeT. *Trudy, 28* (1959), 122-137.

cd   Anon. "Petr Nikolayevich Lebedev i russkaya fizika." *ZhETF, 22* (1952), 257-263.

ce   Anon. "Iz neopublikovannykh dnevnikov, zapisnykh knizhek i pisem Petra Nikolayevicha Lebedeva." *Puti v neznayemoye, 1* (1960), 516-521.

cg   Arkad'yev, V. K. "O P. N. Lebedeve." IIYeT. *Trudy, 28* (1959), 91-105.

ci   Derzhavin, A. N. "Klassiki russkoy fiziki A. G. Stoletov, N. A. Umov, P. N. Lebedev o stroyenii veshchestva." A.abl.vo, 324-332.

ck   Kaptsov, N. A. "Vospominaniya o Petre Nikolayeviche Lebedeve." *UFN, 46* (1952), 325-328.

cl   Kaptsov, N. A. "Rol' Petra Nikolayevich Lebedeva v sozdanii nauchno-issledovatelskikh kadrov." *UFN, 77* (1962), 583-588. (Also in B.lh3.jl, 406-412; in English in *SPU, 5* (1963), 625-628.)

co   Korolev, F. A. "Otkiytiya P. N. Lebedeva i ikh znacheniye dlya sovremennoy fiziki." *VIYeT, 15* (1963), 47-57.

cr   Kravets, T. P. "Detskiye i yunosheskiye gody Petra Nikolayevicha Lebedeva." IIYeT. *Trudy, 28* (1959), 32-44.

cs   Kravets, T. P. "Petr Nikolayevich Lebedev." B.lh3.jl, 391-405.

cv   Vavilov, S. I. "Pamyati P. N. Lebedeva." B.va4.jv, *3,* 165-167, 761-770.

cy   Zernov, V. D. "Petr Nikolayevich Lebedev." C.vm1.pr, 125-150.

db   Akulov, A. I. "Moya rabota u Lebedeva." IIYeT. *Trudy, 28* (1959), 121.

dd   Lazarev, P. P. "K dvadtsatiyatiletiyu so dnya smerti P. N. Lebedeva." *UFN, 17* (1937), 405-420.

de   Lazarev, P. P. "Petr Nikolayevich Lebedev." IIYeT. *Trudy, 28* (1959), 5-31.

df   Lazarev, P. P. "Vospominaniya o P. P. Lebedeve." *UFN, 77* (1962), 571-582.

dg   Lazarev, P. P. "My recollections of P. N. Lebedev." *SPU, 5* (1963), 617-624.

dh   *Lazarev, P. P. "Petr Nikolayevich Lebedev." B.lh3.jk, 11-32.

di   Levshin, V. L. "Zhizn' i nauchnaya deyatel'nost' Petra Nikolayevicha Lebedeva." *UFN, 91* (1967), 331-339.

dk   Rzhevkin, S. N. "Iz vospominaniy o P. N. Lebedeve." IIYeT. *Trudy, 28* (1959), 119-120.

dm   *Sominskiy, M. S. "P. N. Lebedev i progress fiziki." *Zhurnal tekhnicheskoy fiziki, 22* (1952), 1221-1248.

do   Teplyakov, G. M., et al. "Nauchnyye shkoly A. G. Stoletova i P. N. Lebedeva i yevropeyskaya fizika." ICHS, XIII (1971). Section 6. *Actes* (1974), 140-143.

dp   Timiryazev, A. K. "Osnovopolozhniki fiziki v Rossii M. V. Lomonosov, A. G. Stoletov, P. N. Lebedev." *Rol' russkoy nauki v razvitii mirovoy nauki i kul'tury.* Moscow. University. *Uchenyye zapiski, 92* (1946), 3-23.

dq   Timiryazev, A. K. "P. N. Lebedev." C.vb1.ti, 145-163.

dr   Timiryazev, A. K. "Iz vospominaniy o Petre Nikolayeviche Lebedeve." *UFN, 46* (1952), 321-324.

ds   *Timiryazev, A. K. [Essays on Lebedev.] Timiryazev. *Izbrannyye sochineniya.* 2 vols. Moscow, 1957. Vol. *2*, 524-537.

dt   Timiryazev, A. K. "P. N. Lebedev." C.vb1.pr, *1*, 247-64.

du   Timiryazev, A. K. "Petr Nikolayevich Lebedev." B.tk3.jt, 67-78.

ja   *AN. Biblioteka. *Petr Nikolayevich Lebedev: Bibliograficheskiy ukazatel'.* Comp. A. M. Lukomskaya. Ed. K. I. Shafranovskiy. Moscow, 1950.

jb   Kipnis, A. Ya. "Pis'mo P. N. Lebedeva o kriticheskikh yavleniyakh." *VIYeT, 13* (1962), 88-90.

jd   Kravets, T. P. "O perepiske P. N. Lebedeva." *Nauchnoye nasledstvo, 1* (1948), 551-559.

je   Kravets, T. P., and A. A. Yeliseyev. "Iz perepiski P. N. Lebedeva (1891-1912)." *Nauchnoye nasledstvo, 1* (1948), 560-619.

jg   *Kudryavtsev, P. S. "Neizvestnyy avtograf P. N. Lebedeva." *VIYeT, 53* (1976), 38-39.

jk   *Lebedev, P. N. *Izbrannyye sochineniya.* Ed. A. K. Timiryazev. Moscow, 1949.

jl   Lebedev, P. N. *Sobraniye sochineniya.* Moscow, 1963.

jp   Lukomskaya, A. M., ed. *Petr Nikolayevich Lebedev: Bibliograficheskiy ukazatel'.* Moscow, 1950.

js   Serdyukov, A. R. "Pis'mo Lebedeva k N. A. Umovu." *VIYeT, 8* (1959), 106-108.

jz   Zyukov, P. I. "Pis'mo P. N. Lebedeva B. B. Golitsynu." *VIYeT, 2* (1956), 253-259.

ks   *Shugaylin, A. V. *Materialisticheskiye vozzreniya velikogo russkogo fizika P. N. Lebedeva.* Moscow, 1952. (Summary of thesis for AN, Institut filosofii.)

nk   Kaptsov, N. A. "P. N. Lebedev i yego shkola." IIYeT. *Trudy, 28* (1959), 106-110.

nl   Kaptsov, N. A. "Shkola Petra Nikolayevicha Lebedeva." C.vm1.pr, 151-165.

px   *Yerokhin, P. V. "Pedagogicheskaya deyatel'nost' P. N. Lebedeva: Yego vzglyady na formirovaniye fizicheskikh kadrov." A.bh1.vo, 155-163.

pz   Zernov, V. D. "Uchitel' i drug." IIYeT. *Trudy, 28* (1959), 111-118.

See also: B.ag1.bd; C.vm3.se; D.hg1.kn |kb1.mp; E.td1.se; G.ba1.fa, kr |fa2.ki; O.db1.de, il; P.ha1.sh

Lebedinskiy, Vladimir Konstantinovich (1868-1937)

lh6.ar   Rodionov, V. M. *Vladimir Konstantinovich Lebedinskiy.* Moscow, 1970.

cg   Gurevich, L. E., et al. "A. I. Lebedinskiy." *Istorikoastronomicheskiye issledovaniya, 11* (1972), 303-333.

ck   Kononkov, A. F. "Vladimir Konstantinovich Lebedinskiy." *IMYeN: Fizika, 10* (1971), 175-178.

nr Radovskiy, M. I. "V. K. Lebedinskiy—redaktor fizicheskikh zhurnalov." *UFN, 78* (1962), 345-351. (In English in *SPU, 5* (1963), 843-847.)

Lemaître, George (1894-1966)

li6.bd *Dirac, P. A. M. "The scientific work of Georges Lemaître." Pontificia Accademia delle Scienze, Rome. *Acta ?* (1938?), 1-20.

bg Godart, O., and M. Heller. "Un travail inconnu de Georges Lemaître." *RHS, 31* (1978), 345-360.

jg *Godart, O. "Bibliographie des travaux de George Lemaître." Lemaître, *L'hypothèse de l'atome primitif.* Brussels, 1972.

See also: P.kc1.gn, go, gu

Lenard, Philipp Eduard Anton @ $05 (1862-1947)

lj3.aw Weigel, R. G., ed. *Philipp Lenard, der Vorkämpfer der deutschen Physik.* Karlsruhe, 1937. (*Karlsruhe akademische Reden,* 17.)

bf Freund, F. "Lenard's share in the discovery of x-rays." *British journal of radiology, 19* (1946), 131-132.

bt Teichmann, H. "Philipp Lenard und die theoretische Physik." *ZGN, 8* (1942), 137-139.

cb Anon. "Hertz und Lenard." *PB, 13* (1957), 567-569.

ck Kleinert, Andreas. "Lenard, Stark und die Kaiser Wilhelm Gesellschaft." *PB, 36* (1980), 35-43.

cr Ramsauer, Carl. "Zum zehnten Todestag Philipp Lenard." *PB, 13* (1957), 219-222.

ct Wesch, Ludwig. "Philipp Lenard—Vorbild und Verpflichtung." *Zeitschrift für die gesamte Naturwissenschaft, 3* (1937/8), 42-45.

cv Wolf, Franz. "Philipp Lenard zum 100. Geburtstag." *PB, 18* (1962), 271-275.

cw Wolf, Franz. "Zur 100. Wiederkehr des Geburtstages von Philipp Lenard." *Nwn, 49* (1962), 245-247.

gg Stark, Johannes. "Philipp Lenard als deutscher Naturforscher." U.gg3.bk, 10-15. (Also in *Nationalsozialistische Monatshefte, 71* (1936), 106-112.)

gj Kossel, Walther. "Zu Philipp Lenards 50. Doktorjubiläum." *FF, 12* (1936), 247-248.

gl Kubach, F. "Geheimrat Lenards 75. Geburtstag." *Zeitschrift für die gesamte Naturwissenschaft, 3* (1937/8), 164-165.

gp   Kossel, Walther. "Zu P. Lenards 80. Geburtstag." *Nwn, 30* (1942), 317-318.

gq   *Stark, Johannes. *Zum 80. Geburtstag von...Philipp Lenard und zum 70. Geburtstag von Reichspostminister Dr. Ing. e.h. Wilhelm Ohnesorge.* Vienna, 1942.

gr   *Stark, Johannes. "Philipp Lenard als Vorbild." *Zeitschrift für die gesamte Naturwissenschaft, 8* (1942), 100- .

jk   Kleinert, Andreas, and Charlotte Schönbeck. "Lenard und Einstein. Ihr Briefwechsel und ihr Verhältnis vor der Nauheimer Diskussion von 1920." *Gesnerus, 35* (1978), 318-333.

jl   Lenard, Philipp. *Wissenschaftliche Abhandlungen aus den Jahren 1886-1932.* Ed. L. Wesch. 3 vols. Leipzig, 1942-44.

sb   Brüche, Ernst, and H. Marx. "Der Fall Philipp Lenard—Mensch und 'Politiker'." *PB, 23* (1967), 262-267.

sr   Germany. Reichstudentenführer. *Philipp Lenard, der deutsche Naturforscher. Sein Kampf um nordische Forschung.* Munich and Berlin, 1937.

See also: G.qa1.wh; U.gg3.bk

Lennard-Jones, John Edward @ (1894-1954)

lj8.em   Mott, N. F. "John Edward Lennard-Jones." RS. *BM, 1* (1955), 175-184.

et   Tyndall, A. M. "John Edward Lennard-Jones." Physical Society of London. *Proceedings, 67A* (1954), 1128-1129; *67B* (1954), 916-917.

jc   CSAC. *Sir John Lennard-Jones papers at Churchill College, Cambridge.* List 2/73. 7 p.

Leontovich, Mikhail Aleksandrovich (1903-)

lk3.gb   Anon. "Akademik Mikhail Aleksandrovich Leontovich." *ZhETF, 25* (1953), 3-6.

Leprince-Ringuet, Louis (1901)

lk5.al   Leprince-Ringuet, Louis. *Atoms and men.* Tr. Elaine P. Halperin. Chicago, 1961.

ap   Puyo, Jean. *Jean Puyo interroge Louis Leprince-Ringuet de l'Académie Française: Le bonheur de chercher.* Paris, 1976.

Levi-Città, Tullio @ (1873-1941)

lk8.cb   Amaldi, Ugo. "Commemorazione del socio Tullio Levi-Città." Accademia Nazionale dei Lincei. Classe di scienze fisiche, matematiche, e naturali." *Rendiconti, 1* (1946), 1130-1155.

cd   Anon. "Tullio Levi-Città." Pontificia Accademia delle Scienze. *Annuario, 1* (1936/7), 496-511.

eh   Hodge, W. V. D. "Tullio Levi-Città." RS. *Obituary notices, 4* (1942), 151-165.

jl   Levi-Città, Tullio. *Opere matematiche: Memorie e note.* 5 vols. Bologna, 1954-70.

See also: F.ae1.gp

Levshin, Vadim Leonidovich (1896-1969)

ll3.al   *Levshin, L. V., and Yurii Timofeyev. *Vadim Leonidovich Levshin.* Moscow, 1977.

gb   Anon. "V. L. Levshin." *Optika i spektroskopiya, 1* (1956), 441-442.

Lewis, Gilbert Newton @ (1875-1946)

ll8.al   Lachman, Arthur. *Borderland of the unknown: The life of Gilbert Newton Lewis.* NY, 1955.

cg   Giauque, William Francis. "Gilbert N. Lewis." APS. *Yearbook,* 1946, 317-322.

eh   Hildebrand, Joel H. "Gilbert N. Lewis." RS. *Obituary notices, 5* (1947), 491-506.

ei   Hildebrand, Joel H. "Gilbert Newton Lewis." NAS. *BM, 31* (1958), 210-235.

See also: G.ba1.ss; R.bd1

Leybenzon, Leonid Samuilovich @ (1879-1951)

lm3.cm   Myursepp, P. V. "Tartuskiy period deyatel'nosti akademika L. S. Leybenzona." *VIYeT, 34* (1971), 65-68.

es   Sedov, L. I. "Osnovnyye daty zhizni i deyatel'nosti L. S. Leybenzona." *UFN, 7:4* (1952), 127-134.

Lindemann, Frederick Alexander, Viscount Cherwell @ (1886-1957)

lm8.ab   Birkenhead, Frederick W., 2nd Earl. *The professor and the prime minister: The official life of Professor F. A. Lindemann, Viscount Cherwell.* Boston, 1962. (Published in London in 1961 as *The professor in two worlds.*)

ah Harrod, Roy Forbes. *The prof: A personal memoir of Lord Cherwell.* London, 1959.

et Thomson, George P. "Frederick Alexander Lindemann, Viscount Cherwell." RS. *BM, 4* (1958), 45-71.

jc CSAC. *Lord Cherwell papers at Nuffield College, Oxford.* List 80/4/81, 497p.

See also: B.tn3.sr

Linnik, Vladimir Pavlovich (1889-   )

ln3.av *Vladimir Pavlovich Linnik.* Moscow, 1963. (*Mtly*, ser. fiz.-mat.)

cb Anon. "Vladimir Pavlovich Linnik." *Optika i spektroskopiya, 7* (1959), 134-136. (Also in *Optiko-mekhanicheskaya promyshlennost'*, 1959:6, 1-3.)

See also: B.fk1.gb

Lippmann, Gabriel Jonas @ $08 (1845-1921)

ln8.cp Picard, Emile. "La vie et l'oeuvre de Gabriel Lippmann." AS. *Memoirs, 60* (1931), 29p. (Also in *Revue scientifique, 70* (1932), 129-141.)

es S[chuster], A[rthur]. "Gabriel Lippmann." RS. *Proceedings, 101A* (1922), i-iii.

Lockyer, Joseph Norman @ (1836-1920)

lo3.al Lockyer, T. Mary, and Winifred L. Lockyer. *The life and work of Sir Norman Lockyer.* London, 1928.

am Meadows, A. J. *Science and controversy: A biography of Sir Norman Lockyer.* London, 1972.

ef F[owler], A[lfred]. "Norman Lockyer." RS. *Proceedings, 104A* (1923), i-xiv.

Lodge, Oliver Joseph @ (1851-1940)

lo8.ag Gauld, Alan. *The founders of psychical research.* London, 1968.

aj Jolly, William P. *Sir Oliver Lodge.* London, 1974.

al Lodge, Oliver. *Past years, an autobiography.* London, 1931.

an McCabe, Joseph. *The religion of Sir Oliver Lodge.* London, 1914.

ap *Mercier, Charles Arthur. *Spiritualism and Sir Oliver Lodge.* London, 1917.

bw Wilson, David B. "The thought of late Victorian physicists: Oliver Lodge's ethereal body." *Victorian studies,* *15* (1971), 29-48.

eg Gregory, Richard, and A. Ferguson. "Oliver Lodge." RS. *Obituary notices,* *3* (1941), 551-574.

jb Besterman, Theodore. *A bibliography of Sir Oliver Lodge.* London, 1935.

jd Birmingham University Library. *Handlist of the papers of Sir Oliver Lodge.* Birmingham, 1979.

jl Lodge, Oliver. *Letters from Sir Oliver Lodge, psychical, religious, scientific and personal.* Ed. J. Arthur Hill. London, 1932.

London, Fritz Wolfgang @ (1900-1954)

lp1.bn Nordheim, L. W. "Fritz London: 1900-1954, an appreciation of his work." B.lp1.jl, *1*, v-viii.

cl London, Edith. "Fritz London: A brief biography." B.lp1.jl, *1*, x-xiv.

jl London, Fritz W. *Superfluids.* 2nd ed. 2 vols. NY, 1961.

jn London, Edith. "A list of publications of Fritz London." B.lp1.jl, *1*, xv-xviii.

London, Heinz @ (1907-1970)

lp2.es Schoenberg, D. "Heinz London." RS. *BM, 17* (1971), 441-461.

jc CSAC. *Heinz London papers at Bristol University Library.* List 5/73. 10 p.

Lonsdale, Kathleen Yardley @ (1903-1971)

lp3.eh Hodgkin, Dorothy M. C. "Kathleen Lonsdale." RS. *BM, 21* (1975), 447-484.

Lorentz, Hendrik Antoon @ $02 (1853-1928)

lp8.ah Haas-Lorentz, G. L. de, ed. *H. A. Lorentz: Impressions of his life and work.* Tr. J. C. Fagginger Auer. Amsterdam, 1957.

ak Klyaus, Ye. M., et al. *Gendrik Anton Lorents.* Moscow, 1974.

be Fokker, A. D. "The scientific work." B.lp8.ah, 48-81.

bf Frankfurt, Usher I. "G. A. Lorents: Tvorets elektronnoy teorii." *VIYeT, 9* (1960), 83-90.

bp Pol, B. van der. "H. A. Lorentz and the bearing of his work on electromagnetic telecommunication." B.lp8.ah, 121-128.

cc   Casimir, H. B. G. "The influence of Lorentz' ideas on modern physics." B.lp8.ah, 165-172.

ce   Ehrenfest, Paul. "Professor H. A. Lorentz as researcher." B.ec1.je, 471-477.

cg   Einstein, Albert. "H. A. Lorentz, his creative genius and his personality." B.lp8.ah, 5-9.

cl   Haas-Lorentz, G. L. de. "Reminiscences." B.lp8.ah, 15-47, 82-120, 145-153, 160-164.

cn   Haas, W. J. de. "On the occasion of the 100th anniversary of H. A. Lorentz." B.lp8.ah, 10-14.

cw   Watson, E. C. "Photograph of H. A. Lorentz, H. Kamerlingh Onnes, Niels Bohr, and Paul Ehrenfest." *AIP, 21* (1953), 463-464.

eb   Born, Max. "Antoon Lorentz." Akademie der Wissenschaften, Göttingen. *Jahrbuch,* 1927/8, 69-73.

ed   Bragg, William Henry, et al. "Prof. H. A. Lorentz." *Nature, 121* (1928), 287-291.

ef   Broglie, Louis de. "Notice sur la vie et l'oeuvre de Hendrik Antoon Lorentz." AS. *Notices et discours, 3* (1951), 241-276.

eh   Ehrenfest, Paul. "Funeral oration." B.lp8.ah, 154-159.

cp   Planck, Max. "Hendrik Antoon Lorentz." *Nwn, 16* (1928), 549-555.

er   Richardson, O. W. "Hendrik Antoon Lorentz." RS. *Proceedings, 121A* (1928), xx-xxviii.

ez   Zeeman, Pieter. "Hendrik Antoon Lorentz, sa vie et son oeuvre." *Archives néerlandaises des sciences exactes et naturelles, 11A* (1928), 155-166.

gi   Il'in, B. V. "K yubileyu G. A. Lorentsa." *UFN, 5* (1925), 411-414.

gl   Larmor, Joseph. "Hendrik Antoon Lorentz." *Nature, 111* (1923), 1-6.

jh   Hermann, Armin. "H. A. Lorentz, Praeceptor Physicae: sein Briefwechsel mit dem deutschen Nobelpreisträger Johannes Stark." *Janus, 53* (1966), 99-114.

jl   Lorentz, Hendrik Antoon. *Collected papers.* Ed. A. D. Fokker. 9 vols. The Hague, 1934-39.

jt   Leyden. Rijksmuseum voor de Geschiedenis der Natuurwetenschappen. *Tentoonstelling . . . H. A. Lorentz, H. Kamerlingh-Onnes.* Leyden, 1953.

km   Miller, Arthur I. "On Lorentz's methodology." *BJPS, 25* (1974), 29-45.

st   Thijsse, J. T. "Enclosure of the Zuidersee." B.lp8.ah, 129-144.

See also: B.ei7.nm; C.na1.la; E.ae1; F.b

Lorenz, Richard @ (1863-1929)

lq3.eh   Hevesy, Georg von. "Richard Lorenz: Erinnerungen aus den Zürcher Jahren." *Helevetica chimica acta, 13* (1930), 13-17.

em   Magnus, A. "Richard Lorenz." *Zeitschrift für Elektrochemie und angewandte physikalische Chemie, 35* (1929), 815-822.

Love, Augustus Edward Hughes @ (1863-1940)

lr3.em   Milne, E. A. "August Edward Hugh Love." RS. *Obituary notices, 3* (1941), 467-482.

Lukirskiy, Petr Ivanovich (1894-1954)

ls3.ed   Dobretsov, L. N. "Akademik Petr Ivanovich Lukirskiy." *Zhurnal tekhnicheskoy fiziki, 25* (1955), 367-376.

em   Murin, A. "Akademik Petr Ivanovich Lukirskiy." *UFN, 55* (1955), 289-298.

jm   Luk'yanov, S. Yu., et al., eds. *Petr Ivanovich Lukirskiy.* Moscow, 1959. (*Mtly*, ser. fiz., 11.)

Lummer, Otto @ (1860-1925)

lt3.cb   Buchwald, Eberhard. "Erinnerung an Otto Lummer." *PB, 6* (1950), 313-316.

cg   Gehrcke, Ernst. "Erinnerungen an Lummer." *PB, 11* (1955), 315-317.

gs   Schaefer, Clemens. "Otto Lummer: Zum 100. Geburtstag." *PB, 16* (1960), 373-381.

See also: A.bb1.bu

Luzin, Nikolay Nikolayevich @ (1883-1950)

lu3.am   Men'shova, D. Ye., et al., ed. *Nikolay Nikolayevich Luzin.* Moscow and Leningrad, 1948. (*Mtly*, ser. matematiki, 3.)

cb   Bari, N. K., and V. V. Golubev. "Biografiya N. N. Luzina." B.lu3.jl, *3,* 468-483.

gb   Anon. "Nikolay Nikolayevich Luzin." *Uspekhi matematicheskikh nauk, 1:1* (1946), 226-228.

jb   Anon. "Pis'mo akademika N. N. Luzina." *Puti v neznayemoye, 1* (1960), 522-526.

jl   Luzin, N. N. *Sobraniye sochineniya.* 3 vols. Moscow, 1953-59.

Lyapunov, Aleksandr Mikhaylovich @ (1857-1918)

lw3.cb   *Anon. "Kratkiy ocherk zhizni i deyatel'nosti A. M. Lyapunova." AN. *Izvestiya,* otd. fiz.-mat. nauk, 1930:1, 1-24.

ck   Krylov, A. N. "Pamyati Aleksandra Mikhaylovicha Lyapunova." B.kt1.jj, *1:2,* 147-152.

cp   Polak, L. S. "Aleksandr Mikhaylovich Lyapunov." *VIYeT, 5* (1957), 31-38.

ek   Krylov, A. N. "Aleksandr Mikhaylovich Lyapunov." AN. *Bulletin, 13* (1919), 389-394. (Also in B.kt1.al, 461-468.)

es   Steklov, V. A. "Aleksandr Mikhaylovich Lyapunov." AN. *Bulletin, 13* (1919), 367-388.

jb   *AN. Biblioteka. *Aleksandr Mikhaylovich Lyapunov: Bibliografiya.* Comp. A. M. Lukomskaya. Ed. V. I. Smirnov. Moscow, 1953.

js   Smirnov, V. I. "Iz perepiski P. Appelya, Zh. Adamara, G. Burkkhardta, V. Vol'terra, P. Dyugema, S. Zhordana, A. Puankare i N. Rado s akademikom A. M. Lyapunovym." IIYeT. *Trudy, 19* (1957), 690-719.

See also: B.sg5.js; D.cd1.mo; P.ib1.ki

Lyman, Theodore @ (1874-1954)

ly3.eb   Bridgman, Percy W. "Theodore Lyman." NAS. *BM, 30* (1957), 237-250.

ev   Vleck, J. H. Van. "Theodore Lyman." APS. *Yearbook,* 1954, 435-439.

gs   Saunders, F. A. "Professor Theodore Lyman." Optical Society of America. *Journal, 31* (1941), 509.

MacDonald, David Keith Chalmers (1920-1963)

ma2.em   Mendelssohn, Kurt. "David Keith Chalmers MacDonald." RS. *BM, 10* (1964), 207-220.

Macdonald, Hector Munroe (1865-1935)

ma3.ew   Whittaker, E. T. "Hector Munroe Macdonald." RS. *Obituary notices, 1* (1935), 552-558.

Mach, Ernst @ (1838-1916)

GENERAL

mb1.ac   Blackmore, John T. *Ernst Mach: His work, life, and influence.* Berkeley, 1972.

ad   Bouvier, Robert. *La pensée d'Ernst Mach. Essai de biographie intellectuelle et de critique.* Paris, 1923.

af   Elia, Alfonsina d'. *Ernst Mach.* Florence, 1971.

ai   Heller, K. D. *Ernst Mach: Wegbereiter der modernen Physik.* Vienna, 1964.

cc   Blackmore, John T. "Three autobiographical manuscripts by Ernst Mach." *Annals of science, 35* (1978), 401-418.

cd   Blüh, Otto. "Mach: Biographical data." B.mb2.ae, 271-273.

cf   Haubelt, Josef. "K Machove zádosti o profesuru na prazské polytechnice." *Dejiny ved a techniky, 5* (1972), 52-55.

ch   Herneck, Friedrich. "Über eine unveröffentliche Selbstbiographie Ernst Machs." Berlin. University. *Wissenschafliche Zeitschrift, 6* (1956-57), 209-220.

ci   Herneck, Friedrich. "Ernst Mach: Eine bisher unveröffentliche Autobiographie." *PB, 14* (1958), 385-390.

df   Feuer, Lewis S. "Ernst Mach: The unconscious motives of an empiricist." *American image, 27* (1970), 12-39.

eb   Auerbach, Felix. "Ernst Machs Lebenswerk." *Nwn,* 4 (1916), 177-183.

ee   Dingler, Hugo. "Ernst Mach." *Monatschrifte für den naturwissenschaftlichen Unterricht, 9* (1916), 321-329.

eg   Einstein, Albert. "Ernst Mach." *PZ, 17* (1916), 101-104.

ei   Exner, Franz. "Ernst Mach." Akademie der Wissenschaften, Vienna. *Almanach, 66* (1916), 328-334.

ek   Gomperz, H. "Ernst Mach." *Archiv für Geschichte der Philosophie, 29* (1916), 321-328.

em   Helm, Georg. "Ernst Mach, dem naturwissenschaftlichen Denker zum Gedächtnis." Naturwissenschaftliche Gesellschaft Isis, Dresden. *Sitzungsberichte und Abhandlungen,* 1916, 45-54.

en   Höfler, A. "Ernst Mach." *Zeitschrift für den physikalischen und chemischen Unterricht, 29* (1916), 57-63.

eo   *Lampa, Anton. *Ernst Mach.* Prague, 1918.

es   Sommerfeld, Arnold. "Ernst Mach." Akademie der Wissenschaften, Munich. *Jahrbuch,* 1917, 58-67.

ew *Wlassak, Rudolf. *Ernst Mach. Gedächtnisrede.* Leipzig, 1917.

gf Frank, Philipp. "Ernst Mach—The centenary of his birth." *Erkenntnis, 7* (1938), 247-256.

ib Blüh, Otto, and Wolfgang F. Merzkirch. "Mach bibliography." B.mb2.ae, 274-290.

ie Elia, Alfonsina d'. "Recente bibliografia Machiana." *Revista critica di storia della filosofia, 30* (1975), 189-203.

ip *Ackermann, Theodor, Antiquariat. *Bibliothek Ernst Mach.* 2 pts. Munich, 1959-1960.

is *Thiele, Joachim. [Bibliography of Mach's writings.] Mach. *Abhandlungen*. Ed. Thiele. Amsterdam, 1969.

it Thiele, Joachim. "Ernst Mach—Bibliographie." *Centaurus, 8* (1963), 189-237.

iu Thiele, Joachim. "Zur Wirkungsgeschichte der Schriften Ernst Machs." *Zeitschrift für philosophische Forschung, 20* (1966), 118-130.

jb Anon. "Briefe von Richard Avenarius und Ernst Mach an Wilhelm Schuppe." *Erkenntnis, 6* (1936), 73-80.

jd Cafiero, Luca. "Cinque lettere di G. Vailati a E. Mach." *Revista critica di storia della filosofia, 17* (1962), 68-74.

jf Carus, Paul. "A letter from Professor Mach." *Monist, 16* (1906), 628.

jh Häbler, Theodor. "Ein Brief von Ernst Mach." *Zeitschrift für mathematischen und naturwissenschaftlichen Unterricht, 49* (1918), 96-98.

jl Lowie, Robert H. "Letters from Ernst Mach." *Isis, 37* (1947), 65-68.

jp Peter, Gustav. "Kant und Mach: Ein erkenntnistheoretischer Briefwechsel mit F. C. Müller-Lyer." *Annalen der Naturphilosophie, 14* (1921), 97-111.

kb Thiele, Joachim. "Ein Brief Edmund Husserls an Ernst Mach." *Zeitschrift für philosophische Forschung, 19* (1965), 134-139.

kd Thiele, Joachim. "William James und Ernst Mach." *Philosophia naturalis, 9* (1966), 298-310.

ke   Thiele, Joachim. "Briefe von Gustav Theodor Fechner und Ludwig Boltzmann an Ernst Mach." *Centaurus, 11* (1967), 222-235.

kf   Thiele, Joachim. "Zur 'Kritik der Sprache.' Briefe von Fritz Mauthner an Ernst Mach." *Muttersprache, 76* (1966), 78-85.

kh   Thiele, Joachim. "Briefe deutscher Philosophen an Ernst Mach." *Synthèse, 18* (1968), 285-301.

ki   Thiele, Joachim. "Briefe Robert H. Lowies an Ernst Mach." *Isis, 59* (1968), 84-87.

kj   Thiele, Joachim. "Ernst Mach und Heinrich Hertz: Zwei unveröffentliche Briefe aus dem Jahre 1890." *NTM, 5:12* (1968), 132-134.

km   Thiele, Joachim. "Karl Pearson, Ernst Mach, John B. Stallo: Briefe aus den Jahre 1897 bis 1904." *Isis, 60* (1969), 535-542.

kn   Thiele, Joachim. "Einige zeitgenössische Urteile über Schriften Ernst Machs. Briefe von Johnnes Reinke, Paul Volkmann, Max Verwom, Carl Menger, und Jakob von Uexküll." *Philosophia naturalis, 11* (1969), 474-489.

kp   Thiele, Joachim. "Zur Kritik des Empiriomonismus. Briefe von Wilhelm Schuppe, Graf Hermann Keyserling, u. a., an Ernst Mach." *Zeitschrift für philosophische Forschung, 24* (1970), 412-427.

kr   Thiele, Joachim. "Paul Carus und Ernst Mach: Wechselbeziehungen zwischen deutscher und amerikanischer Philosophie um 1900." *Isis, 62* (1971), 208-219.

ks   Thiele, Joachim. "Zur Analyse der Empfindungen: Briefe von Anton Marty und Richard Semon an Ernst Mach." *Zeitschrift für philosophische Forschung, 25* (1971), 590-606.

ku   Thiele, Joachim. "Zur Analyse der Bewegungsempfindungen: Briefe von Josef Breuer an Ernst Mach." *Centaurus, 19* (1975), 40-53.

kv   Thiele, Joachim. "Briefe deutscher Philosophen an Ernst Mach aus den Jahren 1865 bis 1915." *Philosophia naturalis, 16* (1976), 64-84.

kw   Thiele, Joachim. *Wissenschaftliche Kommunikation: Die Korrespondenz Ernst Machs.* Kastellaun, 1978.

kx   Thiele, Joachim. "Briefe Hugo v. Seeligers an Ernst Mach." *Philosophia naturalis, 17* (1979), 391-399.

pc   Blüh, Otto. "Ernst Mach as teacher and thinker." *PT, 20* (Jun. 1967), 32-42.

pd Blüh, Otto. "Ernst Mach: His life as a teacher and thinker." B.mb2.ae, 1-22.

pt *Thiele, Joachim. "Schulphysik von 70 Jahren. Hinweis auf Ernst Machs Lehrbücher der Physik." *Zeitschrift für den mathematischen und naturwissenschaftlichen Unterricht, 19* (1966), 15-17.

xc Blüh, Otto. "Ernst Mach as an historian of physics." *Centaurus, 13* (1968), 62-84.

xh Hiebert, Erwin N. "Mach's philosophical use of the history of science." *MSPS, 5* (1970), 184-203.

xm Mayerhöfer, Joseph. "Ernst Mach as a professor of the history of science." ICHS, X (1962). *Actes, 1* (1964), 337-339.

xn Mayerhöfer, Joseph. "Ernst Machs Berufung an die Wiener Universität 1895." *Clio medica, 2* (1967), 47-55.

xt Thiele, Joachim. "Natur und Geschichte in den wissenschaftshistorischen Schriften Ernst Machs." *Natur und Geschichte. 10. Deutscher Kongress für Philosophie, Kiel 1972.* Hamburg, 1973. Pp. 449-452.

WORKS

Some fifty items dealing with Mach's philosophy have been omitted. They concern (1) philosophical criticism published during his lifetime, (2) strictly philosophical analysis published after his death, (3) parts or chapters on Mach in books on philosophy. References to most of these items will be found in B.mb1.iu, kx.

mb2.ac *Chmelka, F. "Ernst Mach: Physiker und Philosoph." *Universum, 21* (1966), 74-80.

ae Cohen, Robert, and Raymond J. Seeger, eds. *Ernst Mach, physicist and philosopher.* NY and Dordrecht, 1970. (*BSPS, 6.*)

ah Henning, Hans. *Ernst Mach als Philosoph, Physiker und Psycholog.* Leipzig, 1915.

as Sommerfeld, Arnold. "Ernst Mach als Physiker, Psycholog und Philosoph." DPG. *Verhandlungen, 19* (1938), 51-52.

bh Hiebert, Erwin N. "An appraisal of the work of Ernst Mach." W.aa1.ma, 360-389.

bl Lohr, E. "Ernst Mach als Physiker." *Zeitschrift für die gesamte Naturwissenschaft, 4* (1938/9), 108-116.

bt Thirring, Hans. "Ernst Mach als Physiker." Akademie der Wissenschaften, Vienna. *Almanach, 116* (1966), 361-372.

bv Volkmann, P. "Studien über Ernst Mach vom Standpunkt eines theoretischen Physikers der Gegenwart." *Annalen der Philosophie und philosophischen Kritik, 4* (1924), 303-312.

cc Brush, Stephen G. "Mach and atomism." *Synthèse, 18* (1968), 192-215.

ch Hiebert, Erwin N. "The genesis of Mach's early views on atomism." B.mb2.ae, 79-106.

cl Laudan, Laurens. "The methodological foundations of Mach's anti-atomism and their historical roots." W.aa1.ma, 390-417.

cp Petzoldt, Joseph. "Mach und die Atomistik." *Nwn, 10* (1923), 230-231.

cs Seaman, Francis. "Mach's rejection of atomism." *JHI, 29* (1968), 381-393.

df Heller, Michal. "Dzieje pewnego rozumiena zasady Macha." *KHNT, 19* (1974), 59-69.

dh Hönl, Helmut. "Zur Geschichte des Machschen Prinzips." Jena. University.   *Wissenschaftliche   Zeitschrift,   mathematisch-naturphilosophische Reihe, 15:1* (1966), 25-36.

di Hönl, Helmut. "K istorii printsipa Makha." *ES*, 1968, 258-285.

dk Jourdain, Philip E. B. "The principle of least action: Remarks on some passages of Mach's *Mechanics." Monist, 22* (1912), 285-304.

dm Koslow, A. "Mach's concept of mass: Program and definition." *Synthèse, 18* (1968), 216-233.

ds Siedlerová, Irena. "Machuv mechanik." *Dejiny ved a techniky, 5* (1970), 108-112.

dy Yourgrau, Wolfgang, and Alwyn van der Merwe. "Did Ernst Mach 'miss the target'?" *Synthèse, 18* (1968), 234-250.

ec Elek, Tibor. "Zur Geschichte der Beziehungen zwischen Physik und Philosophie: Die philosophische Diskussion zwischen Ernst Mach, Max Planck und Albert Einstein zu Beginn des 20. Jahrhunderts." *Periodica polytechnica, electrical engineering* (Budapest), *11* (1967), 135-157.

ee Goenner, Hubert. "Mach's principle and Einstein's theory of gravitation." B.mb2.ae, 200-215.

eg Heller, Michal. "The influence of Mach's thought on contemporary relativistic physics." *Organon, 11* (1975), 271-283.

ei Holton, Gerald. "Mach, Einstein, and the search for reality." *Daedalus, 97* (1968), 636-673.

ej   Holton, Gerald. "Mach, Einstein and the search for reality."
     B.mb2.ae, 165-199.

ek   Holton, Gerald. "Mach, Einstein, and the search for reality."
     A.aa1.ho, 344-381.

es   Thiele, Joachim. *Die Bedeutung Ernst Machs für die Wende von
     der klassischen zur modernen Physik.* Ph.D. thesis. Hamburg,
     1959.

et   Thiele, Joachim. "Bemerkungen zu einer Äusserung im Vorwort
     der *Optik* von Ernst Mach." *NTM, 2:6* (1965), 10-19.

ey   Zahar, Elie G. "Mach, Einstein, and the rise of modern science."
     BJPS, 28 (1977), 195-213.

fh   Herrmann, Dieter B. "Ernst Mach zur Doppler-Theorie." *Die
     Sterne, 40* (1964), 155-156.

fm   Merzkirch, Wolfgang F. "Mach's contributions to the develop-
     ment of gas dynamics." B.mb2.ae, 41-59.

fs   Seeger, Raymond J. "On Mach's curiosity about shockwaves."
     B.mb2.ae, 60-68.

gp   Ratliff, Floyd. "On Mach's contributions to the analysis of sensa-
     tions." B.mb2.ae, 23-41.

gu   Titchener, E. B. "Mach's 'Lectures on psychophysics'." *American
     journal of psychology, 23* (1922), 213-222.

kc   Bradley, J. *Mach's philosophy of science.* London, 1971.

ke   Cohen, Robert S. "Ernst Mach: Physics, perception, and the phi-
     losophy of science." *Synthèse, 18* (1968), 132-170. (Also in
     B.mb1.b, 126-164.)

kg   Dingler, Hugo. *Die Grundgedanken der Machschen Philosophie.
     Mit Erstveröffentlichungen aus seinen wissenschaftlichen Tage-
     büchern.* Leipzig, 1924.

ki   Frank, Philipp. "Mach and the unity of science." B.mb2.ae,
     235-244.

kl   Kraft, Viktor. "Ernst Mach als Philosoph " Akademie der
     Wissenschaften, Vienna. *Almanach, 116* (1966), 373-387.

lh   Hüfler, A. "Zur Geschichte und Wurzel der Machschen Philoso-
     phie." *Zeitschrift für den physikalischen und chemischen Unterricht,
     23* (1919), 1-16.

mc   Čapek, Milič. "Ernst Mach's biological theory of knowledge."
     BSPS, 5 (1969), 400-420. (Also in *Synthèse, 18* (1968), 171-
     191.)

mm Mises, Richard von. *Ernst Mach und die empiristische Wissenschaftsaufassung.* The Hague, 1938. (*Einheitswissenschaft, 7.*) (Also in B.mb1.ae, 245-270.)

mw Weinberg, Carlton Berenda. *Mach's empirio-pragmatism in physical science.* NY, 1937.

nb Adler, Friedrich. *Ernst Machs Überwindung des mechanischen Materialismus.* Wien, 1918.

ng Gerhards, Karl. "Zur Kontroverse Planck-Mach." *Vierteljahrsschrift für wissenschaftliche Philosophie und Soziologie, 36* (1912), 19-68.

nr Rabel, Gabriele. "Mach und die 'Realität der Aussenwelt.'" *PZ, 21* (1920), 433-437.

nw Wernick, Georg. "Der Begriff des physikalischen Körpers nach Mach." *Vierteljahrsschrift für wissenschaftliche Philosophie und Soziologie, 39* (1915), 82-97, 178-200; *40* (1916), 1-32.

od Diepert, Randall R. "Peirce on Mach and absolute space." Charles S. Peirce Society. *Transactions, 9* (1973), 79-94.

oh Hiebert, Erwin N. "Mach's conception of thought experiments in the natural sciences." W.aa1.el, 339-340.

os Seaman, Francis. "Mach's principle of continuity." ICHS, X (1962). *Actes, 1* (1964), 333-335.

pn Nicolle, Jacques. "Lénine, Mach, et Paul Langevin." *La pensée,* no. 57 (1954), 66-70.

See also: A.cc1.th; B.ei6.km, ko, lh | ei7.rd, rj, ro, rq | pl1.lj; D.hg1.mh; F.fe1.pe; R.dc1.hi

Mache, Heinrich (1876-1954)

mc1.ef   Flamm, Ludwig. "Professor Hofrat Dr. Heinrich Mache." *Acta physica austriaca, 9* (1954), 85-89.

Maclaurin, Richard Cockburn (1867-1920)

mc4.ap   Pearson, Henry Greenleaf. *Richard Cockburn Maclaurin, president of the Massachusetts Institute of Technology.* NY, 1937.

Madelung, Erwin (1881-)

md1.gh Hund, Friedrich. "Erwin Madelung 80 Jahre alt." *FF, 35* (1961), 157.

Majorana, Ettore @ (1906-1938)

md4.as Sciascia, Leonardo. *La scomparsa di Ettore Majorana.* Turin, 1975.

bc Amaldi, Edoardo. "L'opera scientifica di Ettore Majorana." *Physis, 10* (1968), 173-187.

cc Amaldi, Edoardo. "Nota biografica di Ettore Majorana." B.md4.jm, vii-xlix.

cr Recami, E. "I nuovi documenti sulla scomparsa del fisico Ettore Majorana." *Scientia, 110* (1975), 557-588.

jm Majorana, Ettore. *La vita e l'opera.* Rome, 1966.

Mallock, Henry Reginald Arnulph (1851-1933)

md6.eb B[oys], C[harles] V[ernon]. "Henry Reginald Arnulph Mallock." RS. *Obituary notices, 1* (1933), 95-100.

Mandel'shtam, Leonid Isaakovich @ (1879-1944)

me1.bp Rytov, S, M. "L. I. Mandel'shtam i ucheniye o mogulyartsii." AN. *Izvestiya,* ser. fiz., *9* (1945), 77-87.

br Shchegolev, Ye. Ya. "Akademik L. I. Mandel'shtam— radioinzhener." B.me1.ia, 172-184.

bs Tamm, I. Ye. "O rabotakh L. I. Mandel'shtama v oblasti teoreticheskoy fiziki." AN. *Izvestiya,* ser. fiz., *9* (1945), 56-60. (Also in B.me1.av, 131-137.)

bt Tamm, I. Ye. "Characteristic features of the work of Leonid Isaakovich Mandel'shtam." *SPU, 8* (1966), 633-636. (Also in *UFN, 87* (1965), 3-7.)

cc Anon. "Zasedaniye pamyati L. I. Mandel'shtama." AN. *Vestnik,* 1955:3, 116-117.

cd *Anon. "L. I. Mandel'shtam." *Radio,* 1954:12, 18.

ck Krylov, A. N. "Pamyati Leonida Isaakovicha Mandel'shtama." B.kt1.al, 497-499. (Also in B.me1.ia, 85-86.)

cp Papaleksi, N. D. "Leonid Isaakovich Mandel'shtam." B.me1.jm, *1,* 7-66.

cr Papaleksi, N. D. "Leonid Isaakovich Mandel'shtam." B.me1.ia, 5-52.

ek   Khaykin, S. "Leonid Isaakovich Mandel'shtam." Moscow. University. *Uchenyye zapiski, 77:3* (1945), 278-285.

eo   Papaleksi, N. D. "Akademik Leonid Isaakovich Mandel'shtam." AN. *Vestnik, 15:4* (1945), 97-102.

ep   Papaleksi, N. D. "Kratkiy ocherk zhizni i nauchnoy deyatel'nosti Leonida Isaakovicha Mandel'shtama." AN. *Izvestiya,* ser. fiz., *9* (1945), 8-20. (Also in *UFN, 27* (1945), 143-158; and B.pb3.jp, 224-240.)

eq   Papaleksi, N. D. "Iz nauchnykh vospominaniy o Leonide Isaakoviche Mandel'shtame." AN. *Izvestiya,* ser. fiz., *10* (1946), 127-134. (Also in B.pb3.jp, 375-383.)

cs   Rytov, S. M. "Leonid Isaakovich Mandel'shtam." *SPU, 22* (1979), 826-832.

ia   *Akademik L. I. Mandel'shtam: K 100-letiyu so dnya rozhdeniya.* Moscow, 1979.

jl   Mandel'shtam, L. I. "Iz korrespondentsii L. I. Mandel'shtama." B.me1.ia, 53-84.

jm   Mandel'shtam, L. I. *Polnoye sobraniye trudov.* 5 vols. Moscow, 1948-1955.

jp   Vreden-Kobetskaya, T. O., ed. *Leonid Isaakovich Mandel'shtam.* Moscow, 1941. (*Mtly,* ser. fiz., 1.)

pg   Gorelik, G. S. "L. I. Mandel'shtam i prepodavaniye fiziki." AN. *Izvestiya,* ser. fiz., *10* (1946), 135-140.

See also: D.cd1.an, ga; E.td1; G.ca2.ma | da1.ta; I.eg1.go; T.aa1.an

March, Arthur (1891-1957)

mf1.ec   Cap, Ferdinand. "Arthur March." *Acta physica austriaca, 11* (1957), 289-294.

Markov, Moisey Aleksandrovich (1908-   )

mf4.gc   Baldin, A. M., and A. A. Komar. "Moisei Aleksandrovich Markov." *SPU, 21* (1978), 544-548.

kc   Blokhintsev, D. I., et al. "Obsuzhdeniye stat'i M. A. Markova." *Voprosy filosofii,* 1948:1, 203-222.

Marsden, Ernest (1889-1970)

mf7.ef   Fleming, C. A. "Ernest Marsden." RS. *BM, 17* (1971), 463-496.

is   *Sir Ernest Marsden. 80th birthday book.* Wellington, N.Z., 1969.

See also: B.ru1.cb

Martyn, David Forbes (1906-1970)

mf8.em   Massey, H. S. W. "David Forbes Martyn." RS. *BM, 17* (1971), 497-510.

Mascart, Eleuthère Elie Nicolas @ (1837-1908)

mg1.bl   Langevin, Paul. "L'oeuvre de Mascart." *Revue du mois, 8* (1913), 385-406.

    ej   Janet, Paul. "La vie et les oeuvres de E. Mascart." *Revue générale des sciences, 20* (1909), 574-593.

    et   T., F. T. "Eleuthère Elie Nicolas Mascart." RS. *Proceedings, 83A* (1909/10), i-ii.

Mason, Max (1877-1961)

mg4.ew   Weaver, Warren. "Max Mason." NAS. *BM, 37* (1964), 205-236.

Mayer, Maria Goeppert $63 (1906-1972)

mh1.ad   Dash, Joan. *A life of one's own: Three gifted women and the men they married.* NY, 1973.

    cs   Sachs, Robert G. "Maria Goeppert Mayer." NAS. *BM, 50* (1979), 311-328.

McClelland, John Alexander (1870-1920)

mh2.ew   W[ilson], C. T. R. "John Alexander McClelland." RS. *Proceedings, 106A* (1924), v-ix.

McLennan, John Cunningham (1867-1935)

mh4.al   Langton, Hugh Hornby. *Sir John Cunningham McLennan.* Toronto, 1939.

    ee   Eve, A. S. "Sir John Cunningham McLennan." RS. *Obituary notices, 1* (1935), 577-583.

McMillan, Edwin Mattison $51C (1907-)

mh7.pc   Anon. "Ajax...an apparatus for amusement: Dr. McMillan's desktop toy." *PTeach, 12* (1974), 530-531.

Mees, Charles Edward Kenneth (1882-1960)

mi4.ec   Clark, Walter. "Charles Edward Kenneth Mees." RS. *BM, 7* (1961), 173-197.

Meggers, William Frederick @ (1888-1966)

mi8.ef   Foote, Paul D. "William Frederick Meggers." NAS. *BM, 41* (1970), 319-340.

Meinesz, Felix Andries Vening (1887-1966)

mj1.ed   Collette, B. J. "In memoriam." *Geologie en mijnbouw, 45* (1966), 285-290.

Meissner, Walther (1882-1974)

mj4.gg   Grassmann, P. "W. Meissner zum 80. Geburtstag." *PB,* 18 (1962), 572-573.

Meitner, Lise @ (1878-1968)

mk1.ad   Crawford, Deborah. *Lise Meitner, atomic pioneer.* NY, 1969.

    ck   Karlik, Berta. "In memoriam Lise Meitner." *PB, 35* (1979), 49-52.

    cm   Krafft, Fritz. "Lise Meitner und ihre Zeit." *Angewandte Chemie, 90* (1978), 876-892. (In English in *Angewandte Chemie international, 17* (1978), 826-842.

    cp   Meitner, Lise. "Lise Meitner looks back." *Advancement of science, 21* (1964), 39-46. (Also in *BAS, 20* (Nov. 1964), 2-7.)

    ds   Scheel, Walter. "Wissenschaft unter dem Gesetz der Freiheit. Zum 100. Geburtstag von Albert Einstein, Otto Hahn, Lise Meitner und Max von Laue." *PB, 35* (1974), 192-194.

    ef   Frisch, O. R. "Lise Meitner." RS. *BM, 16* (1970), 405-420.

    ek   Karlik, Berta. "Lise Meitner." *Acta physica austriaca, 29* (1969), 391-395.

    el   Karlik, Berta. "Gedenkworte für Lise Meitner." *Akademische Gedenkfeier zu Ehren von Otto Hahn und Lise Meitner.* Munich, 1969.

    gh   Hahn, Otto. "Lise Meitner 70 Jahre." *Zeitschrift für Naturforschung, 3a* (1948), 425-428.

    gi   Hahn, Otto. "Lise Meitner zum 80. Geburtstag." Max-Planck-Gesellschaft. *Mitteilungen,* 1958, 324-328.

    gj   Hahn, Otto. "Lise Meitner 85 Jahre." *Nwn, 50* (1963), 653-654.

    if   Frisch, O. R., et al., eds. *Beiträge zur Physik und Chemie des 20. Jahrhunderts: Lise Meitner, Otto Hahn, Max von Laue zum 80. Geburtstag.* Braunschweig, 1959. (Published simultaneously in NY as *Trends in atomic physics.*)

See also: B.ei4.ud |hb1.bh, cn, gf, gg; I.cd1.zi

Mendenhall, Charles Elwood (1872-1935)

mk4.ev Vleck, J. H. Van. "Charles Elwood Mendenhall." NAS. *BM, 18* (1938), 1-22.

Mendenhall, Thomas Corwin (1841-1924)

mk5.cc Crew, Henry. "Thomas Corwin Mendenhall." NAS. *BM, 16* (1936), 329-351.

Merton, Thomas Ralph (1888-1969)

mk9.eh Hartley, Harold, and Dennis Gabor. "Thomas Ralph Merton." RS. *BM, 16* (1970), 421-440.

Meshcherskiy, Ivan Vsevolodovich @ (1859-1935)

mll.bf Fradlin, V. N. "Ob odnoy zabytoy rabote I. V. Meshcherskogo." *VIYeT, 13* (1962), 75-76.

bt Tyulina, I. A. "Nauchnaya deyatel'nost' I. V. Meshcherskogo." IIYeT. *Trudy, 36* (1960), 264-272.

cg Grigor'yan, A. T. "Ivan Vsevolodovich Meshcherskiy." *VIYeT, 7* (1959), 127-130.

Meyer, Edgar (1879-)

mml.gg Gerlach, Walther. [Edgar Meyer zum 70. Geburtstag.] *Helvetica physica acta, 22* (1949), [100a].

Meyer, Stefan (1872-1949)

mm4.ec Benndorf, H. "Gedächtnisrede auf Stefan Meyer." *Acta physica austriaca, 5* (1951), 152-168.

Michelson, Albert Abraham @ $07 (1852-1931)

mnl.ak Livingston, Dorothy Michelson. *The master of light: A biography of Albert A. Michelson.* NY, 1973.

al Livingston, Dorothy Michelson. *The master of light: A biography of Albert A. Michelson.* Chicago and London, 1979.

ao McAllister, D. T. *Albert Abraham Michelson: The man who taught a world to measure.* China Lake, California, 1970. (Michelson Museum. *Publications,* 3.)

bc Bennett, Jean M., et al. "Albert Michelson, dean of American optics; contributions to science and influence on modern-day physics." *Applied optics, 12* (1973), 2253-2279.

bh Hall, J. E. "Nauchnyye raboty A. A. Maykel'sona (1852-1931)." *Mirovedeniye, 21:3* (1932), 11-18.

bj   Joos, Georg. "Povtoreniye opyta Maykel'sona." *UFN, 12* (1932), 136-147.

bp   Picard, Emile. "L'évolution des idées sur la lumière et l'oeuvre d'Albert Michelson." AS. *Mémoires, 62* (1935), 35p.

ch   Lemon, Harvey B. "Albert Abraham Michelson: The man and the man of science." *AJP, 4* (1936), 1-11.

cj   Livingston, Dorothy Michelson. "Michelson in the Navy, the Navy in Michelson." United States Naval Institute. *Proceedings, 95* (Jun. 1969), 72-79.

cm   Millikan, R. A. "Albert A. Michelson." NAS. *BM, 19* (1938), 120-147.

cn   Millikan, R. A. "Albert Abraham Michelson: The first American Nobel Laureate." *Scientific monthly, 48* (1939), 16-27.

cs   Shankland, R. S. "Michelson: America's first Nobel Prize winner in science." *PTeach, 15* (1977), 19-25.

en   N[ewall], H. F. "Albert Abraham Michelson." RS. *Obituary notices, 1* (1932), 18-25.

ev   Vavilov, S. I. "Albert Maykel'son." B.va4.jv, *3*, 135-137.

gm   Michelson, A. A., et al. "Proceedings of the Michelson meeting." Optical Society of America. *Journal, 18* (1929), 143-286.

nr   Shankland, R. S. "Albert A. Michelson at Case." *AJP, 17* (1949), 487-490.

nt   Smithson, J. R. "Michelson at Annapolis." *AJP, 18* (1950), 425-428.

See also: B.ei5.of |st2.cs, ji; E.az1.sj; F.bc; G.aa1.pi |ba1.ht, hu, ja; P.ib1.de

Mie, Gustav @ (1868-1957)

mo1.bh   Hönl, Helmut. "Intensitäts- und Quantitätsgrossen: In memoriam Gustav Mie." *PB, 24* (1968), 498-502.

Mikhel'son, Vladimir Aleksandrovich (1860-1927)

mp1.bl   Maksimov, S. A. "V. A. Mikhel'son, vydayushchiysya uchenyy-geofizik." A.ab1.vo, 288-295.

bp   Predvoditelev, A. S. "O nauchnykh trudakh V. A. Mikhel'sona." A.ab1.vo, 272-288.

cp   Predvoditelev, A. S., and A. K. Timiryazev. "V. A. Mikhel'son i D. A. Gol'dgammer." C.vb1.ti, 185-195. (Also in C.vb1.pr, *1*, 281-290.)

jk   Kipnis, A. Ya. "Neopublikovannaya rukopis' V. A. Mikhel'sona 'Ob energiyakh vysshego poryadka.'" *VIYeT, 18* (1965), 119-120.

kk   Kudryavtsev, P. S., and G. M. Teplyakov. "V. I. Lenin o stat'ye V. A. Mikhel'sona." *VIYeT, 30* (1970), 58-59.

ps   Sokolov, V. A. "Nauchno-pedagogicheskaya deyatel'nost' V. A. Mikhelsona." *VIYeT, 13* (1962), 141-146.

Miller, Dayton Clarence @ (1866-1941)

mq1.ef   Fletcher, Harvey. "Dayton Clarence Miller." NAS. *BM, 23* (1945), 59-74.

es   Shankland, Robert S. "Dayton Clarence Miller: Physics across 50 years." *AJP, 9* (1941), 273-283.

See also: E.az1.sg

Millikan, Robert Andrews @ $23 (1868-1953)

mq4.am   Millikan, R. A. *Autobiography.* NY, 1950.

bd   DuMond, Jesse W. M. "Editor's introduction." R. A. Millikan. *The electron.* Chicago, 1963. Pp. xi-lvii.

bk   Kargon, Robert H. "The conservative mode: Robert A. Millikan and the 20th-century revolution in physics." *Isis, 68* (1977), 509-526.

cd   DuBridge, L. A., and Paul S. Epstein. "Robert Andrews Millikan." NAS. *BM, 33* (1959), 241-282.

ck   Kevles, Daniel J. "Robert A. Millikan." *Scientific American, 240* (Jan. 1979), 142-151.

cw   Watson, E. C. "Robert Andrews Millikan." *PTeach, 2* (1964), 7-11.

eh   Houston, W. V. "Robert Andrews Millikan." APS. *Yearbook,* 1954, 440-444.

jg   Gunns, Albert F., and Judith R. Goodstein. *Guide to the Robert Andrews Millikan collection.* NY, 1975. (American Institute of Physics. Center for History of Physics. *Report,* 4.)

pe   Epstein, Paul S. "Robert A. Millikan as physicist and teacher." *Reviews of modern physics, 20* (1948), 10-25.

pm   Neher, H. V. "Millikan, teacher and friend." *AJP, 32* (1964), 868-877. (Also in *PTeach, 2* (1964), 374-380.)

pr   Romer, Alfred. "Robert A. Millikan, physics teacher." *PTeach, 16* (1978), 78-85.

ps   Roller, Duane. "Robert Andrews Millikan: Recipient of the 1940 Oersted Medal." *AJP, 9* (1941), 38-41.

sk   *Kevles, Daniel J. "Millikan: Spokesman for science in the twenties." *Engineering and science, 32* (Apr. 1969), 17-22.

See also: E.be1.fr, ho

Milne, Edward Arthur @   (1896-1950)

mr1.em   McCrea, W. H. "Edward Arthur Milne." RS. *Obituary notices, 7* (1951), 421-443.

en   McCrea, W. H., and H. H. Plaskett. "Edward Arthur Milne." RAS. *Monthly notices, 111* (1951), 160-172.

jc   CSAC. *E. A. Milne papers.* List in progress, 1981.

kh   Harder, Allen J. "E. A. Milne, scientific revolutions and the growth of knowledge." *Annals of science, 31* (1974), 351-363.

See also: B.eb1.kc

Milne, John @   (1850-1913)

mr2.ep   P[erry], J[ohn]. "John Milne." RS. *Proceedings, 89A* (1913/14), xxii-xxv.

Minkowski, Hermann (1864-1909)

mr5.bg   Galison, Peter Louis. "Minkowski's space-time: From visual thinking to the absolute world." *HSPS, 10* (1979), 85-121.

cb   Born, Max. "Vospominaniya o Germane Minkovskom." *UFN, 69* (1959), 295-302.

ce   Delone, B. N. "German Minkovskiy." *UFN, 2* (1936), 32-38.

cm   Malkin, I. "A sad anniversary." *Scripta mathematica, 24* (1959), 79-81.

eh   Hilbert, David. "Hermann Minkowski: Gedächtnisrede." Akademie der Wissenschaften, Göttingen. *Nachrichten: Geschäftliche Mitteilungen,* 1909, 72-101. (Also in B.hm1.jh, *3*, 339-364.)

See also: F.bh1.py; T.aa1.il

Mints, Aleksandr L'vovich (1895-1974)

mr7.ab   *Aleksandr L'vovich Mints.* Moscow, 1975. (*Mtly,* ser. fiz.-mat.)

Mises, Richard von @   (1883-1953)

ms1.cb   Bernhardt, Hannelore. "Zum Leben und Wirken des Mathematikers Richard von Mises." *NTM, 16: 2* (1979), 40-49.

Mitra, Sisir Kumar (1890-1963)

ms8.er Ratcliffe, J. A. "Sisir Kumar Mitra." RS. *BM, 10* (1964), 221-228.

Mittasch, Alwin @ (1869-1953)

mt1.ch Holdermann, Karl. "Alwin Mittasch." *Chemische Berichte, 90* (1957), xl-liv.

kf Farber, Eduard. "From chemistry to philosophy: The way of Alwin Mittasch." *Chymia, 11* (1966), 157-178.

Morley, Edward Williams @ (1838-1923)

mv1.aw Williams, Howard Raymond. *Edward Williams Morley.* Easton, Pa., 1957.

Morse, Philip McCord (1903-   )

mv4.am Morse, Philip M. *In at the beginnings: A physicist's life.* Cambridge, Mass., 1977.

Moseley, Henry Gwyn Jeffries @ (1887-1915)

mw1.ah Heilbron, J. L. *H. G. J. Moseley: The life and letters of an English physicist.* Berkeley, 1974.

ak Jaffe, Bernard. *Moseley and the numbering of the elements.* Garden City, NY, 1971.

bg Heilbron, J. L. "The work of H. G. J. Moseley." *Isis, 57* (1966), 336-364.

bj Heimann, P. M. "The work of H. G. J. Moseley." *Isis, 58* (1967), 232-234.

bs Sarton, George. "Moseley: The numbering of the elements." *Isis, 9* (1927), 96-111.

bu Smeaton, William A. "Moseley and the numbering of the elements." *Chemistry in Britain, 1* (1965), 353-355.

cr Redman, L. A. "H. G. J. Moseley." *PTeach, 3* (1965), 151-157.

ct Trenn, Thaddeus J. "A note on H. G. J. Moseley in Manchester." Manchester Literary and Philosophical Society. *Memoirs and proceedings, 120* (1977-80), 94-100.

er Rutherford, Ernest. "Henry Gwyn Jeffreys Moseley." RS *Proceedings, 93A* (1916), xxii-xxviii.

ff Fereira, Ricardo. "Photographs of Moseley." *Isis, 60* (1969), 233.

fj Jaffe, Bernard. "The Moseley photograph." *Isis, 61* (1970), 254.

fk   Kopal, Zdenek. "H. G. J. Moseley." *Isis,* *58* (1967), 405-407.

jt   Trenn, Thaddeus J. "Essay review: Moseley and more Moseleyana." *Annals of science, 33* (1976), 105-109.

nh   Hogg, John T. "Moseley at Oxford." *JCE, 52* (1975), 325-326.

See also: G.na1.he, ru; H.be1.dc |ce1.he

Moyer, Burton Jones (1912-1973)

mw4.es   *In memoriam Burton J. Moyer.* Privately printed, 1973.

Müller, Gustav @ (1851-1925)

mx1.el   Ludendorff, H. "Gustav Müller." Astronomische Gesellschaft. *Vierteljahrsschrift, 60* (1925), 158-177.

Mulliken, Robert Sanderson @ $66C (1896-   )

my1.cn   Nachtrieb, Norman H. "Interview with Robert S. Mulliken." *JCE, 52* (1975), 560-564.

Muskhelishvili, Nikolay Ivanovich (1891-   )

my5.au   Vekua, I. N. *Akademik Nikolay Ivanovich Muskhelishvili.* Novosibirsk, 1961.

aw   Vekua, I. N., and A. P. Epifanova, ed. *Nikolay Ivanovich Muskhelishvili.* Moscow, 1967. (*Mtly*, ser. matematiki, 10.)

Mysovskiy, Lev Vladimirovich (1888-1939)

mz1.ck   Khlopin, V. G. "Pamyati L. V. Mysovskogo." Radiyevyy institut im. Khlopina. *Trudy, 5* (1957), 5-11.

Nagaoka, Hantaro @ (1865-1950)

nd1.cy   Yagi, Eri, and Tōsaku Kimura. "The role of Nagaoka's atomic model (1904) in his research in physics." ICHS, XIV (1974). *Proceedings, 2* (1975), 345-348.

gh   *Anniversary volume dedicated to Professor Nagaoka by his friends and pupils on the completion of twenty-five years of his professorship.* Tokyo, 1925.

jb   Badash, Lawrence. "Nagaoka to Rutherford, 22 February 1911." *PT, 20* (Apr. 1967), 55-60. (In Russian in *UFN, 96* (1968), 169-176.)

See also: G.ea4.na; H.bc1; P.aa1.ki

Natanson, Wladyslaw @ (1864-1937)

ng1.cw *Weyssenhoff, Jan W. "In memory of Wladyslaw Natanson." Polska Akademia Nauk. *Review, 11:3* (1966), 35-39. (In Polish in *Postępy fizyki, 9* (1980).)

   ek Klecki, Leon. "Ladisla Natanson." *Prace matematyczno-fizyczne, 46* (1939), 1-18.

   em Michalski, Konstanty. "Ladislas Natanson, l'homme et l'humaniste." *Acta physica polonica, 6* (1937), 308-324.

   ew Weyssenhoff, Jan W. "Ladislas Natanson." *Acta physica polonica, 6* (1937), 295-307.

See also: R.df1.gu

Nernst, Hermann Walther @ $20C (1864-1941)

nk1.am Mendelssohn, Kurt. *The world of Walther Nernst: The rise and fall of German science.* London, 1973.

   br Rollier, Mario Alberto. "L'opera di Walther Nernst." *Scientia, 72* (1942), 81-88.

   bt Schimank, Hans. "Walther Nernst, neue Grundlagen zur Molekulartheorie und Thermodynamik." A.aj1.sc, 129-138.

   ce Eggert, J. "Walther Nernst." *Angewandte Chemie, 76* (1964), 445-455.

   cg Günther, Paul. "Zum 10. Todestag von Walther Nernst." *PB, 7* (1951), 556-558.

   cm Mendelssohn, Kurt. "Walther Nernst: an appreciation." *Cryogenics, 4* (1964), 129-135.

   eb Bodenstein, Max. "Gedächtnisfeier für Walther Nernst." DPG. *Verhandlungen, 23* (1942), 1-33.

   el Lindemann, F. A., and Franz Simon. "Walther Hermann Nernst." RS. *Obituary notices, 4* (1942), 101-112.

   gl Laue, Max von. [W. Nernst zum 60. Geburtstag]. DPG. *Verhandlungen, 5* (1924), 42-43.

   vh Herrmann, Dieter B. "Walther Nernst und sein Neo-Bechstein-Fügel, eine Episode aus der Geschichte der elektronischen Musik." *NTM 9: 1* (1972), 40-48.

See also: C.gb1.ka; R.de1.hi, su

Neumann, Carl Gottfried @ (1832-1925)

nn1.cs Salié, H. "Carl Neumann." *Bedeutende Gelehrte in Leipzig,* vol 2. Ed. G. Harig. Leipzig, 1965. Pp. 13-23.

Neumann, John Ludwig von @ (1903-1957)

np1.ah   Heims, Steve J. *John von Neumann and Norbert Wiener. From mathematics to the technologies of life and death.* Cambridge, Mass., 1980.

bk   Kuhn, H. W., and A. W. Tucker. "John von Neumann's work in the theory of games and mathematical economics." American Mathematical Society. *Bulletin, 64: 3:2* (1958), 100-122.

bt   Todd, John. "John von Neumann and the National Accounting Machine." *SIAM review, 16* (1974), 526-530.

ch   Halmos, P. R. "The legend of John von Neumann." *American mathematical monthly, 80* (1973), 382-394.

cu   Ulam, Stanislaw, et al. "John von Neumann." U.gb2.fl, 235-269.

eb   Bochner, Salomon. "John von Neumann." NAS. *BM, 32* (1958), 438-457.

eo   Oxtoby, J. C., et al., ed. "John von Neumann." American Mathematical Society. *Bulletin, 64* (1958), 1-129.

eu   Ulam, Stanislaw. "John von Neumann." American Mathematical Society. *Bulletin, 64: 3: 2* (1958), 1-49.

jn   Neumann, John von. *Collected works.* Ed. A. H. Taub. 6 vols. NY, 1961-1963.

js   Szentiványi, Tibor. "Neumann János újabb levelei Ortvay Rudolfhoz." *Fizikai szemle, 29* (1979), 380-390.

See also: D.he1.ha; E.th1.go, sh; L.ii1.ho, sn; O.fc1.bi; T.aa1.ka

Nichols, Edward Leamington (1854-1937)

nt1.em   Merritt, Ernest. "Edward Leamington Nichols." NAS. *BM, 21* (1940), 343-366.

Nichols, Ernest Fox @ (1869-1924)

nu1.en   Nichols, Edward L. "Ernest Fox Nichols." NAS. *BM, 12* (1925), 97-131.

See also: B.hv4.ch

Nicholson, John William @ (1881-1955)

nv1.ew   Wilson, William. "John William Nicholson." RS. *BM, 2* (1956), 209-214.

See also: H.bd1.mc

Noether, Amalie Emmy @ (1882-1935)

nx1.ew   Weyl, Hermann. "Emmy Noether." *Scripta mathematica, 3* (1935), 201-220.

Olszewski, Karol Stanislaw @ (1846-1915)

oc1.bw   Wojtaszek, Zdzislaw. "O dzialalności naukowej Karola Olszewskiego poza dziedzina kriogenik." *Studia i materialy z dziejów nauki polskiej,* ser. C, *9* (1964), 135-173.

cb   Adwentowski, Karol, Antoni Pasternak, and Zdzislaw Wojtaszek. "Karol Olszewski jako uczony i nauczyciel." *Studia i materialy z dziejów nauki polskiej,* ser. C, *3* (1959), 193-229.

cp   Pasternak, Antoni. "Karol Olszewski (1846-1915) i Zygmunt Wroblewski (1845-1888)." *Polscy badacze przyrody.* Warsaw, 1959. Pp. 174-203.

cw   Wojtaszek, Zdzislaw. "On the scientific contacts of Karol Olszewski with William Ramsay." ICHS, XI (1965). *Actes, 4* (1968), 113-116.

es   Smoluchowski, Marian. "Karl Olszewski: Ein Gelehrtenleben." *Nwn, 5* (1917), 738-740.

See also: B.dj1.bd; O.ha1.wo

Onnes, Heike Kamerlingh @ $13 (1853-1926)

of1.ec   Cohen, Ernst. "Kamerlingh Onnes Memorial Lecture." Chemical Society. *Journal,* 1927, 1193-1209.

ed   D[onnan], F. G. "Heike Kamerlingh Onnes." RS. *Proceedings, 113A* (1926/7), i-vi.

ek   Lorentz, Hendrik Antoon, et al. *In Memoriam: Heike Kamerlingh Onnes.* London, 1926.

em   Mathias, E. "H. Kamerlingh Onnes (1853-1926). L'oeuvre et l'homme." *Revue générale des sciences, 37* (1926), 294-298.

See also: B.ei6.ik |lp8.jt; O.ha1.pi

Onsager, Lars $68C (1903-1976)

og1.el   Longuet-Higgins, H. C., and M. E. Fisher. "Lars Onsager." RS. *BM, 24* (1978), 443-471.

gm   Meixner, J. "Chemie-Nobelpreis 1968 für Lars Onsager." *PB, 25* (1968), 65-68.

Oppenheimer, J. Robert @ (1904-1967)

ok1.ac   Chevalier, Haakon M. *Oppenheimer: The story of a friendship.* NY, 1965.

ak   Kugelmas, J. *J. Robert Oppenheimer and the atomic story.* NY, 1953.

am   Michelmore, Peter. *The swift years: The Robert Oppenheimer story.* NY, 1969.

ap   Rouzé, Michel. *Robert Oppenheimer et la bombe atomique.* Paris, 1962. (Russian trn, Moscow, 1965.)

aq   Rouzé, Michel. *Robert Oppenheimer, the man and his theories.* Tr. P. Evans. London, 1964.

as   Royal, Denise. *The story of J. Robert Oppenheimer.* NY, 1969.

br   Serber, Robert, V. F. Weisskopf, Abraham Pais, and Glenn T. Seaborg. "A memorial to Oppenheimer." *PT, 20* (Oct. 1967), 35-53.

bs   Rabi, I. I., Robert Serber, V. F. Weisskopf, Abraham Pais, and Glenn T. Seaborg. *Oppenheimer.* NY, 1969.

co   Oppenheimer, Frank. "In defense of the titular heros." *PT, 22* (Feb. 1969), 77-80.

cp   *Perrin, Francis. "Robert Oppenheimer: La responsabilité du scientifique. Entretien avec Francis Perrin." *Sciences, 170* (1971), 5-13.

eb   Bacher, Robert F. "Robert Oppenheimer." APS. *Proceedings, 116* (1972), 279-293.

ed   [Bethe, Hans A., and Henry D. Smyth]. "J. Robert Oppenheimer, 1904-1967." *BAS, 23* (Aug. 1967), 2-6.

ee   Bethe, Hans A. "Oppenheimer: 'Where he was there was always life and excitement.'" *Science, 155* (1967), 1080-1084.

ef   Bethe, Hans A. "J. Robert Oppenheimer." RS. *BM, 14* (1968), 391-416.

eh   Guth, E. "J. Robert Oppenheimer in memoriam." *Acta physica austriaca, 25* (1967), 371-375.

js   Smith, Alice Kimball, and Charles Weiner, ed. *Robert Oppenheimer: Letters and recollections.* Cambridge, Mass., 1980.

mc   Church, Peggy R. *The house at Otowi Bridge: The story of Edith Warner and Los Alamos.* Albuquerque, 1959.

sb   Alsop, J., and S. Alsop. *We accuse! The story of the miscarriage of justice in the case of J. Robert Oppenheimer.* London, 1955.

sd   Boskin, Joseph, and Fred Krinsky. *The Oppenheimer affair: A political play in three acts* Beverly Hills, 1968.

sf   Calvo-Hernando, Manuel. "Robert Oppenheimer: Un drama de neustro tiempo. Traidor a su patria o intelligencia crucificada?" *Arbor, 66* (1967), 249-263.

sh   Curtis, Charles P. *The Oppenheimer case: The trial of a security system* NY, 1955.

sj   Green, Harold P. "The Oppenheimer case: A study in the abuse of law." *BAS, 33* (Jul. 1977), 12-16, 56-61.

sl   Major, John. *The Oppenheimer hearing* London, 1971.

sn   Putik, Jaroslav. *Svedomi: Pripad Professora Oppenheimera.* Prague, 1963.

sp   Sanders, Jane A. "The University of Washington and the controversy over J. Robert Oppenheimer." *Pacific northwest quarterly, 70* (1979), 8-19.

sr   Santillana, Giorgio de. "Galileo and J. Robert Oppenheimer." *Reporter, 17* (1957), 10-18.

ss   Stern, Philip M., and Harold P. Green. *The Oppenheimer case: Security on trial.* NY, 1969.

st   Strout, Cushing, ed. *Conscience, science and security: The case of Dr. J. Robert Oppenheimer.* Chicago, 1963.

su   Trilling, Diana. "The Oppenheimer case: A reading of the testimony." *Partisan review, 21* (1954), 604-635.

sv   United States. Atomic Energy Commission. *In the matter of J. Robert Oppenheimer: Transcript of hearing before Personnel Security Board.* Washington, D.C., 1954.

sw   United States. Atomic Energy Commission. *In the matter of J. Robert Oppenheimer: Texts of principal documents and letters.* Washington, D.C., 1954. (B.ok1.sv and .sw were issued together and reprinted, Cambridge, Mass., 1970.)

sx   Vilar, Jean. *Le dossier Oppenheimer. D'après le montage scénique d'Heinar Kipphardt et les minutes de la Commission de sécurité de l'énergie atomique.* Geneva, 1965.

See also: B.lg3.ad

Orlov, Sergey Vladimirovich @ (1880-1958)

on1.gf   *Anon. "Sergey Vladimirovich Orlov (k 40-letiyu nauchnoy i pedagogicheskoy deyatel'nosti)." Dushanbe. Astronomicheskaya observatoriya. *Tsirkulyar,* no. 64-65 (1948), 1.

gg   Anon. "Semidesyatiletiye S. V. Orlova." Vsesoyuznoye astronomo-geodezicheskoye obshchestvo. *Byulleten'*, no. 10 (1951), 3-4.

gp   Poloskov, S. M. "Vydayushchiysya issledovatel' komet S. V. Orlov." *Priroda*, 1951:11, 73-75.

gs   *"S. V. Orlov." Dushanbe. Astronomicheskaya observatoriya. *Byulleten'*, no. 14 (1955), 3-4.

ju   "Chestvovaniye chlenakorrespondenta AN SSSR S. V. Orlova." AN. *Vestnik*, 1951:6, 81-83.

See also: I.sa1.za

Ornstein, Leonard Salomon @ (1880-1941)

or1.ao   *L. S. Ornstein: A story of his work from 1908 to 1933.* Utrecht, 1933.

bz   *Zernike, Frits. "Ornsteins levenswerk." *Nederlandsch tijdschrift voor natuurkunde, 8* (1941), 253-265.

ek   Kramers, H. A. "Levensbericht van L. S. Ornstein." Akademie van Wetenschappen, Amsterdam. *Jaarboek*, 1940/1, 225-231.

Ortvay, Rudolf (1885-1945)

See: B.np1.js |wp3.jw

Ostwald, Wilhelm Friedrich @ $09C (1853-1932)

ow1.ao   Ostwald, Wilhelm. *Lebenslinien: Eine Selbstbiographie.* 3 vols. Berlin, 1926-27.

ap   Ostwald, Grete. *Wilhelm Ostwald, mein Vater.* Stuttgart, 1953.

ar   Rodnyy, N. I., and Yu. I. Solov'yev. *Vil'gel'm Ostval'd, 1853-1932.* Moscow, 1969.

bm   Malina, I. K. "O roli V. Ostval'da v razrabotke katalaticheskogo sinteza ammiaka." *VIYeT, 45* (1973), 39-41.

bo   Ostwald, Wilhelm. *Forschen und Nutzen: Wilhelm Ostwald zur wissenschaftlichen Arbeit.* Ed. Günther Lotz, Lothar Dunsch, and Uta Kring. Berlin, 1978.

cg   Günther, Paul. "Wilhelm Ostwald." *PB, 10* (1954), 170-172.

ch   Hermann, Armin. "Wilhelm Ostwald, Svante Arrhenius und van't Hoff: Die Begründer der physikalischen Chemie." *PB, 20* (1964), 524-527.

cj   Hillpern, Edmund P. "Some personal qualities of Wilhelm Ostwald recalled by a former assistant." *Chymia, 2* (1949), 57-64.

jo   Ostwald, Wilhelm. *Aus dem wissenschaftlichen Briefwechsel Wilhelm Ostwalds.* Ed. Grete Ostwald and Hans-Günther Körber. 2 vols. Berlin, 1961-1969.

js   Solov'yev, Yu. I. "Neopublikovannyye pis'ma D. I. Mendeleyeva i V. Ostval'da." *VIYeT, 47-48* (1974), 128.

kj   Jodl, Friedrich. "Wilhelm Ostwald als Philosoph." Jodl. *Vom Lebenswege. Gesammelte Vorträge,* vol. 1. Stuttgart, 1916. Pp. 478-489.

ps   Solov'yev, Yu. I., and N. I. Rodnyy. "Russische Wissenschaftler im Leipziger Laboratorium von Wilhelm Ostwald." *NTM, 4:9* (1967), 50-59.

See also: A.cc1.kn, ko; H.ab1.ho; R.ag1.ku

Paalzow, Carl Adolf (1823-1908)

pa3.er   Rubens, Heinrich. "A. Paalzow." DPG. *Verhandlungen, 10* (1908), 451-463.

Pacinotti, Antonio (1841-1912)

pa7.ao   Polvani, Giovanni. *Antonio Pacinotti: la vita, l'opera.* Milan, 1932.

ap   Polvani, Giovanni. *Antonio Pacinotti, la vita e l'opera.* 2 vols. Pisa, 1933-34.

ar   Telò-Pacinotti, M. A. *Mio padre Antonio Pacinotti.* Pisa, 1962.

co   Polvani, Giovanni. "La vita e l'opera di Antonio Pacinotti." *Nuovo cimento, 18* (1941), 425-446.

cp   Puccianti, Luigi. "Profilo di A. Pacinotti." B.pa7.ap, *1,* xvii-xxv.

Paneth, Friedrich Adolf @ (1887-1958)

pb1.ee   Emeléus, H. J. "Friedrich Adolf Paneth." RS. *BM, 6* (1960), 227-246.

Papaleksi, Nikolay Dmitriyevich (1880-1947)

pb3.cb   Anon. "Nikolay Dmitriyevich Papaleksi." *Zhurnal tekhnicheskoy fiziki, 11* (1941), 3-6.

cc   Chestnov, F. "Vydayushchiysya uchenyy." *Radio,* 1952:2, 9-10.

cg   Gorelik, G. S. "Neskol'ko zamechaniy o stile nauchnogo tvorchestva N. D. Papaleksi." AN. *Izvestiya,* ser. fiz., *12* (1948), 22-24.

cr   Rytov, S. M. "Nikolay Dmitriyevich Papaleksi: Kratkaya nauchnaya biografiya." B.pb3.jp, 9-36.

cs   Shchegolev, Ye. Ya. "Chetvert' veka tomu nazad: Iz vospom-
      inaniy o sovmestnoy rabote s N. D. Papaleksi." AN. *Izvestiya*,
      ser. fiz., *12* (1948), 25-33.

er   Rytov, S. M. "Nikolay Dmitriyevich Papaleksi." *UFN, 31* (1947),
      429-446.

es   Rytov, S. M. "Akademik Nikolay Dmitriyevich Papaleksi." AN.
      Izvestiya, ser. fiz., *12* (1948), 7-21.

gc   Anon. "N. D. Papalexi: On the occasion of his sixtieth birthday."
      Journal of physics, 4 (1941), 5-8.

gv   Vavilov, S. I. "Akademik N. D. Papaleksi (k shestidesyatiletiyu
      so dnya rozhdeniya)." *Tekhnicheskaya kniga*, 1940:12, 17.

gz   *Zhezherin, R. P. "Akademik Nikolay Dmitriyevich Papaleksi: K
      60-letiyu so dnya rozhdeniya." *Elektrichestvo*, 1941:3.

jm   Vreden-Kobetskaya, T. O., and Ye. I. Okulich, ed. *Nikolay Dmi-
      triyevich Papaleksi.* Moscow, 1941. (*Mtly*, ser. fiziki, 2.)

jp   Papaleksi, N. D. *Sobraniye trudov.* Ed. S. M. Rytov. Moscow,
      1948.

See also: B.fk1.gb; P.hf1.gi

Parsons, Charles A. (1854-1931)

pb7.aa   Appleyard, Rollo. *Charles Parsons, his life and work.* London,
          1933.

ee   E[wing], J. A. "Charles Parsons." RS. *Proceedings, 131A* (1931),
      v-xxv.

Paschen, Louis Carl Heinrich Friedrich @ (1865-1947)

pc3.cf   Forman, Paul. "Paschen, Louis Carl Heinrich Friedrich." *DSB, 10*
          (1974), 345-350.

et   Tolansky, S. "Friedrich Paschen." Physical Society of London.
      Proceedings, 59 (1947), 1040-1041.

gb   Bohr, Niels. "Friedrich Paschen zum siebzigsten Geburtstag."
      Nwn, 23 (1935), 73.

gg   Gerlach, Walther. "Friedrich Paschen zum siebzigsten
      Geburtstag." *FF, 11* (1935), 50-51.

gr   Runge, Carl. "Friedrich Paschen." *Nwn, 13* (1925), 133-134.

Pauli, Wolfgang, Jr. @ $45 (1900-1958)

pd3.be   Enz, Charles P. "W. Pauli's scientific work." A.ad1.me, 766-799.

cb   Bohr, Niels. "Foreword." B.pd3.if, 1-4.

ci   Jordan, Pascual. "Erinnerungen an Wolfgang Pauli." *PB, 29* (1973), 291-298.

cj   Jordan, Pascual. "My recollections of Wolfgang Pauli." Tr. Ira M. Freeman. *AJP, 43* (1975), 205-208.

el   Landau, L. D. "Wolfgang Pauli." *SPU, 2* (1959), 624-627. (In Russian in *UFN, 68* (1959), 557-559.)

ep   Peierls, R. E. "Wolfgang Ernst Pauli." RS. *BM, 5* (1959), 175-192.

gw   Weyl, Hermann. "Encomium." *Science, 103* (1946), 216-218.

if   Fierz, Markus, and V. F. Weisskopf, ed. *Theoretical physics in the twentieth century: A memorial volume to Wolfgang Pauli.* NY, 1960. (Russian trn by L. D. Puzikov and A. A. Sazykin. Moscow, 1962.)

jb   Pauli, Wolfgang. *Collected scientific papers* Ed. R. Kronig and V. F. Weisskopf. 2 vols. NY, 1964.

jf   Pauli, Wolfgang. *Aufsätze und Vorträge über Physik und Erkenntnistheorie.* Braunschweig, 1961.

ji   CERN. *Catalogue of reprints of scientific papers in the Pauli collection* Geneva, 1969. (CERN. *Bibliographies,* 8.)

jm   Pauli, Wolfgang. *Wissenschaftlicher Briefwechsel mit Bohr, Einstein, u. a.* Vol 1. *1919-1929.* Ed. Armin Hermann, Karl von Meyenn, and Viktor F. Weisskopf. NY, 1979.

kh   Heisenberg, Werner. "Wolfgang Paulis philosophische Auffassungen." *Nwn, 46* (1959), 661-663.

See also: E.bf1.ri; H.cg1; I.ee1.go; L.db1.me

Pegram, George Braxton (1876-1958)

pe1.ce   Embrey, Lee Anna. "George Braxton Pegram." NAS. *BM, 41* (1970), 357-407.

Peierls, Rudolf (1907-   )

pe3.jm   CSAC. *Sir Rudolf Peierls papers at the Bodleian Library, Oxford.* List 52/6/77, 71 p.

Peirce, Benjamin Osgood II @ (1854-1914)

pe5.eh   Hall, Edwin H. "Benjamin Osgood Peirce." NAS. *BM, 8* (1919), 435-466.

Pérot, Jean-Baptiste Gaspard G. A. @ (1863-1925)

pe7.ef   Fabry, Charles. "Jean Baptiste Gaspard Gustave Alfred Pérot." *Astrophysical journal, 64* (1926), 209-214.

Perrin, Jean Baptiste @ $26 (1870-1942)

pf3.al   Lot, Fernard. *Jean Perrin.* Paris, 1963.

am   *Nye, Mary Jo. *Jean Perrin and molecular reality.* Ph.D. thesis. Univ. of Wisconsin, 1970. (*DAI, 31*, 715A.)

an   Nye, Mary Jo. *Molecular reality: A perspective on the scientific work of Jean Perrin.* London and NY, 1972.

bb   Broglie, Louis de. "La réalité des molécules et l'oeuvre de Jean Perrin." AS. *Mémoires, 67* (1945), 29 p.

bp   Perrin, Francis. "L'Oeuvre scientifique de Jean Perrin." AS. *Notices et discors, 4* (1962), 662-674.

cb   Blum, Léon. "Jean Perrin." Perrin. *La science et l'espérance.* Paris, 1948. Pp. xxix-xxxv.

cd   Broglie, Louis de. "Jean Perrin." Perrin. *La science et l'espérance.* Paris, 1948. Pp. ix-xxviii.

ce   Broglie, Louis de. "Jean Perrin physicien." *RHS, 24* (1971), 99-105.

cg   Coulomb, Jean. "Jean Perrin fondateur du Centre National de la Recherche Scientifique." AS. *Notices et discours, 4* (1962), 675-683.

ci   Couderc, Paul. "Jean Perrin et l'astronomie." *RHS, 24* (1971), 117-122.

cr   Raman, Varadaraja V. "Jean Baptiste Perrin: Advocate for the atoms." *PTeach, 8* (1970), 380-386.

cv   Vavilov, S. I. "Pamyati Zhana Perrena." B.va4.jv, *3*, 286-287.

cw   Weart, Spencer. "Jean Perrin and the reorganization of science." *PT, 32* (Jun. 1979), 42-51.

ec   Cabannes, Jean. "Transfert des cendres de Jean Perrin." AS. *Notices et discours, 2* (1937-48), 713-717.

et   Townsend, J. S. "Jean Baptiste Perrin." RS. *Obituary notices, 4* (1943), 301-305.

gb   Broglie, Louis de. "Hommage à Jean Perrin." AS. *Notices et discours, 4* (1962), 657-661.

gd   Courtines, Marcel. *La lumière, principe du monde, à propos de Jean Perrin, prix Nobel de physique 1926.* Paris, 1927.

jb   Perrin, Jean. *Oeuvres scientifiques.* Paris, 1950.

sn   Nye, Mary Jo. "Science and socialism: The case of Jean Perrin in the Third Republic." *French historical studies,* 9 (1975), 141-169.

sr   Ranc, Albert. *Jean Perrin, un grand savant au service du socialisme.* Paris, 1945.

See also: R.ag1.sa

Perucca, Eligio (1890-1965)

pf7.ew   Wataghin, Gleb. "Eligio Perucca, 1890-1965." Rome, 1966. (Accademia Nazionale dei Lincei. *Problemi attuali di scienze e cultura. Quaderni,* 77.)

Petavel, Joseph Ernest (1873-1936)

pg1.er   Robertson, Robert. "Joseph Ernest Petavel." RS. *Obituary notices,* 2 (1936), 183-203.

Pettersson, Hans (1888-1966)

pg2.ed   Deacon, G. E. R. "Hans Pettersson." RS. *BM, 12* (1966), 405-421.

Piccard, Auguste @ (1884-1962)

ph3.al   Latil, Pierre de, and Jean Rivoire. *Le professeur Auguste Piccard.* Paris, 1962.

ho   Honour, Alan. *Ten miles high, two miles deep: The adventures of the Piccards.* NY, 1957.

Pienkowski, Stefan (1883-1953)

pi3.es   Soltan, A. "Stefan Pienkowski." *Acta physica polonica, 13* (1954), 309-313.

Pierce, George Washington @ (1872-1956)

pi7.es   Saunders, Frederick A., and Frederick V. Hunt. "George Washington Pierce." NAS. *BM, 33* (1959), 351-380.

Piola, Franceso (1865-1926)

pj1.gm   Majorana, Quirino. "Commemorazione del Prof. Francesco Piola." *Nuovo Cimento, 4* (1927), 153-157.

Pippard, Alfred John Sutton (1891-1969)

pj3.es   Skempton, A. W. "Alfred John Sutton Pippard." RS. *BM, 16* (1970), 463-478.

Placzek, George (1905-1955)

pk3.eb   Amaldi, Edoardo. "George Placzek." *Ricerca scientifica, 26* (1956), 2038-2042.

Planck, Max Karl Ernst Ludwig @ $18 (1858-1947)

pl1.ab   Akademie der Wissenschaften, Berlin. *Max Planck zum Gedanken* Berlin, 1959.

ad   Gerlach, Walther. *Die Quantentheorie. Max Planck, sein Werk und seine Wirkung.* Bonn, 1948.

ae   Giua, Michele. *Storia delle scienze ed epistemologia: Galilei, Boyle, Planck.* Turin, 1945.

af   Hartmann, Hans. *Max Planck als Mensch und Denker.* Basil, 1953.

ag   Hermann, Armin. *Max Planck in Selbstzeugnissen und Bilddokumenten.* Hamburg, 1973.

ai   *Hönl, Helmut. *Max Planck und die Physik. Gedenkrede.* Freiburg, 1949. 30p.

am   Planck, Max. *Wissenschaftliche Selbstbiographie.* Leipzig, 1948. (English trn by F. Gaynor, NY, 1949; Italian trn by A. Gamba, Turin, 1956; French trn by A. George, Paris, 1960.)

an   Planck, Max. *Erinnerungen.* Ed. W. Keiper. Berlin, 1948. (*Das Dokument. Gestalt und Gestalten der Kultur. Alfred Nobel Reihe, 1.*)

au   Unsöld, Albrecht. *Max Planck: Physik und Historie.* Kiel, 1958. (Schleswig-Holsteinische Universitätsgesellschaft. *Veröffentlichungen,* 24.)

bg   Kapustinskiy, A. F. "Maks Plank kak termodinamik i fiziko-khimik." B.pl1.ig, 109-125.

bi   Jordan, Pascual. "Max Plancks wissenschaftliche Leistung." *PB, 4* (1948), 134-137.

bj   Lamla, Ernst. "Max Planck, die Eröffnung des Atomzeitalters durch die Quantentheorie." A.aj1.sc, 38-46.

bk   Laue, Max von. "Das wissenschaftliche Lebenswerk Max Plancks." *Angewandte Chemie, 61* (1949), 114-115. (Also in B.pll.jo, *3*, 424-426.)

bm   *Needell, Allan A. *Irreversibility and the failure of classical dynamics: Max Planck's work on the quantum theory, 1900-1915.* Ph.D. diss., Yale University, 1980.

bo   Päsler, Max. *Vorlesungen über Thermodynamik von Max Planck.* Berlin, 1964.

bp   Planck, Max. "Zwanzig Jahre Arbeit am physikalischen Weltbild." *Physica, 9* (1929), 193-222.

br   Polak, L. S., and Yu. I. Solov'yev. "Maks Plank kak fizikokhimik." IIYeT. *Trudy, 22* (1959), 13-31.

bs   Solov'yev, Yu. I. "M. Plank kak fiziko-khimik." B.pll.jp, 745-753.

bw   Warburg, Emil. "Über Plancks Verdienste um die experimentelle Physik." *Nwn, 6* (1918), 202-203.

cb   Anon. "Vor 20 Jahren starb Max Planck." *PB, 23* (1967), 473.

cc   Balmer, Heinz. "Planck und Einstein beantworten eine wissenschaftliche Rundfrage." *PB, 25* (1969), 558.

cd   Bertholet, Alfred. "Erinnerungen an Max Planck." *PB, 4* (1948), 161-162.

ce   Biermann, Kurt-R. "Versuch einer Leonhard-Euler-Ausgabe von 1903-07 und ihre Beurteilung durch Max Planck." *FF, 37* (1963), 236-239.

cf   Ehrenhaft, Felix, et al. "Erinnerungen an Max Planck." *PB, 4* (1948), 161-174.

cg   Einstein, Albert. "Max Planck als Forscher." *Nwn, 1* (1913), 1077-1079.

ci   George, André. "Introduction." B.pll.jq, 1-60.

ck   Gerlach, Walther. "Max Planck und sein Werk." *Universitas, 13* (1958), 803-812.

cm   Hahn, Otto. "Einige persönliche Erinnerungen an Max Planck." Max-Planck-Gesellschaft. *Mitteilungen,* 1957, 243-246. (Also in B.pll.jo, *3*, 421-423.)

cq   Hermann, Armin. "Max Planck zum Gedenken." *PB, 28* (1972), 437-442.

cr   Hermann, Armin. "Max Planck: Praeceptor physicae." *PB, 29* (1973), 483-487.

cs   Hönl, Helmut. "Zum hundertsten Geburtstag von Max Planck." *Schweizer Monatsheft, 38* (1958), 22-30.

ct   Ioffe, A. F. "Maks Plank: Vospominaniya." B.pl1.ig, 89-93.

cu   Ioffe, A. F. "Maks Plank." A.aj1.io, 221-224.

cv   Ivanenko, D. D. "Plankovskiye tvorzhestva v Berline i Leyptsige." *UFN, 66* (1958), 523-542. (In English in *SPU, 1* (1958), 287-297.)

cw   Jordan, Pascual. "Max Planck." *Neues Europa. Halbmonatshefte für Völkerverständigung, 20* (1947), 29.

cx   Jordan, Pascual. "Max Plancks wissenschaftliche Leistung." *PB, 4* (1948), 134-137.

cz   *Kommerell, Otto. "Die Planck in Untergruppenbach." *Südwestdeutsche Blätter für Familien- und Wappenkunde, 11* (1960), 77-85.

db   Lamla, Ernst. "Zur 25. Wiederkehr des Todestages von Max Planck: Physiker-Gräber auf dem Göttinger Friedhof." *PB, 28* (1972), 443-446.

dc   *Laue, Max von. "Max Planck." Max-Planck-Gesellschaft. *Mitteilungen, 3* (1952), 1-6.

dd   Laue, Max von. "Traueransprache." B.pl1.jo, *3*, 417-420. (In French in B.pl1.jq, 61-65.)

de   Laue, Max von. "Zu Max Plancks 100. Geburtstage." *Nwn, 45* (1958), 221-226. (Also in B.lf6.jl, *3*, 257-262.)

df   Laue, Max von. "Delo zhizni Maksa Planka." B.pl1.ig, 126-131. (Also in *VIYeT, 6* (1958), 52-55.)

dg   Laue, Max von. "Pamyati Maksa Planka." B.pl1.ig, 132-133. (Also in *UFN, 64* (1958), 639-640.)

di   Meissner, Walther. "Max Planck, the man and his work." *Science, 113* (1951), 75-81.

dj   Meitner, Lise. "Max Planck als Mensch." *Nwn, 45* (1958), 406-408.

dl   O'Flaherty, James C. "A humanist looks at Max Planck." *American scientist, 47* (1959), 68-79.

dm   Planck, Max. "Persönliche Erinnerungen aus alten Zeiten." *Nwn, 33* (1946), 230-235.

dn   Planck, Max. "Aus der wissenschaftlichen Selbstbiographie." *PB, 14* (1958), 145-152.

do   Planck, Max. "Maks Plank v Sovetskom Soyuze v 1925 godu." B.pl1.ig, 76-85.

dq Regato, Juan A. del. "Max Planck." *International journal of radiation oncology and biological physics,* 5 (1979), 2097-2111.

dr Rutherford, Ernest. "Note." *Nwn, 17* (1929), 483.

ds Starosel'skaya-Nikitina, O. A., and L. S. Polak. "Maks Plank i Pervyy Sol'veyevskiy kongress." B.pl1.ig, 221-244.

dt *Stickler, Bernard. "Max-Planck: Mensch und Werk." *Mathematik und Naturwissenschaften im Unterricht, 20:7* (1967), 241-249.

du Unsöld, Albrecht. "Max Planck, seine Zeit und unsere Zeit: Gedanken zur Max-Planck-Ausstellung in Hamburg und Kiel." *PB, 23* (1967), 405-409.

dw Westphal, Wilhelm H. "Max Planck als Mensch." *Nwn, 45* (1958), 234-236.

ea Andrade, E. N. da C. "Max Planck." *Nature, 161* (1948), 284, 751.

ec Becker, Richard, Albert Einstein, and Werner Heisenberg. [Max Planck.] *Angewandte Chemie, 61* (1949), 113-118.

ee Bopp, Fritz. "Vorstellung und Wirklichkeit in der Physik." *NR, 2* (1949), 1-5.

ef Born, Max. "Max Karl Ernst Ludwig Planck." RS. *Obituary notices, 6* (1948), 161-168.

eg Bose, D. M. "Max Planck." *Science and culture, 13* (1947), 237-242.

ei Broglie, Louis de. "Max Planck." *Revue de questions scientifiques,* 9 (1948), 155-165.

el Franck, James. "Max Planck." APS. *Yearbook,* 1947, 284-292.

ep Laue, Max von. "Nachruf auf Max Planck." Akademie der Wissenschaften, Berlin. *Jahrbuch,* 1946-49, 217-220.

eq Laue, Max von. "Max Planck." *Nwn, 35* (1948), 1-7.

gb Sommerfeld, Arnold. "Max Planck zum 60. Geburtstage." *Nwn,* 6 (1918), 195-202.

gd Wachsmuth, F. B. Richard. "Max Planck zu seinem 60. Geburtstag." Physikalischer Verein, Frankfurt. *Jahresbericht,* 1918/9, 13-18.

gf Blokh, M. A. "Maks Plank." *Priroda,* 1926:3-4, 3-10.

gi Lorentz, H. A., and Max Planck. [Speeches at presentation of the Lorentz medal to Planck.] Akademie van Wetenschappen, Amsterdam. Afdeeling Natuurkunde. *Verslag, 36:1* (1927), 532-538.

gk   Laue, Max von. "Zum 70. Geburtstag von Max Planck." *FF, 4* (1928), 144.

gm   Akademie der Wissenschaften, Berlin. "Adresse an Hrn. Max Planck zum 50. Doktorjubiläum." Akademie der Wissenschaften, Berlin. Phil.-Hist. Klasse. *Sitzungsberichte,* 1929:1, 431-432.

gn   Haber, Fritz. "Zum 75. Geburtstag des...Max Planck." *Nwn, 21* (1933), 293.

go   Laue, Max von. "Zu Plancks 75. Geburtstage." *PZ, 34* (1933), 305.

gq   Kemble, E. C. "The eightieth birthday of Max Planck." *Science, 87* (1938), 360-361.

gr   Laue, Max von. "Zum 80. Geburtstag von Max Planck." *Annalen der Physik, 32* (1938), 2-4.

gs   Laue, Max von. "Max Planck on the occasion of his 80th birthday." *Research and progress, 4* (1938), 103-108.

gt   Ramsauer, Carl, E. Grüneisen, and Max Planck, et al. "Feier des 80. Geburtstages des Ehrenmitgliedes...Max Planck." DPG. *Verhandlungen, 19* (1938), 57-76.

gu   Sommerfeld, Arnold. "Max Planck zum 80. Geburtstag." *Münchener medezinische Wochenschrift, 85* (1938), 829-830.

gv   Becker, Richard. "Gedenktage." *FF, 19* (1943), 146-147.

gx   *Broglie, Louis de. "Zum 90. Geburtstag Max Plancks." *Natur und Technik, 2* (1948), 311-315.

ig   Ioffe, A. F., and A. T. Grigor'yan, eds. *Maks Plank, 1858-1958: Sbornik k stoletiyu so dnya rozhdeniya Maksa Planka.* Moscow, 1958.

ik   Kockel, B., W. Macke, and A. Papapetron, eds. *Max-Planck-Festschrift 1958.* Berlin, n.d.

jb   Akademie der Wissenschaften, Berlin. *Max Planck in seinen Akademie Ansprachen.* Berlin, 1948.

jn   Planck, Max. *Physikalische Rundblicke. Gesammelte Reden und Aufsätze.* Leipzig, 1922. (Subsequently published as *Wege zur physikalischen Erkenntnis.*)

jo   Planck, Max. *Physikalische Abhandlungen und Vorträge.* 3 vols. Braunschweig, 1958.

jp   Planck, Max. *Izbrannyye trudy: Termodinamika, teoriya otnositel'nosti.* Ed. L. S. Polak. Moscow, 1975.

jq   Planck, Max. *Autobiographie scientifique et derniers écrits.* Ed. André George. Paris, 1960.

jr   Planck, Max. *Vorträge und Erinnerungen* Stuttgart, 1949.

jt   Planck, Max. *Yedinstvo fizicheskoy kartiny mira: Sbornik statey.* Moscow, 1966.

ju   University of California, Berkeley. Office for History of Science and Technology. *Max Planck. A bibliography of his non-technical writings* Berkeley, 1977.

jz   Zhigalova, L. V., and M. I. Radovskiy. "Iz perepiski s russkimi uchenymi." B.pl1.ig, 64-75.

kc   *Ciri, Giuseppe. *Problemi filosofici della scienza fisica: Il realismo di Max Planck* Siena, 1974?

kd   Daisomont, E. H. *Max Planck et la philosophie religieuse* 2nd ed. Bruges, 1943.

kf   Ferguson, Allan. "Prof. Planck and the principle of causality in physics." *Nature, 130* (1932), 45-48.

kg   Hartmann, Hans. "Max Planck im Kampf um seine Grundideen." *NR, 11* (1958), 128-131.

kh   Hartmann, Hans. "Die Gedanken Plancks und Einsteins als Pole künftiger Naturphilosophie." International Congress of the Philosophy of Science, II (1954). *Proceedings, 4* (1955), 124-126.

ki   Heisenberg, Werner. "Otkrytiye Planka i osnovnyye filosofskiye voprosy ucheniya ob atomakh." *Voprosy filosofii,* 1958:11, 61-69.

kl   Herneck, Friedrich. "Bemerkung zur Religiosität Max Plancks." *PB, 16* (1960), 382-384.

km   Jánossy, L. "Plancks philosophische Ansichten in der Physik." B.pl1.ik, 389-407.

ko   Kretzschmar, Hermann. *Max Planck als Philosoph* Munich, 1967.

kp   Kuznetsov, I. V. "Maks Plank i yego bor'ba za nauchnoye mirovozzreniye v yestestvoznanii." *Voprosy filosofii,* 1958:5, 88-101.

kr   *Lankenau, Ehrfried. *Max Planck und die Philosophie* Bonn, 1957.

ks   Lenzen, Victor F. "Planck's philosophy of science." *Men and moments in the history of science* Ed. Herbert M. Evans. Seattle, 1959. Pp. 112-129.

ku   Lewi, Sabina. "O przeciwfenomenalistycznej postawie Maxa Plancka." *KHNT, 12* (1967), 331-340.

kv   Planck, Max. "The concept of causality." Institute of Physics and the Physical Society. *Proceedings, 44* (1932), 529-539.

lc   Reinhardt, R. Rembert. "Vom Geschehen und seinem Gesetz-lichkeit in der unbelebten Natur; mit einem Nachwort zu Max Plancks Wunderauffassung." *Franziskanische Studien, 25* (1938), 354-369.

lg   Sauchkov, Yu. V., and E. M. Chudinov. "Filosofskiye vzglyady M. Planka." B.pl1.jp, 757-761.

lj   Thiele, Joachim. "Einige zeitgenössische Urteile über die Kontroverse zwischen Max Planck und Ernst Mach." *Centaurus, 13* (1968), 85-90.

lp   Vogel, Heinrich. *Zum philosophischen Wirken Max Plancks: Seine Kritik am Positivismus.* Berlin, 1961.

See also: B.mb2.ec, ng; C.ga4.bq, pl; F.bh1.go, it; H.ab1.jp; L.b; R.dc1.fr, hi

Pohl, Robert Wichard (1884-1976)

pm1.ch   Hempstead, Colin A. "Statement from R. Pohl, 25 July 1974." RS. *Proceedings, 371A,* 112-115.

Poincaré, Jules Henri @ (1854-1912)

pm3.ab   Adhémar, Robert, Vicomte d'. *Henri Poincaré.* Paris, 1914.

ad   Anon. *Le livre du centenaire de la naissance de Henri Poincaré, 1854-1954.* Paris, 1955. (Also in B.pm3.jq.)

af   Appell, Paul. *Henri Poincaré (1854-1912).* Paris, 1925.

ag   Bellivier, André. *Henri Poincaré: ou la vocation souveraine.* 2nd ed. Paris, 1956.

al   Lebon, Ernest. *Henri Poincaré; Biographie, bibliographie analytique des ecrits.* Paris, 1909.

ap   Poincaré, Henri. *El legado de Henri Poincaré al siglo XX.* Ed. Desiderio Papp. Buenos Aires, 1944.

as   Sagerat, Jules. *Henri Poincaré.* Paris, 1911.

at   Toulouse, Edouard. *Enquête médico-psychologique sur la supériorité intellectuelle: Henri Poincaré.* Paris, 1896.

av   Volterra, Vito, Jacques Hadamard, Paul Langevin, and Pierre Boutroux. *Henri Poincaré: L'oeuvre scientifique, l'oeuvre philosophique.* Paris, 1914.

aw   *Wright, Susan Presswood. *Henri Poincaré: A developmental study of his philosophical and scientific thought.* Ph.D. diss. Harvard Univ., 1975.

bb   Aleksandrov, P. S. "Poincaré and topology." *Russian mathematical surveys, 27:1* (1972), 157-168.

bd   Appell, P. "Henri Poincaré, en mathématiques spéciales à Nancy." *Acta mathematica, 38* (1921), 189-195.

bf   Broglie, Louis de. "Henri Poincaré et les théories de la physique." Société Astronomique de France. *L'astronomie, 68* (1954), 217-229.

bh   Hadamard, Jacques. "L'oeuvre mathématique de Poincaré." *Acta mathematica, 38* (1921), 203-287.

bl   Langevin, Paul. "Le physicien." B.pm3.av, 115-202.

bn   Lorentz, H. A. "Deux mémoires de Henri Poincaré sur la physique mathématique." *Acta mathematica, 38* (1921), 293-308.

bp   Poincaré, Henri. "Analyse de ses travaux scientifiques." *Acta mathematica, 38* (1921), 3-135.

bs   Sretenskiy, L. N. "Tvorchestvo Anri Puankare." *VIYeT, 15* (1963), 30-46.

bt   Subbotin, M. F. "Raboty Anri Puankare v oblasti nebesnoy mekhaniki." *VIYeT, 2* (1956), 114-123.

bv   Volterra, Vito. "L'oeuvre mathématique." B.pm3.av, 3-49.

bw   Wien, Wilhelm. "Die Bedeutung Henri Poincarés für die Physik." *Acta mathematica, 38* (1921), 289-291.

bz   Zeipel, H. van. "L'oeuvre astronomique d'Henri Poincaré." *Acta mathematica, 38* (1921), 309-385.

cc   Cath, P. G. "Jules Henri Poincaré." *Euclides, 20* (1954/5), 265-275.

cf   Freytag, Otto. "Henri Poincaré." *ZGN, 3* (1937/8), 220-222.

ch   Hadamard, Jacques. "Le centenaire de Henri Poincaré." *RHS, 7* (1954), 101-108.

ck   Kobzarev, I. Yu. "Henri Poincaré's St. Louis lecture and theoretical physics on the eve of the theory of relativity." *SPU, 17* (1975), 584-592.

cl   Lalande, André. "From *Science and Hypothesis* to *Last Thoughts* of H. Poincaré." *JHI, 15* (1954), 596-598.

co   Malgrange, Bernard. "Le centième anniversaire de la naissance d'Henri Poincaré." *La pensée,* no. 58 (1954), 113-115.

cp   Painlevé, Paul. "Henri Poincaré." *Acta mathematica, 38* (1921), 399-402.

cq   *Petruccioli, S. "La fisica dei principi di Henri Poincaré e la 'crisi' delle teorie di fine ottocento." *Alcuni aspetti dello sviluppo delle teorie fisiche, 1743-1911.* Pisa, 1972. Pp. 169-238. (Domas Galilaeana. *Quaderni*

cr   Volterra, Vito. "Henri Poincaré." Rice Institute. *Pamphlets, 1* (1915), 133-162.

eb   B., H. F. "Jules Henri Poincaré." RS. *Proceedings, 91A* (1915), vi-xvi.

ed   "Eloge historique d'Henri Poincaré." AS. *Mémories, 52* (1913), lxxxi-cxlvii.

em   Merlin, Jean. "Henri Poincaré." Astronomische Gesellschaft. *Vierteljahrsschrift, 49* (1914), 3-11.

es   Somigliana, Carlo. "Henri Poincaré." Accademia della scienze, Turin. *Atti, 49* (1914), 45-54.

jb   Boutroux, Pierre. "Lettre [sur Poincaré]." *Acta mathematica, 38* (1921), 197-201.

jk   Nörland, N. E., ed. "Correspondance de Henri Poincaré et de Felix Klein." *Acta mathematica, 39* (1923), 94-132.

jq   Poincaré, Henri. *Oeuvres..* 11 vols. Paris, 1916-56.

jz   Zorin, V. K. "On Poincaré's letter to Brouwer." *Russian mathematical surveys, 27:1* (1972), 166-168.

kb   Boutroux, Pierre. "L'oeuvre philosophique." B.pm3.av, 205-259.

kd   Dantzig, Tobias. *Henri Poincaré, critic of crisis.* NY, 1954.

kg   Giedgmin, Jerzy. "On the origin and significance of Poincaré's conventionalism." *SHPS, 8* (1977), 271-301.

kn   Nye, Mary Jo. "The Boutroux circle and Poincaré's conventionalism." *JHI, 40* (1979), 107-120.

ko   O'Gorman, F. P. "Poincaré's conventionalism of applied geometry." *SHPS, 8* (1977), 303-340.

See also: B.lw3.js; D.cg1.br; F.be1.cu, cv |fc1.ba; L.cc1.mc, pl

Polanyi, Michael (1891-1976)

pm6.es   S[hils], E[dward]. "A great citizen of the republic of science." *Minerva, 14* (1976), 1-5.

ew   Wigner, Eugene P., and R. A. Hodgkin. "Michael Polanyi." RS. *BM, 23* (1977), 413-448.

kl Langford, Thomas A., and William Poteat, ed. *Intellect and hope: Essays in the thought of Michael Polanyi.* Durham, N. C., 1968.

sb Baker, John R. "Michael Polanyi's contributions to the cause of freedom in science." *Minerva, 16* (1978), 382-396.

Pollock, James Arthur (1865-1922)

pm9.et T., R. "James Arthur Pollock." RS. *Proceedings, 104A* (1923), xv-xxii.

Pomeranchuk, Isaak Yakovlevich (1913-1966)

pn3.cb Berestetskiy, V. B. "Isaak Yakovlevich Pomeranchuk." B.pn3.jp, *1*, 7-17.

eb Berestetskiy, V. B. "Isaak Yakovlevich Pomeranchuk." *UFN, 92* (1967), 355-365.

jp Pomeranchuk, Isaak Yakovlevich. *Sobraniye nauchnykh trudov.* Ed. V. B. Berestetskiy. 3 vols. Moscow, 1972.

Popov, Aleksandr Stepanovich @ (1859-1906)

po3.aa *IIYeT. *Aleksandr Stepanovich Popov v kharakteristikakh i vospominaniyakh sovremennikov.* Comp. M. I. Radovskiy. Ed. K. K. Baumgart. Leningrad, 1958.

ab Berg, A. I. *A. S. Popov i izobreteniye radio.* Leningrad, 1935.

ac Berg, A. I., and M. I. Radovskiy. *Aleksandr Stepanovich Popov: K 50-letiyu izobreteniya radio.* Moscow, 1945.

ad Berg, A. I., and M. I. Radovskiy. *Izobretatel' radio A. S. Popov.* Moscow, 1945, 1948, 1950.

ak *Klyatskina, I. G., ed. *A. S. Popov, izobretatel' radio: Zhizn' i deyatel'nost.* Moscow, 1945.

ap *Radovskiy, M. I. *Aleksandr Stepanovich Popov: Biograficheskiy ocherk.* Moscow, 1956.

aq Radovskiy, M. I. *Alexander Popov: Inventor of radio.* Moscow, 1957.

ar Radovskiy, M. I. *Aleksandr Stepanovich Popov: K stoletiyu so dnya rozhdeniya.* Moscow and Leningrad, 1959.

as Radovskiy, M. I. *Aleksandr Stepanovich Popov, 1859-1905.* Moscow, 1963.

av *Vvedenskiy, B. A. *A. S. Popov: Izobretatel' radio.* Moscow and Leningrad, 1948.

ca   Bailey, V. A., and K. Landecker. "On the 'inventor' of radiocommunication." *Australian journal of science, 9* (1947), 126-129.

cb   Berg, A. I. "A. S. Popov—izobretatel' radio." E.tc1.po, 7-58.

cg   Guéorguievsky, N. N. "Les travaux de Popov avant sa découverte de la télégraphie sans fils." *Elektrichestvo, 4:4* (1925), 10-13.

ck   Kaptsov, N. A. "A. S. Popov." C.vb1.th, 163-170.

cl   Kaptsov, N. A. "A. S. Popov." C.vb1.pr, *1*, 264-269.

cn   Lebedinskiy, V. S. "Le professeur Alexandre Stépanovich Popov." *Elektrichestvo, 4:4* (1925), 4-9.

cp   Petrovskiy, A. A. "Le professeur Alexandre Popov devant son auditoire." *Elektrichestvo, 4:4* (1925), 16-17.

ja   *AN. Biblioteka. *Aleksandr Stepanovich Popov: Bibliograficheskiy ukazatel'*. Comp. A. M. Lukomskaya. 2nd ed. Moscow, 1951.

jg   *Golovin, G. I., and R. I. Karlina, ed. *A. S. Popov: Sbornik dokumentov*. Leningrad, 1945.

jk   *K'yandskiy, G. A. [Letters of Popov.] *Radio* (1947:5), 21- .

jm   *IIYeT. *Izobreteniye radio: A. S. Popov; Dokumenty i materialy*. Ed. A. I. Berg. Moscow, 1966.

js   Shertsnev, B. A. "100 let Tsentral'nogo Muzeya Svyazi im A. S. Popova." *VIYeT, 43* (1973), 87-88.

See also: E.tc1.br, os, su | td1.po

Poray-Koshits, Aleksandr Yevgen'yevich (1877-1949)

po5.jm   *Aleksandr Yevgen'yevich Poray-Koshits*. Moscow, 1948. (*Mtly*, ser. khim., 48.)

Porter, Alfred William (1863-1939)

po8.er   Rankine, A. O. "Alfred William Porter." RS. *Obituary notices, 3* (1940), 87-88.

Powell, Cecil Frank @ $50 (1903-1969)

pp3.ef   Frank, F. C., D. H. Perkins, and A. M. Tyndall. "Cecil Frank Powell." RS. *BM, 17* (1971), 541-563.

jc   CSAC. *Cecil Powell papers at Bristol University library.* List 12/6/74, 15 pp.

jp   Powell, Cecil Frank. *Selected papers.* Ed. E. H. S. Burhop, W. O. Lock and M. G. K. Menon. Amsterdam and NY, 1972.

Poynting, John Henry @ (1852-1914)

pq3.cl   Lodge, Oliver, J. J. Thomson, and Joseph Larmor. "[John Henry Poynting]." B.pq3.jp, ix-xxvi.

  et   Thomson, J. J. "John Henry Poynting." RS. *Proceedings, 92A* (1915/6), i-ix.

  jp   Poynting, John Henry. *Collected scientific papers* Cambridge, 1920.

Prandtl, Ludwig @ (1875-1953)

pr1.eb   Busemann, A. "Ludwig Prandtl." RS. *BM, 5* (1959), 193-205.

  gs   Sommerfeld, Arnold. "Zu L. Prandtls 60. Geburtstag." *Zeitschrift für angewandte Mathematik und Mechanik, 15* (1935), 1-2.

See also: D.eb1.pr

Pringsheim, Ernst @ (1859-1917)

pr3.es   Schaefer, Clemens. "Ernst Pringsheim." Schlesische Gesellschaft für vaterländische Kultur. *Jahresbericht, 95:1* (1917), 32-36.

Pringsheim, Peter (1881-1963)

pr5.ef   Franck, James, and R. W. Pohl. "Peter Pringsheim." *PB, 20* (1964), 133-134.

Prokof'yev, Vladimir Konstantinovich (1898-)

ps3.cb   "Vladimir Konstantinovich Prokof'yev." *Optiko-mekhanicheskaya promyshlennost'*, 1958:3, 1-2.

Proudman, Joseph (1888-1975)

pt1.ec   Cartwright, D. E., and F. Ursell. "Joseph Proudman." RS. *BM, 22* (1976), 319-333.

Pulfrich, Carl @ (1858-1927)

pu3.cl   Lacmann, O. "Prof. Dr. Pulfrich." *Archives internationales de photogrammétrie, 7:2* (1932), 1-7.

  cs   Schneider, Friedrich. "Prof. Dr. Carl Pulfrich zu seinem 100. Geburtstag." *Jenaer Rundschau, 3* (1958), 127-128.

  ek   Löwe, F. "Carl Pulfrich." *Zeitschrift für Instrumentenkunde, 47* (1927), 561-567.

  el   Löwe, F. "Carl Pulfrich." Astronomische Gesellschaft. *Vierteljahrsschrift, 63* (1928), 7-12.

See also: G.da1.ma, mb, mc

Pupin, Michael Idvorsky @ (1858-1935)

pv3.ap   Pupin, Michael. *From immigrant to inventor.* NY, 1923.

ed   Davis, Bergen. "Michael Idvorsky Pupin." NAS. *BM, 19* (1938), 307-323.

Quincke, Georg Hermann @ (1834-1924)

qu1.ek   Kalähne, Alfred. "Dem Andenken an Georg Quincke." *PZ, 25* (1924), 649-659.

el   König, Walter. "Georg Hermann Quinckes Leben und Schaffen." *Nwn, 12* (1924), 621-627.

es   S[chuster], A[rthur]. "Georg Hermann Quincke." RS. *Proceedings, 105A* (1924), xiii-xv.

gb   Braun, F. "Hermann G. Quincke zum 70. Geburtstag." *Annalen der Physik, 15* (1904), i-iv.

Rabi, Isidor Isaac $44 (1898-   )

ra3.ar   Rabi, Isidor Isaac. *My life and times as a physicist.* Claremont, Calif., 1960.

cb   Bernstein, Jeremy. "Profiles. Physicist: I. I. Rabi." *New Yorker, 51* (13 Oct. 1975), 47-110; *51* (20 Oct. 1975), 47-101.

gp   Putlitz, Gisbert zu. "Zum 80. Geburtstag von Isidor Isaac Rabi." *PB, 34* (1978), 431-434.

im   Motz, Lloyd, ed. *A Festschrift for I. I. Rabi.* NY, 1977. (New York Academy of Sciences. *Transactions,* 38.)

See also: K.da1.mi

Raman, Chandrasekhara Venkata @ $30 (1888-1970)

ra7.cm   Meggers, W. F. "Sir C. V. Raman." Optical Society of America. *Journal, 31* (1941), 510-511.

eb   Bnagavantam, S. "Chandrasekhara Venkata Raman." RS. *BM, 17* (1971), 565-592.

ef   Broglie, Louis de. "Notice sur la vie et l'oeuvre de Sir Chandrasekhara Venkata Raman." AS. *Notices et discours, 6* (1973), 60-72.

gi   Indian Academy of Sciences. *Sir Chandrasekhara Venkata Raman, 1888—7th November—1948.* Bangalore, 1948.

See also: O.fc1.br

Ramsauer, Carl Wilhelm @ (1879-1955)

rb3.ar   Ramsauer, Carl. *Physik-Technik-Pädagogik. Erfahrungen und Erinnerungen.* Karlsruhe, 1949.

cb   Boeters, Karl-Ernst. "In memoriam Carl Ramsauer." *PB, 35* (1979), 664-666.

cd   Brüche, Ernst. "Erinnerungen an Carl Ramsauer." *PB, 25* (1969), 451-452; *PB, 32* (1976), 405-408.

eb   Brüche, Ernst. "Abschied von Carl Ramsauer." *PB, 12* (1956), 49-54.

gb   Brüche, Ernst. "Carl Ramsauer zum 70. Geburtstag." *PB, 5* (1949), 51-53.

Ramsay, William @ $04C (1852-1916)

rb7.ac   Chaudhuri, Tarini Charan. *Sir William Ramsay as a scientist and man.* Calcutta & London, 1918.

ah   Solov'yev, Yu. I., and L. P. Petrov. *Vil'yam Ramzay, 1852-1916.* Moscow, 1971.

am   Tilden, William A. *Sir William Ramsay, K.C.B., F.R.S.; Memorials of his life and work.* London, 1918.

at   Travers, Morris William. *William Ramsay and University College London.* London, 1952.

au   Travers, Morris William. *A life of Sir William Ramsay, K.C.B., F.R.S.* London, 1956.

bb   Balbiani, Luigi. "L'opera sperimentale di Guglielmo Ramsay." Accademia delle scienze, Turin. *Atti, 52* (1916/7), 29-38.

bh   Havlik, Robert J. "William Ramsay." *Argon. helium, and the rare gases.* Ed. Gerhard A. Cook. Vol. 1, NY, 1961. 17-34.

bt   Taylor, F. Sherwood. "The work of Sir William Ramsay." *American scientist, 41* (1953), 449-452.

ch   Hartley, Harold. "The Ramsay centenary." RS. *Notes and records, 10* (1953), 71-80.

ct   Travers, Morris William. "Ramsay and helium." *Nature, 135* (1935), 619.

cu   Travers, Morris William. "Sir William Ramsay." *Endeavour, 12* (1952), 126-131.

ec   Collie, J. Norman. "Sir William Ramsay." RS. *Proceedings, 93A* (1917), xliii-liv.

eg   Guye, Philippe-A. "Sir William Ramsay." *Journal de chimie physique, 16* (1918), 377-387. (Also in *Revue générale des sciences, 29* (1918), 567-572.)

eh   Harrow, Benjamin. "Sir William Ramsay." *Scientific monthly, 9* (1919), 167-178.

el   Moore, Richard B. "Sir William Ramsay." Franklin Institute. *Journal, 186* (1918), 29-55.

em   Moureu, Charles. "Un grand chimiste, un grand anglais: Sir William Ramsay." *Revue scientifique, 57* (1919), 609-618.

en   Moureu, Charles. "A great chemist: Sir William Ramsay." Smithsonian Institution. *Annual report,* 1919, 531-546.

er   Richards, T. W. "Sir William Ramsay." APS. *Proceedings, 56* (1917), 3-8.

es   Sabatier, Paul. "Sir William Ramsay et son oeuvre." *Revue scientifique, 54* (1916), 609-616.

go   Ostwald, Wilhelm. "Scientific worthies XXXVII: Sir William Ramsay." *Nature, 88* (1912), 339-342.

gp   Ostwald, Wilhelm. "Sir William Ramsay." *Weltall,* Mar. 1914, 156-160.

jr   Ramsay, William. "Pis'mo Y. Ramzaya I. I. Borgmanu." *VIYeT, 29* (1969), 128-129.

jv   Volkova, T. V. "Pis'mo V. Ramzaya k D. I. Mendeleyevu." *Priroda,* 1946:5, 76-81.

See also: B.oc1.cw; R.c

Rankine, Alexander Oliver @ (1881-1956)

rc3.et   Thomson, George P. "Alexander Oliver Rankine." RS. *BM, 2* (1956), 249-255.

Rayleigh *see* **Strutt**

Rebinder, Petr Aleksandrovich (1898-1972)

rc5.jm   *Petr Aleksandrovich Rebinder.* Moscow, 1958; 2nd ed., 1971. (*Mtly,* ser. khim., 27, 45.)

Reczynski, Czeslaw (1878-1936)

rc7.ck   Klemensiewicz, Z. "Czeslaw Reczyński." *Acta physica polonica, 6* (1936), 1-5.

Regener, Erich Rudolf Alexander @ (1881-1955)

rd3.eg   Gerlach, Walther. "Erich Rudolf Alexander Regener." Akademie der Wissenschaften, Munich. *Jahrbuch,* 1956, 222-229.

gb   Bothe, Walther, and Otto Hahn. "Erich Regener zum 70. Geburtstag." *Zeitschrift für Naturforschung, 6a* (1951), 565-569.

Reichenbach, Hans F. @ (1891-1953)

rd7.jr   Reichenbach, Hans. *Selected writings.* Ed. Maria Reichenbach and Robert S. Cohen. 2 vols. Dordrecht, 1978.

Reid, Harry Fielding @ (1859-1944)

re3.eb   Berry, Edward W. "Memorial to Harry Fielding Reid." Geological Society of America. *Proceedings,* 1944, 292-298.

Reynolds, Osborne @ (1842-1912)

re7.bt   Trevena, David H. "Reynolds and the internal cohesion of liquids." *AJP, 47* (1979), 341-345.

cb   Allen, Jack. "The life and work of Osborne Reynolds." *Osborne Reynolds and engineering science today.* Ed. D. M. McDowell and J. D. Jackson. Manchester, 1970. Pp. 1-82.

cg   Gillespie, E. S. "Osborne Reynolds." *PE, 7* (1972), 427-428.

el   Lamb, Horace. "Osborne Reynolds." RS. *Proceedings, 88A* (1912/3), xv-xxi.

See also: D.ec1.gi

Ribaud, Gustav Marcel (1884-1963)

rf3.ek   Kastler, Alfred. "Notice sur la vie et les travaux de Gustav Ribaud." AS. *Notices et discours, 5* (1965), 231-244.

Ricci-Curbastro, Gregorio @ (1853-1925)

rf7.cn   Natucci, A. "Nel primo centanaio della nascità di Gregorio Ricci-Curbastro." *Giornale di matematiche, 2* (1954), 437-442.

ct   Tonolo, Angelo. "Commemorazione di Gregorio Ricci-Curbastro nel primo centenario della nascità." Padua. University. Seminario matematico. *Rendiconti, 23* (1954), 1-24.

el   Levi-Cività, Tullio. "Commemorazione del socio prof. Gregorio Ricci-Curbastro." Accademia nazionale dei Lincei. *Memorie, 1* (1926), 555-567.

Riccò, Annibale @ (1844-1919)
See: C.ic1.ab

Richardson, Owen Willans @ $28 (1879-1959)
rg5.ew   Wilson, William. "Owen Willans Richardson." RS. *BM, 5* (1959), 207-215.

Richtmeyer, Floyd Karker @ (1881-1939)
rg7.ei   Ives, Herbert E. "Floyd Karker Richtmeyer." NAS. *BM, 22* (1941), 71-81.

  pa   Andrews, C. L. "Memories of a great teacher." *PTeach, 14* (1976), 27-29.

Riecke, Eduard @ (1845-1915)
rh3.ev   Voigt, Woldemar. "Eduard Riecke als Physiker." *PZ, 16* (1915), 219-221.

Righi, Augusto @ (1850-1920)
rh7.bb   Amaduzzi, Lavoro. "L'oeuvre scientifique d'Augusto Righi." *Scientia, 28* (1920), 467-472.

  ca   *Angelini, A. M. "Rievocazione di Augusto Righi." *Elettrotecnica, 58* (1971), 57-75.

  cg   Graffi, Dario. "Nel 50° aniversario della morte di A. Righi." Accademia della scienze dell'Istituto di Bologna. *Rendiconti, 8* (1971), 34-42.

  ct   Tabarroni, Giorgio. "La formazione di Augusto Righi nella Bologna di un secolo fa." *Strenna storica bolognese, 19* (1969), 271-292.

  cv   *Valle, G. "Discorso commemorativo di Augusto Righi." *Elettrotecnica, 37* (1950), 483-487.

  eb   Amaduzzi, Lavoro. "Augusto Righi." *Archiginnasio, 15* (1920), 222-226.

  ec   *Amaduzzi, Lavoro. "Commemorazione di A. Righi." *Elettrotecnica, 8* (1921), 62-68.

  ee   Cardani, Pietro. "In memoria di Augusto Righi." *Nuovo cimento, 21* (1921), 51-186.

  ef   Corbino, O. M. "Commemorazione del socio Righi Augusto." Accademia dei Lincei. Classe di scienze fisiche. *Atti 30:1* (1921), 215-221.

jr　*Righi, Augusto. *Scelta di scritti.* Ed. G. C. della Noce and G. Valle. Bologna, 1950.

See also: E.tc1.ta; G.qa1.ti

Ritz, Walther @ (1878-1909)

ri3.cf　Forman, Paul. "Ritz, Walther." *DSB, 11* (1975), 475-481.

ch　Hagenbach, August. "J. J. Balmer und W. Ritz." *Nwn, 9* (1921), 451-455.

cw　Weiss, Pierre. "[Biographical] Préface." B.ri3.jr, vii-xxii.

ef　Fueter, Rudolf. "Walter Ritz." Schweizerische Naturforschende Gesellschaft. *Verhandlungen, 92* (1909), 96-104.

jr　Ritz, Walther. *Gesammelte Werke—Oeuvres.* Paris, 1911.

Robb, Alfred Arthur (1873-1936)

rj3.el　Larmor, Joseph. "Alfred Arthur Robb." RS. *Obituary notices, 2* (1938) 315-321.

See also: F.cd1.br

Robertson, Howard Percy (1903-1961)

rj7.eg　Greenstein, Jesse L., and Frederick Seitz. "Howard Percy Robertson." NAS. *BM, 51* (1980), 343-364.

Robinson, Harold Roper (1889-1955)

rk3.eb　Andrade, E. N. da C. "Harold Roper Robinson." RS. *BM, 3* (1957), 161-172.

Rodebush, Worth Hoff (1887-1959)

rk4.em　Marvell, Carl S., and Frederick T. Wall. "Worth Huff Rodebush." NAS. *BM, 36* (1962), 277-288.

Röntgen, Wilhelm Conrad @ $01 (1845-1923)

rk7.ag　Glasser, Otto. *Wilhelm Conrad Röntgen and the early history of the Röntgen rays.* London, 1934. (German edn, Berlin, 1931.)

ah　Glasser, Otto. *Wilhelm Conrad Röntgen und die Geschichte der Röntgenstrahlen.* 2nd ed. Berlin, 1959.

aj　Glasser, Otto. *Dr. W. C. Röntgen.* 2nd ed. Springfield, Ill., 1958.

am　Nicolle, Jacques. *Röntgen.* Paris, 1965.

an   Nicolle, Jacques. *W. C. Röntgen (1845-1923) et l'ère des rayons X.* Paris, 1967. (Paris. Palais de la Découverte. *Conferences, D115.*)

ap   Nitske, W. Robert. *The life of Wilhelm Conrad Röntgen, discoverer of the x-ray.* Tucson, 1971.

aq   Otremba, Heinz. *Wilhelm Conrad Röntgen; ein Leben in Dienste der Wissenschaft; eine Dokumentation.* Würzburg, 1965.

as   *Schreus, Hans Theo. *W. C. Röntgen, Entdecker neuer Strahlen: Ein kritischer Essay.* Düsseldorf, 1964.

at   Streller, Ernst, Rolf Winau, and Armin Hermann. *Wilhelm Conrad Röntgen.* Bonn, 1973.

bc   Chaston, J. C. "Discoveries by accident." *Nature, 151* (1943), 55.

bg   Gerlach, Walther. "W. C. Röntgen, der Forscher und sein Werk in der Auswirkung für die Entwicklung der exakten Naturwissenschaften." *Strahlentherapie, 47* (1933), 3-11.

bi   Ioffe, A. F. "Istoricheskoye znacheniye otkrytiya Rentgena." AN. *Izvestiya,* ser. fiz., *10* (1946), 343-349.

br   Romer, Alfred. "Accident and Professor Röntgen." *AJP, 27* (1959), 275-277.

bs   Soto, Oscar. "Roentgen y su obra." Sociedad Peruana de Historia de la Medicina. *Anales, 8* (1946), 9-27.

bt   Tomas, V. K. "Pervyye otkliki na otkrytiye Rentgena." *VIYeT, 32* (1970), 57-58.

bw   Winau, Rolf. "Röntgens Entdeckung und die Medizin." B.rk7.at, 21-52.

by   Zehnder, Ludwig. "W. C. Röntgen und seine Entdeckung der X-Strahlen." *Radiologica clinica, 14* (1945), 1-9.

ca   Andreae, Horst. "Wilhelm Conrad Röntgen starb vor 50 Jahren." *PB, 29* (1973), 85-86.

cb   Boveri, Margret. "Persönliches über W. C. Röntgen." B.rk7.ah, 117-175.

cf   *Dillon, Ya. G. "Vil'gel'm Konrad Rentgen." *Klinicheskaya meditsina, 16* (1938), 1460-1462.

ch   Evers, G. A., and E. Wölfflin. "De nederlandsche periode von Wilhelm Conrad Röntgen." *Natuur en mensch, 51* (1931), 159-161; *52* (1932), 33-35.

cj   Garin, G. "Yubiley Rentgena v 'Tret'yey imperii.'" *Arkhiv istorii nauki i tekhniki, 8* (1936), 301-309.

cl *Gerlach, Walther. [W. C. Röntgen]. Röntgen, *Über eine neue Art von Strahlen.* Ed. Fritz Kraft. Munich, 1972.

cm Glasser, Otto. "The human side of science." *Cleveland clinical quarterly, 20* (1953), 400-406.

cn Hahn, K. "Erinnerungen an Röntgen und Drude." *PB, 1* (1944), 95-96.

cp Heuss, Theodor. "Conrad Wilhelm Röntgen." *PB, 6* (1950), 49-51.

cr *Ioffe, A. F. "Vil'gel'm Konrad Rentgen." Röntgen. *O novom rode luchey.* Ed. Ioffe. Moscow and Leningrad, 1933. Pp. 5-24.

cs Ioffe, A. F. "Vil'gel'm Konrad Rentgen, 1845-1923." *Priroda,* 1938:2, 107-112.

ct Ioffe, A. F. "Vospominaniya o Vil'gel'me Konrade Rentgene." *Ocherki razvitiya meditsinskoy rentgenologii.* Moscow, 1948. Pp. 29-38.

cu Ioffe, A. F. "Vil'gel'm Konrad Rentgen." A.aj1.io, 188-196.

cw Kolomý, Rudolf. "K di'lu W. C. Röntgena." *Djiny vêd a techniky, 9* (1976), 160-175.

cx Krafft, Ernest. "W. C. Roentgen, his friendship with Ludwig Zehnder." *New York State journal of medicine, 73* (1973), 1002-1008.

db Krause, Paul. *Röntgen-Gedächtnis-Heft anlässlich der Enthüllungsfeier des Röntgendenkmals in Lennep am 29. u. 30. November 1930. (Arbeiten zur Kenntnis der Geschichte der Medizin im Rheinland und in Westfalen,* 8.)

dg Laue, Max von. "Zum Gedächtnis Wilhelm Conrad Röntgens." *Nwn, 33* (1946), 3-7. (Also in B.lf6.jl, *3,* 193-197.)

dn *Roffo, Angel H. "Guillermo Conrado Roentgen. En el primer centenario de su nacimiento." *Revista argentina de historia de la medicina, 4* (1945), 5-21.

do Schimank, H. "Wilhelm Conrad Röntgen." *PB, 2* (1946), 55-56.

dp Schinz, H. R. "Röntgen und Zürich, aus alten Akten." *Acta radiologica, 15* (1934), 562-575.

ds Sirkar, S. C. "Birth centenary of Wilhelm Konrad Röntgen." *Science and culture, 11* (1945), 283-286.

dt Streller, Ernst. "Röntgens Leben und Werk." B.rk7.at, 5-20.

dv Wölfflin, Ernst. "Personal recollections of Wilhelm Conrad Röntgen." *Ciba symposium, 5* (1957), 111-119.

dw   Yakovenko, E. I. "Iz vospominaniy Yakovenko: Chestvovaniye Vil'gel'ma Konrada Rentgena v Vyurtsburge." *Ocherki razvitiya meditsinskoy rentgenologii.* Moscow, 1948. Pp. 26-28.

dx   Zehnder, Ludwig. "Persönliche Erinnerungen an W. C. Röntgen und über die Entwicklung der Röntgenröhren." *Helvetica physica acta, 6* (1933), 608-632. (In French in Institut Adrien Guébhard-Séverine. *Annales, 9* (1933), 351-364.)

ef   Friedrich, Walther. "Wilhelm Konrad Röntgen." *PZ, 24* (1923), 353-360.

ei   Ioffe, A. F. "Vil'gel'm Konrad Rentgen." *UFN, 4* (1924), 1-10.

ew   Wien, Wilhelm. "Röntgen." *Annalen der Physik, 70* (1923), between 332 and 333, 4 p.

gb   Akademie der Wissenschaften, Berlin. "Adresse an Hrn. W. C. Röntgen zum 50. Doktorjubiläum." Akademie der Wissenschaften, Berlin. *Sitzungsberichte,* 1919:1, 522-524.

jg   Glasser, Otto. "The life of Wilhelm Conrad Röntgen as revealed in his letters." *Scientific monthly, 45* (1937), 193-206.

jk   Klickstein, Herbert S. *Wilhelm Conrad Röntgen on a new kind of rays: A bibliographical study.* [St. Louis], 1966. (*Mallinkrodt classics of radiology,* 1.)

jm   Krebs, Hans. "Two letters by Wilhelm Conrad Röntgen." RS. *Notes and records, 28* (1973), 83-92.

jr   Tomas, V. K. "Tri pis'ma russkikh fizikov V. K. Rentgenu." *UFN, 90* (1966), 541-544.

js   Tomas, V. K. "Three letters of Russian physicists to W. K. Roentgen." *SPU, 9* (1967), 913-915.

jt   Tomas, V. K. "Nemetskiy muzey Rentgena." *VIYeT, 32* (1970), 58-59.

jy   Zehnder, Ludwig. *W. C. Röntgen, Briefe an L. Zehnder.* Zurich 1935.

pk   Kuhn, Karl. "Erinnerungen an die Vorlesungen von W. C. Röntgen und L. Grätz." *PB, 18* (1962), 314-316.

See also: A.cc1.st |pe1.kn; G.k; G.l

Ronchi, Vasco (1897-   )

rl3.kt   *Trogu, Gianni. "Vasco Ronchi's revolution in optics." *Telos, 8* (1971), 3-20.

Rood, Ogden Nicholas @ (1831-1902)

rl7.cn   Nichols, Edward L. "Ogden Nicholas Rood." NAS. *BM, 6* (1909), 447-472.

Roozeboom, Hendrik Willem Bakhuis @ (1854-1907)

rm3.ch   *Hooykaas, R. [H. W. B. Roozeboom]. *Geloof en wetenschap, 53* (1955), 68-77.

eb   Bemmelen, J. M. van. "Het leven en de werken van H. W. Bakhuis Roozeboom in zijnen Leidschen tijd." *Chemisch weekblad, 4* (1907), 249-285.

eh   Holleman, A. F. "H. W. Bakhuis Roozeboom." *Chemisch weekblad, 4* (1907), 119-132.

es   Stortenbeker, W. "Henri-Guillaume Bakhuis Roozeboom." *Recueil des travaux chimiques des Pays-Bas et de la Belgique, 27* (1908), 360-410.

Rosen, Louis (1918-   )

rm7.cr   Rosen, Louis. "A scientific autobiography." *Adventures in experimental physics, 5* (1976), 74-75.

Rosenberg, Hans Oswald @ (1879-1940)

rn3.cg   *Gleissberg, W. "Hans Rosenberg." İstanbul. University. Orman Fakültesi. *Yayinlari, 13* (1940), - .

Rosenfeld, Léon (1904-1975)

rn7.cp   Rosenfeld, Léon. [Interview.] A.ajl.bu, 17-33.

cr   Rosenfeld, Léon. "My initiation." *BSPS, 21* (1979), xxxi-xxxiv.

jr   Rosenfeld, Léon. *Selected papers* Ed. R. S. Cohen and J. J. Stachel. Dordrecht, 1979. (*BSPS, 21.*)

See also: I.dal.rp; L.hal.ro |hdl.ta

Rowland, Henry Augustus @ (1848-1901)

ro3.am   *Miller, John David. *Henry Augustus Rowland and his electromagnetic researches.* Ph.D. thesis. Oregon State Univ., 1970. (*DAI, 30,* 5391A.)

cc   Crew, Henry. "Some recollections of Henry A. Rowland, 1848-1901." *AJP, 17* (1949), 576-577.

cr   Reid, Harry Fielding. "A great American physicist: Henry Augustus Rowland." *AJP, 9* (1941), 117-119.

cs   Rezneck, Samuel. "The education of an American scientist: H. A. Rowland 1848-1901." *AJP, 28* (1960) 155-162.

ct   Rezneck, Samuel. "An American physicist's year in Europe: Henry Rowland, 1875-1876." *AJP, 30* (1962), 877-886.

em   Mendenhall, Thomas C. "Henry Augustus Rowland." NAS. *BM, 5* (1905), 115-140.

See also: E.bd1.mi

Rozenberg, L. D. (1908-   )

ro4.gb   Anon. "L. D. Rozenberg." *Akusticheskiy zhurnal, 4* (1958), 290-291.

Rozhanskiy, Dmitriy Apollinariyevich (1882-1936)

ro6.cd   Anon. "Pamyati Dmitriya Apollinariyevicha Rozhanskogo." *Radiotekhnika, 16:9* (1961), 68-69.

cp   *Polyakova, N. L. "Dmitriy Apollinariyevich Rozhanskiy." Kharkov. University. *Uchenyye zapiski, 49* (1953), 5-15.

Rozhdestvenskiy, Dmitriy Sergeyevich (1876-1940)

ro7.af   Frish, S. E. *Dmitriy Sergeyevich Rozhdestvenskiy: Zhizn' i deyatel'nost'.* Leningrad, 1954.

ag   Frish, S. E., and A. I. Stozharov, eds. *Vospominaniya ob akademike D. S. Rozhdestvenskom: K 100-letiyu so dnya rozhdeniya.* Leningrad, 1976.

bo   *Osinovskiy, A. N. "D. S. Rozhdestvenskiy—borets za nerazryvnuyu svyaz' nauki s proizvodstvom." A.bh1.vo, 81-89.

cf   Frish, S. E. "Dmitriy Sergeyevich Rozhdestvenskiy." *UFN, 44* (1951), 238-254.

cg   Frish, S. E. "On the centenary of the birth of D. S. Rozhdestvenskii." *SPU, 19* (1976), 275-284. (Also in *UFN, 118* (1976), 565-582.)

co   *Osinovskiy, A. N. *Akademik D. S. Rozhdestvenskiy i yego rol' v razvitii sovetskoy fiziki.* Moscow, 1954. (Summary of thesis for Moscow Pedagogicheskiy Institut.)

eb   Baumgart, K. K. "Dmitriy Sergeyevich Rozhdestvenskiy." *UFN, 25* (1941), 230-240.

jo   Osinovskiy, A. N., and A. M. Tolmacheva. "Osnovnyye daty zhizni i nauchnoy deyatel'nosti akademika D. S. Rozhdestvenskogo (arkhivnyye materialy)." *IMYeN, 8* (1970), 250-270.

jr   Rozhdestvenskiy, D. S. *Izbrannyye trudy.* Leningrad, 1964.

nb   *Baumgart, K. K. "Professor universiteta Dmitriy Sergeyevich Rozhdestvenskiy: Osnovatel' Gosudarstvennogo opticheskogo instituta." Leningrad. Gosudarstvennyy opticheskiy institut. *Trudy, 24* (1957), 65-73.

See also: C.vl2.fr; G.dal.ga, le, li, lj |ea4.ro |hal.fr, kv, te; H.cfl.fr

Rubens, Heinrich @ (1865-1922)

rp3.cw   Westphal, Wilhelm H. "Dem Andenken an Heinrich Rubens zur 30. Wiederkehr seines Todestages." *PB, 8* (1952), 323-324.

ef   Franck, James, and Robert Pohl. "Heinrich Rubens." *PZ, 23* (1922), 377-382.

eg   Franck, James. "Heinrich Rubens." DPG. *Verhandlungen, 3* (1922), 76-91.

ep   Planck, Max. "Gedächtnisrede auf Heinrich Rubens." Akademie der Wissenschaften, Berlin. Phil.-Hist. Klasse. *Sitzungsberichte,* 1923, cviii-cxiii.

er   Regener, E. "Rubens und die Experimentierkunst." *Nwn, 10* (1922), 1021-1024.

ew   Westphal, Wilhelm H. "Heinrich Rubens." *Nwn, 10* (1922), 1017-1020.

See also: E.abl.he; G.fa2.ba, kd, kf; L.cal.fr, he

Rüdenberg, Reinhold @ (1883-1961)

rq3.eh   Hieronimus, Ekkehard. "Reinhold Rüdenberg." *Leben und Schicksal: Zur Einweihung der Synagoge in Hannover.* Hanover, 1963. Pp. 143-149.

gj   Jacottet, P., and R. Strigel. "Reinhold Rüdenberg zum 75. Geburtstag." *Elektrotechnische Zeitschrift, 79:4* (1958), 97-100.

Runge, Carl David Tolmé @ (1856-1927)

rr3.ar   Runge, Iris. *Carl Runge und sein wissenschaftliches Werk.* Göttingen, 1949. (Akademie der Wissenschaften, Göttingen. Math.-Phys. Klasse. *Abhandlungen,* 23.)

cf   Forman, Paul. "Runge, Carl David Tolmé." *DSB, 11* (1975), 610-615.

ec   Courant, Richard. "Carl Runge als Mathematiker." *Nwn, 15* (1927), 229-231.

ek   Kienle, Hans. "Carl Runge." Astronomische Gesellschaft, Leipzig. *Vierteljahrsschrift, 62* (1927), 173-177.

ep   Paschen, Friedrich. "Carl Runge." *Astrophysical journal, 69* (1929), 317-321.

eq   Paschen, Friedrich. "Carl Runge als Spektroskopiker." *Nwn, 15* (1927), 231-233.

es   Prandtl, Ludwig. "Carl Runge." Akademie der Wissenschaften, Göttingen. *Jahrbuch,* 1926/7, 58-62.

Russell, Henry Norris (1877-1957)

rs3.bh   Hunter, A., and E. G. Martin. "Fifty years of trigonometrical parallaxes." *Vistas in astronomy, 2* (1956), 1023-1030.

ck   Kron, Katherine G. "Henry Norris Russell (1877-1957): Some recollections." *Vistas in astronomy, 12* (1970), 3-6.

em   Menzel, Donald H. "Henry Norris Russell." APS. *Yearbook,* 1958, 139-143.

es   Shapley, Harlow. "Henry Norris Russell." NAS. *BM, 32* (1958), 354-378.

eu   Stratton, F. J. M. "Henry Norris Russell." RS. *BM, 3* (1957), 173-191.

See also: P.hb1 |ib1.sz

Rutherford, Ernest @ $08C (1871-1937)

ru1.ab   Allibone, Thomas E. *Rutherford: The father of nuclear energy.* Manchester, 1973.

ac   Andrade, E. N. da C. *Rutherford and the nature of the atom.* Garden City, NY, 1964.

ad   Birks, J. B., ed. *Rutherford at Manchester.* London, 1962. (Rutherford Jubilee International Conference. *Proceedings.*)

ae   Bunge, M., and W. Shea, eds. *Rutherford and physics at the turn of the century.* NY and Folkstone, 1979.

af   Crowther, James G. *Ernest Rutherford.* London, 1972.

ag   Danin, D. S. *Rezerford.* Moscow, 1966. (*Zhizn' zamechatel'nykh lyudey; seriya biografiy, 18.*)

ai   Evans, Ivor B. N. *Man of power: The life story of Baron Rutherford of Nelson, O.M., F.R.S.* London, 1939; 1943.

aj   Eve, Arthur S. *Rutherford: Being the life and letters of the Rt. Hon. Lord Rutherford, O.M.* NY, 1939.

ak   Feather, Norman. *Lord Rutherford.* London, 1940; reprinted 1973.

al   *Kapitsa, P. L. *Zhizn' dlya nauki: Lomonosov, Franklin, Rezerford, Lanzheven.* Moscow, 1965.

an   Kedrov, Fedor Borisovich. *Ernest Rezerford* Moscow, 1965.

ao   Kelman, Peter, and A. Harris Stone. *Ernest Rutherford: Architect of the atom* Englewood Cliffs, N.J., 1969.

ap   *Mann, Frederick George. *Lord Rutherford on the golf course.* Cambridge, 1976.

aq   McKown, Robin. *Giant of the atom, Ernest Rutherford* NY, 1962.

ar   Moon, P. B. *Ernest Rutherford and the atom* London, 1974.

as   Oliphant, Mark. *Rutherford: Recollections of the Cambridge days.* NY, 1972.

au   Rowland, John. *Ernest Rutherford: Atom pioneer.* NY, 1957.

av   Rowland, John. *Ernest Rutherford: Master of the atom* London, 1964.

aw   *Rutherford by those who knew him. Being the collection of the first five Rutherford lectures of the Physical Society.* London, 1954.

ax   Shire, Edward S. *Rutherford and the nuclear atom* London, 1972.

ay   Starosel'skaya-Nikitina, O. A. *Ernest Rezerford, 1871-1937.* Moscow, 1967.

bb   Badash, Lawrence. "The origins of big science: Rutherford at McGill." B.rul.ae, 23-41.

bc   Br[üche, Ernst]. "Helmholtz und Rutherford." *PB, 4* (1948), 21-22.

bd   Burcham, W. E. "Rutherford at Manchester, 1907-1919." *Contemporary physics, 5* (1964), 304-308.

bf   Devons, Samuel. "Recollections of Rutherford and the Cavendish." *PT, 24* (Dec. 1971), 39-45.

bg   Geake, J. E. "Rutherford in Manchester." *CP, 3* (1961), 155-158.

bj   Jaki, Stanley. "The reality beneath: The world view of Rutherford." B.rul.ae, 110-123.

bl   Marsden, Ernest. "Rutherford: His life and work, 1871-1937." RS. *Proceedings, 226A* (1954), 283-305.

bm   Mott, Nevill F. "Rutherford and theory " RS. *Notes and records, 27* (1972), 65-66.

br   Robinson, H. R. "Rutherford: Life and work to the year 1919." *Nature, 150* 1942), 591-593.

bs   Thomson, George P. "Rutherford in nineteenth-century Cambridge." RS. *Proceedings, 283A* (1965), 481-490.

bt   Trenn, Thaddeus J. "Rutherford in the McGill Physical Laboratory." B.rul.ae, 89-109.

ca   Andrade, E. N. da C. "Rutherford at Manchester." B.rul.ad, 27-44.

cb   Andrade, E. N. da C. "Some reminiscences of Ernest Marsden's days with Rutherford at Manchester." RS. *Notes and records, 23* (1968), 247-250.

cc   Anon. "Ernest Rutherford (1871-1937)." *PTeach,* 9 (1971), 382-383.

cd   Anon. "A memorial to Ernest Rutherford." *Endeavour, 10* (Jan. 1951), 3-4.

ce   Badash, Lawrence. "The importance of being Ernest Rutherford." *Science, 173* (1971), 873.

cf   Blackett, P. M. S. "The Rutherford Memorial Lecture, 1958." RS. *Proceedings, 251A* (1959), 293-305.

cg   Blackett, P. M. S. "Memories of Rutherford." B.rul.ad, 102-113.

ch   Blackett, P. M. S. "Rutherford." RS. *Notes and records, 27* (1972), 57-59.

ci   Bohr, Niels. "Reminiscences of the founder of nuclear science and of some developments based on his work." RS. *Proceedings, 78* (1961), 1083-1115. (Also in B.bol.je, 30-73, and B.rul.ad, 114-167.)

cj   Bohr, Niels. "Vospominaniya ob E. Rezerforde, osnovopolozhnike nauki o yadre: Dal'neysheye razvitiye yego rabot." *UFN, 80* (1963), 215-250.

ck   Bronson, H. L., and Otto Hahn. "Some reminiscences of Professor Ernest Rutherford during his time at McGill University, Montreal." B.rul.jn, 163-168.

cm   Dale, Henry. "Some personal memories of Lord Rutherford of Nelson." *Cawthron Lecture Series,* no. 25 (1950).

cn   Dee, P. I. "The Rutherford memorial." *Nature, 166* (1950), 917-919.

cp   Feather, Norman. "Ernest Rutherford." A.pc1.lu, 189-215.

cq   Feather, Norman. "Rutherford—Faraday—Newton." RS. *Notes and records, 27* (1972), 45-55.

cr   Geiger, Hans, E. N. da C. Andrade, and A. D. Wood. "Some reminiscences of Rutherford during his time in Manchester." B.rul.jn, 295-311.

cs   Jacobs, D. J. "Lord Rutherford." *PE, 7* (1972), 170-172.

cu Kapitsa, P. L. "Vospominaniya o Prof. E. Rezerforde." *UFN, 19* (1938), 1-17.

cv Kapitsa, P. L. "Recollections of Lord Rutherford." RS. *Proceedings, A294* (1966), 123-137. (Original in Russian in *Novyy mir,* 1966:8, 205-215.)

cw Kapitsa, P. L. "Recollections of Lord Rutherford." *Nature, 210* (1966), 780-783.

cx Kapitsa, P. L. "Recollections of Lord Rutherford." A.ad1.me, 749-765.

cy Kapitsa, P. L. "Rutherford and creativity in science." *New scientist, 51* (1971), 639-640.

cz Kapitsa, P. L. "Nauchnaya deyatel'nost' Rezerforda. Moi vospominaniya o Rezerforde." B.ru1.jq, 495-516.

dc Kay, William Alexander. "Recollections of Rutherford. Being the personal reminiscences of Lord Rutherford's laboratory assistant published for the first time." *Natural philosopher, 1* (1963), 129-155.

dd Keys, David A. "Rutherford and nuclear power." *Nature, 197* (1963), 842-843.

de Kedrov, B. M. "Droga geniusze—droga myśli ludzkiej (W stulecie urodzin Ernesta Rutherforda)." *KHNT, 17* (1972), 219-226.

dg Leibfried, Günther. "Sir Ernest Rutherford, der Begründer der Atom- und Kernphysik." A.aj1.sc, 63-70.

dh Lewis, W. Bennett. "Some recollections and reflections on Rutherford." RS. *Notes and records, 27* (1972), 61-63.

dj Marsden, Ernest. "Rutherford Memorial Lecture (1948)." Institute of Physics and the Physical Society. *Proceedings, 63A* (1950), 305-322.

dk *Marsden, Ernest. "Rutherford the man." *New Zealand science review, 9:7* (1951), 113- .

dl Marsden, Ernest. "Rutherford at Manchester." B.ru1.ad, 1-16.

dn Oliphant, Mark L. "Some personal recollections of Rutherford, the man." RS. *Notes and records, 27* (1972), 7-23.

do Oliphant, Mark L. "The two Ernests—I." *PT, 19* (Sep. 1966), 35-49.

dp Oliphant, Mark L. "The two Ernests—II." *PT, 19* (Oct. 1966), 41-51.

dr O'Shea, P. P. "Ernest Rutherford: His honors and distinctions." RS. *Notes and records, 27* (1972), 67-74.

ds   Regato, J. A. del. "Ernest Rutherford." *International journal of radiation oncology and biological physics, 5* (1979), 539-552.

dt   Robinson, H. R. "Rutherford: Life and work to the year 1919, with personal reminiscences of the Manchester period." B.ru1.ad, 53-86.

du   Russell, A. S. "Lord Rutherford: Manchester, 1907-1919." B.ru1.ad, 87-101.

dv   Rutherford Centenary Celebration. RS. *Notes and records, 27* (1972), 1-74.

dx   Snow, C. P. "The age of Rutherford." *Atlantic monthly, 202* (Nov. 1958), 76-81.

dy   Tizard, Henry. "Lord Rutherford." RS. *Notes and records, 4* (1966), 103-108.

dz   Tizard, Henry. "The Rutherford memorial lectures." Chemical Society. *Journal*, 1946, 980-986.

eb   Burton, E. F. "Ernest Rutherford." *University of Toronto quarterly, 7* (1938), 329-338.

ed   Eve, Arthur S., and James Chadwick. "Ernest Rutherford." RS. *Obituary notices, 2* (1938), 395-423.

ee   Eve, Arthur S., et al. "The Right Hon. Lord Rutherford of Nelson, O.M., F.R.S." *Nature, 140* (1937), 746-754; *141* (1938), 244.

ef   Farr, C. C., et al. "Ernest Rutherford." Physical Society of London. *Proceedings, 50* (1938), 441-466.

eg   Geiger, Hans. "Das Lebenswerk von Lord Rutherford of Nelson." *Nwn, 26* (1938), 161-164.

eh   Geiger, Hans. "Lord Rutherford zum Gedächtnis." Akademie der Wissenschaften, Göttingen. *Nachrichten: Geschäftliche Mitteilungen,* 1937-38, 19-25.

ei   Gueben, Georges. "Lord Rutherford of Nelson." *Revue des questions scientifiques, 113* (1938), 5-19.

em   Marsden, Ernest, and C. M. Focken. "Baron Rutherford of Nelson." Royal Society of New Zealand. *Transactions and proceedings, 68* (1938), 4-25.

eo   Meyer, Stefan, et al. "Further tributes to the late Lord Rutherford." *Nature, 140*:suppl. (1937), 1047-1054.

gb   Bohr, Niels. "Sir Ernest Rutherford." *Nature, 118*:suppl. (1926), 51-52.

gd Broglie, Maurice de. "Scientific worthies: The Right Hon. Lord Rutherford of Nelson." *Nature, 129* (1932), 665-669.

gf Crowther, J. G. "Lord Rutherford." *Great contemporaries.* London, 1935. Pp. 359-370.

gh Hahn, Otto, and Lise Meitner. "Lord Rutherford zum sechzigsten Geburtstag." *Nwn, 19* (1931), 729.

jb Badash, Lawrence, ed. *Rutherford and Boltwood: Letters on radioactivity.* New Haven, 1969.

jc Badash, Lawrence. *Rutherford correspondence catalog.* NY, 1974. (American Institute of Physics. Center for History of Physics. *Report,* 3.)

jd Bond, Elizabeth B., and W. L. Bragg. "The Rutherford papers in the library of the Cavendish Laboratory." *Nature, 158* (1946), 714.

jf Kapitsa, P. L., ed. *Rezerford, uchenyy i uchitel': K 100-letiyu so dnya rozhdenia, sbornik statey.* Moscow, 1973.

ji Birks, J. B. "The publications of the late Lord Rutherford." B.rul.ad, 316-333.

jn Rutherford, Ernest. *Collected papers.* Ed. James Chadwick. 3 vols. London, 1962-1965.

jo Feather, Norman. "An essay-review of volume one of Rutherford's collected papers." *CP, 4* (1962), 73-76.

jq Rutherford, Ernest. *Izbrannyye nauchnyye trudy: Stroyeniye atoma i iskusstvennoye prevrashcheniye elementov.* Moscow, 1972.

jr "Rutherford's den." Canterbury, New Zealand. University. *Chronicle, 13:15* (1978), 2.

jt Taranaki, New Zealand. *Herald.* [Excerpts from letters among members of Ernest Rutherford's family.] Aug.-Sep., 1935.

ju Terroux, F. R. "The Rutherford collection of apparatus at McGill University." Royal Society of Canada. Section III. *Transactions, 32* (1938), 9-16.

jv University of California, Berkeley. Office for History of Science and Technology. *Ernest Rutherford. A bibliography of his nontechnical writings.* Berkeley, 1979.

pf Fainbaum, Iosif. "Rutherfords russische Schüler." *Ideen des exakten Wissens,* 1971, 731-737.

See also: C.bm1.sh |cc1.he; H.bf; I.bd; I.bf; I.ra; I.rb; P.da1.ba; T.gb1.tq

Rydberg, Johannes Robert @ (1854-1919)

rv3.cm   Meggers, William F. "Opening address [of Rydberg centennial conference on atomic spectroscopy]." Lund. University. *Årsskrift, Avd. 2, 50:21* (1954), 13-14.

    cn   Nepomucene, Sister St. John. "Rydberg: The man and the constant." *Chymia, 6* (1960), 127-145.

See also: H.gc1.pa

Rytov, Sergey Mikhaylovich (1908-   )

ry3.ga   Akhmanov, S. A., et al. "Sergei Mikhailovich Rytov (on his seventieth birthday)." *SPU, 21* (1978), 643-644.

Rzhevkin, Sergey Nikolayevich (1891-   )

rz3.gb   "Sergey Nikolayevich Rzhevkin." *Akusticheskiy zhurnal, 7* (1961), 503-504.

Sabine, Wallace Clement Ware @ (1868-1919)

sa3.ao   Orcutt, William Dane. *Wallace Clement Sabine: A study in achievement.* Norwood, Mass., 1933.

    eh   Hall, Edwin H. "Wallace Clement Ware Sabine." NAS. *BM, 11* (1924), 19 p.

    js   Sabine, Wallace Clement. *Collected papers on acoustics.* Cambridge, Mass., 1927.

Sadovskiy, Mikhail Aleksandrovich (1932-   )

See: G.qa1.ma

Sagnac, Georges M. M. @ (1869-1928)

sa9.cc   Chappell, John E., Jr. "Georges Sagnac and the discovery of the ether." *AIHS*, no. 72-73 (1965), 175-190.

    gl   Lippmann, G. J., et al. "M. Georges Sagnac." AS. *Comptes rendus, 169* (1919), 1227-1232.

Saha, Meghnad @ (1893-1956)

sb2.as   Saha, Meghnad. *My experiences in Soviet Russia.* Calcutta, 1947.

    at   *Sen, Samarendra Nath, ed. *Professor Meghnad Saha: His life, work, and philosophy.* Calcutta, 1954.

    ek   Kotori, D. S. "Meghnad Saha." RS. *BM, 5* (1958), 217-236.

    ga   *Anon. [Meghnad Saha]. *Science and culture, 19* (1954), 442-444; *22* (1956), - .

js   Saha, Meghnad. *Collected scientific papers.* Ed. Santimay Chatterjee. New Delhi, 1969.

Sakata, Shoichi (1911-1970)

sb5.js   Sakata, Shoichi. *Scientific works.* Tokyo, 1978.

Sano, Shizuwo (1869-1925)

sb8.js   Sano, Shizuwo. *Scientific papers.* Tokyo, 1926.

Saunders, Frederick Albert (1875-1963)

sc1.eo   Olson, Harry F. "Frederick Albert Saunders." NAS. *BM, 39* (1967), 403-416.

Schaefer, Clemens (1878-1968)

sc4.gb   Bergmann, Ludwig. "Clemens Schaefer 70 Jahre Alt." *PB, 4* (1948), 119-120.

gl   Lohr, Erwin. "Clemens Schaefer." *Acta physica austriaca, 2* (1948), 214-218.

gn   Matossi, F. "Clemens Schaefer wird 90 Jahre alt." *PB, 24* (1968), 120-121.

Scheel, Karl (1866-1936)

sc7.cb   Brüche, Ernst. "Erinnerungen an Karl Scheel: Zum 20. Todestag." *PB,12* (1956), 511-516.

cc   Brüche, Ernst. "Unser Geheimrat Scheel: Erinnerungen und Gedanken zur 100sten Wiederkehr seines Geburtstages." *PB, 22* (1966), 121-128.

Scheiner, Julius @ (1858-1913)

sd1.ef   Frost, E. B. "Julius Scheiner." *Astrophysical journal, 41* (1918), 1-9.

ew   Wilsing, J. "Julius Scheiner." Astronomische Gesellschaft. *Vierteljahrsschrift, 49* (1914), 22-36.

Scherrer, Paul (1890-1969)

sd3.if   Frauenfelder, H., and O. Huber, eds. *Beiträge zur Entwicklung der Physik: Festgabe zum 70. Geburtstag von Professor Paul Scherrer.* Basel and Stuttgart, 1960. (*Helvetica physica acta, 5,* supplement.)

Schönflies, Arthur Moritz @ (1853-1928)

See: B.ff1.jf

Schonland, Basil Ferdinand Jamieson @ (1896-1972)

sd7.ea   Allibone, T. E. "Basil Ferdinand Jamieson Schonland." RS. *BM, 19* (1973), 629-653.

Schott, G. Adolf (1868-1937)

sd9.ec   Conway, A. W. "Professor G. A. Schott." RS. *Obituary notices, 2* (1939), 451-454.

Schrödinger, Erwin @ $33 (1887-1961)

se1.as   Scott, William Taussig. *Erwin Schrödinger: An introduction to his writings.* Amherst, 1967.

    bo   Olby, Robert. "Schrödinger's problem: What is life?" *Journal of the history of biology, 4* (1971), 119-148.

    ch   Hanle, Paul A. "Erwin Schrödinger's reaction to Louis de Broglie's thesis on the quantum theory." *Isis, 68* (1977), 606-609.

    cj   Hermann, Armin. "Erwin Schrödinger, eine Biographie." Schrödinger, *Die Wellenmechanik.* Ed. A. Hermann. Stuttgart, 1963. Pp. 173-192. (*Dokumente der Naturwissenschaft. Abteilung Physik, 3.*)

    cm   Matthew, J. A. D. "Erwin Schrödinger, 1887-1961." *PE, 10* (1975), 357-360.

    cy   Yourgrau, Wolfgang. "Marginal notes on Schrödinger." *Biology, history, and natural philosophy.* Ed. A. D. Breck and W. Yourgrau. NY, 1972. Pp. 331-344.

    eb   Born, Max. "Erwin Schrödinger." *PB, 17* (1961), 85-87.

    ef   Flamm, Ludwig. "Erwin Schrödinger." Österreichische Akademie der Wissenschaften. *Almanach, 111* (1961), 402-411.

    eh   Heisenberg, Werner. "Erwin Schrödinger." Akademie der Wissenschaften, Munich. *Jahrbuch,* (1961), 194-196.

    ei   Heitler, Walther. "Erwin Schrödinger." RS. *BM, 7* (1961), 221-228.

    gk   *Katscher, F. "Zum 70. Geburtstag von Erwin Schrödinger." *Christ und Welt, 32* (1957), - .

    gt   Thirring, Hans. "Erwin Schrödinger." *Acta physica austriaca, 1* (1947), 105-109. (Also in *Neue Auslese, 2* (1947), 121-124.)

ks   Schrödinger, Erwin. *Meine Weltansicht.* Frankfurt and Hamburg, 1963. (English trn by C. Hastings. Cambridge, 1964).

See also: D.hc1.ha; L.ec1.ha, ra, we, wf |fe1.ha |id1.ha; P.mb1.yo

Schuster, Arthur @ (1851-1934)

se4.as   Schuster, Arthur. *Biographical fragments.* London, 1932.

es   Simpson, G. C. "Sir Arthur Schuster." RS. *Obituary notices, 1* (1935), 409-423.

Schwarzschild, Karl @ (1873-1916)

se8.bb   Bruggencate, Paul ten. "Karl Schwarzschild, der Schöpfer der heutigen Astrophysik." A.aj1.sc, 232-239.

cf   Fracastoro, Mario G. "Karl Schwarzchild." Fondazione Giorgio Ronchi. *Atti, 28* (1973), 565-569.

ck   *Kienle, Hans. "Auf den Spuren Karl Schwarzschilds." *Sterne und Weltraum,* 1974, 79-82.

co   Oppenheim, S. "Karl Schwarzschild, zur 50. Wiederkehr seines Geburtstages." Astronomische Gesellschaft. *Vierteljahresschrift, 58* (1923), 191-209.

eb   Blumenthal, Otto. "Karl Schwarzschild." Deutsche Mathematiker-vereinigung. *Jahresbericht, 26* (1918), 56-75.

ee   Eddington, A. S. "Karl Schwarzschild." RAS. *Monthly notices, 77* (1917), 314-319.

eh   Hertzsprung, Ejnar. "Karl Schwarzschild." *Astrophysical journal, 45* (1917), 285-292.

es   Sommerfeld, Arnold. "Karl Schwarzschild." *Nwn, 4* (1916), 453-457.

See also: P.ha1.tr

Schweidler, Egon Ritter von (1873-1948)

sf2.eb   Benndorf, H. "Egon Schweidler." *Acta physica austriaca, 3* (1949), 296-302.

Schwinger, Julian Seymour $65 (1918-)

sf5.js   Schwinger, Julian, ed. *Selected papers on quantum electrodynamics.* NY, 1958.

Seaborg, Glenn Theodore $51C (1912-   )

sf9.js   Seaborg, Glenn T. *Nuclear milestones: A collection of speeches.*
           San Francisco, 1972.

Searle, George Frederick Charles (1864-1954)

sg2.et   Thomson, George P. "George Frederick Charles Searle." RS.
           BM, 1 (1955), 247-252.

See also: A.bg1.wo

Sechenov, Ivan Mikhaylovich @ (1829-1905)

sg5.al   *Laroshevskiy, M. G. *I. M. Sechenov.* Leningrad, 1968.

   as   Sechenov, I. M. *Avtobiograficheskiye zapiski.* Moscow, 1945.

   js   Sechenov, I. M. "Pis'ma I. M. Sechenova A. M. Lyapunovu."
           Nauchnoye nasledstvo, 3 (1956), 225-230.

Sedov, Leonid Ivanovich (1907-   )

sg8.ac   Cuny, Hilaire. *Leonide Sedov et l'astronomie.* Paris, 1961.

See, Thomas Jefferson Jackson @ (1866-1962)

sh2.aw   Webb, William Larkin. *Brief biography and popular account of the
           unparalleled discoveries of T. J. J. See.* Lynn, Mass. 1913.

Seitz, Frederick (1911-   )

sh3.se   Seitz, Frederick. "Biographical notes." RS. *Proceedings, 371A,*
           84-99.

Semenov, Nikolay Nikolayevich $56C (1896-   )

sh5.jm   *Nikolay Nikolayevich Semenov.* Moscow and Leningrad, 1946; 2nd
           ed., 1966.

   js   Semenov, N. N. *Nauka i obshchestvo: Staty i rechi.* Moscow,
           1973.

Shal'nikov, Aleksandr Iosifovich (1905-   )

See: O.hb1.tu

Sharonov, Vsevelod Vasil'yevich @ (1901-1964)

sh9.bb   Bronshten, V. A. "Leningradskiy issledovatel' planet." *Zemlya i
           vselennaya,* 1969:5, 70-71.

   eb   Anon. "Pamyati V. V. Sharonov." AN. Astrosovet. Komissiya po
           fizike planet. *Izvestiya,* no. 5 (1965), 105-111.

Shaw, William Napier (1854-1945)

si3.eg Gold, E. "William Napier Shaw." RS. *Obituary notices, 5* (1945), 202-230.

eh Gold, E. "Sir William Napier Shaw." Royal Meteorological Society. *Quarterly journal, 71* (1945), 187-194.

Shayn, Grigoriy Abramovich @ (1892-1956)

si6.eb Anon. "Grigoriy Abramovich Shayn." *Astronomicheskiy zhurnal, 33* (1956), 465-468.

ed Dobronravin, P. P. "Grigoriy Abramovich i Pelageya Fedorovna Shayn." *Peremennyye zvezdy, 11* (1956), 321-324.

ee *Dobronravin, P. P. "Grigory Abramovich Shayn." AN. Krymskaya astrofizicheskaya observatoriya. *Izvestiya, 17* (1957), 3-10.

ep *Pikel'ner, S. B. "G. A. Shayn." *Istoriko-astronomicheskie issledovaniya, 3* (1957), 551-607.

jm Dobronravin, P. P. *Grigory Abramovich Shayn.* Moscow, 1960. (*Mtly*, ser. astron., 2.)

Shmidt, Otto Yul'yevich (1891-1956)

si9.ak Alexandrov, P. S., and Ya. B. Kogan, eds. *Otto Yul'yevich Schmidt: Zhizn' i deyatel'nost'.* Moscow, 1959.

cp Podvigina, Ye. P., and L. K. Vinogradov. "Gosudarstvennaya deyatel'nost' O. Yu. Shmidta v pervyye gody sovetskoy vlasti (1917-1922 gg.)." B.si9.ak, 127-139.

cs Shcherbakov, D. I. "O. Yu. Shmidt—vydayushchiy sovetskiy geograf." *VIYeT, 13* (1962), 135-137.

cy Yanitskiy, N. F. "Otto Yul'yevich Schmidt." B.si9.ak, 9-50.

js [On personal archive of O. Yu. Schmidt.] *Voprosy istorii KPSS,* 1958:2, 219.

nn Nakoryakov, N. N. "Zachinatel' novykh putey sovetskogo knigoizdatel'stva." B.si9.ak, 160-168.

pk Kurosh, A. G. "Osnovopolozhnik sovetskoy algebraicheskoy shkoly." B.si9.ak, 51-63.

sp Petrov, F. N. "Na fronte kul'tury i nauki." B.si9.ak, 140-159.

Shubnikov, Aleksey Vasil'yevich (1887-1970)

sj2.cb Balabekyan, O. I. "Lev Vasil'evich Shubnikov." *SPU, 9* (1966), 455-459.

jm   *Aleksey Vasil'yevich Shubnikov.* Moscow, 1941. (*Mtly,* ser. fiz.-
      mat.)

Shuleykin, Mikhail Vasil'yevich (1884-1939)

sj5.av   Vvedenskiy, B. A., ed. *Mikhail Vasil'yevich Shuleykin.* Moscow,
          1952.

Siegbahn, Manne $24 (1886-1979)

sj8.gl   *Lindh, A. "En svensk Nobelpristagare." *Kosmos, 5* (1925/6),
          5-63.

is   *Manne Siegbahn. 1886 3/12 1951.* Uppsala, 1951.

See also: C.su1.fr, no

Simon, Franz Eugen @ (1893-1956)

sk3.ab   Arms, Nancy. *A prophet in two countries: The life of F. E. Simon.*
          London, 1966.

ek   Kurti, N. "Franz Eugen Simon." RS. *BM, 4* (1958), 225-256.

ss   Simon, F. E. *The neglect of science.* Oxford, 1951.

Simpson, George Clarke (1878-1965)

sk4.eg   Gold, E. "George Clarke Simpson." RS. *BM, 11* (1965),
          157-175.

Sitter, Willem de @ (1872-1934)

See: B.ei6.ns

Skinner, Herbert Wakefield Banks (1900-1960)

sk8.ej   Jones, H. "Herbert Wakefield Banks Skinner." RS. *BM, 6*
          (1960), 259-268.

Skobel'tsyn, Dmitriy Vladimirovich (1892-   )

sk9.gb   Anon. "Akademik D. V. Skobel'tsyn." *ZhETF, 23* (1952),
          485-487.

gc   Anon. "Dmitriy Vladimirovich Skobel'tsyn." *UFN, 49* (1953),
          297-299. (In English in *SPU, 5* (1963), 1024-1028.)

jm   Vernov, S. N., et al., ed. *Dmitriy Vladimirovich Skobel'tsyn.* Mos-
          cow, 1962. (*Mtly,* ser. fiz.-mat., 15.)

Slater, John Clarke (1900-1976)

sl3.as   Slater, John C. *Solid-state and molecular theory: A scientific biography.* NY, 1975.

il   Löwdin, Per-Olov, ed. *Quantum theory of atoms, molecules, and the solid state; A tribute to John C. Slater.* NY, 1966.

Smekal, Adolf Gustav Stephan @ (1895-1959)

sl6.ef   Flamm, Ludwig. "Adolf Gustav Smekal." Akademie der Wissenschaften, Vienna. *Almanach, 109* (1959), 421-427.

See also: O.ba1.ru

Smirnov, Vladimir Ivanovich (1887-1974)

sm1.jm   Sobolev, S. L., and A. P. Epifanova, ed. *Vladimir Ivanovich Smirnov.* Moscow and Leningrad, 1949. (*Mtly*, ser. matematiki, 5.)

Smith, Frank Edward (1876-1970)

sm3.eg   Goodeve, Charles. "Frank Edward Smith." RS. *BM, 18* (1972), 525-548.

jc   CSAC. *Frank Smith papers at Imperial College of Science and Technology.* List 9/3/74. 3 p.

Smith, Samuel Walter Johnson (1871-1948)

sm4.et   Thomas, J. S. G. "Samuel Walter Johnson Smith." RS. *Obituary notices, 6* (1949), 579-598.

Smits, Andreas @ (1870-1948)

sm5.gb   Bijvoet, J. M. "Prof. Dr. A. Smits." *Chemisch weekblad, 28* (1931), 555-559.

gg   Gerding, H. "Professor Dr. A. Smits." *Chemisch weekblad, 37* (1940), 430-436.

gs   Scheffer, F. E. C. "Het 25-jarig hoogleeraarschap van Prof. Dr. A. Smits." *Chemisch weekblad, 28* (1931), 560-566.

Smoluchowski, Marian @ (1872-1917)

sm8.ak   Krajewski, W. *Swiatopoglad Mariana Smoluchowskiego.* Warsaw, 1956.

at   Teske, Armin. *Marian Smoluchowski. Leben und Werk.* Warsaw, 1977. (Polish ed.: *Marian Smoluchowski: Zycie i Twórczość.* Warsaw, 1955.)

bl   *Loria, S. "Marian Smoluchowski i jego dzielo." *Postępy fizyki, 4* (1953), 5- .

ct   Teske, Armin. "Szkic Twórczości Mariana Smoluchowskiego. W Pięćdziesięciolecie śmierci." *KHNT, 12* (1967), 707-713.

cu   Teske, Armin. "Szkic Twórczości Mariana Smoluchowskiego." Polska Akademia Nauk. Zaklad historii nauki i techniki. *Studia,* 1968, 14-20.

eb   Anon. "M. von Smoluchowski und sein Lebenswerk." Physikalischer Verein, Frankfurt. *Jahresbericht,* 1917/8, 3-16.

es   Sommerfeld, Arnold. "Zum Andenken an Marian von Smoluchowski." *PZ, 18* (1917), 533-539.

js   Smoluchowski, Marian. *Pisma.* Ed. W. Natanson and J. Stock. Cracow, 1924.

kk   *Kapuściński, W. "Poglądy filozoficzne Mariana Smoluchowskiego." *Fizyka i chemia, 6* (1953), 200- .

See also: B.cv1.aj |ei6.os; D.hh1.te, ul; H.ab1.kr

Soddy, Frederick @ $21C (1877-1956)

sn2.ah   Howorth, Muriel. *Atomic transmutation: The greatest discovery ever made, from memoirs of Professor Frederick Soddy.* London, 1953.

ai   Howorth, Muriel. *Pioneer research on the atom: Rutherford and Soddy in a glorious chapter of science. The life story of Frederick Soddy.* London, 1958.

ak   Krivomazov, A. N. *Frederik Soddi, 1877-1956.* Moscow, 1978.

cc   Cruickshank, A. O. "Soddy at Oxford." *BJHS, 12* (1979), 277-288.

ck   Kent, A. "Frederick Soddy." Chemical Society of London. *Proceedings,* 1963, 327-331.

ct   Trenn, Thaddeus J. "The central role of energy in Soddy's holistic and critical approach to nuclear science, economics, and social responsibility." *BJHS, 12* (1979), 261-276.

ef   Fleck, Alexander. "Frederick Soddy." RS. *BM, 3* (1957), 203-216.

jc   CSAC. *Frederick Soddy papers at the Bodleian Library, Oxford.* List 14/8/74, 29 p.

See also: I.bd1.fr, ts

Sokolov, Sergey Yakovlevich (1897-1957)

See: D.kc1.me

Solomon, Jacques (1908-1942)

sn9.cc Cogniot, Georges. "A la mémoire de Jacques Solomon." *La pensée*, no. 122 (1965), 34-39.

cr Rosenfeld, Léon. "Jacques Solomon." *BSPS, 21* (1979), 297-301.

Sommerfeld, Arnold Johannes Wilhelm @ (1868-1951)

sol.ab Benz, Ulrich. *Arnold Sommerfeld. Lehrer und Forscher an der Schwelle zum Atomzeitalter, 1868-1951.* Stuttgart, 1975.

bh Hermann, Armin. "Sommerfeld und die Technik." *Technikgeschichte, 34* (1967), 311-322.

bl Laue, Max von. "Sommerfelds Lebenswerk." B.lf6.jl, *3*, 213-218. (*Nwn, 38* (1951), 513-518.)

bp Pauli, Wolfgang. "Sommerfelds Beiträge zur Quantentheorie." *Nwn, 35* (1948), 129-132. (Also in B.pd3.jb, *2*, 1103-1106.)

ce Ewald, P. P. "Arnold Sommerfeld als Mensch, Lehrer, und Freund." B.sol.ib, 8-16.

ch Heisenberg, Werner. "Ausstrahlung von Sommerfelds Werk in der Gegenwart." *PB, 24* (1968), 530-537. (In English in B.sol.ib, 44-52).

cj Hermann, Armin. "Der Brückenschlag zwischen Mathematik und Technik: Arnold Sommerfelds Verdienste um eine wissenschaftliche technische Mechanik." *PB, 23* (1967), 442-449.

cs Sommerfeld, Arnold. "Autobiographische Skizze." B.sol.js, *4*, 673-682.

eb Born, Max. "Arnold Johannes Wilhelm Sommerfeld." RS. *Obituary notices, 8* (1952), 275-296.

ej Joos, Georg. "Arnold Sommerfeld." Akademie der Wissenschaften, Munich. *Jahrbuch*, 1951, 152-155.

el Jordan, Pascual. "Nachruf auf Arnold Sommerfeld." Akademie der Wissenschaften und der Literatur, Mainz. *Jahrbuch*, 1951, 143-154.

gb Bopp, Fritz. "Zum 80. Geburtstag Arnold Sommerfelds." *NR, 1* (1948), 232.

gc Buchwald, Eberhard. "Arnold Sommerfeld zum 80. Geburtstag." *PB, 4* (1948), 457-459.

gg   Heisenberg, Werner. "Arnold Sommerfeld zum 5. Dezember 1948." *Zeitschrift für Naturforschung, 3a* (1948), 429.

gi   Hund, Friedrich. "Arnold Sommerfeld zum 70. Geburtstag." *FF, 14* (1938), 403-404.

gk   Kirkpatrick, Paul. "Arnold Sommerfeld, recipient of the 1948 Oersted Medal for notable contributions to the teaching of physics." *AJP, 17* (1949), 312-314.

gl   Laue, Max von. "Arnold Sommerfeld." Deutsche Chemische Gesellschaft. *Berichte, 72A* (1939), 46-47.

gp   Planck, Max. "Arnold Sommerfeld zum siebzigsten Geburtstag." *Nwn, 26* (1938), 777-779.

gt   Thirring, Hans. "Zum 80. Geburtstag Arnold Sommerfelds." *Acta physica austriaca, 2* (1949), 221-223.

ib   Bopp, Fritz, and H. Kleinpoppen, ed. *Arnold Sommerfeld centennial meeting, Munich, 1968: Physics of one and two electron atoms.* Amsterdam, 1969.

id   Debye, Peter, ed. *Probleme der modernen Physik. Arnold Sommerfeld zum 60. Geburtstag gewidmet.* Leipzig, 1928.

je   Hermann, Armin. "Sommerfeld und Einstein. Aus dem Briefwechsel der beiden Physiker." *PB, 24* (1968), 543-549.

js   Sommerfeld, Arnold. *Gesammelte Schriften.* Ed. F. Sauter. 4 vols. Braunschweig, 1968.

jt   Sommerfeld, Arnold. *Puti poznaniya v fizike: Sbornik statey.* Moscow, 1973.

pb   Benz, Ulrich. "Der akademische Lehrer Arnold Sommerfeld." *PB, 28* (1972), 292-299.

pd   Born, Max. "Sommerfeld als Begründer einer Schule." *Nwn, 16* (1928), 1035-1036.

ps   Sommerfeld, Arnold. "Some reminiscences of my teaching career." *AJP, 17* (1949), 315-316.

See also: B.ei6.ps; D.be1.de; G.qa1.ns; H.cc1.bo; L.ce1; O.ab1.we

Southwell, Richard Vynne (1888-1970)

so3.ec   Christopherson, Derman. "Richard Vynne Southwell." RS. *BM, 18* (1972), 549-565.

Stark, Johannes @ $19 (1874-1957)

See: B.ei6.qf |lj3.ck |lp8.jh; L.ce1.he

Steacie, Edgar William Richard (1900-1962)

sp2.em   Marion, L. "E. W. R. Steacie." RS. *BM, 10* (1964), 257-281.

Stebbins, Joel (1878-1966)

sp3.cw   Whitford, A. E. "Joel Stebbins." NAS. *BM, 49* (1978), 293-316.

Steklov, Vladimir Andreyevich @ (1864-1926)

sp5.ai   Ignatsius, Georgiy Ivanovich. *Vladimir Andreyevich Steklov, 1864-1926.* Moscow, 1967.

ck   Kol'tsov, A. V. "Akademik V. A. Steklov vitse-prezident Akademii Nauk SSSR." *VIYeT, 7* (1959), 107-112.

cm   Krylov, A. N. "Pamyati V. A. Steklova." B.kt1.jj, *1:2,* 187-189.

ep   Parfent'yev, N. N. "Nauchnaya kharakteristika akademika V. A. Steklova." Kazan. University. Fiz.-mat. obshchestva. *Izvestiya,* ser. 3, *1* (1926), 2-13.

eu   Uspenskiy, Ya. V. "Vladimir Andreyevich Steklov." AN. *Bulletin, 20* (1926), 837-856.

pm   Markush, I. I. "V. A. Steklov i N. M. Gyunter o magisterskoy dissertatsii V. I. Smirnova." *VIYeT, 50* (1975), 41-45.

Stepanov, Aleksandr Vasil'yevich (1908-1972)

sp8.jm   Voinova, A. A., ed. *Aleksandr Vasil'yevich Stepanov.* Moscow, 1976. (*Mtly,* seria fiziki, 20.)

Stepanov, Boris Ivanovich (1913-   )

sp9.ag   *Grivkovskiy, V. P., and Ye. P. Gridasova, ed. *Boris Ivanovich Stepanov.* Minsk, 1973.

Stern, Otto @ $43 (1888-1969)

sq3.og   Gerlach, Walther. "Otto Stern zum Gedenken." *PB, 25* (1969), 412-413.

es   Segrè, Emilio. "Otto Stern." NAS. *BM, 43* (1973), 215-236.

ie   Estermann, Immanuel, ed. *Recent research in molecular beams: A collection of papers dedicated to Otto Stern.* NY, 1959.

See also: K.dd1.ge

Stewart, George Walter (1876-1956)

sq6.ef   Fletcher, Harvey. "George W. Stewart." NAS. *BM, 32* (1958), 379-398.

gw   Worthing, A. G. "George Walter Stewart, nominee for the 1942 Oersted Award." *AJP, 11* (1943), 89-91.

Stormer, Frederik Carl Muelertz @ (1874-1957)

sq9.eh   Harang, L. "Minnetale over professor Carl Stormer." Norske Videnskapsakademi. *Árbok*, 1958, 81-85.

Stokes, George Gabriel @ (1819-1903)

sr4.cb   Barr, E. Scott. "Men and milestones in optics, I. George Gabriel Stokes." *Applied optics, 1* (1962), 69-73.

es   Strutt, John William, Third Baron Rayleigh. "Sir George Gabriel Stokes." RS. *Proceedings, 75* (1905), 199-216.

jr   Stokes, George Gabriel. *Mathematical and physical papers.* Ed. G. Stokes and J. Larmor. 5 vols. Cambridge, 1880-1905. (Reprinted with additions, NY, 1966.)

js   Larmor, Joseph, ed. *Memoir and scientific correspondence of the late Sir George Gabriel Stokes.* 2 vols. Cambridge, 1907.

jt   Wilson, David B. *Catalogue of the manuscript collections of Sir George Gabriel Stokes and Sir William Thomson, Baron Kelvin of Largs, in Cambridge University Library.* Cambridge, 1976.

Stoner, Edmund Clifton (1899-1968)

sr6.eb   Bates, L. F. "Edmund Clifton Stoner." RS. *BM, 15* (1969), 201-237.

jc   CSAC. *Edmund Stoner papers at Leeds University Library.* List 6/73, 20 p.

Stoney, George Johnstone @ (1826-1911)

sr8.ej   J[oly], J[ohn]. "George Johnstone Stoney." RS. *Proceedings, 86A* (1911/12), xx-xxxv.

See also: E.bb1.oh

Strutt, John William, Third Baron Rayleigh @ $04 (1842-1919)

st2.ag   Gavin, William. *Ninety years of family farming: The story of Lord Rayleigh's and Strutt and Parker farms.* London, 1967.

al   Lindsay, Robert Bruce. *Men of physics: Lord Rayleigh, the man and his work.* Oxford and NY, 1970.

as   Strutt, Robert John, Fourth Baron Rayleigh. *John William Strutt: Third Baron Rayleigh.* London, 1924.

at Strutt, Robert John, Fourth Baron Rayleigh. *Life of John William Strutt,* (Reprint of B.st2.as with additions.) Madison, 1968.

bh Howard, John N. "The optics papers of John W. Strutt, third Baron Rayleigh." *Applied optics, 3* (1964), 1102-1104.

bi Howard, John N., et al. "Discussion of the scientific work of the Third Baron Rayleigh." B.st3.ji, 25-43.

bl Lodge, Oliver. "The scientific work of Lord Rayleigh." *The national review, 32* (1898/9), 89-102.

bt Tooley, Peter. "The Terling laboratory." *Chemistry in Britian, 15* (1979), 284-285.

ch Howard, John N. "John William Strutt, Third Baron Rayleigh." *Applied optics, 3* (1964), 1091-1101.

ci Howard, John N. "Eleanor Mildred Sidgwick and the Rayleighs." *Applied optics, 3* (1964), 1120-1122.

cs Shankland, Robert S. "Rayleigh and Michelson." *Isis, 58* (1967), 86-88.

el Lodge, Oliver. "In memory of Lord Rayleigh." Society for Psychical Research. *Proceedings, 31* (1921), 1-11.

es Schuster, Arthur. "John William Strutt, Baron Rayleigh." RS. *Proceedings, 98A* (1921), i-l.

eu Thomson, J. J., et al. "Strutt, J. W. Baron Rayleigh." *Nature, 103* (1919), 365-369.

ga Anon. "The Rayleigh memorial. The unveiling in Westminster Abbey." *Nature, 108* (1921), 471-474.

jh Howard, John N. "The Rayleigh notebooks." *Applied optics, 3* (1964), 1129-1133.

ji Howard, John N. "The Michelson-Rayleigh correspondence of the AFCRL Rayleigh archives." *Isis, 58* (1967), 88-89.

jj Howard, John N. "The scientific papers of the Lords Rayleigh." ICHS, XI (1965), *Actes, 4* (1968), 315-318.

js Strutt, John William, Third Baron Rayleigh. *Scientific papers.* Cambridge, 1899-1920.

nb Barrell, H. "The Rayleighs and the National Physical Laboratory." *Applied optics, 3* (1964), 1125-1128.

See also: B.lo8.ag; B.st3; G.ha1.po; R.c

Strutt, Robert John, 4th Baron Rayleigh @ (1875-1947)

st3.as   Strutt, Guy Robert. *The airglow Rayleigh; Robert John Strutt, fourth Baron Rayleigh.* Ed. J. N. Howard. Bedford, Mass., 1969.

cs   Strutt, Guy Robert. "Robert John Strutt, Fourth Baron Rayleigh." *Applied optics, 3* (1964), 1105-1112.

ee   Egerton, Alfred C. "Lord Rayleigh." RS. *Obituary notices, 6* (1949), 503-530.

jh   *Howard, John N., ed. *Robert John Strutt, 4th Baron Rayleigh: Unpublished manuscripts and reviews of his work.* Bedford, Mass., 1971.

ji   Howard, John N., ed. *The Rayleigh Archives dedication.* Bedford, Mass., 1967. (United States Air Force. Cambridge Research Laboratories. *Special report, 63.)*

js   Strutt, Robert John, Fourth Baron Rayleigh. *Summaries and abstracts of the scientific writings.* Ed. John N. Howard. Bedford, Mass., 1969. (United States Air Force. Cambridge Research Laboratories. [*Report.*])

See also: B.st2; P.fc1.ch

Struve, Otto @ (1897-1963)

st6.ec   Cowling, T. G. "Otto Struve." RS. *BM, 10* (1964), 283-304.

Sutherland, William @ (1859-1912)

su2.ao   Osborne, William Alexander. *William Sutherland.* Melbourne, 1920.

Svedberg, The @ $26C (1884-1971)

su5.ck   Kinell, Per-Olof. "Theodor Svedberg, Kolloidchemiker, Molecülforscher, Atomfachmann." A.aj1.sc, 191-198.

ec   Claesson, S., and K. O. Pedersen. "The Svedberg." RS. *BM, 18* (1972), 595-627.

gt   Tiselius, Arne, and K. O. Pedersen. *The Svedberg, 1884-1944.* Uppsala, 1944.

See also: H.ab1.ke, sc; R.af1.ti

Sverdrup, Harald Ulrik @ (1888-1957)

su9.ed   Devik, Olaf, and S. Richter. "Minnetale [og Bibliografi] over H. U. Sverdrup." Norske Videnskapsakademi. *Årbok,* 1958, 49-73.

Sveshnikov, Boris Yakovlevich (1901-1963)

sv3.gb   Anon. "Boris Yakovlevich Sveshnikov." *Optika i spektroskopiya, 11* (1961), 437-438.

    gc   Aristov, A. V., et al. "Boris Yakovlevich Sveshnikov." *SPU, 6* (1964), 755-763.

Swann, William Francis Grey @ (1884-1962)

sv6.ep   Pomerantz, Martin A. "William Francis Grey Swann." APS. *Yearbook,* 1962, 178-184.

Swinne, Johan Richard (1885-1939)

See: I.cb1.st

Swinton, Alan A. Campbell (1863-1930)

See: E.te1.mc

Synge, John Lighton (1897-)

sy2.io   O'Raifeartaigh, L., ed. *General relativity: Papers in honour of J. L. Synge.* Oxford, 1972.

Syrkin, Yakov Kivovich (1894-1974)

sy5.jm   *Yakov Kivovich Syrkin.* Moscow, 1971. (*Mtly,* ser. khim., 48.)

Szilard, Leo @ (1898-1964)

sz2.cs   Szilard, Leo. "Reminiscences." U.gb2.fl, 94-151.

    ew   Wigner, Eugene P. "Leo Szilard." NAS. *BM, 40* (1969), 337-341.

    jj   American Institute of Physics. "[Letter from Szilard to Joliot, 1940.]" Center for History of Physics, *Newsletter, 8:2* (1976), 2.

    js   Szilard, Leo. *Collected works.* vol. 1. *Scientific papers.* Ed. Bernard T. Field and Gertrud Weiss Szilard. Cambridge, Mass., 1972.

    jt   Szilard, Leo. *His version of the facts: Selected recollections and correspondence.* Ed. Spencer R. Weart and Gertrud Weiss Szilard. Cambridge, Mass., 1978.

    ju   Szilard, Leo. "Leo Szilard: His version of the facts." *BAS, 35* (Feb. 1979), 37-40; (Mar. 1979), 55-59; (Apr. 1979), 28-32; (May 1979), 34-35. (Excerpts from B.sz2.jt)

See also: B.fg1.bd |fp1.er; I.tc1.an

Tamm, Igor' Yevgen'yevich @ $58 (1895-1971)

ta3.cf   *Feynberg, Ye. L. "Vospominaniya ob I. Ye. Tamme." *VIYeT,* 1980:2, 147-156.

ct   Anon. "Akademik Igor' Yevgen'yevich Tamm (k 60-letiyu so dnya rozhdeniya)." *ZhETF, 29* (1955), 3-5.

gg   Ginzburg, V. L., and Ye. L. Feynberg. "Igor' Yevgen'yevich Tamm." *UFN, 56* (1955), 469-475.

gh   Ginzburg, V. L., and Ye. L. Feynberg. "Igor' Yevgen'yevich Tamm." *UFN, 86* (1965), 353-356.

jb   Borotovskiy, B. M., and V. Ya. Frenkel'. "Pis'mo I. Ye. Tamma L. I. Mandel'shtamu." *Priroda,* 1974:2, 100.

jm   Ginzburg, V. L., et al., ed. *Igor' Yevgen'yevich Tamm.* Moscow, 1959. (*Mtly,* ser. fiziki, 9.)

jt   *Akademik Igor' Yevgen'yevich Tamm: Sbornik statey.* Ed. B. M. Bolstovskiy and V. Ya. Frenkel'. Moscow, 1973.

pg   Ginzburg, V. L., and Ye. L. Feynberg. "Kratkiy ocherk nauchnoy i pedagogicheskoy deyatel'nosti." B.ta3.jm, 5-11.

See also: B.cf1.gk; I.dd1.ft

Tammann, Gustav Heinrich J. A. @ (1861-1938)

ta6.cb   Boström, S. "Gustav Tammann." *Baltische Hefte, 10* (1964), 139-150.

ch   Hausen, Josef. *Was nicht in den Annalen steht.* Weinheim, 1958.

ck   Köster, Werner. "Zum 100 Geburtstag von Gustav Tammann." *Zeitschrift für metallkunde, 52* (1961), 379-381.

eb   Anon. "Nachruf auf Gustav Tammann." Akademie der Wissenschaften, Göttingen. *Jahrbuch,* 1938/9, 54-66.

gb   Biltz, Wilhelm. "Gustav Tammann zum siebzigsten Geburtstag." *Zeitschrift für anorganische und algemeine Chemie, 198* (1931), 1-31.

See also: O.ba1.gr, ko, ks, ma

Tate, John Torrence (1889-1950)

ta9.cn   Nier, Alfred O. C. "John Torrence Tate." NAS. *BM, 47* (1975), 461-484.

Taylor, Geoffrey Ingram (1886-1975)

tb3.eb   Batchelor, G. K. "Geoffrey Ingram Taylor." RS. *BM, 22* (1976), 565-633.

jc   CSAC. *Sir Geoffrey Taylor papers at Trinity College Library, Cambridge.* List 67/5/79, 99 p.

Teller, Edward (1908-   )

tc3.ab   Blumberg, Stanley A., and Gwinn Owens. *Energy and conflict: The life and times of Edward Teller.* NY, 1976.

gw   Wigner, E. P. "An appreciation on the 60th birthday of Edward Teller." B.tc3.im, 1-6.

im   Mark, Hans, and Sidney Fernbach, eds. *Properties of matter under unusual conditions. In honor of Edward Teller's 60th birthday.* NY, 1969.

See also: H.ea1.tu

Terenin, Aleksandr Nikolayevich (1869-1967)

td3.en   Neporent, B. S. "Aleksandr Nikolaevich Terenin." *SPU, 12* (1970), 575-579.

gb   Anon. "Chestvovaniye akademika A. N. Terenina." AN. *Vestnik,* 1956:8, 86-87.

gd   Anon. "Akademik Aleksandr Nikolayevich Terenin (K 60-letiyu so dnya rozhdeniya)." *Optiko-mekhanicheskaya promyshlennost',* 1956:2, 1-4.

gv   *Vartanyan, A. T. "Akademik A. N. Terenin (K 60-letiyu so dnya rozhdeniya)." *Zhurnal nauchnoy i prikladnoy fotografii i kinematografii, 1* (1956), 310-312.

jm   *Aleksandr Nikolayevich Terenin.* Moscow, 1971. (*Mtly,* ser. khim., 47.)

Tesla, Nikola @ (1856-1943)

te3.ab   Belgrad. Muzej Nikole Tesle. *Centenary of the birth of Nikola Tesla, 1856-1956.* Belgrad, 1959.

ah   Hunt, Inez, and Wanetta W. Draper. *Lightning in his hand: The life and story of Nikola Tesla.* Denver, 1964.

an   O'Neill, John J. *Prodigal genius: The life of Nikola Tesla.* NY, 1944.

ap   Popović, Vojin, ed. *A tribute to Nikola Tesla: Presented in articles, letters, and documents.* Belgrade, 1961.

bb   Blondel, André. "L'oeuvre de Tesla vu par un de ses contemporains." B.te3.ap, A144-A148.

bd   Bokšan, Slavko. "Nikola Tesla, der Begründer der Hochfrequenz- und der Radiotechnik." B.te3.ap, A112-A122.

bf   Fleming, Arthur P. M. "Tesla's contribution to the development of electrotechnics." B.te3.ap, A295-A299.

bk   Kiebitz, Franz. "Nikola Tesla als Wegbereiter der drahtlosen Telegraphie." B.te3.ap, A155-A160.

br   Rzhonsnitskiy, B. N. "Vydayushchiysya elektrotekhnik Nikola Tesla." *VIYeT, 1* (1956), 192-203. (Also in B.te3.ap, A285-A294.)

cb   Bethenod, Joseph. "Nikola Tesla." B.te3.ap, A196-A202.

cc   Cohen, Samuel. "Lightning made to order." B.te3.ap, A93-A97.

cd   Damjanovič, Aleksandar. "La vie et l'oeuvre de Nikola Tesla." B.te3.ap, A235-A256.

ce   Eccles, W. H. "Dr. Nikola Tesla." B.te3.ap, A203-A204.

cf   Fleming, Arthur P. M. "Nikola Tesla." B.te3.ap, A215-A230.

cg   Girardeau, Emile. "Pourquoi Nikola Tesla, créateur de la radioélectricité, a-t-il été longtemps méconnu." B.te3.ap, A188-A195.

ch   Giazanov, V. N. "Veliky syn yugoslavskogo naroda." B.te3.ap, A278-A284.

ci   Holmgren, E. J. "Nikola Tesla." B.te3.ap, A337-A339.

cj   Jakubowski, J. L. "Wysokosč napieč stosowanych przez Nikole Tesle." B.te3.ap, A340-A345.

ck   Jovanovič, Vladislav. "Nikolo Tesla." B.te3.ap, A133-A143.

cl   Landolt, Max K. "Aus dem Leben und Werk von Nikola Tesla." B.te3.ap, A369-A394.

cm   Miljanič, Pavle. "Nikola Tesla, Fondateur de l'electrotechnique industrielle moderne." B.te3.ap, A123-A127.

cn   Nagler, Josef. "Nikola Tesla." B.te3.ap, A257-A259.

co   Swezey, Kenneth M. "Nikola Tesla, pathfinder of the electrical age." *Electronical engineering, 75* (1956), 786-790.

cp   Swezey, Kenneth M. "Nikola Tesla." *Science, 127* (1958), 1147-1159.

cq   Swezey, Kenneth M. "Nikola Tesla." B.te3.ap, A346-A368.

cv   Voyevodin, P. I. "Nikola Tesla (1856-1943)." B.te3.ap, A231-A234.

cz   Zenneck, Jonathan. "Nikola Tesla." B.te3.ap, A128-A132.

ge   Electrical Review and Western Electrician. "Nikola Tesla receives Edison Medal [1917]." B.te3.ap, A98-A107.

See also: D.td1.pi; E.tb1

Thirring, Hans (1888-1976)

tf3.eu   Urban, Paul. "Hans Thirring." Akademie der Wissenschaften, Vienna. *Almanach, 127* (1977), 477-483.

gf   Flamm, Ludwig. "Hans Thirring zu seinem 70. Geburtstag." *Acta physica austriaca, 12* (1958), 1-8.

gu   Urban, Paul. "Hans Thirring 80 Jahre." *Acta physica austriaca, 28* (1969), 1-7.

Thompson, Silvanus Phillips @ (1851-1916)

tg3.at   Thompson, Jane Smeal, and Helen G. Thompson. *Silvanus Phillips Thompson: His life and letters.* London, 1920.

ep   P[erry], J[ohn]. "Silvanus Phillips Thompson." RS. *Proceedings, 94A* (1917/18), xvi-xix.

Thomson, George Paget $37 (1892-1975)

th3.em   Moon, P. B. "George Paget Thomson." RS. *BM, 23* (1977), 529-556.

jc   CSAC. *Sir George Thomson papers at Trinity College Library, Cambridge.* List 75/5/80. 167p.

Thomson, Joseph John @ $06 (1856-1940)

th5.ap   Pla, Cortés. *Semblanza de Sir Joseph John Thomson.* Rosario, Argentina, 1941.

ar   Strutt, Robert John, Fourth Baron Rayleigh. *The life of Sir J. J. Thomson, O.M., sometime master of Trinity College, Cambridge.* Cambridge, 1943.

as   Thomson, George P. *J. J. Thomson and the Cavendish Laboratory in his day.* London, 1964.

at   Thomson, J. J. *Recollections and reflections.* NY, 1937.

bp   Saltzman, H. "J. J. Thomson and the modern revival of dualism." *Journal of chemical education, 50* (1973), 59-61.

bt   Topper, David R. "Commitment to mechanism: J. J. Thomson, the early years." *AHES, 7* (1971), 393-410.

bu   Topper, David R. "'To reason by means of images': J. J. Thomson and the mechanical picture of nature." *Annals of science, 37* (1980), 31-57.

bw   Wendling, A. V. "Le decouvreur du corpuscule électronique: Sir Joseph John Thomson." *Ingénieur* (Montreal), *27* (1941), 34-51.

cm   Price, Derek J. "Sir J. J. Thomson, O.M., F.R.S., A centenary biography." *Discovery, 17* (1956), 494-502.

cp   Thomson, George P. "J. J. Thomson." *Nature, 178* (1956), 1317-1319. (Also in RI, *Proceedings, 36* (1957), 532-540.)

cq   Thomson, George P., and Joan Thomson. "J. J. Thomson as we remember him." RS. *Notes and records, 12* (1957), 201-210.

ct   Thomson, J. J. "Retrospect." *Nature, 118*: Suppl. (1926), 41-44.

cu   Thomson, J. J. "Reminiscences of physics and physicists." *Science, 80* (1934), 169-173. (Also in RI. *Proceedings, 28* (1935), 183-194; reported in *Engineering, 137* (16 Feb. 1934), 196-197.)

eb   Born, Max. "Sir J. J. Thomson." Institute of Physics and the Physical Society. *Proceedings, 53* (1941), 305-310.

ed   Crowther, J. A., et al. "Sir J. J. Thomson, O.M., F.R.S." *Nature, 146* (1940), 351-357.

ee   Crowther, J. A. "[Sir J. J. Thomson]." Institute of Physics and the Physical Society. *Proceedings, 53* (1941), 311-316.

ek   Kaptsov, N. A. "Dzhozef Dzhon Tomson." *Sovetskaya nauka,* 1940:10, 88-108.

es   Strutt, Robert John, Fourth Baron Rayleigh. "Sir Joseph John Thomson." RS. *Obituary notices, 3* (1941), 587-609.

ew   Whittaker, E. T. "Sir Joseph John Thomson." Royal Society of Edinburgh. *Proceedings, 60* (1940), 410-415.

gb   Bohr, Niels, et al. "Sir J. J. Thomson's seventieth birthday." *Nature, 118* (1926), 879-885.

gl   Lodge, Oliver. "Sir J. J. Thomson." *Nature, 118*: Suppl. (1926), 49-51.

gr   Righi, Augusto. "Scientific worthies, XL: Sir J. J. Thomson." *Nature, 91* (1913), 1-5.

gt   Rutherford, Ernest. "Dinner in honor of Sir J. J. Thomson." *Science, 65* (1927), 31-32.

jc   CSAC. *Sir J. J. Thomson papers at Trinity College Library, Cambridge.* List of additions 74/4/80, 14 p.

See also: E.ab1.to |bb1.th; G.qa1.mc

Thomson, William, Lord Kelvin @ (1824-1907)

th9.ab   *Bowden, Ralph Charles. *An analysis of Lord Kelvin's scientific career.* Ph.D. thesis. Univ. of North Carolina, 1972. (*DAI, 34,* 240A.)

ak   Ring, Agnes Gardner. *Kelvin the man. A biographical sketch by his niece.* London, 1925.

ar   Russell, Alexander. *Lord Kelvin, his life and work.* London, Edinburgh, and NY, 1939.

as   Sharlin, Harold Issadore. *Lord Kelvin: The dynamic Victorian.* University Park, Pa., 1979.

at   Thompson, Silvanus P. *The life of William Thomson, Baron Kelvin of Largs.* 2 vols. London, 1910.

ay   Young, Arthur Primrose. *Lord Kelvin, physicist, mathematician, engineer.* London, 1948.

cp   Picard, Emile. "Notice historique sur la vie et l'oeuvre de Lord Kelvin." AS. *Mémoires, 57* (1920), i-xxxix.

el   Larmor, Joseph. "William Thomson, Baron Kelvin of Largs." RS. *Proceedings, 81A* (1908), iii-lxxvi.

ew   Wien, Wilhelm. "Lord Kelvin." *Annalen der Physik, 25* (1908), 1-6.

See also: B.hg1.cg |sr4.jt; H.ab1.si

Threlfall, Richard (1861-1932)

ti3.ct   Threlfall, R. E. "Sir Richard Threlfall, G.B.E., F.R.S., (1861-1932): Some personal memories." RS. *Notes and records, 10* (1961), 234-242.

et   Thomson, J. J., and W. B. H. "Sir Richard Threlfall." RS. *Obituary notices, 1* (1932), 45-53.

Tikhov, Gavriil Adrianovich @ (1875-1960)

tj3.bs   *Shtaude, N. M. "Osnovnyye cherty nauchnogo tvorchestva G. A. Tikhova po lichnym vpechatleniam za 40 let." AN Kazakhskoy SSR. *Izvestiya*, no. 90, ser. astrobot., no. 1-2 (1950), 19-24.

gs   Sharonov, V. V. "Gavriil Adrianovich Tikhov." *Priroda*, 1950:8, 85-88.

Tilden, William Augustus @ (1842-1926)

tj8.ep   P., J. C. "William Augustus Tilden." RS. *Proceedings, 117A* (1927/8), i-v.

Timiryazev, Arkadiy Kliment'yevich (1880-1955)

tk3.jt   Timiryazev, A. K. *Nauka i demokratiya: Sbornik statey 1904-1919 gg.* Moscow, 1963.

Timoshenko, Stepan Prokof'yevich (1878-1972)

tl3.at   Timoshenko, Stephen P. *As I remember.* Tr. Robert Addis. Princeton, 1968.

em   Mansfield, E. H., and D. H. Young. "Stephen Prokofievitch
      Timoshenko." RS. *BM, 19* (1973), 679-694.

Titchmarsh, Edward Charles @ (1899-1963)

tm3.jc   CSAC. *E. C. Titchmarsh papers at New College Archives, Oxford.*
          List 44/8/76, 4 p.

Tizard, Henry (1885-1959)

tn3.ac   Clark, Ronald W. *Tizard.* Cambridge, 1965.

  cj   Jones, R. V. "Scientists and statesmen: The example of Henry
          Tizard." *Minerva, 4* (1966), 202-214.

  ef   Farren, W. S. "Henry Thomas Tizard." RS. *BM, 7* (1961),
          313-348.

  sr   Snow, Charles Percy. *Science and government.* London, 1961.

  ss   Snow, Charles Percy. *Appendix to Science and government.* Cam-
          bridge, Mass., 1962.

See also: U.kb1.bl

Tolansky, Samuel (1907-1973)

to3.ed   Ditchburn, R. W., and G. D. Rochester. "Samuel Tolansky." RS.
          BM, 20 (1974), 429-455.

  jc   CSAC. *Samuel Tolansky papers at University of London Library.*
          List 24/1/75, 36 p.

Tolman, Richard Chance @ (1881-1948)

to8.ek   Kirkwood, John G., et al. "Richard Chance Tolman." NAS.
          BM, 27 (1952), 139-153.

Tomonaga, Sin-itiro $65 (1906-   )

tp3.jt   Tomonaga, Sin-itiro. *Scientific papers.* Ed. Tatsuoki Miyazima. 2
          vols. Tokyo, 1971-76.

Topchiyev, Aleksandr Vasil'yevich (1907-1962)

tq3.jm   *Aleksandr Vasil'yevich Topchiyev.* Moscow, 1964. (*Mtly,* ser.
          khim., 34.)

Townsend, John Sealy Edward @ (1868-1957)

tr3.ct   Trenn, Thaddeus J. "Townsend, John Sealy Edward." *DSB, 13*
          (1976), 445-447.

ee   Engel, A. von. "John Sealy Edward Townsend." RS. *BM, 3* (1957), 257-272.

jc   CSAC. *Sir John Townsend papers at the Bodleian Library, Oxford.* List 8/2/74, 3 p.

Traubenberg, Heinrich Rausch von (1880-1944)

ts3.es   Sommerfeld, Arnold. "Heinrich Freiherr Rausch v. Traubenberg." *Zeitschrift für Naturforschung, 1* (1946), 420.

Travers, Morris William @ (1872-1961)

tt3.ct   Trenn, Thaddeus J. "Travers, Morris William." *DSB, 11* (1975), 277-284.

eb   Bawn, C. E. H. "Morris William Travers, 1872-1961." RS. *BM, 9* (1963), 301-313.

Trouton, Frederick Thomas @ (1863-1922)

tu3.cp   P., A. W. "Frederick Thomas Trouton." RS. *Proceedings, 110A* (1926), iv-ix.

Trowbridge, Augustus (1870-1934)

tv3.ec   Compton, Karl T. "Augustus Trowbridge." NAS. *BM, 18* (1938), 219-244.

jt   Trowbridge, Augustus. "War letters of Augustus Trowbridge: August 28, 1917 to January 19, 1919." New York Public Library. *Bulletin, 43* (1939), 591-617, 645-666, 725-738, 830-844, 901-914; *44* (1940), 8-35, 117-130, 331-350.

Trowbridge, John @ (1843-1923)

tv5.ch   Hall, Edwin H. "John Trowbridge." NAS. *BM, 14* (1932), 183-204.

Tudorovskiy, Aleksandr Illarionovich (1875-1964)

tw3.gb   Anon. "Aleksandr Illarionovich Tudorovskiy (K 85-letiyu so dnya rozhdeniya)." *Optiko-mekhanicheskaya promyshlennost'*, 1960:8, 4-5.

gt   Anon. "Semidesyatipyatiletniy yubiley Aleksandra Illarionovicha Tudorovskogo." *Zhurnal tekhnicheskoy fiziki, 20* (1950), 1285-1286.

Turkevich, Anthony (1916-   )

tx3.ct   Turkevich, Anthony. "A scientific autobiography." *Adventures in experimental physics, 4* (1974), 60-62.

Tyndall, Arthur Manning (1881-1961)

ty3.em   Mott, N. F., and C. F. Powell. "Arthur Manning Tyndall." RS. *BM, 8* (1962), 159-165.

Uhlenbeck, George Eugene (1900-   )

uh1.cu   Uhlenbeck, George E. "Personal reminiscences." *PT, 29* (Jun. 1976), 43-48.

Umarov, Sultan Umarovich (1908-1964)

um1.ad   *Dobrovol'skiy, O. V., and L. V. Tursynova. *Sultan Umarovich Umarov.* Dushanbe, 1965.

Umov, Nikolay Alekseyevich (1846-1915)

um4.ab   *Bachinskiy, A. Y. *Nikolay Alekseyevich Umov.* Moscow, 1905.

   af   *Gulo, D. D. *N. A. Umov i yego nauchnaya deyatel'nost'.* Moscow, 1953. (Summary of thesis for Moscow University.)

   ag   Gulo, D. D. *Nikolay Alekseyevich Umov, 1846-1914.* Moscow, 1971.

   ap   *Moscow. University. Biblioteka. *Nikolay Alekseyevich Umov.* Ed. A. S. Predvoditelev et al. Moscow, 1950.

   bg   Gulo, D. D. "Yestestvennonauchnyye i filosofskiye vzglyady N. A. Umova." *IMYeN: Fizika, 1* (1960), 115-140.

   ci   *Mechnikov, I. I. "Pamyati N. A. Umova." *Akademicheskoye sobraniye sochineniy.* Ed. N. N. Anichkov et al. 16 vols. Moscow, 1950-64. Vol. 14, 75-79. (Also in U.da1.me, 67-69.)

   cl   Predvoditelev, A. S. "Russkiy uchenyy-fizik N. A. Umov." *Sovetskaya nauka,* 1940:7, 121-133.

   cm   Predvoditelev, A. S. "Nikolay Alekseyevich Umov." C.vm1.pr, 81-106.

   cn   Predvoditelev, A. S., and A. A. Maksimov. "N. A. Umov." C.vb1.th, 130-145.

   co   Predvoditelev, A. S. "Nikolay Alekseyevich Umov (1846-1915)." B.um4.jv, 511-527.

   cp   Predvoditelev, A. S. "N. A. Umov." C.vb1.pr, *1*, 235-247.

   cs   Shpol'skiy, E. V. "Nikolay Alekseyevich Umov (1846-1915)." *UFN, 31* (1947), 129-146.

ct   Timiryazev, A. K. "Moi vospominaniya o Nikolaye Alekseyev-
     iche Umove." Moscow. University. *Vestnik,* seriya fiz.-mat i
     yestest. nauk, 1954:9, 149-152.

cu   *Umov, N. A. "Avtobiograficheskiy ocherk." *Sbornik statey po
     voprosam fiziko-matematicheskikh nauk i ikh prepodavaniya.* Mos-
     cow, 1924. Vol. 1, 84-105. (Also in B.um4.jv, 7-28.)

cw   Umov, N. A. "Avtobiografiya." *Nauchnoye nasledstvo, 2* (1951),
     363-397.

cz   Zubov, V. P. "Rabota N. A. Umova nad svoye avtobiografiyey."
     Nauchnoye nasledstvo, 2 (1951), 357-362.

jc   Chertov, A. G. "Neizvestnaya stat'ya N. A. Umova." Moscow.
     University. *Vestnik,* ser. fiz.-mat. i yest. nauk, 1954:2, 133-134.

ju   *Umov, N. A. *Sobraniye sochineniy.* Ed. A. I. Bachinskiy. 3
     vols.? Moscow, 1916.

jv   Umov, N. A. *Izbrannyye sochineniya.* Ed. A. S. Predvoditelev.
     Moscow and Leningrad, 1950.

kk   Kompaneyets, A. I. *Bor'ba N. A. Umova za materializm v fizike.*
     Moscow, 1954.

nl   Lazarev, P. P. *Nikolay Alekseyevich Umov, prezident Moskovsogo
     obshchestva ispytateley prirody (1846-1915).* Moscow, 1940.

nm   *Lazarev, P. P. "N. A. Umov v Moskovkom universitete."
     C.vm1.mo, 357-360.

np   Predvoditelev, A. S. "Primechaniya redaktora." B.um4.jv, 530-
     553.

See also: B.lh3.al, ci, js; D.be1.ba, gu; G.ca2.um; P.ca1.ar, gu

Unsöld, Albrecht (1905-   )

uo1.au   Unsöld, Albrecht. *Sterne und Menschen: Aufsätze und Vorträge.*
         Berlin, 1972.

Urbain, Georges @ (1872-1938)

uv1.cc   Courier, Robert. "Notice sur la vie et les travaux de Georges Ur-
         bain." AS. *Notices et discours, 6* (1972), 1-28.

Vavilov, Sergey Ivanovich @ (1891-1951)

va4.ab   Artobelevskiy, I. I. *Vydayushchiysya sovetskiy uchenyy i obshchest-
         vennyy deyatel' Sergey Ivanovich Vavilov.* Moscow, 1951; Baku,
         1952.

ad   *Bazhenov, A. N. *S. I. Vavilov.* Moscow, 1961.

aj   Keler, V. L. *Sergey Vavilov.* Moscow, 1961.

ak   Lazarevich, E. A. *Iskusstvo populyarizatsii akademiki S. I. Vavilov, V. A. Obruchev, A. Ye. Fersman.* Moscow, 1960.

al   Levshin, L. V. *Sergey Ivanovich Vavilov.* Moscow, 1960.

am   Levshin, L. V. *Sergey Ivanovich Vavilov.* Moscow, 1977.

an   *Nesmeyanov, A. N., et al., eds. *Pamyati Sergeya Ivanovicha Vavilova.* Moscow, 1952.

ar   Rayevskaya, M. A. *Vydayushchiysya sovetskiy uchenyy akademik S. I. Vavilov.* Moscow, 1952.

as   *Shpol'skiy, E. V. *Vydayushchiysya sovetskiy uchenyy S. I. Vavilov.* Moscow, 1956.

au   *Terenin, A. N., et al., eds. *Trudy sessii, posvyashchennoy pamyati akademika Sergeya Ivanovich Vavilova.* Moscow, 1953.

bd   Feofilov, P. P. "S. I. Vavilov: Sozdatel' sovetskoy shkoly lyuminestsentsii." *UFN, 75* (1961), 277-286. (In English in *SPU, 4* (1962), 770-775.)

bf   Feofilov, P. P. "The contributions of Academician S. I. Vavilov to the study of light." *SPU, 10* (1967), 1-5. (Also in *UFN, 91* (1967), 3-9.)

bl   Levshin, V. L., et al. "Razvitiye rabot S. I. Vavilova v oblasti fiziki." *UFN, 75* (1961), 215-225. (In English in *SPU, 4* (1962), 730-736.)

bn   Mints, A. L. "Nochaya beseda." *UFN, 111* (1973), 185-187.

bs   Stepanov, B. I. "Zakon Vavilova." *UFN, 58* (1956), 3-36.

bt   Terenin, A. N., and P. P. Feofilov. "Krupneyshiy sovetskiy uchenyy optik." AN. *Vestnik*, 1951:3, 111-121.

cb   Anon. "Sergey Ivanovich Vavilov." *Synthèse, 5* (1946), 422-424.

cd   Chenakal, V. L. "S. I. Vavilov: Issledovatel' tvorchestva M. V. Lomonosova." IIYeT. *Trudy, 17* (1957), 44-65.

ce   Feofilov, P. "Sergey Ivanovich Vavilov." *Optika i spektroskopiya, 1* (1956), 107-112.

cg   Frank, I. M. "Fiziki o Vavilove." *UFN, 111* (1973), 173-179.

ch   *Kravets, T. P. "Prezident Akademii Nauk S. I Vavilov." *Elektrichestvo*, 1945:8, 1-3.

ci   Landsberg, G. S., et al. "Iz vospominaniy o Sergeye Ivanoviche Vavilove." IIYeT. *Trudy, 17* (1957), 137-153.

cl   Levshin, V. L. "Sergey Ivanovich Vavilov." B.va4.jv, *1*, 7-48.

cm   Levshin, V. L. "Sergey Ivanovich Vavilov." *UFN, 73* (1961), 373-380. (In English in *SPU, 4* (1961), 374-379.)

cn   Nesmeyanov, A. N. "S. I. Vavilov: Vydayushchiysya uchenyy i organizator sovetskoy nauki." *UFN, 75* (1961), 205-213. (In English in *SPU, 4* (1962), 725-729.)

cp   Shpol'skiy, E. V., et al. "Nabroski k portretu S. I. Vavilova." *UFN, 117* (1975), 159-179.

cr   Skobel'tsyn, D. V. "Krupneyshiy russkiy fizik S. I. Vavilov." *UFN, 75* (1961), 227-230.

cs   Sveshnikov, B. "Sergey Ivanovich Vavilov." *Optika i spektroskopiya, 10* (1961), 426-428.

ct   Tolstoy, N. A. "Sergey Ivanovich Vavilov." *Optikomekhanicheskaya promyshlennost'*, 1961:3, 2-7.

cv   Vvedenskiy, B. A. "Iz vospominaniy o Sergeye Ivanoviche Vavilove." *UFN, 111* (1973), 181-185.

db   Anon. "Pamyati S. I. Vavilova." AN. *Vestnik*, 1961:6, 103-106.

dd   Bolotovskiy, B. M. "Pamyati S. I. Vavilova." AN. *Vestnik*, 1956:4, 138-139.

df   Frank, I. M., et al. "Nabroski k portretu S. I. Vavilova." *UFN, 114* (1974), 533-554.

di   Idel'son, N. I. "Pamyati S. I. Vavilova." IIYeT. *Trudy, 17* (1957), 127-136.

dl   Levshin, L. V. "Akademik S. I. Vavilov—vydayushchiysya sovetskiy fizik-optik." A.ab1.vo, 259-272.

dn   Nesmeyanov, A. N. "Vystupleniye, posvyashchennoye pamyati S. I. Vavilova." Nesmeyanov. *Izbrannyye trudy.* 4 vols. Moscow, 1959. Vol. 4, 181-184.

ds   Shubnikov, A. V. "To, chto sokhranila pamyat'." *UFN, 111* (1973), 179-181.

eb   Anon. "Zhizn', otdannaya rodine, sovetskoy nauke, velikomu delu kommunizma." AN. *Vestnik, 1951:2, 35-44.*

ed   Anon. "Otkrytiye memorial'noy doski, posvashchennoy S. I. Vavilova." AN. *Vestnik*, 1952:2, 74-80.

ee   Anon. "Sergey Ivanovich Vavilov." *ZhETF, 21* (1951), 99-104.

ek   Kravets, T. P. "Sergey Ivanovich Vavilov: Uchenyy i deyatel'." AN. *Izvestiya*, ser. fiz. *15* (1951), 523-532.

el   Kravets, T. P. "Sergey Ivanovich Vavilov: Ocherk zhizni i deyatel'nosti." *UFN, 46* (1951), 3-22.

en   Kuznetsov, I. V. "S. I. Vavilov—uchenyy-patriot, voinstvu-yushchiy materialist-dialektik." *Voprosy filosofii*, 1951:1, 62-82.

es   Shpol'skiy, E. V. "Sergey Ivanovich Vavilov." *UFN, 43* (1951), 327-346. (Also in B.va4.is, 5-19.) Moscow, Leningrad, 1951. Pp. 5-19.)

gb   Anon. "Prezident Akademii Nauk SSSR akademik Sergey Ivanovich Vavilov." AN. *Vestnik*, 1945:7-8, 29-31.

gd   *Anon. "Pamyati zamechatel'nogo uchenogo. (K 70-letiyu so dnya rozhdeniya akad. S. I. Vavilova.)" AN Kazakhskoy SSR. *Vestnik*, 1961:3, 100-102.

is   *Shpol'skiy, E. V., ed. *Problemy fizicheskoy optiki i drugiye voprosy fiziki: Sbornik statey*. Moscow and Leningrad, 1951.

jj   Koryakov, P. N., B. A. Mal'kevich, and N. M. Raskin. "Obzory arkhivnykh fondov S. I. Vavilova." IIYeT. *Trudy, 17* (1957), 154-155.

jk   Koryakov, P. N., B. A. Mal'kevich, and N. M. Raskin. "Pis'mo V. I. Vernadskogo S. I. Vavilovu." IIYeT. *Trudy, 17* (1957), 121-122.

jl   Kuvanova, L. K. "Kratkoye obozreniye arkhivnogo fonda S. I. Vavilova, khranyashchegosya v moskovskom otdelenii Arkhiva AN SSSR." IIYeT. *Trudy, 17* (1957), 155-160.

jm   Levshin, V. L., and T. O. Vreden-Kobetskaya, ed. *Sergey Ivanovich Vavilov*. Moscow and Leningrad, 1949. (*Mtly*, ser. fiziki, 3.)

ju   *AN. *Pamyati Sergeya Ivanovicha Vavilova: Sbornik statey*. Moscow, 1952.

jv   Vavilov, S. I. *Sobraniye sochineniy*. 4 vols. Moscow, 1954-56.

kk   Kuznetsov, I. V. "Trudy S. I. Vavilova po filosofii i istorii yestestvoznaniya." *UFN, 75* (1961), 251-258. (In English in *SPU, 4* (1962), 753-758.)

nf   Feynberg, Ye. L. "S. I. Vavilov i vavilovskiy FIAN." *VIYeT*, 1980:4, 123-132.

ni   Kol'tsov, A. V. "S. I. Vavilov kak istorik Akademii nauk SSSR." *VIYeT, 19* (1965), 148-150.

nk   Kravets, T. P. "Iz vystupleniya chl.-korr. AN SSSR T. P. Kravtsa ot litsa obshchestvennosti Leningradskogo gos. universiteta im. A. A. Zhdanova za kandidaturu akademika S. I. Vavilova v deputaty Verkhovnogo soveta RSFSR." IIYeT. *Trudy, 17* (1957), 123-125.

nr   Rusevich, E. "S. I. Vavilov i pol'skaya nauka." *VIYeT, 49* (1974), 21-23.

nv   Veksler, V. I. "S. I. Vavilov v FIANe." *UFN, 111* (1973), 187-190.

pl   Levshin, V. L. "Nauchnaya i pedagogicheskaya deyatel'nost' S. I. Vavilova." Moscow. University. *Vestnik,* seriya fiz.-mat. i yestest. nauk, 1953:5, 3-15.

pr   Radovskiy, M. I. "S. I. Vavilov: Organizator nauchno-populyarnykh izdaniy." *UFN, 47* (1952), 477-481.

xk   Kuznetsov, Boris Grigor'yevich. "S. I. Vavilov kak istorik nauk." IIYeT. *Trudy, 4* (1952), 5-17.

xy   Yushkevich, A. P. "S. I. Vavilov kak issledovatel' tvorchestva I. N'yutona." IIYeT. *Trudy, 17* (1957), 66-89.

See also: E.td1.fe; G.ba1.fe |ca2.va |pa1.ko, ld, lf, lg, te

Vekshinskiy, Sergey Arkad'yevich (1896-   )

vc4.gb   Anon. "Vekshinskiy, S. A.: K 60-letiyu so dnya rozhdeniya." *Radiotekhnika, 12:1* (1957), 78-79.

Veksler, Vladimir Iosifovich @ (1907-1966)

ve4.er   Rabinovich, M. S. "Pamyati V. I. Vekslera." *UFN, 91* (1967), 161-165. (In English in *SPU, 10* (1967), 112-116.)

See also: T.ga1.ko

Vernov, Sergey Nikolayevich (1910-   )

vf4.gd   Dobrotin, N. A., et al. "Sergey Nikolayevich Vernov." *UFN, 72* (1960), 153-155.

Villard, Paul Ulrich @ (1860-1934)

vh4.ep   Picard, Emile. "La vie et l'oeuvre de Paul Villard et de Georges Gouy." AS. *Mémoires, 63* (1937), 29p.

gm   Mascart, Eleuthère, et al. "Paul Villard." AS. *Comptes rendus, 145* (1907), 1002-1005.

Vleck, John Hasbrouck Van $7 / (1899-1980)

See: E.mb1.an; L.ah1.vv

Vogel, Hermann Carl @ (1841-1907)

vn4.el   Lohse, O. "Hermann Carl Vogel." *Astronomische Nachrichten, 175* (1907), 373-378.

em   Müller, G. "Hermann Carl Vogel." Astronomische Gesellschaft. *Vierteljahrsschrift, 42* (1907), 323-339.

Voigt, Woldemar @ (1850-1919)

vo4.el   L[amb], H[orace]. "Woldemar Voigt." RS. *Proceedings, 99A* (1921), xxix-xxx.

er   Runge, Carl. "Woldemar Voigt." *PZ, 21* (1920), 81-82.

es   Runge, Carl. "Woldemar Voigt." Akademie der Wissenschaften, Göttingen. *Nachrichten,* 1920, 46-52.

See also: O.fa1.pa

Volterra, Vito @ (1860-1940)

vq4.ab   Arangio-Ruiz, Vincenzo, et al. *Vito Volterra nel I centenario della nascità (1860-1960).* Rome, 1961. (Accademia Nazionale dei Lincei. *Problemi attuali di scienza e cultura. Quaderni,* 51.)

ap   Polishchuk, Ye. M. *Vito Vol'terra.* Leningrad, 1977.

ew   Whittaker, E. T. "Vito Volterra." RS. *Obituary notices, 3* (1941), 690-729.

jv   Volterra, Vito. *Opere matematiche.* 5 vols. Rome, 1954-62.

See also: B.lw3.js

Vul'f, Yuriy Viktorovich (1863-1925)

vu4.ci   Il'in, B. V. "Yuriy Viktorovich Vul'f." B.vm1.pr, 188-198.

See also: B.ff1.jd

Vvedenskiy, Boris Alekseyevich (1893-1969)

vv4.gb   Anon. "Chestvovaniye akademika B. A. Vvedenskogo." AN. *Vestnik,* 1953:5, 64-67.

gd   *Anon. "Akademik B. A. Vvedenskiy: K 60-letiyu so dnya rozhdeniya." *Radiotekhnika, 8:3* (1953), 5-7.

jm   Arenburg, A. G., and A. P. Epifanova, ed. *Boris Alekseyevich Vvedenskiy.* Moscow and Leningrad, 1950. (*Mtly,* ser. fiziki, 4.)

Walker, George Walker (1874-1921)

wa2.et   T., H. H., et al. "George Walker Walker." RS. *Proceedings, 102A* (1922/3), xxii-xxvi.

Walsh, Arthur Donald (1916-1977)

wa4.ep   Price, W. C. "Arthur Donald Walsh." RS. *BM, 24* (1978), 569-582.

Warburg, Emil Gabriel @ (1846-1931)

wa6.cg   Gehrcke, Ernst. "Warburg als Physiker." *Zeitschrift für technische Physik, 3* (1922), 186-192.

ef   Franck, James. "Emil Warburg zum Gedächtnis." *Nwn, 19* (1931), 993-997.

ep   Paschen, Friedrich. "Gedächtnisrede... auf Emil Warburg." Akademie der Wissenschaften, Berlin. *Sitzungsberichte,* 1932, cxv-cxxii.

ge   Einstein, Albert. "Emil Warburg als Forscher." *Nwn, 10* (1922), 823-828.

gr   *Rubens, Heinrich. "Adresse an Hrn. Emil Warburg zum 50. Doktorjubiläum." Akademie der Wissenschaften, Berlin. *Sitzungsberichte,* 1917, 269- .

pg   Gehlhoff, Georg. "E. Warburg als Lehrer." *Zeitschrift für technische Physik, 3* (1922), 193-194.

Watson-Watt, Robert Alexander (1892-1973)

wa8.er   Ratcliffe, J. A. "Robert Alexander Watson-Watt." RS. *BM, 21* (1975), 549-568.

Webster, Arthur Gordon (1863-1923)

wb3.cb   Ames, Joseph S. "Arthur Gordon Webster." NAS. *BM, 18* (1938), 337-347.

ed   Duff, A. Wilmer. "Arthur Gordon Webster: Physicist, mathematician, linguist, and orator." *AJP, 6* (1938), 181-194.

Wegener, Alfred Lothar @ (1880-1930)

wc3.aw   Wegener, Else, ed. *Greenland journey. The story of Wegener's German expedition to Greenland in 1930-31.* London, 1939.

bw   Wegner, Kurt. "Alfred Wegner, die Entstehung der Kontinente und Ozeane." A.ajl.sc, 295-302.

eb   Benndorf, H. "Alfred Wegener." *Beiträge zur Geophysik, 31* (1931), 337-377.

eg   George, J. "Memories of Alfred Wegener." *Continental Drift.* Ed. S. K. Runcorn. London, 1962. Pp. 309-324.

jw   Wegener, Else. *Alfred Wegener: Tagebücher, Briefe, Erinnerungen.* Wiesbaden, 1960.

Wehnelt, Arthur Rudolph Berthold @ (1871-1944)

wd3.cb   Biguenet, C. "Arthur Wehnelt: 50 Jahre Oxydkathode." *PB, 11* (1955), 30-32.

Weiss, Pierre-Ernst @ (1865-1940)

we3.if   France. Centre National de la Recherche Scientifique. *Colloque national de magnétisme commémoratif de l'oeuvre de Pierre Weiss.* Paris, 1958.

Weisskopf, Victor Frederick (1908-   )

we6.cs   Spruch, Grace Marmor. "Victor Weisskopf, international scientist." *New scientist, 46* (1970), 387-388.

   cw   Weisskopf, V. F. "Physics and physicists the way I knew them." A.ad1.we, 435-446.

   gp   Paul, W. "Victor Frederick Weisskopf 60 Jahre." *PB, 24* (1968), 417-418.

   gr   Rechenberg, Helmut. "Victor F. Weissskopf—Ein herzlicher Gruss zum 70. Geburtstag." *PB, 34* (1978), 434-436.

   ih   Huang, Kerson, ed. *Physics and our world: A symposium in honor of Victor F. Weisskopf.* NY, 1976.

   is   Shalit, Amos de, H. Feshbach, and L. Van Hove, eds. *Preludes in theoretical physics, in honor of V. F. Weisskopf.* Amsterdam, 1966.

   jw   Weisskopf, Victor F. *Physics in the 20th century: Selected essays.* Cambridge, 1972.

Weizsäcker, Carl Friedrich von (1912-   )

wf3.bd   Dingler, Hugo. "Methode der Physik. Zu einem Aufsatz von Karl Friedrich Weizsäcker." *ZGN, 6* (1940), 75-88.

   cb   Born, Max. "Carl Friedrich Freiherr von Weizsäcker: Bindeglied zwischen zwei Kulturen." *PB, 19* (1963), 518-520.

   cw   Weizsäcker, C. F. von. [Interview.] A.aj1.bu, 62-70.

   gh   Heisenberg, Werner. "C. F. v. Weizsäcker zum 60. Geburtstag." *PB, 28* (1972), 319-321.

   is   Scheibe, Erhard, and Georg Süssmann, eds. *Einheit und Vielheit. Festschrift für Carl Friedrich v. Weizsäcker zum 60. Geburtstag.* Göttingen, 1973.

   kl   Labérenne, Paul. "De Broglie, Carnap, Ambartsoumian, von Weizsäcker." *La pensée,* no. 178 (1974), 89-99.

ks   Strobl, Wolfgang. "Carl Friedrich von Weizsäcker y el pensamiento contemporáno." *Atlantida, 1* (1963), 442-448.

Wentzel, Gregor (1898-1978)

wg3.if   Freund, P. G. O., C. J. Goebel, and Y. Nambu, eds. *Quanta: Essays in theoretical physics dedicated to Gregor Wentzel.* Chicago, 1970.

Westphal, Wilhelm H. (1882-1978)

wh3.cw   Westphal, Wilhelm H. "68 Jahre als Physiker in Berlin." *PB, 28* (1972), 258-265.

gb   Brüche, Ernst. "Wilhelm H. Westphal zum 80. Geburtstag." *PB, 18* (1962), 127-130.

See also: B.kd1.ck

Weyl, Hermann @ (1885-1955)

wi3.cb   Beisswanger, Peter. "Hermann Weyl and mathematical texts." *Ratio, 8* (1966), 25-45.

cc   Chevalley, Claude, and A. Weil. "Hermann Weyl." *L'Enseignement mathématique, 3* (1957), 157-187.

cf   Freudenthal, Hans. "Hermann Weyl, der Dolmetscher zwischen Mathematikern und Physikern um die moderne Interpretation von Raum, Zeit und Materie." A.aj1.sc, 357-366.

en   Newman, M. H. A. "Hermann Weyl." RS. *BM, 3* (1957), 305-328.

jv   Weyl, Hermann. *Selecta Hermann Weyl.* Basel, 1956.

jw   Weyl, Hermann. *Gesammelte Abhandlungen.* 4 vols. Berlin and NY, 1968.

Wheeler, John Archibald (1911-)

wj3.ck   Klauder, John R. "Magic without magic: John Archibald Wheeler." B.wj3.ik, 1-14.

cw   Wheeler, John A. [Interview.] A.aj1.bu, 51-61.

ik   Klauder, John R., ed. *Magic without magic: John Archibald Wheeler, a collection of essays in honour of his sixtieth birthday.* San Francisco, 1972.

Whiddington, Richard D. (1885-1970)

wk3.ef   Feather, Norman. "Richard Whiddington." RS. *BM, 17* (1971), 741-755.

jc   CSAC. *Richard Whiddington papers at Leeds University Library.*
       List 7/1/74, 6 p.

Whittaker, Edmund Taylor @ (1873-1956)

wl3.ek Martin, D. "Sir Edmund Whittaker." Edinburgh Mathematical
        Society. *Proceedings, 11* (1958), 1-9.

   em   McCrea, W. H. "Edmund Taylor Whittaker." London
        Mathematical Society. *Journal, 32* (1957), 234-256.

   et   Temple, G. F. J. "Edmund Taylor Whittaker." RS. *BM, 2*
        (1956), 299-325.

   km   McCronell, James. "Whittaker's correlation of physics and philo-
        sophy." Edinburgh Mathematical Society. *Proceedings, 11* (1958),
        57-68.

   xh   Hardie, C. D. "Professor Whittaker and the history of physics."
        Isis, 34 (1943), 344-346.

See also: F.dc1.sy

Wiechert, Emil @ (1861-1928)

wm3.cb *Anon. "Zum Gedenken Emil Wiecherts anlässlich der 100
        Wiederkehr seines Geburtstags." Jena. Insititut für Boden-
        dynamik und Erdbebenforschung. *Veröffentlichungen*, no. 72
        (1962), 5-21.

Wien, Wilhelm Carl W. O. @ $11 (1864-1928)

wn3.as Steenbeck, Max. *Wilhelm Wien und sein Einfluss auf die Physik
        seiner Zeit.* Berlin, 1964. (Akademie der Wissenschaften, Berlin.
        Vorträge und Schriften, 94.)

   aw   Wien, Wilhelm. *Aus dem Leben und Wirken eines Physikers.*
        Leipzig, 1930.

   ed   Laue, Max von, and E. Rüchardt. "Willy Wien" *Nwn, 17* (1929),
        675-681. (Also in B.lf6.jl, *3*, 173-179.

Wiener, Norbert @ (1894-1964)

wo3.aw Wiener, Norbert. *Ex-prodigy: My childhood and youth.* Cam-
        bridge, Mass., 1953.

   ax   Wiener, Norbert. *I am a mathematician: The later life of a prodi-
        gy.* Cambridge, Mass., 1956.

   bg   Guillaumaud, Jacques. *Norbert Wiener et la cybernétique.* Paris,
        1971.

Wiener, Otto Heinrich @ (1862-1927)

wo8.el   Lichtenecker, Karl. "Otto Wiener." *PZ, 29* (1928), 73-78.

ew   Weikmann, L. "Nachruf auf Otto Wiener." Akademie der Wissenschaften, Leipzig. Math.-Phys. Klasse. *Berichte, 79* (1927), 107-123.

Wigner, Eugene Paul $63 (1902-   )

wp3.cw   Walsh, John. "A conversation with Eugene Wigner." *Science, 181* (1973), 527-533.

gb   Bargman, V., et al. "In commemoration of the sixtieth birthday of Eugene Paul Wigner." *Reviews of modern physics, 34* (1962), 587-591.

gp   Päsler, Max. "Eugene Wigner zum 75. Geburtstag." *PB, 74* (1978), 29-31.

gs   Seitz, Frederick. "Eugene Wigner, a tribute on his seventieth birthday." *PT, 25* (Oct. 1972), 40-43.

jo   Wigner, Eugene Paul. "Wigner Jenö levelei Ortvay Rudolfhoz." *Fizikai szemle, 22* (1972), 45-58.

jw   Wigner, Eugene P. *Symmetries and reflections. Scientific essays.* Bloomington, 1967.

Williams, Evan James (1903-1945)

wq3.eb   Blackett, P. M. S. "Evan James Williams." RS. *Obituary notices, 5* (1945-48), 387-406.

Williams, John Harry (1908-1966)

wq8.cn   Nier, Alfred O. C. "John Harry Williams." NAS. *BM, 42* (1971), 339-355.

Wilson, Charles Thomas Rees @ $27 (1869-1959)

wr3.cw   Wilson, C. T. R. "Reminiscences of my early years." RS. *Notes and records, 14* (1960), 163-173.

eb   Blackett, P. M. S. "Charles Thomson Rees Wilson." RS. *BM, 6* (1960), 269-295.

jd   Dee, P. I., and T. W. Wormell. "An index to C. T. R. Wilson's laboratory records and notebooks in the library of the Royal Society." RS. *Notes and records, 18* (1963), 54-66.

See also: B.npl.ah

Wilson, Edwin Bidwell (1879-1964)

wr8.eh   Hunsaker, Jerome, and Saunders MacLane. "Edwin Bidwell Wilson." NAS. *BM, 43* (1973), 285-320.

Wilson, Harold Albert (1874-1964)

wr9.et   Thomson, George P. "Harold Albert Wilson." RS. *BM, 11* (1965), 187-201.

Wilson, Robert Rathburn (1914-)

ws1.cr   Wilson, Robert R. "The conscience of a physicist." *BAS, 26* (Jun. 1970), 30-34. (Also in U.gk5.le, 67-76.)

    cw   Wilson, Robert R. "My fight against team research." A.aa1.ho, 468-479.

    cx   Wilson, Robert R. "A recruit for Los Alamos." *BAS, 31* (Mar. 1975), 41-47.

Wilson, William (1887-1948)

ws4.et   Temple, G., and H. T. Flint. "William Wilson." RS. *BM, 13* (1967), 387-391.

Wood, Robert Williams @ (1868-1955)

wt3.as   Seabrook, William B. *Doctor Wood: Modern wizard of the laboratory.* NY, 1941.

    at   Seabrook, William B. *Robert Vil'yams Vud: Sovremennyy charodey fizicheskoy laboratorii.* Tr. V. S. Vavilov. Moscow and Leningrad, 1946.

    co   Osinovskiy, A. N., and F. A. Uvarov. "Robert Vud." *IMYeN: Fizika, 10* (1971), 179-185.

    ed   Dieke, G. H. "Robert Williams Wood." RS. *BM, 2* (1956), 327-345.

Woodward, Robert Simpson @ (1849-1924)

wu3.ew   Wright, F. E. "Robert Simpson Woodward." NAS. *BM, 19* (1938), 1-24.

Yel'yashevich, Mikhail Aleksandrovich (1908-)

ye1.gb   "M. A. Yel'yashevich: K 50-letiyu so dnya rozhdeniya." *Optika i spektroskopiya, 6* (1959), 127-128.

    gf   *"K 50-letiyu so dnya rozhdeniya i 30-letiyu nauchnoy deyatel'nosti M. A. Yel'yashevicha." AN BSSR. Institut fiziki i matematiki. *Trudy,* 1959:3, 3-8.

Young, Sydney (1857-1937)

yo1.ea Atkins, W. R. G. "Sydney Young." RS. *Obituary notices, 2* (1938), 370-379.

ef Francis, F. "Sydney Young." *Journal of the chemical society*, 1937, 1332-1336.

Yukawa, Hideki $49 (1907-)

yu1.ky Yukawa, Hideki. *Creativity and intuition: A physicist looks at East and West.* Tr. John Bester. Tokyo, 1973.

Zakrzevsky, Konstantin (1876-1948)

za1.ep Piech, Tadeusz. "Konstanty Zakrzewski." *Acta physica polonica, 9* (1948), 65-70.

Zeeman, Pieter @ $02 (1865-1943)

ze1.es Strutt, Robert John, Fourth Baron Rayleigh. "Pieter Zeeman." RS. *Obituary notices, 4* (1944), 591-595.

gl Lorentz, H. A. "Prof. Dr. P. Zeeman, 1900-1925." *Physica, 5* (1925), 73-77.

gm Meggers, W. F. "The progress of science: The seventieth anniversary of Professor P. Zeeman." *Scientific monthly, 41* (1935), 85-87.

gw Waals, J. D. van der, Jr. "Toespraak tot Professor Doctor Pieter Zeeman den 25sten Mei 1935." B.ze1.ih, 1-7.

ih *Pieter Zeeman 1865—25 Mei—1935. Verhandlingen op 25 Mei 1935 aangeboden an Prof. Dr. P. Zeeman.* The Hague, 1935.

See also: G.ba1.le; G.e; H.db1.ka, ro

Zehnder, Ludwig Albert (1854-1949)

ze4.bd Dingler, Hugo. "Ludwig Zehnder. Ein Vorkämpfer der klassischen Physik." *ZGN, 6* (1940), 131-133.

km Müller, Wilhelm. "Über Zehnders Darstellung des physikalischen Weltganzen." *ZGN, 6* (1940), 134-135.

Zel'dovich, Yakov Borisovich (1914-)

zf3.gg Gershtein, S. S. "Yakov Borisovich Zel'dovich." *UFN, 112* (1974), 533-540. (In English in *SPU, 17* (1974), 276-282.)

gs Smorodinskiy, Ya. A., and D. A. Frank-Kamenetskiy. "Yakov Borisovich Zel'dovich." *UFN, 82* (1964), 567-574. (In English in *SPU, 7* (1962), 332-338.)

Zemplen, Győző (1879-1916)

zf5.cs   Szilard, Josef. "Zemplén Gyözö, Eötvös tanitvanya." *Fizika szemle, 26* (1976), 252-258.

Zenneck, Jonathan (1871-1959)

zf8.ed   Dieminger, Walter. *Jonathan Zenneck.* Munich, 1961. (Deutsches Museum. *Abhandlungen und Berichte, 29:1.*)

Zernike, Frits @ $53 (1888-1960)

zg3.bn   Nijboer, B. R. A. "Het door Prof. Dr. F. Zernike in de laatste twintig jaren verrichte wetenschappelijke werk." *Nederlands tijdschrift voor natuurkunde, 19* (1953), 320-328.

bp   Prins, J. A. "Het oudere wetenschappelijke werk van Prof. Dr. F. Zernike." *Nederlands tijdschrift voor natuurkunde, 19* (1953), 314-319.

ep   Prins, J. A. "Frits Zernike." Akademie van Wetenschappen, Amsterdam. *Jaarboek,* 1965/6, 370-377.

et   Tolansky, Samuel. "Frits Zernike." RS. *BM, 13* (1967), 393-402.

gb   Brinkman, H. "Bij de zeventigste verjaardag van Prof. Dr. F. Zernike." *Nederlands tijdschrift voor natuurkunde, 24* (1958), 139.

See also: G.da6.ze

Zhukovskiy, Nikolay Yegorovich @ (1847-1921)

zh3.ab   Arlazorov, M. *Zhukovskiy.* 2nd ed. Moscow, 1964.

al   *Leybenzon, L. S. *Nikolay Yegorovich Zhukovskiy: K stoletiyu so dnya rozhdeniya.* Moscow and Leningrad, 1947.

cv   Vavilov, S. I. "Iz vstupitel'nogo slova na torzhestvennom zasedanii, posvyashchennom stoletiyu so dnya rozhdeniya N. Ye. Zhukovskogo." IIYeT. *Trudy, 17* (1957), 93-95.

js   *Semenova, N. M. *Iz neopublikovannoy perepiski N. Ye. Zhukovskogo.* Moscow, 1957.

jz   *Zhukovskiy, N. Ye. *Sobraniye sochineniy.* 7 vols. Moscow, 1948-50.

See also: B.kt1.jh; D.eb1.ss |ta1.kn

C. INSTITUTIONS

Austria/Hungary

aa1.an   Anon. "Aus der Geschichte der Österreichischen Physikalischen Gesellschaft." *PB, 25* (1969), 418-420.

mc   McCagg, William O., Jr. *Jewish nobles and geniuses in modern Hungary.* NY, 1972.

ap1.kl   Kleinert, Andreas. "Anton Lampa and Albert Einstein, die Neubesetzung der physikalischen Lehrstühle an der Deutschen Universität Prag 1909 und 1910." *Gesnerus, 32* (1975), 285-292.

av1.he   Herneck, Friedrich. "Wiener Physik vor 100 Jahren." *PB, 17* (1961), 455-461.

av2.he   Hess, Victor F. "Persönliche Erinnerungen aus dem ersten Jahrzehnt des Instituts für Radiumforschung." C.av2.vi, 43-45.

hf   Hevesy, Georg von. "Erinnerungen an die alten Tage am Wiener Institut für Radiumforschung." C.av2.vi, 47-48.

ka   Karlik, Berta. "[Institut für Radiumforschung] 1938 bis 1950." C.av2.vi, 35-41.

me   Meyer, Stefan. "Die Vorgeschichte der Grundung und das erste Jahrzehnt des Institutes für Radiumforschung." C.av2.vi, 1-26.

pa   Paneth, Friedrich A. "Aus der Frühzeit des Wiener Radiuminstituts: Die Darstellung des Wismutwasserstoffs." C.av2.vi, 49-52.

pr   Przibram, Karl. "[Institut für Radiumforschung] 1920 bis 1938." C.av2.vi, 27-34.

ps   Przibram, K. "Erinnerungen an ein altes physikalisches Institut." B.mk1.if, 1-6.

vi   Vienna. Universität. Institut für Radiumforschung. *Festschrift des Instituts... anlässlich seines 40-jährigen Bestandes.* Vienna, 1950. (Akademe der Wissenschaften, Vienna. Math.-Natur. Klasse. *Sitzungsberichte, 159:2a* (1950), 1-57.)

Britain

ba1.cr   Crowther, James G. *British scientists of the twentieth century.* London, 1952.

mo   Moseley, Russell. "Tadpoles and frogs: Some aspects of the professionalization of British physics, 1870-1939." *SSS, 7* (1977), 423-446.

we   *Werskey, P. Gary. *The visible college: A study of left-wing scientists in Britain, 1918-1939.* Ph.D. thesis. Harvard Univ., 1974.

wf   Werskey, P. Gary. *The visible college: The collective biography of British scientific socialists in the 1930s.* NY, 1979.

See also: C.ga2.fp |va4.an;   D.kt1.ha;   E.tf1.kr;   F.ae1.go;   H.da1.lo; U.gb1.ra |gd1.fi, fj

ba2.ho Howarth, O. J. R. *The British Association for the Advancement of Science: A retrospect, 1831-1931.* 2nd ed. London, 1931.

lo   Lodge, Oliver. *Advancing science: Being personal reminiscences of the British Association in the nineteenth century.* London, 1932.

ba3.gs *Gummett, Philip J. *Scientists in Whitehall.* Manchester, 1980.

gu   Gummett, Philip J., and Geoffrey L. Price. "An approach to the central planning of British science: The formation of the Advisory Council on Scientific Policy." *Minerva, 15* (1977), 119-143.

hu   Hutchinson, Eric. "Scientists as an inferior class: The early years of the DSIR." *Minerva, 8* (1970), 396-411.

ma   MacLeod, Roy M., and E. Kay Andrews. "The Committee of Civil Research: Scientific advice for economic development, 1925-1930." *Minerva, 7* (1969), 680-705.

mc   McGucken, William. "The Royal Society and the genesis of the Scientific Advisory Committee to Britain's War Cabinet, 1939-1940." RS. *Notes and records, 33* (1978), 87-116.

sp   Spear, Frederick Gordon, and K. Griffiths. *The radium commission: A short history of its origin and work, 1929-1948.* London, 1951.

va   Varcoe, Ian. "Scientists, government, and organised research in Great Britain, 1914-1916: The early history of the DSIR." *Minerva, 8* (1970), 192-216.

vb   Varcoe, Ian. *Organizing science in Britain.* Oxford, 1974.

ba4.ki Kingslake, Hilda G. "Institute of Optics, 1929-1979: A brief commemorative." *Applied optics, 18* (1979), 3223-3229.

bc1.ca Campbell, N. R. "1903-1909." C.bc1.hi, 221-249.

cr   Crowther, J. A. "Research work in the Cavendish Laboratory in 1900-1918." *Nature, 118:* Suppl. (1926), 58-60.

cs   Crowther, James G. *The Cavendish Laboratory, 1874-1974.* NY, 1974.

da   Dampier, William Cecil. *Cambridge and elsewhere.* London, 1950.

gl   Glazebrook, Richard T. "The Cavendish Laborarory: 1876-1900." *Nature, 110:* Suppl. (1926), 52-58.

hi   *A history of the Cavendish Laboratory.* London, 1910.

ku   Kudryavtsev, P. S. "K 100-letiyu otkrytiya Kavendishskoy laboratorii." *VIYeT, 49* (1974), 73-75.

la   Larsen, Egon. *The Cavendish Laboratory: Nursery of genius.* London, 1962.

ne   Newall, H. F. "1885-1894." C.bc1.hi, 102-158.

pr   Price, Derek J. "The Cavendish laboratory archives." RS. *Notes and records, 10* (1953), 139-147.

ra   Rabel-Cheveley, Gabriele. "Die Geschichte des 'Cavendish'." *PB, 5* (1949), 17-21.

ru   Rutherford, Ernest. "1895-1898." C.bc1.hi, 159-194.

sa   Satterly, John. "The postprandial proceedings of the Cavendish Society." *AJP, 7* (1939), 179-185, 244-248.

sv   Sviedrys, Romualdas. "An analysis of the Cavendish Laboratory (1874-1914)." ICHS, XII (1968). *Actes, 11* (1971), 123-127.

th   Thomson, J. J. "Survey of the last twenty-five years." C.bc1.hi, 75-101.

wi   Wilson, C. T. R. "1899-1902." C.bc1.hi, 195-220.

See also: B.th5.as

bc2.ha   Hall, A. R. *The Cambridge Philosophical Society: A history, 1819-1969.* Cambridge, 1969.

bc3.st   Stratton, F. J. M. *The history of the Cambridge Observatory.* Cambridge, 1949. (Cambridge, Eng. Solar Physics Observatory. *Annals,* 1.)

bh1.gb   Great Britain. Ministry of Supply. *Harwell. The British Atomic Energy Research Establishment, 1946-1951.* London, 1952.

gh   *Great Britain. Ministry of Supply. *Atomic energy research at Harwell.* London, 1955.

sp   Spence, R. "Twenty-one years at Harwell." *Nature, 214* (1967), 343-344, 436-438.

bj1.lo   Lovell, Bernard. *The story of Jodrell Bank.* London and NY, 1968.

lp   Lovell, Bernard. *Out of the zenith: Jodrell Bank, 1957-1970.* NY, 1973.

bl1.ba   Barrell, H. "A short history of measurement standards at the National Physical Laboratory." *CP, 9* (1968), 205-226.

hu   Hutchinson, Eric. "Scientists and civil servants: The struggle over the National Physical Laboratory in 1918." *Minerva, 7* (1969), 373-398.

mo   Moseley, Russell. "The origins and early years of the National Physical Laboratory: A chapter in the pre-history of British science policy." *Minerva, 16* (1978), 222-250.

sl   Sloman, H. A. "Extension to the metallurgy division of the National Physical Laboratory." *Nature, 173* (1954), 808-809.

sm   *Smithe, E. E. *Radiation science at the National Physical Laboratory, 1912-1955.* London, 1975.

te   Teich, Albert H., and Henry Lambright. "The redirection of a large national laboratory." *Minerva, 14* (1977), 447-474.

See also: B.st2.nb

bl2.ar   Armstrong, Henry E. "Low-temperature research at the Royal Institution, 1900-1907." RI. *Proceedings, 19* (1909), 354-412.

as   Armstrong, Henry E. "Low-temperature at the Royal Institution, 1908-1916." RI. *Proceedings, 21* (1916), 735-785.

co   Cory, Ralph. "Fifty years at the Royal Institution." *Nature, 166* (1950), 1049-1053.

wa   Watson, E. C. "Paintings of lectures at the Royal Institution: A Friday evening discourse on liquid hydrogen by Sir James Dewar, 1904." *AJP, 9* (1941), 41-44.

bm1.bi   Birks, J. B. "Papers published from the physical laboratories, University of Manchester, 1907-1919." B.ru1.ad., 334-361.

ha   Harker, J. R. "Some scientific centres, XI. The physical laboratories of Manchester University." *Nature, 76* (1907), 640-642.

hb   Harker, J. R. "The extension of the physical and electrotechnical laboratories of the University of Manchester." *Nature, 89* (1912), 46.

sh   *Shilov, N. A. "Laboratoriya professora Rezerforda: Pis'mo iz Manchestera." *Priroda,* 1914: 7-8, - .

See also: D.td1.ba

bm2.ca   Cardwell, D. S. L., ed. *Artisan to graduate. Essays to commemorate the foundation in 1824 of the Manchester Institute of Science and Technology.* Manchester, 1974.

bo1.me   Mendelssohn, Kurt. "The world of cryogenics, IV. The Clarendon Laboratory, Oxford." *Cryogenics, 6:3* (1966), 129-140.

See also: O.fd1.co, jo

Commonwealth

ca1.ed Tomlin, S. G. "Physics at Adelaide University. The Kerr Grant Era." *The Australian physicist, 2* (Apr. 1977), 55-60.

ro *Royal Society of New South Wales, Sydney. *A century of scientific progress.* Sydney, 1968.

cc1.ev Eve, Arthur S. "Some scientific centres, VIII. The Macdonald Physics Building, McGill University, Montreal." *Nature, 74* (1906), 272-275.

he Heilbron, J. L. "Physics at McGill in Rutherford's time." B.ru1.ae, 42-73.

mi Middleton, W. E. Knowles. *Physics at the National Research Council of Canada, 1929-1952.* Waterloo, Ontario, 1979.

th Thistle, Mel W. *The inner ring. The early history of the National Research Council of Canada.* Toronto, 1968.

See also: B.ru1.bt; C.lb1.py; P.ca1.ja

China

da1.le League of Nations. Mission of Educational Experts. *The reorganization of education in China.* Paris, 1932.

ts Tsyan', San'-tsyan. "Kratkaya istoriya fiziki v Kitaye." AN, *Vestnik,* 1953:5, 17-21.

dz1.mo Moidrey, J. de. "Louis A. Bauer and the Zi-ka-wei Observatory." *Terrestrial magnetism and atmospheric electricity, 37* (1932), 217-218.

France

fa1.bl *Blancpain, Frédéric. "La création du CNRS: Histoire d'une décision, 1901-1939." Institut International de l'Administration Publique. *Bulletin, 32* (1974), 93-143.

cr Crawford, Elisabeth. "The prize system of the Academy of Sciences, 1850-1914." U.ba1.fo, 283-307.

da Day, C. R. "Education for the industrial world: Technical and modern instruction in France under the Third Republic, 1870-1914." U.ba1.fo, 127-153.

fo Fox, Robert. "The *savant* confronts his peers: Scientific societies in France, 1815-1914." U.ba1.fo, 241-282.

pa Paul, Harry W. *The edge of contingency: French Catholic reaction to scientific change from Darwin to Duhem.* Gainesville, Florida, 1979.

pb Paul, Harry W. *The sorcerer's apprentice: The French scientist's image of German science, 1840-1919.* Gainesville, 1972.

pc   Paul, Harry W. "Apollo courts the Vulcans: The applied science institutes in 19th-century French science faculties." U.ba1.fo, 155-181.

re   Reynier, Marguerite, and Félix Broutet. *Quelques français, hommes de science et d'action.* Paris, 1944.

sh   Shinn, Terry. "The French science faculty system, 1808-1914: Institutional change and research potential in mathematics and the physical sciences." *HSPS, 10* (1979), 271-332.

we   Weart, Spencer R. *Scientists in power.* Cambridge, Mass., and London, 1979.

wf   Weart, Spencer R. "Scientists in power: France and the origins of nuclear energy, 1900-1950." *BAS, 35* (Mar. 1979), 41-50. (Excerpts from C.fa1.we.)

wh   Weisskopf, Victor. "Physics in France." *PT, 4* (Dec. 1951), 6-11.

See also: B.cv3.jj |pf3.sn; G.ca6.fi |pa1.nx

fa5.la   Langevin, Jean. "Paul Langevin et le *Journal de physique.*" *La pensée,* no. 165 (1972), 127-134.

fp1.la   Langevin, Paul. "La physique au Collège de France." Paris. Collège de France. *Centenaire.* Paris, 1932. Pp. 61-79.

See also: B.jj1.nr

fp2.br   Broglie, Louis de. "L'activité du centre de théories physiques de l'Institut Henri Poincaré pendant les dernières années." *Experientia, 2* (1946), 33-36.

fp3.zw   Zwerling, Craig. "The emergence of the Ecole Normale Supérieure as a centre of scientific education in the 19th century." U.ba1.fo, 31-60.

fp7.ro   Fose, A. J., et al. "Le XXXe aniversaire du Palais de la Découverte (1937-1967)." Paris. University. *Annales, 38* (1968), 185-222.

ft1.ny   Nye, Mary Jo. "The scientific periphery in France: The faculty of sciences at Toulouse (1880-1930)." *Minerva, 13* (1975), 374-403.

Germany

ga1.ab   Abb, Gustav, ed. *Aus fünfzig Jahren deutscher Wissenschaft, die Entwicklung ihrer Fachgebiete in Einzeldarstellungen.* Berlin, 1930. (Friedrich Schmidt-Ott Festschrift.)

bo   Bothe, Walther, and Siegfried Flügge, eds. *Nuclear physics and cosmic rays.* 2 parts. Wiesbaden, 1948. (Office of Military Government for Germany. Field Information Agencies Technical. *FIAT review of German science, 1939-1946.*)

cl   Clusius, Klaus, ed. *Physical chemistry.* Wiesbaden, 1948. (Office of Military Government for Germany. Field Information Agencies Technical. *FIAT review of German science, 1939-1946.*)

fr   Franck, James. "Experimentalphysik." C.ga1.ab, 310-322.

ha   Hartkopf, Werner, and Gerhard Dunken. *Von der Brandenburgischen Sozietät der Wissenschaften zur Deutschen Akademie der Wissenschaften zu Berlin.* Berlin, 1967.

hb   Hartmann, Max, ed. *Die Naturwissenschaften* Berlin, 1936. (*25 Jahre Kaiser-Wilhelm Gesellschaft,* vol. 2.)

he   Hermann, Armin. "Theoretische Physik in Deutschland." *Berichte zur Wissenschaftsgeschichte, 1* (1978), 163-172.

mu   Müller, Wilhelm. "Die Lage der theoretischen Physik an den Universitäten." *ZGN, 6* (1940), 281-298.

na   Nachmansohn, David. *German-Jewish pioneers in science, 1900-1933.* NY, 1979.

pl   Planck, Max. "Theoretische Physik." C.ga1.ab, 300-303.

ze   Zenneck, Jonathan. "Technische Physik." C.ga1.ab, 323-328.

See also: B.ha7.nf; C.fa1.pb |ua1.ra; I.df1.hd

ga2.do   Donini, Elisabetta. "Scienze a Weimar, um nodo storico." *Testi e contesti, 1* (1979), 13-24.

dp   Donini, Elisabetta. "La svolta quantistica, dall' interno e dall' esterno." *Testi e contesti, 2* (1979), 122-129.

fm   Forman, Paul. *Environment and practice of atomic physics in Weimar Germany.* Ph.D. thesis, Univ. of California, Berkeley, 1967. (*DAI, 29,* 200A.)

fn   Forman, Paul. "Weimar culture, causality, and quantum theory, 1918-1927: Adaptation by German physicists and mathematicians to a hostile intellectual environment." *HSPS, 3* (1971), 1-115.

fo   Forman, Paul. "Scientific internationalism and the Weimar physicists: The ideology and its manipulation in Germany after World War I." *Isis, 64* (1973), 151-180.

fp   Forman, Paul. "The reception of an acausal quantum mechanics in Germany and Britain." *The reception of unconventional science.* Ed. S. H. Mauskopf. Boulder, Co., 1979. Pp. 11-50.

fq   Forman, Paul. "Kausalität, Anschaulichkeit e Individualität: ovvero, come i valori culturali prescissero il carattere e gli insegnamenti attributi alla meccanica quantistica." U.aa1.fi, 15-34.

ft   Friedrich, A. "Der mathematisch-naturwissenschaftliche Unterricht in den letzten 100 Jahren." *PB, 1* (1944), 200-204.

hi   Hirsch, W. "The autonomy of science in totalitarian societies: The case of Nazi Germany." *Determinants and controls of scientific development.* Ed. Karin D. Knorr et al. Dordrecht, 1975. Pp. 343-366.

mc   McCormmach, Russell. "On academic scientists in Wilhelmian Germany." *Daedalus, 103* (1974), 157-171. (Also in *BSPS, 33* (1976), 157-171.)

pe   Pyenson, Lewis, and Daniel Skopp. "Educating physicists in Germany *circa* 1900." *SSS, 7* (1977), 329-366.

ri   Richter, Steffen. "Die Kämpfe innerhalb der Physik in Deutschland nach dem ersten Weltkrieg." *Sudhoffs Archiv, 57* (1973), 195-207.

so   Sommerfeld, Arnold. "Die Entwicklung der Physik in Deutschland seit Heinrich Hertz." *Deutsche Revue, 43:3* (1918), 122-132.

vo   Voigt, Woldemar. *Physikalische Forschung und Lehre in Deutschland während der letzten 100 Jahre.* Göttingen, 1912.

See also: B.ei9.fv | lj3.bt; U.gg3.be, ri, st, su, sv

ga3.bq   Brüche, Ernst. "Die Versammlungen Deutscher Naturforscher und Ärzte in Wien." *PB, 17* (1961), 402-469.

br   Brüche, Ernst. "Wer nennt die Namen?" *PB, 18* (1962), 30-34. (About the 1913 meeting of the Gesellschaft deutscher Naturforscher und Ärzte.)

ga4.bq   Brüche, Ernst. "Max Planck und die Physikalische Gesellschaft." *PB, 4* (1948), 152-160.

br   Brüche, Ernst. "Aus der Vergangenheit der Physikalischen Gesellschaft." *PB, 16* (1960), 499-505; *17* (1961), 17-33, 120-127, 225-232, 400-410.

bu   Buchwald, E. "Die Deutsche Physikalische Gesellschaft an der Schwelle ihres zweiten Jahrhunderts." *PB, 2* (1946), 97-106.

eb   Ebert, H. "Die DPG in den letzten 25 Jahren. Zur Feier ihres 125 jährigen Bestehens." *PB, 26* (1970), 121-125.

he   Hermann, Armin. "130 Jahre Deutsche Physikalische Gesellschaft." *PB, 31* (1975), 544-547.

io   Ioffe, A. F. "Zum 90 Jahrestag der Deutschen Physikalischen Gesellschaft." *Physikalische Zeitung der Sowjet Union, 7* (1935), 128.

la   Laue, Max von. [Zur Feier des 80 jährigen Bestehens der DPG]. DPG. *Verhandlungen, 6* (1925), 1-3.

pl   Planck, Max. "Persönliche Erinnerungen." DPG. *Verhandlungen, 16* (1935), 11-16.

ra   Ramsauer, Carl. "Zur Geschichte der Deutschen Physikalischen Gesellschaft in der Hitlerzeit." *PB, 3* (1947), 110-114.

sc   Scheel, Karl. [Zur Feier des 90 jährigen Bestehens der DPG zu Berlin]. DPG. *Verhandlungen, 16* (1935), 2-11.

See also: A.bb1.bu

ga5.ka   Kaiser Wilhelm Gesellschaft zur Förderung der Wissenschaften. *25 Jahre Kaiser Wilhelm Gesellschaft.* Berlin, 1936.

ma   Max-Planck Gesellschaft zur Förderung der Wisenschaften. *50-Jahre Kaiser-Wilhelm Gesellschaft und Max-Planck-Gesellschaft zur Förderung der Wissenschaften, 1911-1961.* Göttingen, 1961.

we   Wendel, Günter. *Die Kaiser-Wilhelm-Gesellschaft, 1911-1914. Zur Anatomie einer imperialistischen Forschungsgesellschaft.* Berlin, 1975. (Akademie der Wissenschaften, Berlin. *Studien zur Geschichte der Akademie,* 4.)

See also: B.lj3.ck

ga6.fo   Forman, Paul. "The financial support and political alignment of physicists in Weimar Germany." *Minerva, 12* (1974), 39-66.

fp   Forman, Paul. "L'appoggio economico ai fisici tedeschi durante la Repubblica di Weimar e lo spettro delle loro posizioni politiche." U.aa1.fi, 278-308.

he   *Hermann, Armin. "Forschungsförderung der Deutschen Forschungsgemeinschaft und der Physik der letzten 50 Jahren." Deutsche Forschungsgemeinschaft. *Mitteilungen,* 1970, 21-34.

hf   *Hermann, Armin. "50 Jahre Forschungsförderung der DFG." *Physik in unserer Zeit, 2* (Jan. 1971).

hg   Hermann, Armin. "The role of the German Research Council, 'Deutsche Forschungsgemeinschaft,' in the development of physics." ICHS, XIII (1971). Section 2. *Actes* (1974), 279-283.

ri   Richter, Steffen. "Das Wirken der Notgemeinschaft der Deutschen Wissenschaft: Erläutert am Beispiel der Relativitätstheorie in Deutschland, 1920-1930." *PB, 27* (1971), 497-504.

rj   Richter, Steffen. *Forschungsförderung in Deutschland, 1920-1936. Dargestellt am Beispiel der Notgemeinschaft der deutschen Wissenschaft und ihrem Wirken für das Fach Physik.* Düsseldorf, 1972.

sc   Schlicker, Wolfgang. "Forschung und Gesellschaft—Vergesellschaftung der Forschung. Zur Stellung der Notgemeinschaft der deutschen Wissenschaft in der bürgerlichen Forschungspolitik der Weimarer Republik." *NTM, 12:1* (1975), 45-55.

ga7.br Brüche, Ernst. "25 Jahre Physik Verlag in Mosbach: Vom Beginn der *Physikalischen Blätter* (1943) bis zur Lizenz des Physik Verlags (1952)." *PB, 28* (1972), no. 12: suppl., 1-16.

eg   Eggert, John. "'Ceterum   censeo'—ein   zeitgeschichtlicher Rückblick auf dreihundert 'Letzte Seiten.'" *PB, 29* (1973), 51-58.

he   Hermann, Armin. "25 Jahre *Physikalische Blätter.*" *PB, 25* (1969), 547-551.

gb1.an Anon. "Berliner Physiker in Bildern." *PB, 23* (1967), 409-416.

br   Brüche, Ernst. "Ereignisreiche Jahre in der Berliner Physik." *PB, 23* (1967), 417-424.

hf   Herrmann, Dieter B. "Julius Scheiner und der erste Lehrstuhl für die Astrophysik an der Universität Berlin." *NTM, 14:1* (1977), 33-42.

ka   Kant, Horst. "Zum Problem der Forschungsprolifirierung am Beispiel der Nernstschen Schule während ihrer Berliner Zeit von 1905 bis 1914." *NTM, 11:2* (1974), 58-68.

See also: B.fp1.cr

gb2.ha *Hartkopf, Werner. *Die Akademie der Wissenschaften der DDR: Ein Beitrag zu ihrer Geschichte.* Berlin, 1975.

ki   Kirsten, Christa, and Hans-Günther Körber, eds. *Physiker über Physiker: Wahlvorschläge zur Aufnahme von Physikern in die Berliner Akademie 1870 bis 1929 von Hermann v. Helmholtz bis Erwin Schrödinger.* Berlin, 1975. (*Studien zur Geschichte der Akademie der Wissenschaften der DDR, 1.*)

pl   Planck, Max. *Max Planck in seinen Akademie-Ansprachen: Erinnerungsschrift der Deutschen Akademie der Wissenschaften zu Berlin.* Berlin, 1948.

See also: B.ei9.jt

gb3.cb *Cassidy, David. "Gustav Hertz, Hans Geiger und das Physikalische Institut der TH Berlin in den Jahren 1933 bis 1945." *Wissenschaft und Gesellschaft: Beiträge zur Geschichte der TH/TU Berlin, 1879-1979.* Ed. R. Rürup. Berlin and NY, 1979.

pa Päsler, Max. "30 Jahre Technische Universität Berlin." *PB, 32* (1976), 511-514.

we Westphal, Wilhelm H. "Das Physikalische Institut der TU Berlin." *PB, 11* (1955), 554-558.

gb4.bu Burchardt, Lothar. "Der Weg zur PTR." *PB, 32* (1976), 289-297.

ha Hauser, Wilfried, and Helmut Klages. "Die Entwicklung der PTR zum metrologischen Staatsinstitut." *PB, 33* (1977), 457-464

mo Moser, Hans, ed. *Forschung und Prüfung: 75 Jahre Physikalisch-Technische Bundesanstalt/Reichsanstalt.* Braunschweig, 1962.

pf Pfetsch, Frank. "Scientific organisation and science policy in imperial Germany, 1871-1914: The foundation of the Imperial Institute of Physics and Technology." *Minerva, 8* (1970), 557-580.

re Reishaus, Heike. "Der Einfluss der Chemiemonopole auf die Aufgabenstellung der Chemisch-Technischen Reichsanstalt während der Weimar Republik." *NTM, 9:2* (1972), 34-48.

ss Stark, Johannes. *Forschung und Prüfung. 50 Jahre Physikalisch-Technische Reichsanstalt.* Leipzig, 1937.

st Stenzel, Rudolf. "Begründung für die Verschmelzung der Reichsanstalt für Mass und Gewicht mit der Physikalisch-Technischen Reichsanstalt in Berlin im Jahre 1923." *Annals of science, 33* (1976), 289-306.

See also: G.ea4.ho

gb5.bo Borrmann, G. "Max Von Laue und das Fritz-Haber-Institut." *PB, 15* (1959), 453-456.

me Meitner, Lise. "Einige Erinnerungen an das Kaiser-Wilhelm-Institute für Chemie in Berlin-Dahlem." *Nwn, 41* (1954), 97-99.

zi Zimen, Karl Erik. "Einige Errinerungen an das Kaiser-Wilhelm-Institut für Chemie." B.mk1.if, 79-84.

See also: B.lf6.cd

gb6.ja Jaekel, W. "Hundert Jahre Siemens." *PB, 3* (1947), 305-307.

gd1.br Bruche, Ernst. "Danzig: 60 Jahre Technische Hochschule und Physikalisches Institut." *PB, 20* (1964), 529-531.

wo Wolf, Franz. "Gedenkstunde für die ehemalige TH Danzig," *PB, 31* (1975), 74-77.

gg1.hu Hund, Friedrich. "Höhepunkte der Göttinger Physik." *PB, 25* (1969), 145-153, 210-215.

py Pyenson, Lewis. "Mathematics, education, and the Göttingen approach to physical reality, 1890-1914." *Europa* (Montréal), *2:2* (1979), 91-127.

See also: B.fp1.co; F.ae1.px; O.aa1.br

gh1.an   Andrade, E. N. da C. "A physics research student at Heidelberg in the old days." *PE, 1* (1966), 69-78.

    be   Becker, A. "Das Philipp-Lenard-Institut der Universität Heidelberg." *ZGN, 3* (1937/8), 45-51.

    dr   Drysdale, N. "Physics at Heidelberg." *PE, 4* (1969), 167-172.

    mo   Moser, W. "Über das Wirken von Juden am Chemischen Institut der Universität Heidelberg." *ZGN, 3* (1937/8), 166-171.

    sc   Schmidt, F. "Die physikalisch-technische Abteilung des Philipp-Lenard-Instituts." *ZGN, 3* (1937/8), 51-55.

    st   Stevens, E. H. "The Heidelberg physical laboratory." *Nature, 65* (1902), 587.

gj1.he   Heermann, Christian. "Karl Snell und Hermann Schäffer als Hochschulpädagogen: Zur Geschichte des Experimentellunterrichtes in Physik an der Universität Jena in der zweiten Hälfte des 19. Jahrhunderts." *NTM, 2:6* (1965), 23-36.

gj2.bq   Brüche, Ernst. "100 Jahre Carl Zeiss Jena." *PB, 2* (1946), 193-200, 223.

    br   Brüche, Ernst. "Ernst Abbe und sein Werk: Ein Rückblick auf das 120 jährige Bestehen der Werkstatt von Carl Zeiss." *PB, 21* (1965), 261-269.

See also: G.da1.ha, ze

gk1.wo   Wolf, Franz. "Aus der Geschichte der Physik in Karlsruhe." *PB, 24* (1968), 388-400.

gk5.sc   Schönbeck, Charlotte. *300 Jahre Physik und Astronomie an der Kieler Universität.* Kiel, 1965.

gm1.ew   Ewald, P. P. "Erinnerungen an das Münchner Physikalischen Kolloquium." *PB, 24* (1968), 538-542.

    ge   Gerlach, Walther. "Münchner Erinnerungen: Aus der Zeit von Max von Laues Entdeckung vor 50 Jahren." *PB, 19* (1963), 97-103.

gm2.fu   Fuchs, Franz. *Der Aufbau der Physik im Deutschen Museum, 1905-1933.* Munich, 1957. (Deutsches Museum. *Abhandlungen und Berichte,* 25:3.)

gp1.gu   Gussmann, E. A. "100 Jahre Astrophysikalisches Observatorium Potsdam: Arbeiten zur Theorie der Sternatmosphären." *Sterne, 51* (1975), 219-227.

he   Herrmann, Dieter B. "Zur Vorgeschichte des Astrophysikal-ischen Observatoriums Potsdam." *Astronomische Nachrichten, 296* (1975), 245-259.

sc   Scholz, G. "100 Jahre Astrophysikalisches Observatorium Potsdam: Arbeiten zur Spektroskopie." *Sterne, 51* (1975), 207-218.

we   Wempe, J. "Zum 100. Jahrestag der Gründung des Astrophysi-kalischen Observatoriums Potsdam." *Sterne, 51* (1975), 193-206.

India

ha1.ra   Ramanna, R. "Razvitiye fiziki v Indii." *UFN, 61* (1957), 23-26.

Italy

ia1.am   Amaldi, Edoardo. "Gli anni della Ricostruzione." *Scientia, 114* (1979), 29-50, 421-437.

bu   *Buck, Barbara R. *Italian physicists and their institutions, 1861-1911.* Ph.D. thesis. Harvard Univ., 1980.

iv   Ivanenko, D. D. "Fizicheskaya nauk Italii." *UFN, 62* (1957), 523-537.

po   Polvani, Giovanni. "Fisica." C.ia1.so, *1,* 555-699.

se   Segrè, Emilio. "A prophetic achievement in science policy. An introductory note to 'The new goals of experimental physics' by Orso Mario Corbino." *Minerva, 9* (1971), 528-538.

so   Società Italiana per il Progresso delle Scienze. *Un secolo di pro-gresso scientifico italiano, 1839-1939.* 7 vols. Milan, 1939-1940.

See also: A.ah1.le; E.aa1.co|tc1.ta; F.ae1.gp, gp; G.ca6.ar; I.de1; O.ba1.za; P.aa1.st|bg1.re|fd1.ri

ic1.ab   Abetti, Giorgio. "Annibale Ricco, l'Accademia Gioenia, e l'Osservatorio Astrofisico di Catania." Accademia Gioenia di Scienze Naturali, Catania. *Bollettino, 3* (1955), 13-25.

ip1.oc   Occhialini, Augusto. *Notizie sull' Istituto di Fisica Sperimentale della studio Pisano.* Pisa, 1914.

ip2.po   *Polvani, Giovanni. "Cenni storici sull' Istituto di Fisica Tecnica della Regia Scuola di Ingegneria di Pisa." Pisa. Scuola di Ingeg-neria. *Annuario,* 1927.

ip3.ab   Abetti, Giorgio. "Thirty years of solar work at Arcetri." *Vistas in astronomy, 1* (1955), 624-630.

See also: P.ie1.ac

ir1.ma   Marcolonogo, Roberto. "Le scienze fisiche e matematiche in Roma." C.ir1.ro, 351-372.

ro   Rome. Istituto di Studi Romani. *Le scienza fisiche e biologiche in Roma e nel Lazio.* Rome, 1933.

See also: I.de1.am, ho, se; K.ac1.am

Japan

ja1.fu   Fukushima, Y. "The history of the development of the organization for promotion of science and technology in Japan after the World War II." ICHS, XIII (1971). Section 2. *Actes* (1974), 244-251.

hi   Hirosige, Tetu. "Social conditions for the researches of nuclear physics in pre-war Japan." *JSHS, 2* (1963), 80-93.

hj   Hirosige, Tetu. "Social conditions for prewar Japanese research in nuclear physics." C.ja1.na, 202-220.

ka   Kamatuni, Chikayoshi. "The history of research organization in Japan." *JSHS, 2* (1963), 1-79.

ko   *Koizumi, Kenkichiro. *The development of physics in Meiji Japan: 1868-1912.* Ph.D. thesis. Univ. of Pennsylvania, 1973. (*DAI, 34,* 1828A.)

kp   Koizumi, Kenkichiro. "The emergence of Japan's first physicists: 1868-1900." *HSPS, 6* (1975), 3-108.

lo   Lockheimer, F. Roy. "Prerequisites, receptivity, and change: Government and the development of science in Japan." U.be1.si, 154-170.

na   Nakayama, Shigeru, David L. Swain, and Eri Yagi, eds. *Science and society in modern Japan.* Tokyo, 1974.

nb   Nakayama, Shigeru. *Characteristics of scientific development in Japan.* New Delhi, 1977.

tu   *Tuge, Hideomi. *Historical development of science and technology in Japan.* Tokyo, 1968.

ya   Yagi, Eri. "The statistical analysis of the growth of physics in Japan." C.ja1.na, 108-113.

yu   Yukawa, Hideki. "Hundred years of science in Japan from a physicist's point of view." ICHS, XIV (1974). *Proceedings, 2* (1975), 3-15.

See also: I.bg1.ta |tj1.do, sh; K.fc1.ka, ta; R.af1.ko

jr1.ki Kiyonobu, Itakura, and Eri Yagi. "The Japanese research system and the establishment of the Institute of Physical and Chemical Research." C.ja1.na, 158-201.

jt1.ko Koizumi, Kenkichiro. "The Tokyo School of Physics and the University of Tokyo: Two approaches to the institutionalization of physics in Japan." ICHS, XIV (1974). *Proceedings, 3* (1975), 227-230.

Latin America

la1.az Azevedo, Fernando de, ed. *As ciências no Brasil.* 2 vols. n.p., n.d.

fe Ferraz, J. de Sampaio. "A meteorologia no Brasil." C.la1.az, *1*, 203-240.

rh Rheinboldt, Heinrich. "A química no Brasil." C.la1.az, *2*, 9-89.

rk Ribeiro, J. Costa. "A fisica no Brasil." C.la1.az, *1*, 163-201.

ro Rowe, James W. "Science and politics in Brazil: Background of the 1967 debate on nuclear energy policy." U.be1.si, 91-122.

lb1.py Pyenson, Lewis. "The incomplete transmission of a European image: Physics at greater Buenos Aires and Montreal, 1890-1920." APS. *Proceedings, 122* (1978), 92-114.

Netherlands

na1.ku Kuenen, J. P., ed. *Het aandeel van Nederland in de ontwikkeling der natuurkunde gedurende de laatste 150 jaren.* Rotterdam, 1919.

la *Lazarev, P. P. "Yubiley G. A. Lorentsa i gollandskaya nauka." *Nauchnyy rabotnik,* 1926:1, 120-127.

nl1.he Henning, F. "Das physikalische Institut der Universität Leiden in den Jahren 1904 bis 1922." *Nwn, 11* (1923), 429-430.

le Leyden. University. Kamerlingh-Onnes Laboratorium. *Het natuurkundig laboratorium der Rijksuniversiteit te Leiden in de jaren 1882-1904.* Leyden, 1904.

lf Leyden. University. Kamerlingh-Onnes Laboratorium. *Het natuurkundig laboratorium der Rijksuniversiteit te Leiden in de jaren 1904-1922.* Leyden, 1922.

See also: R.ds1.si

Poland

pa1.hu Hurwic, Jósef. "The Polish contribution to mathematical and physical sciences in the years 1918-1970." *Organon, 12/13* (1976/7), 261-274.

ka   *Kaminski, Wieslaw A., and Stanislaw Szpikowski. "Recepcja mechaniki kwantowej w Polskich ośrodkach naukowych w latach dwudziestych." *Studia i materialy z dziejów nauki polskiej, ser. C., 23* (1979), 105-109.

ma   Mazurkiewiczowie, Danuta, and Zbigniew Mazurkiewiczowie. "Polskie tradycje w zakresie mechaniki teoretycznej i stosowanej." *KHNT, 18* (1973), 123-144.

sr   Średniawa, Bronislaw. "Szkic historii fizyki polskiej w okresie międzywojennym 1918-1939." Polska Akademia Nauk. Zaklad Historii Nauki i Techniki. *Studia* (1968), 133-153.

sz   *Szymborski, Krzysztof. "Dzieje Polskich badań w dziedzinie fizyki w latach 1860-1918." *Studia i materialy z dziejów nauki polskiej, ser. C., 22* (1978), 33-78.

See also: C.ba1 | ga2.fp | va4.an; D.kt1.ha; E.tf1.kr; F.ae1.go; H.da1.lo; I.ae1.st; U.gb1.ra | gd1.fi, fj

pa2.ja   Jaczewski, Bohdan. "Dzialalnošč polskiego przedstawiciela naukowego we Francji w okresie międzywojennym." *KHNT, 20* (1975), 313-328.

ro   Róziewicz, Jerzy. "Kontakty naukowe Polsko-Radzieckle w latach 1919-1939." *KHNT, 12* (1967), 769-799.

rp   Róziewicz, Jerzy. "Uczeni radzieccy czlonkami Polskiej Akademii Umiejętności." *KHNT, 17* (1972), 719-742.

st   *Stroński, Ignacy. "Chemicy i fizycy na pietnastu zjazdach lekarzy i przyodników Polskich, 1869-1937." *Studia i materialy z dziejów nauki polskiej, ser. C., 22* (1978), 115-145.

Scandinavia

sa1.gu   Gustavson, Torsten. "Svensk fysik under 30 år." *Svensk naturvetenskap,* 1975, 26-53.

li   Lindroth, Sten, ed. *Swedish men of science, 1650-1950.* Stockholm, 1952.

sc1.ha   Hall, R. B. "Copenhagen revisited." *PE, 13* (1978), 337-340.

mo   Møller, Christian. "Nogle erindringer fra livet på Bohrs Institut: Sidste halvdel af tyverne." *Fysik tidsskrift, 60* (1962), 54-64.

ro   Robertson, Peter. *The early years: The Niels Bohr Institute, 1921-1930.* Copenhagen, 1979.

See also: B.bo1.nk, np; P.mc1.lf; T.ga2.ho, la

sl1.hu   Hulthén, Erik. "1900-1925, fysikalisk forskning i Lund under ett kvartsekel." B.sj8.as, 1-8.

ta   Tanberg, J. "Notiser från arbetet och kamratlivet på fysicum i Lund." B.sj8.as, 9-12.

ss1.we   Westgren, Arne. "Vetenskapsakademiens forskningsinstitut för fysik." B.sj8.as, 31-34.

su1.fr   Friesen, Sten von. "Manne Siegbahn och fysikum i Uppsala 1928-1937." B.sj8.as, 23-30.

no   Nordhult, Axel Larsson. "Manne Siegbahn och fysikum i Uppsala 1923-1930." B.sj8.as, 13-22.

sl   Slätis, Hilding. "Forskningsinstitut för fysik." B.sj8.as, 35-58.

Switzerland

tz1.mu   Muheim, Jules T. "Die ETH und ihre Physiker und Mathematiker, eine Chronologie der Periode 1855-1955." *Neue Zürcher Zeitung,* 9 Apr. 1975, Beilage, 10 p.

we   *Weyl, Hermann. "Rückblick auf Zürich aus dem Jahre 1930." *Schweizerische Hochschulzeitung, 28* (1955), 1-8.

USA

ua1.cp   Condon, E. U. "The development of American physics." *AJP, 17* (1949), 404-408.

cr   Crowther, James G. *Famous American men of science.* NY, 1937.

da   Darrow, Karl K. "Twenty-five years of American physics." *AJP, 17* (1949), 127-136.

gr   Gromeka, V. E., et al. *S.Sh.A.: Nauka i obrazovaniye.* Moscow, 1974.

ke   *Kevles, Daniel J. *The study of physics in America, 1865-1916.* Ph.D. thesis. Princeton Univ., 1964. (*DAI, 25,* 5239.)

kf   Kevles, Daniel J. *The physicists. The history of a scientific community in modern America.* NY, 1978.

ra   *Ramsauer, Carl. *Über Leistung und Organisation der angelsächsischen Physik: Mit Ausblicken auf die deutsche Physik.* Berlin, 1943.

re   Reingold, Nathan, ed. *The sciences in the American context: New perspectives.* Washington, D.C., 1979.

ru   Rubinshtein, M. I. *Burzhuaznaya nauka i tekhnika na sluzhbe amerikanskogo imperializma.* Moscow, 1951.

ze   Zenneck, Jonathan. "Meine Eindrücke und Erfahrungen in den USA." *PB, 18* (1962), 72-77, 472-475; *19* (1963), 169-173.

See also: B.cv1.tc |hc1.sk; E.ba1.da; G.oa1.hu

ua2.co　Coben, Stanley. "The scientific establishment and the transmission of quantum mechanics to the United States, 1919-1932." *American historical review, 76* (1971), 442-466.

do　Donini, Elisabetta. "Aspetti scientifici e di contesto storico nel passaggio della meccanica quantistica negli Stati Uniti." U.aa1.fi, 159-187.

dp　Donini, Elisabetta. "La meccanica quantistica tra Germania e USA." U.aa1.fi, 309-326.

he　Heilbron, J. L. "La fisica negli Stati Uniti subito prima della meccanica quantistica." U.aa1.fi, 135-158.

hu　Hull, Gordon Ferrie. "The new spirit in American physics." *AJP, 11* (1943), 23-30.

se　Seidel, Robert. "Aspetti istituzionali della trasmissione della meccanica quantistica agli Stati Uniti." U.aa1.fi, 189-213.

va　Vleck, John H. Van. "American physics comes of age." *PT, 17* (Jun. 1964), 21-26.

we　Weart, Spencer R. "The physics business in America, 1919-1940: A statistical reconnaissance." C.ua1.re, 295-358.

wf　Weiner, Charles. "Physics in the great depression." *PT, 23* (Oct. 1970), 31-38.

See also: L.ah1.sl, so

ua3.bi　Birr, Kendall. "Industrial research laboratories." C.ua1.re, 193-207.

fa　Fagen, Mortimer D., ed. *A history of engineering and science in the Bell System: The early years, 1875-1925.* NY, 1975.

fb　Fagen, Mortimer D., ed. *A history of engineering and science in the Bell System: National service in war and peace (1925-1975).* N.p., 1978.

ha　Hammond, John Winthrop. *Men and volts. The story of General Electric.* NY, 1941.

mi　Miller, John Anderson. *Men and volts at war: The story of General Electric in World War II.* NY, 1947.

wi　Wise, George. "Physics yesterday: A career in research." *PT, 29* (Jul. 1976), 9-11.

ua4.an　Anon. "AIP—40 years." *PT, 24* (Jun. 1971), 29-37.

ba　Barr, E. Scott. "Men and milestones in optics, IV. The first fifty years of the Optical Society of America." *Applied optics, 5* (1966), 357-368.

co　Compton, Karl T. "The founding of the American Institute of Physics." *PT, 5* (Feb. 1952), 4-7.

da   Darrow, Karl K. "My sixty years with the American Physical Society." *PT, 27* (Jan. 1974), 38-42.

ea   Eaton, V. E. "The history of the American Association of Physics Teachers." American Association of Physics Teachers. *History and Activities.* NY, 1958.

hi   Hirsh, F. R., Jr. "Academic origins of fellows of the American Physical Society." *AJP, 23* (1955), 255-256.

hj   Hirsh, F. R., Jr. "Concerning the fellows of the American Physical Society." *AJP, 25* (1957), 303-305.

ov   Overbeck, C. J. "The history of the first twenty-five years of the American Association of Physics Teachers." American Association of Physics Teachers. *History and activities.* NY, 1955. Pp. 1-4.

we   Webster, David L. "Reminiscences of the early years of the association." *AJP, 25* (1957), 131-134.

wf   Weiner, Charles. "*Physics today* and the spirit of the forties." *PT, 26* (May 1973), 23-28.

ua5.ca   Cameron, Frank. *Cottrell: Samaritan of science.* Garden City, N.Y., 1952.

co   Coben, Stanley. "Foundation officials and fellowships: Innovation in the patronage of science." *Minerva, 14* (1976), 225-240.

cp   Coben, Stanley. "American foundations as patrons of science: The commitment to individual research." C.ua1.re, 229-247.

da   Davis, Lance E., and Daniel J. Kevles. "The National Research Fund: A case study in the industrial support of academic science." *Minerva, 12* (1974), 207-220.

fo   Fosdick, Raymond B. *The story of the Rockefeller Foundation.* NY, 1952.

fp   Fosdick, Raymond B. *Adventure in giving. The story of the General Education Board.* NY, 1962.

ko   Kohler, Robert E. "A policy for the advancement of science: The Rockefeller Foundation, 1924-1929." *Minerva, 16* (1978), 480-515

le   *Levine, Arthur Louis. *United States aeronautical research policy, 1915-1958: A study of the major policy decisions of the National Advisory Committee for Aeronautics.* Ph.D. thesis. Columbia Univ., 1963. (*DAI, 24,* 3827.)

mi   Miller, Howard S. *Dollars for research: Science and its patrons in nineteenth-century America.* Seattle, 1970.

we   Weaver, Warren. *Scene of change: A lifetime in American science.* NY, 1970.

 uc1.al   Alvarez, Luis W. "Berkeley: A lab like no other." *BAS, 30* (Apr. 1974), 18-23.

he   Heilbron, J. L., Seidel, R. W., and Wheaton, B. R. *Lawrence and his laboratory. Nuclear science at Berkeley, 1931-1961.* Berkeley, 1981.

ka   Kamen, Martin D. "The birthplace of Big Science." *BAS, 30* (Nov. 1974), 42-46.

la   Lawrence, Ernest O. "The growth of the physics department." University of California, Berkeley. *Symposium* (1958), 12-27.

se   *Seidel, Robert. *Physics research in California: The rise of a leading sector in American physics.* Ph.D. thesis. Univ. of California, Berkeley, 1978. (*DAI, 39,* 5685A.)

sf   Seidel, R. W. "The origins of academic physics research in California." *Journal of college teaching, 6* (1976), 10-24.

See also: K.da1.ni; O.ba1.pa

uc2.ad   Adams, Walter S. "Early days at Mount Wilson." Astronomical Society of the Pacific. *Publications, 59* (1947), 213-231, 285-304.

ae   Adams, Walter S. "Early solar research at Mount Wilson." *Vistas in astronomy, 1* (1955), 619-623.

ka   Kargon, Robert H. "Temple to science: Cooperative research and the birth of the California Institute of Technology." *HSPS, 8* (1977), 3-31.

se   Servos, John W. "The knowledge corporation: A. A. Noyes and chemistry at Cal-Tech, 1915-1930." *Ambix, 23* (1976), 175-186.

st   Struve, Otto. "The story of an observatory." *Popular astronomy, 55* (1947), 223-244.

uc3.yo   York, Herbert F. "The origins of Lawrence Livermore Laboratory." *BAS, 31* (Sep. 1975), 8-14.

uc4.wr   Wright, Helen. *Palomar, the world's largest telescope.* NY, 1952.

uc5.ed   Eddy, John A. "The Schaeberle 40-ft. eclipse camera of Lick Observatory." *Journal for the history of astronomy, 2* (1971), 1-22.

ue1.br   Brown, Sanborn C., and Leonard Rieser. *Natural philosophy at Dartmouth.* Hanover, N.H., 1974.

ui1.gr   Greenbaum, Leonard. *A special interest: The Atomic Energy Commission, Argonne National Laboratory, and the midwestern universities.* Ann Arbor, 1971.

ui3.ad   Adams, Walter S. "Some reminiscences of the Yerkes Observatory." *Science, 106* (1947), 196-200.

uk1.go   Goudsmit, Samuel A. "The Michigan Symposium in Theoretical Physics." *Michigan Alumni quarterly review, 4* (1965), 181-182.

uk2.ba   Barber, William Harley. "Forty years of physics at Ripon College." *AJP, 16* (1948), 107-109.

um1.ha   Hall, Edwin H. "Physics teaching at Harvard fifty years ago." *AJP, 6* (1938), 17-20.

um2.ba   Bailey, Solon I. *The history and work of the Harvard Observatory.* NY, 1931.

     jo   Jones, Bessie Zaban, and Lyle Gifford Boyd. *The Harvard College Observatory: The first four directorships, 1839-1919.* Cambridge, Mass., 1971.

un1.fe   Fermi, Enrico. "Physics at Columbia University, The genesis of the nuclear energy project." *PT, 8* (Nov. 1955), 12-16. (Also in B.fg1.jj, 996-1003.)

See also: K.da1.mi

un3.ra   Ramsey, Norman F. "Early history of Associated Universities and Brookhaven National Laboratory." *Brookhaven National Laboratory lectures in science, vistas in research,* vol. 2. NY, 1968. Pp. 182-198.

uw1.am   Ambler, Ernest. "75 years of physics at NBS." *PT, 29* (Aug. 1976), 33-38.

     co   Cochrane, Rexmond C. *Measures for progress: A history of the National Bureau of Standards.* Washington, D.C., 1966.

See also: G.ea4.me

uw2.ca   Carter, Luther J. "Office of Naval Research: 20 years bring change." *Science, 153* (1966), 397-400.

     ol   [Old, Bruce S., et al.]. "The evolution of the Office of Naval Research." *PT, 14* (Aug. 1961), 30-35.

     sa   Sanderson, John A. "Optics of the Naval Research Laboratory." *Applied optics, 6* (1967), 2029-2043.

uw3.jo   Jones, Bessie Zaban. *Lighthouse of the skies, the Smithsonian Astrophysical Observatory: Background and history 1846-1955.* Washington, 1965.

uw4.ke   *Keller, Michael David. *A history of the Langley Research Center, 1917-1947.* Ph.D. thesis. Univ. of Arizona, 1968. (*DAI, 29,* 1194A.)

USSR

va1.am   *AN. *Voprosy istorii otechestvennoy nauki.* Moscow, 1949.

     an   Anuchin, D. N. *O lyudyakh russkoy nauki i kultury.* Moscow, 1950.

fi   Figurovskiy, N. A., et al. *Istoriya yestestvoznaniya v Rossii.* 3 vols in 4 vols. Moscow, 1957-62. *Fiziko-matematicheskiye i khimicheskiye nauki: Vtoraya polovina XIX-nachalo XX veka,* vol. 2. Moscow, 1960.

gr   Grigor'yan, A. T. "Rozwój nauk matematyczno-fizycznych w Rosji i ZSRR." *KHNT, 20* (1975), 25-35.

ko   Kokin, Lev. *Yunost' akademikov.* Moscow, 1970.

ku   Kuznetsov, I. V., ed. *Lyudi russkoy nauki.* Moscow, 1948; 1961.

la   Lazarev, P. P. *Ocherki istorii russkoy nauki.* Moscow and Leningrad, 1950.

me   Melinskaya, S. I. *Soviet science, 1917-1970.* Ed. Paul K. Urban and Andrew I. Lebed. Metuchen, New Jersey, 1971.

pe   Perel', Yu. G. *Vydayushchiyesya russkiye astronomy.* Moscow, 1951.

ry   Ryazanovskiy, V. A. *Razvitiye russkoy nauchnoy mysli v XVIII-XX st.st.* NY, 1949.

vu   Vucinich, Alexander. *Science in Russian culture, 1861-1917.* Stanford, 1970.

See also: B.at1.cs | bp1.jz | bp4.cf | ow1.ps | sb2.as; D.ab1.go, hq, hr | bb1.gr | cd1.bo, pc | kb1.am, an, rx | kt1.an | td1.ar | te1.te; E.bi1.ka | ma1.ko | tb1.so | td1.vv, vw | te1.ka | tf1.sp | tt1.bo; F.dd1.iw; G.ao1.ma | ca4.ch, ci, fr, ga, kr, ro, ts, va | da1.ro | da3.tu | ea1.fr | ea2.fr, km, ne, st | oa1.go, gp | pa1.ld, le, lh, te; H.ac1.vi | ac1.fl, yc | cd1.sm | dd1.ar, da; O.ab1.ar, kt, ku | ac1.ar | bb1.sk | bc1.da | da1.sh | hb1.an; P.aa1.ma; R.ac1.pr, ps | ad1.sq; U.gb1.ra | kh1.er; W.bb1

va2.an *AN. *Yubileynyy sbornik, posvyashch. 30-letiyu Velikoy Oktyabr'skoy sotsialisticheskoy revolyutsii.* Ed. S. I. Vavilov. 2 parts. Moscow, 1947.

ar   Artsikhovskiy, A. V. *Ocherki po istorii sovetskoy nauki i kul'tury.* Moscow, 1968.

fh   Figurovskiy, N. A. "40 Jahre Geschichte der Naturwissenschaft und Technik in der USSR." C.va2.ha, 1-17.

fi   Fiodorov, Aleksandr S., and S. J. Plotkin. "Rozwój przyrodoznawstwa w ZSRR." *KHNT, 12* (1967), 681-699.

go   Gokhberg, B. I., and M. S. Sominskiy. "Dostizheniya tekhnicheskoy fiziki v SSSR za 25 let." *Zhurnal tekhnicheskoy fiziki, 12* (1942), 663-678.

gr   Grigor'yan, A. T., and L. A. Filatova. "Fifty years of Soviet science and technology." *Organon, 5* (1968), 65-72.

gs   Grigor'yan, A. T. "Aus der Geschichte der Entwicklung der sowjetischen Wissenschaft und Technik." *NTM, 5:11* (1968), 11-22.

ha   Harig, Gerhard, ed. *Sowjetische Beiträge zur Geschichte der Naturwissenschaft.* Berlin, 1960.

io   *Ioffe, A. F. *Development of the exact sciences in the U.S.S.R.* NY, 1943.

ip   *Ioffe, A. F. "Razvitiye tochnykh nauk v SSSR za 25 let." AN. *Vestnik,* 1943:1-2, 10-22.

ke   Keldysh, M. V., et al. *Oktyabr' i nauchnyy progress.* 2 vols. Moscow, 1967.

ti   Timoshenko, S. P., and Ya. V. Uspenskiy. "Remarks in the history of science in Russia." *Science, 100* (1944), 193-194.

va   Vavilov, S. I. *Sovetskaya nauka na novom etape.* Moscow and Leningrad, 1946. (Also in B.va4.jv, *3,* 591-645.)

vb   Vavilov, S. I. "Twenty-eight years of Soviet science." *Synthèse, 5* (1946), 57-59.

vc   Vavilov, S. I. "Thirty years of Soviet science." *Synthèse, 6* (1948), 318-329.

vd   Vavilov, S. I. *Nauka stalinskoy epokhi.* Moscow, 1950. (Trans. in part as *The progress of Soviet science.* Moscow, 1951.)

ve   Vavilov, S. I. "Tridtsat' let sovetskoy nauki." B.va4.jv, *3,* 730-760.

we   Westphal, Wilhelm H. "Erster Besuch eines deutschen Wissenschaftlers in Sowjetrussland 1922." *PB, 20* (1964), 578-584.

See also: E.ta1.lu

va3.ak   *Akademiya nauk SSSR za desyat' let, 1917-1927.* Leningrad, 1927.

an   *AN. Vsesoyuznyy komitet po provedeniyu 220-letiya Akademii nauk. *Ocherki po istorii Akademii nauk: Fiziko-matematicheskiye nauki.* Moscow, 1945.

bq   Brasch, Frederick. "History and activities of the U.S.S.R. Academy of Sciences during the past twenty-five years." *Science, 99* (1944), 437-441.

br   Bryksin, V. V. "The USSR Academy of Sciences: 250 years." *SPU, 17* (1974), 289-304.

fi   Fiodorov, Aleksandr S., and S. J. Plotkin. "250 lat Akademii nauk ZSRR." *KHNT, 19* (1974), 219-223.

gr   *Graham, Loren R. *The transformation of Russian science and the Academy of Sciences, 1927-1932.* Ph.D. thesis. Columbia Univ., 1964. (*DAI, 28,* 591A.)

ko   Kol'tsov, A. V. "K istorii organizatsii respublikanskikh Akademii nauk." *VIYeT, 41* (1972), 23.

va   Vavilov, S. I. "Fizicheskiy kabinet, Fizicheskaya laboratoriya, Fizicheskiy institut Akademii nauk SSSR za 220 let." B.va4.jv, *3,* 468-529.

vb   Vavilov, S. I. "Ocherk razvitiya fiziki v Akademii nauk SSSR za 220 let." B.va4.jv, *3,* 530-532.

va4.an IIYeT. *USSR Academy of Sciences: Scientific relations with Great Britain.* Moscow, 1977.

gr   Graham, Loren R. "The formation of Soviet research institutes: A combination of revolutionary innovation and international borrowing." ICHS, XIV (1974). *Proceedings, 1* (1974), 25-52. (Also in *SSS, 5* (1975), 303-329.)

ja   Janouch, Fr. "Die tschechoslowakisch-sowjetischen Beziehungen in der Physik." *PB, 24* (1968), 462-466.

ki   Kisieliow, Igor N. "Wspólpraca naukowa Akademii Nauk ZSRR z Polską Akademia Nauk." *KHNT, 16* (1971), 301-306.

ko   Korneyev, S. G., and Yu. A. Timofeyev. "U.S.S.R. Academy of Sciences: Relations with research institutions and scholars of Britain (1917-1975)." C.va4.an, 8-69.

va5.ka Kapitsa, P. L. "100-letiye *Zhurnala eksperimental'noy i teoreticheskoy fiziki* i rol' zhurnalov v razvitii nauk." AN. *VIYeT, 47-48* (1974), 9-17. (Also in *UFN, 111* (1973), 535-543, and *SPU, 16* (1974), 928-933.)

vb1.ku Kuznetsov, B. G. *Ocherki istorii russkoy nauki.* Moscow and Leningrad, 1940.

pr   Predvoditelev, A. S., and B. I. Spasskiy, eds. *Razvitiye fiziki v Rossii.* 2 vols. Moscow, 1970.

te   Ternov, I. M. "Otdeleniye eksperimental'noy i teoreticheskoy fiziki." *IMYeN: Fizika, 6* (1968), 29-38.

th   *Timiryazev, A. K. "Iz istorii russkoy fiziki." *Sovetskaya nauka,* 1940:1, 94-105.

ti   Timiryazev, A. K., ed. *Ocherki po istori fiziki v Rossii.* Moscow, 1949.

vo   *Voprosy istorii fiziki i yeye prepodavaniya.* Tambov, 1961.

vb2.by   *Bykova-Orlova, Ye. G. "Razvitiye fizicheskikh laboratoriy v
         Rossii vo vtoroy polovine XIX, nachale XX veka." C.vb1.vo,
         193-207.

ku   Kudryavtsev, P. S., et al. "Fizika." C.va1.fi, 318-501.

vi   *Vinokurov, B. Z. "Nekotoryye voprosy razvitiya fiziki v Rossii
         v nachale XX veka." C.vb1.vo, 125-130.

vj   *Vinokurov, B. Z. "Kharakteristika sostoyaniya russkoy fiziki v
         nachale XX veka." C.vb1.vo, 165-178.

vb3.io   *Ioffe, A. F. "Razvitiye sovetskoy fiziki." *Fizika v shkole,* 1948:4,
         5-11. (Also in *Elektrichestvo,* 1948:1, 3-9.)

ip   *Ioffe, A. F. "Puti razvitiya sovetskoy fiziki." AN. *Obshcheye
         sobraniye.* Moscow and Leningrad, 1948. Pp. 379-392.

iq   Ioffe, A. F., and D. N. Nasledov. "O nedostatkakh i nekotorykh
         problemakh razvitiya sovetskoy fiziki." *Front nauki i tekhniki,*
         1934:4, 32-36.

iu   Ivanenko, D. D. "Sovetskaya fizika. Obshchiy ocherk." C.vb1.ti,
         297-302.

iv   Ivanenko, D. D. "Main periods of Soviet physics." ICHS, XII
         (1968). *Actes, 5* (1971), 55-57.

ku   Kuznetsov, B. G. *Fizika i ekonomika.* Moscow, 1967.

pr   Predvoditelev, A. S. "O nauchnykh sovetskikh shkolakh."
         C.vb1.ti, 303-325.

sh   Shpol'skiy, E. V. "Fifty years of Soviet physics." *SPU, 10*
         (1968), 678-720.

si   Shpol'skiy, E. V. *Ocherki po istorii razvitiya sovetskoy fiziki,
         1917-1967.* Moscow, 1969.

so   Sokolov, Yuriy Lukich. "Iz vospominaniy fizika." *Puti v
         neznayemoye, 5* (1965), 460-489.

vb4.an   AN. Otdeleniye matematicheskikh i yestestvennykh nauk. *Ma-
         tematika i yestestvoznaniya v SSSR.* Moscow, 1938.

in   *Ioffe, A. F. "Fizika za desyat' let." *Nauka i tekhnika SSSR,
         1917-1927.* Ed. Ioffe et al. Moscow, 1927. Vol. 1, 75-88.
         (Also in *Narodnyy uchitel',* 1928:1-2, 135-155.)

io   Ioffe, A. F. "Fizika v rekonstruktivnyy period." AN. *Vestnik,*
         1931:1, 26-38.

ip   Ioffe, A. F. "Sovetskaya fizika za 15 let." *Front nauki i tekhniki,*
         1933:10-11, 116-120.

iq   Ioffe, A. F. "Sovetskaya fizika za dvadtsat' let." *ZhETF, 7* (1937), 1189-1193. (Also in *Physikalische Zeitschift der Sowjetunion, 12* (1937), 493-505.).

ir   Ioffe, A. F. "Sovetskiye fiziki i dorevolyutsionnaya fizika v Rossii." *UFN, 33* (1947), 453-468.

iv   Ivanenko, D. D. "Early years of Soviet physics." ICHS, VIII (1956). *Actes, 1* (1958), 265-268.

ru   Ruhemann, Martin. "Soviet physics in the 1930's." *New scientist, 36* (1967), 276-277.

sh   Shpol'skiy, E. V. "Fizika v SSSR, 1917-1937 gg." *UFN, 18* (1937), 295-322.

vb5.am   Anon. "Put' razvitiya fiziki v SSSR za sorok let Sovetskoy vlasti." *ZhETF, 33* (1957), 1081-1084.

an   *Anon. "K 40-letiyu Velikoy Oktyabr'skoy sotsialisticheskoy revolyutsii." *Pribory i tekhnika eksperimenta,* 1957:6, 3-5.

io   Ioffe, A. F. "Sovetskaya fizika za 30 let." AN. *Izvestiya,* ser. fiz., *11* (1947), 581-590.

ip   Ioffe, A. F. "Razvitiye fiziko-matematicheskikh nauk v stalinskuyu epokhu." AN. *Izvestiya,* ser. fiz., 1950:1, 7-14.

ka   Kapitsa, P. L. "Put' razvitiya fiziki v SSSR za sorok let sovetskoy vslasti." *ZhETF, 33* (1957), 1081-1084. (In English in *Soviet physics—JETP, 6* (1958), 835.)

sg   Shpol'skiy, E. V. "Sorok let sovetskoy fiziki." *UFN, 63* (1957), 461-501. (Also expanded and published separately, Moscow, 1958; in English in *SPU, 63* (1957), 625-677.)

sh   Shpol'skiy, E. V. "Pyat'desyat let sovetskoy fiziki." *UFN, 93* (1967), 197-276.

vb6.bl   Blokhintsev, D. I. "Uspekhi teoreticheskoy fiziki v Sovetskom Soyuze za 20 let." *ZhETF, 7* (1937), 1203-1208. (In English in *Physikalische Zeitschrift der Sowjetunion, 12* (1937), 542-549.)

bm   Blokhintsev, D. I. "Puti razvitiya teoreticheskoy fiziki v SSSR." *UFN, 33* (1947), 285-293.

fr   Frenkel', Ya. I. "Teoreticheskaya fizika v SSSR za 30 let." *UFN, 33* (1947), 294-317. (Also in B.fr1.jf, 306-337.)

ku   Kudryavtsev, P. S. "Iz istorii stanovleniya sovetskoy teoreticheskoy fiziki." C.vb1.pr, *2,* 6-25.

vo   Vonsovskiy, S. V. "Nekotoryye voprosy razvitiya issledovaniy po teoreticheskoy fizike v Sverdlovske." *Uchenyye Urala v bor'be za tekhnicheskiy progress.* Sverdlovsk, 1959. Pp. 127-136.

vb7.ig   Igonin, V. V. "The main stages and principal trends in the development of nuclear physics in the USSR." A.aa1.an, 29-45.

pe   *Petrov, K., and G. I. Golovin. "Korifei sovetskoy radiofiziki." *Voyennyy svyazist,* 1948:11, 12-17.

ve1.ka   Karakeyev, K. *Razvitiye nauki v sovetskom Kirgizstane.* Frunze, 1962.

kb   Karakeyev, K., et al. *Lenin i nauka sovetskogo Kirgizstana.* Frunze, 1970.

ve2.ev   Evladov, V. *130 meridianov.* Moscow, 1967.

ve3.as   Asimov, M. S., et al. *Nauka sovetskogo Tadzhikistana.* Dushanbe, 1974.

ve4.az   Azimov, P. A., et al. *Razvitiye nauki v sovetskom Turkmenistane.* Ashkhabad, 1971.

ve5.ab   Abdullayev, Kn. M. *Sorok let sovetskoy nauki v Uzbekistane.* Tashkent, 1958.

az   Azimov, S. A., et al. *Nauka v Uzbekistane,* vol. 1. *Yestestvennyye nauki.* Tashkent, 1974.

ko   *Kori-Niëzii, T. N., et al., eds. *25 let sovetskoy nauki v Uzbekistane.* Tashkent, 1942.

sh   *Shuppe, G. N. "Ocherk po istorii razvitiya fizicheskikh issledovaniy v Uzbekistane." AN Uzbekskoy SSR. Fiziko-tekhnicheskiy institut. *Trudy, 4* (1952), 3-61.

st   Starodubtsev, S. V. "Razvitiye fiziko-matematicheskikh nauk v Uzbekistane za gody Sovetskoy vlasti (1917-1957 gg.)." Akademiya Nauk, Uzbekistan. *Izvestiya.* Ser. fiz.-mat. nauk, 1957:4, 5-14.

vl1.am   *AN. Fiziko-tekhnicheskiy institut. *Problemy sovremennoy fiziki v rabotakh instituta.* Moscow and Leningrad, 1936.

an   AN. *A. F. Ioffe Physico-Technical Institute, 1918-1978* [and other pamphlets on the Institute's work]. Ed. V. Ya. Frenkel. 6 vols. Leningrad, 1978.

fr   Frenkel', V. Ya. "Pyat'desyat let Fiziko-tekhnicheskomu institutu im. A. F. Ioffe, AN SSSR." *UFN, 96* (1968), 529-568.

fs   Frenkel', V. Ya. "Fiftieth anniversary of the A. F. Ioffe Physicotechnical Institute." *SPU, 11* (1969), 831-854.

ft   Frenkel', V. Ya. "50-letiye Fiziko-tekhnicheskogo instituta im. A. F. Ioffe." AN. *Vestnik,* 1969:2, 71-76.

io   *Ioffe, A. F. "Fiziko-tekhnicheskiy institut za 15 let." *Sorena,* 1933:8, 160-164.

tu   Tuchkevich, V. M., and V. Ya. Frenkel'. "Fiziko-tekhnicheskiy institut imeni A. F. Ioffe v gody voyny." *VIYeT, 51* (1975), 13-20.

vl2.ch *Chekhmatayev, D. P. "20 let Gosudarstvennogo opticheskogo instituta." Leningrad. Gosudarstvennyy opticheskiy institut. *Trudy, 14* (1941), 5-8. (Also in *Sbornik statey k 20-letiyu [GOI].* Moscow, 1941. Pp. 5-8.)

fr   Frish, S. E., and K. K. Baumgart. "Akademik D. S. Rozhdest-venskiy i Leningradskaya shkola optikov." Leningrad. University. *Vestnik,* 1946:2, 116-122.

va   *Vavilov, S. I., ed. *Pyatnadtsat' let Gosudarstvennogo opticheskogo instituta.* Leningrad, 1934.

vb   Vavilov, S. I. "Puti razvitiya Opticheskogo instituta." AN. *Izvestiya,* ser. fiz., 1936:1-2, 163-188. (Also in *UFN, 16* (1936), 872-896.)

vc   Vavilov, S. I. "Tvorcheskaya rabota Gosudarstvennogo opticheskogo instituta." *UFN, 27* (1945), 106-117.

vl3.an *AN. *Fiziko-matematicheskiy institut.* Leningrad, 1925.

vl4.io *Ioffe, A. F. "Rol' Leningradskogo politekhnicheskogo instituta v razvitii dorevolyutsionnoy i sovetskoy fiziki." Leningrad. Politekhnicheskiy institut. *Yubileynaya nauchno-tekhnicheskaya konferentsiya.* Leningrad, 1949. Pp. 4-6.

vml.ar *Arkad'yev, V. K. *Laboratoriya elektromagnetizma im. Makswella 1919-1939.* Moscow, 1940.

ch   *Chertov, A. G. "Publichnyye lektsii fizikov Moskovskogo universiteta i I. F. Usagin." *Ivan Filippovich Usagin.* Moscow, 1959. Pp. 118-129.

kl   Klement'yev, S. D. "Laboratoriya elektromagnetizma pri Kafedre teoreticheskikh osnov elektrotekhniki Fizicheskogo fakul'teta MGU." Moscow. University. *Vestnik,* ser. fiz.-mat. i yest. nauk, 1949:9, 186-190.

ko   *Kononkov, A. F. "Fizicheskiy kabinet v period deyatel'nosti A. G. Stoletova i I. F. Usagina." *Ivan Filippovich Usagin.* Moscow, 1959. Pp. 241-257.

kp   *Kononkov, A. F., and S. I. Usagin. "Fizicheskiy kabinet i yego laboratorii v period deyatel'nosti N. A. Umova i I. F. Usagina." *Ivan Filippovich Usagin.* Moscow, 1959. Pp. 257-278.

kq *Kononkov, A. F. "Fizicheskiy kabinet Moskovskogo univer-siteta s yego osnovaniya do nashikh dney." C.vb1.vo, 143-154.

kr Kononkov, A. F. "Fizicheskiy fakul'tet Moskovskogo univer-siteta." *IMYeN: Fizika, 6* (1968), 15-28.

mo *Moscow. University. *Moskovskiy universitet v vospominaniyakh sovremennikov.* Moscow, 1956.

na Nasledov, D. N. "K istorii otdeleniya geofiziki fizicheskogo fakul'teta MGU." *IMYeN, 8* (1970), 211-222.

pr Predvoditelev, A. S., and A. S. Timiryazev, ed. *Fizika v Moskovskom universitete, 1755-1940 gg.* Moscow, 1940. (Moscow. Universitet. *Uchenyye zapiski, 52.*)

sh Shost'in, N. A. "Laboratoriya elektromagnetizma pri Fizi-cheskom fakul'tete MGU." *UFN, 38* (1949), 133-135.

so Sokolov, A. A., and B. K. Kerimov. "Kafedra teoreticheskoy fiziki v Moskovskom universitete." *IMYeN: Fizika, 6* (1968), 86-106.

sp Sominskiy, M. S. "Reforma F. F. Petrushevskogo." *UFN, 37* (1949), 378-387.

zy Zyukov, P. I. "Novyye materialy o deyatel'nosti B. B. Golitsyna v Moskovskom Universitete." IIYeT. *Trudy, 5* (1955), 216-240.

vm2.ka Kapitsa, P. L. "The construction and work of the Institute of Physical Problems of the U.S.S.R. Academy of Sciences." AN. SSSR. *Izvestiya,* ser. fiz., *2* (1937), 278-286.

See also: D.cd1.ir; E.ab1.ar; G.ca6.mo; I.dd1.fr; R.ba1.kn

vm3.an Anon. "220-letiye Fizicheskogo instituta im. P. N. Lebedeva." AN. *Vestnik,* 1945:7-8, 153-159.

se *Serdyukov, A. R. *Rol' P. N. Lebedeva i yego shkoly v organizatsii i razvitii otechestvennoy fiziki.* Moscow, 1953. (Summary of thesis for Moscow University.)

sk Skobel'tsyn, D. V., and I. M. Frank. "Fizicheskiy institut im. P. N. Lebedeva." *UFN, 63* (1957), 503-525.

va Vavilov, S. I. "Fizicheskiy institut im. P. N. Lebedeva." *Vestnik, 7:10-11* (1937), 37-46.

vm4.ko Kolotyrkin, Ya. M. "Fiziko-khimicheskii institut imeni P. Ya. Karpova v gody voyny." *VIYeT, 51* (1975), 21-23.

li Lipshits, S. Yu. *Moskovskoye Obshchestvo ispytateley prirody za 135 let yego sushchestvovaniya 1805-1940.* Moscow, 1940.

vm5.an *AN. *25 let Radiyevogo instituta.* Moscow and Leningrad, 1947.

my   *Mysovskiy, L. V. "Fizicheskiy otdel Gosudarstvennogo radi-
      yevogo instituta." AN. Radiyevyy institut.   *Trudy, 4* (1938),
      28-34.

za   Zaytseva, L. L. "Pervaya radiologicheskaya laboratoriya v Rossii."
      IIYeT.   *Trudy, 19* (1957), 197-218.

vr1.mi   Mikheyev, M. N. "Institut fiziki metallov na Urale." *Zhurnal
         tekhnicheskoy fiziki, 18* (1948), 125-130.

mj   Mikheyev, M. N. "Institut fiziki metallov na Urale..., 1932-
      1947." AN. Ural. filial. Institut fiziki metallov.   *Trudy, 12*
      (1949), 3-8.

vr2.al   Al'tshuler, S. A. "Razvitiye fiziki v Kazanskom universitete
         posle Velikoy Oktyabr'skoy sotsialisticheskoy revolyutsii." Kazan.
         University. *Uchenyye zapiski, 120:7* (1960), 3-13.

fe   *Fesenkov, V. G. "O nekotorykh voprosakh razvitiya fiziko-
      matematicheskikh nauk v Kazakhstane." AN Kazakhskoy SSR.
      Vestnik, 1947:11(32), 25-26.

ko   Kononkov, B. F., and A. V. Dikarev. "Raboty Radiolaboratorii
      2-y bazy radiotelegrafnykh formirovaniy v Kazani." *IMYeN: Fizi-
      ka, 10* (1971), 196-242.

tu   Tumashev, G. G. "Razvitiye mekhaniki v Kazanskom Universi-
      tete za 40 let." Kazan. University. *Uchenyye zapiski, 120:7*
      (1960), 14-23.

See also: I.ee1.ko

SOUTHERN REPUBLICS

vs1.al   Ambartsumyan, V. A., and L. V. Mirzoyan. "Byurakanskaya
         astrofizicheskaya observatoriya Akademii nauk Armyanskoy
         SSR." IIYeT. *Trudy, 17* (1957), 485-492.

am   Ambartsumyan, V. A. *Nauka v Armenii za 40 let.* Yerevan,
      1960.

an   *Anon. "Razvitiye fiziko-matematicheskikh nauk v Armenii za
      period Sovetskoy vlasti." AN Armyanskoy SSR. *Izvestiya,* ser.
      fiz.-matem. nauk, 1957:5, 3-18.

vs2.am   *Amirkhanov, Kh. I., et al. "Razvitiye fiziki v Azerbaydzhane za
         30 let." AN Azerbaydzhanskoy SSR. Institut fiziki i matematiki.
         Trudy, ser. fiz., *3* (1948), 3-15.

an   *Anon. "Energeticheskiy institut k 30-y godovshchine
      ustanovleniya Sovetskoy vlasti v Azerbaydzhane." AN Azerbayd-
      zhanskoy SSR. Energeticheskiy institut. *Trudy, 9* (1950), 5-9.

do *Dorfman, Ya. G., and A. P. Mikhalevskiy. "Fizika i geofizika v Azerbaydzhane za 20 let." AN Azerbaydzhanskoy SSR. *Izvestiya,* 1940:2, 140-144.

kh *Khalilov, Z. I. "Razvitiye fiziko-matematicheskikh nauk v Sovetskom Azerbaydzhane." AN Azerbaydzhanskoy SSR. *Izvestiya,* 1957:10, 25-38.

lo *Lopukhin, Ye. B., et al. "Razvitiye fiziki." AN. Azerb. filial. *Trudy, 30* (1936), 79-93.

na Nagiyev, M. F. "Itogi nauchno-issledovatel'skikh rabot v oblasti fiziko-tekhnicheskikh nauk." *10 let Akademii nauk Azerbaydzhanskoy SSR.* Baku, 1957. Pp. 94-103.

ve Veisov, A. B. "Aus der Geschichte der Entwicklung der Physik in der Sowjetrepublik Azerbajdzan." *NTM, 13:2* (1976), 62-69.

vs3.dy Dzhikiya, D. K. *Iz istori fiziki v Sovetskoy Gruzii.* Tbilisi, 1972.

dz Dzhikiya, D. K. "Nekotoryye voprosy razvitiya fiziki v Gruzii za 50 let." *IMYeN: Fizika, 12* (1972), 73-101.

pa Parkadze, V. D. "Le développement de la physique en Géorgie au XXe siècle." ICHS, XII (1968). *Actes, 5* (1971), 75-79.

ve Vekua, I. N., et al. *Akademiya Nauk SSSR i razvitiye gruzinskoy nauki, 1724-1974.* Tbilisi, 1974.

vs4.mi Mitt, A. "Fizika v Tartuskom universitete (1802-1918)." *Iz istorii yestestvoznaniya i tekhniki Pribaltiki, 3* (1971), 69-80.

pr Pryuller, P. K. "Vklad uchenykh Tartuskogo universiteta v razvitiye fiziki i geofiziki za period c 1802 po 1940 g." ICHS, XIII (1971). Section 6. *Actes* (1974), 143-145.

UKRAINE

vu1.ak Akademiya Nauk Ukrains'koi RSR. *Istoriia Akademii Nauk Ukrains'koi RSR.* 2 vols., Kiev, 1967.

an Anon. "Fizichni nauki." C.vu1.ak, 488-531.

ko Kordun, G. G. "Razvitive fiziki na Ukraine." *IMYeN: Fizika, 10* (1971), 77-111.

kp Kordun, G. G. "K istorii razvitiya fiziki v Sovetskoy Ukraine." ICHS, XIII (1971). Section 6. *Actes* (1974), 149-152.

See also: D.ab1.an, pu

vu2.ge *Geguzin, Ya. Ye. "K istorii kafedry fiziki tverdogo tela." Kharkov. University. *Uchenyye zapiski, 60* (1955), 81-92.

le *Lemmleyn, G. A. "Vospominaniya o kafedre fiziki Khar'kovskogo universiteta i o moyey rabote na ney s 1902 po 1906 g." Kharkov. University. *Uchenyye zapiski, 60* (1955), 51-55.

po *Polyakova, N. L. "Fizika v Khar'kovskom universitete ot yego osnovaniya do Velikoy Oktyabr'skoy sotsialisticheskoy revolyutsii." Kharkov. University. *Uchenyye zapiski, 60* (1955), 5-50.

pp *Polyakova, N. L. "Fizika v Khar'kovskom universitete s 1917 po 1930 g." Kharkov. University. *Uchenyye zapiski, 60* (1955) 57-62.

ve *Verkin, V. I., et al. "Kafedry eksperimental'noy, teoreticheskoy i obshchey fiziki fiziko-matematicheskogo fakul'teta (1930-1955 gg.)." Kharkov. University. *Uchenyye zapiski, 60* (1955), 63-79.

See also: I.dd1.tk

vu3.ga Gayduk, Yu. M., and I. A. Naumov. "Poltavskiy kruzhok lyubiteley fiziko-matematicheskikh nauk (1898-1917)." AN. *VIYeT, 26* (1969), 33-34.

D. MECHANICS

General accounts

aa1.pn Pogrebysskiy, I. B. "Quelques aspects de l'évolution de la mécanique classique (Newtonienne) au XXe siècle." ICHS, XII (1968). *Actes, 4* (1971), 143-146.

po Polak, L. S. "Nekotoryye tendentsii razvitiya printsipov dinamiki sistemy v XIX v. i pervoy chetverti XX v." IIYeT. *Trudy, 19* (1957), 538-543.

wi Wiechert, Emil. "Die Mechanik im Rahmen der allgemeinen Physik." *Kultur der Gegenwart.* Ed. Paul Hinneberg. Vol. 3:3:1 (1915), 1-78.

See also: B.bo4.bl | ei2.qm | th5.bt, bu

ab1.am *Anon. *Mekhanika v SSSR za 30 let, 1917-1947.* Moscow and Leningrad, 1950.

an Anon. "Mekhanika." C.vu1.ak, 436-487.

bl Bogolyubov, A. N. "Raboty sovetskikh issledovateley po istorii mekhaniki." *VIYeT, 36-37* (1971), 22-30.

gn Golubev, V. V. "Russkiye raboty po mekhanike i vliyaniye ikh na razvitiye mirovoy nauki." Moscow University. *Uchenyye zapiski, 91* (1947), 97-104.

go Golubev, V. V. "Mekhanika v Moskovskom universitete pered Velikoy Oktyabr'skoy sotsialisticheskoy revolyutsiyey i v sovetskiy period." *Istoriko-matematicheskiye issledovaniya, 8* (1955), 77-126.

hq Grigor'yan, A. T. "The main trends in the development of mechanics in the USSR." *AIHS,* no. 60-61 (1962), 267-279.

hr Grigor'yan, A. T. "The development of analytical mechanics in the U.S.S.R." ICHS, XI (1965). *Actes, 3* (1968), 383-386. (Also in *AIHS,* nos. 78-79 (1967), 39-42.)

hs Grigor'yan, A. T., and V. N. Fradlin. "Zum 60. Jahrestag der Oktoberrevolution: Forschungen zur Geschichte der Mechanik in der UdSSR." *NTM, 14:2* (1977), 1-7.

ht Grigor'yan, A. T., and I. B. Pogrebysskiy. "Die Entwicklung der Mechanik in der UdSSR seit 1917." *NTM, 5:11* (1968), 23-43.

hu Grigor'yan, A. T., and L. S. Polak. "Ocherki istorii mekhaniki v Rossii vo vtoroy polovine XIX i nachale XX veka (1861-1917)." IIYeT. *Trudy, 10* (1956), 85-164.

hv   Grigor'yan, A. T., and L. S. Polak. "Mekhanika." C.va1.fi, *2*, 222-283.

ii   IIYeT. *Ocherki istorii matematiki i mekhaniki.* Ed. A. T. Grigor'yan. Moscow, 1963.

is   *Ishlinskiy, Aleksandr Yul'yevich, ed. *Razvitiye mekhaniki v SSSR, 1917-1967.* Moscow, 1967.

mi   Mitropol'skiy, Yu. A. "Le développement des idées de la mécanique non-linéaire en U.R.S.S." ICHS, XII (1968). *Actes, 4* (1971), 123-126.

mo   *Moscow. Moskovskoye vyssheye tekhnicheskoye uchilishche. Kafedra teoreticheskoy mekhaniki. *Mekhanika: Sbornik statey.* Moscow, 1956.

pu   *Putyata, T. V., and V. N. Fradlin. "O tvorcheskom sodruzhestve uchenykh Ukrainy i Rossii v oblasti mekhaniki." Kiev. Politekhnicheskiy institut. *Izvestiya, 15* (1954), 220-227.

See also: C.vr2.tu

General concepts

ba1.hu   Hund, Friedrich. "Kräfte und ihre begriffliche Fassung." DPG. *Verhandlungen, 24* (1943), 12-20.

ja   Jammer, Max. *Concepts of force.* Cambridge, Mass., 1957.

to   Tonnelat, M. A. "L'évolution de la notion de force du 17e au 20e siècle." ICHS, VII (1953). *Actes,* 1953?, 610-614.

bb1.gr   Grigor'yan, A. T. "La contribution des savants soviétiques au développement de la mécanique des corps de masse variable." ICHS, XII (1968). *Actes, 4* (1971), 79-82. (Also in *AIHS*, nos. 86-87 (1969), 45-49.)

gs   Grigor'yan, A. T. "Die Mechanik der Körper veränderlicher Masse und ihre Entwicklung in der UdSSR." *NTM, 11:2* (1974), 44-57.

jb   Jammer, Max. *Concepts of mass.* Cambridge, Mass., 1961.

ty   Tyulina, I. A. "Dva podkhoda k postroyeniyu modeli tela peremennoy massy." ICHS, XIII (1971). Section 5. *Actes* (1974), 247-250.

bc1.ku   Kul'betsas, L. L. "O popytkakh aksiomatizirovat' vremya v klassicheskoy mekhanike." ICHS, XIII (1971). Section 5. *Actes* (1974), 236-238.

ma   Mays, Wolfe. "Whitehead and the philosophy of time." *Studium generale, 23* (1970), 509-524.

mi   Mittelstaedt, Peter. *Der Zeitbegriff in der Physik: Physikalische und philosophische Untersuchungen in der klassischen und in der relativistischen Physik.* Mannheim, 1976.

pa   Park, David. "The changing concepts of space and time in physics." *Studium generale, 20* (1967), 10-14.

pr   Prigogine, Ilya. "Time, irreversibility and structure." A.ad1.me, 561-593. (1973), 561-593.

bd1.ak Akchurin, I. A., and M. D. Akhundov. "Eynshteyn i razvitiye ponyatiya prostranstva." B.ei7.ae, 163-201.

go   Gould, James A. "The concept of absolute space." *JHI, 21* (1961), 119-120.

jb   Jammer, Max. *Concepts of space.* 2nd ed. Cambridge, Mass., 1969.

le   Leclerc, Ivor. "Whitehead and the problem of extension." *Journal of philosophy, 58* (1961), 559-565.

be1.ba Bachinskiy, A. I. "K istorii russkoy nauki: Vzglyady N. A. Umova na potentsial'nuyu energiyu, na silu, deystvuyushchiye na rassgoyanii, i na massu." *UFN, 3* (1923), 256-261.

de   Debye, Peter. "Arnold Sommerfeld und die Überlichtgeschwindigkeit." *PB, 16* (1960), 568-570.

gu   Gulo, D. D. "O rabotakh N. A. Umova po lokalizatsii i dvizheniyu energii." ICHS, XI (1965). *Actes, 3* (1968), 414-417.

kr   Kravets, T. P. "Evolyutsiya ucheniya ob energii (1847-1947)." *UFN, 36* (1948), 338-358.

ku   Kuznetsov, B. G., and U. I. Frankfurt. "K istorii zakona sokhraneniya i prevrashcheniya energii." IIYeT. *Trudy, 28* (1959), 339-376.

bg1.di Dicke, R. H. "The Eötvös experiment." *Scientific American, 205* (Dec. 1961), 84-94.

pe   Pekár, Dezsö. "Gravitációs mérések." *Matematikai és physikai lapok, 27* (1918), 147-187.

pf   Pekár, Dezsö, and Jenö Fekete. "A gravitáció és tehetetlenség arányosságáról." *Matematikai és physikai lapok, 27* (1918), 188-205.

re   Renner, J. "The Eötvös experiment." Budapest University. *Annales: sectio geologica, 7* (1964), 9-18.

rw   Rybar, István. "Vizsgálatok a Földön mozgó szerkezetek nehézségröl." *Matematikai és physikai lapok, 27* (1918), 230-234.

rx   Rybar, István. "Elöadásairól és eredeti elöadási kīsérleteiröl."
     Matematikai és physikai lapok, 27 (1918), 235-256.

va   Varnello, V. V. "Istoricheskoye razvitiye metodov opredeleniya
     tverdosti." Novosibirskiy institut inzhenerov vodnogo transporta.
     Trudy, 2 (1956), 235-243.

ze   Zemplén, Jolán M. "The Eötvös experiment and modern phys-
     ics." ICHS, XII (1968). *Actes, 5* (1971), 121-125.

See also: F.de1

Classical theory

ca1.gr   Grigor'yan, A. T. "O rozwoju zasad wariacyjnych mechaniki."
         Polska Akademia Nauk. Zaklad Historii Nauki i Techniki. *Studia*
         (1968), 154-165.

gs   Grigor'yan, A. T. "Iz istorii integral'nykh variatsionnykh prin-
         tsipov mekhaniki." *VIYeT, 1* (1956), 24-33.

gt   Grigor'yan, A. T. "On the development of variational principles
         of mechanics." *AIHS,* no. 70-71 (1965), 23-35.

cb1.fr   Fradlin, V. N. "K istorii dinamiki negolonomnykh sistem." *VI-
         YeT, 11* (1961), 61-69.

fs   Fradlin, V. N. "Petr Vasil'yevich Voronets: Odin iz
         osnovopolozhnikov negolonomnoy mekhaniki." IIYeT. *Trudy,*
         43 (1961), 422-469.

ft   Fradlin, V. N. "Nauchnyye trudy S. A. Chaplygina po negolo-
         nomnoy mekhanike i ikh dalneysheye razvitiye." D.ab1.ii, 147-
         190.

fu   Fradlin, V. N. "Ob odnoy oshibke v negolonomnoy mekhanike."
         IIYeT. *Trudy, 43* (1961), 470-477.

gr   Grigor'yan, A. T., and V. N. Fradlin. "Über die Entwicklung der
         Mechanik nichtholonomer Systeme in den Arbeiten deutscher
         Wissenschaftler." *NTM, 16:1* (1979), 43-48.

po   Pogrebysskiy, I. B. "O mekhanike sistem s ideal'nymi neuder-
         zhivayushchimi svyazyami." IIYeT. *Trudy, 34* (1960), 226-240.

ra   Rabinowicz, Ernest. "Resource letter F-1." *Friction: Selected re-*
         prints. NY, 1963. Pp. 1-4.

cc1.gr   Grigor'yan, A. T. "Les travaux sur la mécanique non-
         euclidienne en Russie." *Scientia, 95* (1960), 347-350.

gs   Grigor'yan, A. T. "Raboty po neyevklidovoy mekhanike v Ros-
         sii." IIYeT. *Trudy, 43* (1961), 363-377.

gt   Grigor'yan, A. T., and Boris A. Rozenfeld. "Mechanika neyeuklidesowa." *KHNT, 16* (1971), 273-280.

cd1.an   Andronov, A. A. "L. I. Mandel'shtam i teoria nelineynykh kolebaniy." AN. *Izvestiya,* ser. fiz., *9* (1945), 30-55. (Also in B.me1.ia, 98-130.)

bo   Bojko, Evgenija S. "Zasada izomorfizmu i teoria dragań w pracach szkoly moskiewsko-gorkowskiej." *KHNT, 20* (1975), 479-489.

ga   Gaponov-Grekhov, A. V., and M. I. Rabinovich. "L. I. Mandel'shtam and the modern theory of nonlinear oscillations and waves." *SPU, 22* (1979), 590-614.

ir   Ivankov, A. G. *Razvitiye ucheniya ob avtokolebaniyakh v Moskovskom universitete.* Moscow, 1956. (Summary of thesis, IIYeT.)

kh   Khaykin, S. E. "Razvitiye ucheniya o kolebaniyakh." C.vb4.an, 253-262.

mo   Moiseyev, N. D. "A. M. Lyapunov i yego trudy po teorii ustoychivosti." Moscow. University. *Uchenyye zapiski, 91* (1947), 129-147.

pb   Papaleksi, N. D. "Razvitiye ucheniya o nelineynykh kolebaniyakh i ikh primenenii." AN. *Izvestiya,* ser. fiz., *9* (1945), 145-160.

pc   Papaleksi, N. D., et al. "Nekotoryye issledovaniya v oblasti nelineynykh kolebanii, provedennyye v SSSR, nachinaya c 1935 g." *UFN, 33* (1947), 335-352.

ce1.iv   Ivashkevich, V. Yu. "K istorii razvitiya osnovnykh predposylok invariantnoy teorii mekhaniki." IIYeT. *Trudy, 43* (1961), 378-405.

cf1.be   Berkson, William. *Fields of force: The development of a world view from Faraday to Einstein.* NY, 1974.

ei   Einstein, Albert. "Staryye i novyye teorii polya." *VIYeT, 17* (1964), 16-21.

he   Heisenberg, Werner. "Zamechaniya k eynshteynovskomu nabrosku yedinoy teorii polya." IIYeT. *Trudy, 34* (1960), 3-8.

hg   Hesse, Mary B. *Forces and fields. The concept of action at a distance in the history of physics.* London, 1961.

cg1.br   Brillouin, Léon. "Poincaré and the shortcomings of the Hamilton-Jacobi method for classical or quantized mechanics." *Archive for rational mechanics and analysis, 5* (1960), 76-94.

fr   Fradlin, V. N. "Kratkii istoricheskiy ocherk razvitiya problemy *n* tel." IIYeT. *Trudy, 34* (1960), 198-225.

ha   Hadamard, Jacques. "Le problème des trois corps." B.pm3.av, 51-114.

Matter in bulk

da1.ey   Eyring, Dean Henry. "Introduction [on properties of matter]." B.ld3.jl, *8*, xvii-xxix.

ha   Harker, David. "Introduction [on structure of matter]." B.ld3.jl, *6*, xvii-xxxiv.

hi   Higgins, Thomas James. "Comprehensive review of Saint-Venant's torsion problem." *AJP, 10* (1942), 248-259.

ra   Rakcheyev, E. N. "Ocherk razvitiya teorii uprugosti v Rossii vo vtoroy polovine XIX- nachale XX veka (1861-1917)." IIYeT. *Trudy, 22* (1959), 214-239.

rf   Reytman, M. I., et al. "O razvitii mekhaniki deformiruyemykh tverdykh tel v XX v." ICHS, XIII (1971). Section 5. *Actes* (1974), 268-271.

Fluid mechanics

ea1.em   Emrich, Raymond J., and François N. Frenkel. "[Twenty years of] fluid dynamics." *PT, 21* (May 1968), 44-46.

en   Emrich, Raymond J., et al. "Thirty years of fluid dynamics." *PT, 31* (Sep. 1978), 38-46.

go   Goldstein, Sidney. "Fluid mechanics in the first half of this century." *Annual review of fluid mechanics, 1* (1969), 1-28.

ne   Neményi, P. F. "The main concepts and ideas of fluid dynamics in their historical development." *AHES, 2* (1962-66), 52-86.

rp   Rouse, Hunter, and Simon Ince. *History of hydraulics.* State University of Iowa, 1957; NY, 1963.

eb1.ch   Chaplygin, S. A., and V. V. Golubev. "Raboty po gidromekhanike v SSSR." C.vb4.an, 101-120.

gr   Grigor'yan, A. T. "Die Entwicklung der Hydrodynamik und Aerodynamik in den Arbeiten von N. I. Shukowski und S. A. Tschaplygin." *NTM, 2:5* (1965), 39-62.

me   Meshcherskiy, I. "Trudy A. A. Fridmana po gidromekhanike." Leningrad. Glavnaya geofizicheskaya observatoriya. *Geoficheskiy sbornik, 5:1* (1927), 57-60.

pr   Prandtl, Ludwig. "Mein Weg zu hydrodynamischen Theorien." *PB, 4* (1948), 89-92.

ss   Stepanov, G. Yu. "Teoriya gidrodinamicheskikh reshetok v rabotakh N. Ye. Zhukovskogo i S. A. Chaplygina i yeye
posledyushcheye razvitiye." ICHS, XIII (1971). Section 5. *Actes*
(1974), 271-274. (Also in AN. *Izvestiya,* ser. mekh. zhidkosti i
gaza, no.2 (1972), 3-8.)

ec1.gi Gibson, A. H. *Osborne Reynolds and his work in hydraulics and
hydrodynamics.* London, 1946.

See also: B.re7.bt

eg1.mb Markovitz, Hershel. "The emergence of rheology." *PT, 21* (Apr.
1968), 23-30.

mc   Marvin, Robert S. "[Twenty years of] rheology." *PT, 21* (May
1968), 52-53.

eh1.ku Kutateladze, S. S. "Problema turbulentnosti." ICHS, XIII
(1971). Section 5. *Actes* (1974), 274-276.

ei1.bi Bikerman, Jacob J. "Theories of capillary attraction." *Centaurus,
19* (1975), 182-205.

ta   Tangl, Károly. "Vizsgálatok a kapillaritásról." *Matematikai és
physikai lapok, 27* (1918), 115-129.

Statistical mechanics

ha1.be Bellone, Enrico. *Aspetti dell'approccio statistico alla meccanica,
1849-1905.* Florence, 1977.

br   Brush, Stephen G. "Foundations of statistical mechanics, 1845-
1915." *AHES, 4* (1967), 145-183.

co   Cohen, E. G. D., ed. *Statistical mechanics at the turn of the decade.* NY, 1971.

du   Dugas, René. *La théorie physique au sens de Boltzmann et ses pro-
longements modernes.* Neuchâtel-Suisse, 1959.

jo   Jordan, Pascual. "Die Statistik in der modernen Physik."
Friedrich Burgdörfer, ed. *Die Statistik in Deutschland nach ihrem
heutigen Stand.* Berlin, 1940. Pp. 1280-1287.

ka   Kac, M. "The emergence of statistical thought in exact sciences."
A.aa1.nf, 433-444.

hb1.ca Caldirola, Piero. "Osservazioni sulle statistiche intermedie."
Ricerca scientifica, 12 (1941), 1020-1027.

gl   Glebov, L. A. "O roli metoda srednikh v statisticheskoy
mekhanike." *VIYeT, 34* (1971), 50-51.

mc   Mehra, Jagdish. "Einstein and the foundations of statistical
mechanics." *Physica, 79A* (1975), 447-477.

mi   Migdal, A. B., and V. A. Fok. "Vzglyady N. S. Krylova na obosnovaniye statisticheskoy fiziki." Nikolay Sergeyevich Krylov. *Raboty po obosnovaniyu statisticheskoy fiziki.* Moscow, 1950. Pp. 5-14.

ro   Rosenfeld, Léon. "On the foundations of statistical thermodynamics." *Acta physica polonica, 14* (1955), 3-39.

sp   Spasskiy, Boris I. "Ob issledovaniyakh N. N. Pirogova po statisticheskomy obosnovaniyu vtorogo nachala termodinamiki." *IMYeT: Fizika, 1* (1960), 61-88.

hc1.ha *Hanle, Paul Arthur. *Erwin Schrödinger's statistical mechanics, 1912-1925.* Ph.D. thesis. Yale Univ., 1975. (*DAI, 36,* 7598A.)

mo   Møller, Christian. "Statisticheskaya mekhanika Gibbsa i teoriya otnositel'nosti." *ES,* 1971, 114-162.

he1.be Bernhardt, Hannelore. "Über die Entwicklung und Bedeutung der Ergodenhypothese in den Anfängen der statistischen Mechanik." *NTM, 8:1* (1971), 13-25.

ha   Halmos, Paul R. "Von Neumann on measure and ergodic theory." American Mathematical Society. *Bulletin 64:3:2* (1958), 86-94.

hf1.be Bernhardt, Hannelore. "Der Wiederkehreinwand gegen Boltzmanns H-Theorem und der Begriff der Irreversibilität." *NTM, 6:2* (1969), 27-36.

co   Cohen, E. G. D., and W. Thirring, eds. *The Boltzmann equation, theory and applications.* Vienna, 1973.

du   Dutta, Mahadev. "A hundred years of entropy." *PT, 21* (Jan. 1968), 75-79.

po   Popper, Karl R. "Irreversibility; or, entropy since 1905." *BJPS, 8* (1957), 151-155.

re   Rechenberg, Helmut. "Ist das Gibbssche Paradoxon paradox ? Die Vollendung der statistischen Mechanik, aufgezeigt an der Entwicklung des Entropiebegriffs." *PB, 31* (1975), 456-470.

ro   Rosenfeld, Léon. "Max Planck and the statistical definition of entropy." *BSPS, 21* (1979), 235-246. (In French in B.pl.ik, 203-211.)

sv   Sviridonov, M. N. "Razvitiye ponyatiya entropii v rabotakh T. A. Afanas'yevoy-Erenfest." *IMYeN: Fizika, 10* (1971), 77-111.

hg1.br Brush, Stephen G. *Kinetic theory.* 3 vols. Oxford, 1965-1972.

bs   Brush, Stephen G. "The development of the kinetic theory of gases, VII. Heat conduction and the Stefan-Boltzmann Law." *AHES, 11* (1973), 38-96.

bt   Brush, Stephen G. "The development of the kinetic theory of gases, VIII. Randomness and irreversibility." *AHES, 12* (1974), 1-88.

bu   Brush, Stephen G., and C. W. F. Everitt. "Maxwell, Osborne Reynolds, and the radiometer." *HSPS, 1* (1969), 105-125.

bv   Brush, Stephen G. "Interatomic forces and gas theory from Newton to Lennard-Jones." *Archive for rational mechanics and analysis, 39:1* (1970), 1-29.

bw   Brush, Stephen G. *The kind of motion we call heat.* 2 vols. Amsterdam, 1976.

go   Goncharov, V. P. "Teoriya real'nykh gazov N. N. Pirogova." *IMYeN: Fizika, 1* (1960), 89-97.

kn   Knyazheskiy, P. N. "Raboty uchenikov P. N. Lebedeva po issledovaniyu razrezhennykh gazov." *IMYeN: Fizika, 10* (1971), 171-174.

me   Merkulova, N. M. "La dynamique des gaz au XXe siècle: Tendances de son évolution." ICHS, XII (1968). *Actes, 4* (1971), 111-113.

mf   Merkulova, N. M. "K istorii formirovaniya osnovnykh ponyatiy gazovoy dinamiki." ICHS, XIII (1971). Section 5. *Actes* (1974), 281-284.

mh   Merzkirch, Wolfgang F. "Mach's contribution to the development of gas dynamics." *BSPS, 6* (1970), 42-59.

hh1.be   Bessenrodt, Rüdiger. "Brownsche Bewegung: Hundert Jahre Theorie der wichtigsten Brücke zwischen Mikro- und Makrophysik." *PB, 33* (1977), 7-16.

br   Brush, S. G. "A history of random processes. I. Brownian movement from Brown to Perrin." *AHES, 5* (1968-69), 1-36.

la   Layman, Ronald. "Feyerabend, Brownian motion, and the hiddenness of refuting facts." *PS, 44* (1977), 225-247.

te   Teske, Armin. "Einstein und Smoluchowski: Zur Geschichte der Brownschen Bewegung und der Opaleszenz." *Sudhoffs Archiv, 53* (1969), 292-305.

ul   Ulam, Stanislaw. "Marian Smoluchowski and the theory of probabilities in physics." *AJP, 25* (1957), 475-481.

Acoustics

ka1.li   Lindsay, Robert Bruce, ed. *Acoustics: Historical and philosophical development.* Stroudsburg, Pa., 1973.

lj Lindsay, R. Bruce. "[Twenty years of] acoustics." *PT, 21* (May 1968), 60.

ok Okhotnikov, V. D. *V mire zastyvshikh zvukov.* Moscow and Leningrad, 1948.

kb1.am Anon. "Sovetskaya akustika za 40 let." *Akusticheskiy zhurnal, 3* (1957), 299-321.

an Anon. "Soviet acoustics during the last fifty years." *Soviet physics, acoustics, 13:4* (1968), 415-454.

gu Gulo, D. D. "Raboty otechestvennykh fizikov po akustike v kontse XIX- nachale XX v." C.vb1.pr, *1,* 364-380.

is Isakovich, M. A. "L. I. Mandel'shtam and the propagation of sound in microscopically inhomogeneous media." *SPU, 22* (1979), 928-933.

mp *Moroz, L. I. "Raboty prof. P. N. Lebedeva i yego shkoly v oblasti akustiki." Nauchno-tekhnicheskoye obshchestvo vodnogo transporta. Leningradskoye basseinovoye pravleniye. *Sbornik trudov,* 1954:1, 105-121.

mq *Moroz, L. I. *K istorii razvitiya otechestvennoy akustiki.* Leningrad, 1952. (Summary of thesis for Leningrad, Politekhnicheskiy Institut.)

ri Rimskiy-Korsakov, A. V. "Raboty B. P. Konstantinova po fizicheskoy akustike." B.kn4.it, 14-25.

rw Rzhevkin, S. N. "Uspekhi sovetskoy akustiki." *UFN, 34* (1948), 1-12.

rx Rzhevkin, S. N. "Raboty uchenykh Moskovskogo universiteta v oblasti akustiki." A.ab1.vo, 306-318.

kc1.kl Klein, Elias. "Background history of ultrasonics." Acoustical Society of America. *Journal, 20* (1948), 601-604.

me Merkulov, L. G., and V. F. Nozdrev. "Raboty prof. S. Ya. Sokolova po ul'trazvukoskopii." A.ab1.vo, 318-324.

rw Rzhevkin, S. N. "Akustika i ul'trazvuk." C.vb1.pr, *2,* 197-242.

vv *Vvedenskiy, B. A. "Nashi raboty po rasprostraneniyu ul'trakorotkikh voln." AN. *Yubileynyy sbornik, 2,* 598-607.

kd1.kn Knudsen, Vern O. "The propagation of sound in air and water." A.ad1.un, 79-90.

ma Matthäus, Wolfgang. "Experimente zur Messung der Schallgeschwindigkeit im Wasser und Meerwasser im 19. und zu Beginn des 20. Jahrhunderts." *NTM, 10:2* (1973), 39-49.

kt1.an   Andreyev, N. N., et al. "Arkhitekturnaya akustika v SSSR." *UFN, 37* (1949), 269-315.

ha   Hackmann, W. D. "Underwater acoustics and the Royal Navy, 1893-1930." *Annals of science, 36* (1979), 255-278.

kl   Klein, Elias. "Underwater sound and naval acoustical research and applications before 1939." Acoustical Society of America. *Journal, 43* (1968), 931-947.

See also: B.mb2.fh

Applications

ta1.ab   Abbot, Charles Greeley. "The 1914 tests of the Langley 'Aerodrome.'" Smithsonian Institution, Washington. *Miscellaneous collections, 103:8* (1942).

gr   Grigor'yan, A. T. "The contribution of Russian scientists to the development of aerodynamics." ICHS, X (1962). *Actes, 2* (1964), 793-796. (In French in *Scientia, 98* (1963), 46-50.)

kb   Kármán, Theodor von. *Aerodynamics: Selected topics in the light of their historical development.* Cornell, 1954.

kc   Kármán, Theodor von. "Some significant developments in aerodynamics since 1946." *Journal of the aero-space sciences, 26* (1959), 129-144.

kn   Kosmodem'yanskiy, A. A. "Osnovopolozhniki sovremennoy aeromekhaniki: N. Ye. Zhukovskiy i S. A. Chaplygin." Moscow. University. *Uchenyye zapiski, 91* (1947), 105-128.

ko   Kosmodem'yanskiy, A. A. "O nekotorykh rabotakh S. A. Chaplygina po teorii profilya kryla." ICHS, XIII (1971). Section 5. *Actes* (1974), 259-261.

ve   Vetchinkin, V. P. "Aerodinamika." C.vb4.an, 121-138.

tb1.bl   Blitzer, Leon. "Resource letter SO-1." *Kinematics and dynamics of satellite orbits: Selected reprints.* NY, 1963. Pp. 1-4.

br   Braun, Wernher von, and Frederick I. Ordway. *History of rocketry and space travel.* NY, 1969.

dy   Dyson, Freeman. "Experiments with bomb-propelled spaceship models." *Adventures in experimental physics, 2* (1972), 323-326.

em   Emme, Eugene. *The history of rocket technology.* Detroit, 1964.

tc1.fi   Firsov, G. A. "Raboty A. N. Krylova po teorii korablya." B.kt1.as, 53-72.

sh   *Shimanskiy, Yu. A. "Raboty A. N. Krylova v oblasti kachki korablya na volnenii." C.va2.an, *2*, 545-558.

td1.ar   Artobelevskiy, I. I. "Russkaya shkola teorii mekhanizmov i mashin." Moscow. University. *Uchenyye zapiski, 91* (1947), 149-156.

ay   Ayzerman, M. A. "Obzor deyatel'nosti A. A. Andronova v oblasti avtomaticheskogo regulirovaniya." B.ao1.ec, 20-32.

ba   Bailey, R. W. "The contribution of Manchester researchers to mechanical science." Institution of Mechanical Engineers. *Proceedings, 2* (1929), 613-683.

bo   Bogolyubov, A. N. "Razvitiye idey mekhaniki mashin v XX v." ICHS, XIII (1971). Section 5. *Actes* (1974), 306-309.

gr   Grigor'yan, A. T. "Einige Entwicklungsprobleme der technischen Mechanik in Russland in der zweiten Hälfte des 19. und Anfang des 20. Jahrhunderts." *NTM, 7:1* (1970), 23-32.

pi   Pio-Ulsky, G. "Die Arbeiten Nikola Teslas auf dem Gebiete der angewandten Mechanik." B.te3.ap, A161-A171.

te1.si   Sigachev, N. I. "Raboty A. N. Krylova v oblasti giroskopii." B.kt1.as, 103-116.

te   Temtchenko, Marie E. "Researches on the theory of gyroscopes in the USSR for 50 years." ICHS, XII (1968). *Actes, 4* (1971), 175-178.

E. ELECTRICITY AND MAGNETISM

Electrodynamics

aal.ba Bauer, Edmond. *L'électromagnétisme: Hier et aujourd'hui.* Paris, 1949.

br *Bragg, W. H. *The story of electromagnetism.* London, 1941.

ch Chappell, John E., Jr. "The forgotten tradition in electromagnetics, and why it must be revived." ICHS, XIII (1971). *Actes, 6* (1974), 44-50.

cj Chernyshev, A. A. "Elektrofizika." C.vb4.an, 284-309.

co Corbino, O. M. "Il contributo italiano ai progressi della elettrologia nell'ultimo cinquantennio." SIPS. *Atti, 5* (1911), 275-306.

ro Robinson, Myron. "A history of the electric wind." *AJP, 30* (1962), 366-372.

st Stein, Howard. "On the notion of field in Newton, Maxwell, and beyond." A.aal.st, 264-287.

wh Whittaker, Edmund Taylor. *A history of the theories of aether and electricity.* 2 vols. London, 1910-53.

abl.ar *Arkad'yev, V. K. *Elektromagnitnaya teoriya sveta i rabotu laboratorii imenl Maksvella pri Fizicheskom fakul'tete za 25 let.* Moscow, 1944.

he Hertz, Gustav. "Rubens und die Maxwellsche Theorie." *Nwn, 10* (1922), 1024-1027.

kn Knudsen, Ole. "Electric displacement and the development of optics after Maxwell." *Centaurus, 22* (1978), 53-60.

ku Kudryavtsev, P. S. "Razrabotka russkimi fizikami XIX veka problem maksvellovskoy elektrodinamiki." *VIYeT, 3* (1957), 197-199.

kv Kudryavtsev, P. S. "Razvitiye teorii elektromagnitnogo polya." A.abl.gr, 236-262.

to *Topper, David Roy. *J. J. Thomson and Maxwell's electromagnetic theory.* Ph.D. thesis. Case Western Reserve Univ., 1970. (*DAI, 32,* 341A.)

acl.fr Frankfurt, Usher I. "Elektrodinamika Gel'mgol'tsa i yeye evolyutsiya." *VIYeT, 14* (1963), 49-55.

adl.do *Doran, Barbara Jean Giusti. *Contributions of British physics to the first electron theory of matter and the first electromagnetic view of nature: Sir Joseph Larmor's 1893 theory of aether and matter.* Ph.D. thesis. Johns Hopkins Univ., 1973.

ki   Kittel, Charles. "Larmor and the prehistory of the Lorentz transformations." *AJP, 42* (1974), 726-729.

va   *Vasil'yev, M. B. "Elektrodinamika dvizhushchikhsya tel Larmora." Ulan-Ude. Buryatskiy zooveterinarnyy institut. *Trudy, 13* (1958), 351-353.

wh   Whyte, Lancelot Law. "A forerunner of twentieth century physics: A re-view of Larmor's 'Aether and matter.'" *Nature, 186* (1960), 1010-1014.

ae1.da   Agostino, Salvo d'. "L'elettrodinamica di Lorentz sino alla soglia della teoria speciale di relatività di Einstein." *Physis, 15* (1973), 260-279.

gr   Grünbaum, Adolf. "The falsifiability of the Lorentz-Fitzgerald contraction hypothesis." *BJPS, 10* (1959), 48-50.

hi   Hirosige, Tetu. "Lorentz's theory of electrons and the development of the concept of electromagnetic field." *JSHS, 1* (1962), 101-110.

hj   Hirosige, Tetu. "Electrodynamics before the theory of relativity, 1890-1905." *JSHS, 5* (1966), 1-49.

mc   McCormmach, Russell. "Einstein, Lorentz, and the electron theory." *HSPS, 2* (1970), 41-87.

md   McCormmach, Russell. "H. A. Lorentz and the electromagnetic view of nature." *Isis, 61* (1970), 459-497.

sc   Schaffner, Kenneth F. "The Lorentz electron theory of relativity." *AJP, 37* (1969), 498-513.

sd   Schaffner, Kenneth F. "Interaction of theory and experiment in the development of Lorentz's contraction hypothesis." ICHS, XII (1968). *Actes, 5* (1971), 87-90.

af1.mi   Miller, Arthur I. "A study of Henri Poincaré's 'Sur la dynamique de l'électron.'" *AHES, 10* (1973), 207-328.

ag1.go   Goldberg, Stanley. "The Abraham theory of the electron: The symbiosis of experiment and theory." *AHES, 7* (1971), 7-25.

sa   Sandor, Mikola. "Eletrajz." *Matematikai és physikai lapok, 27* (1918), 257-283.

az1.da   Dauvillier, Alexandre. "L'ère prérélativiste et les paradoxes de l'éther, d'Olbers et de Seeliger." *Revue de synthèse, 93* (1972), 245-266.

di   Dingle, Herbert. "A re-examination of the Michelson-Morley experiment." *Vistas in astronomy, 9* (1967), 97-100.

hh Hirosige, Tetu. "The decline of the ether." ICHS, XII (1968). *Actes, 5* (1971), 45-48.

hi Hirosige, Tetu. "The ether problem, the mechanistic world view, and the origins of the theory of relativity." *HSPS, 7* (1976), 3-82.

ja Jackson, A. T. "Detection of the ether." *PE, 9* (1974), 265-268.

lb *Lafuente-García, Antonio. "La hipótesis del éter en España." *Llull, 3* (1979), 15-28. (Sociedad Española de Historia de las Ciencias. *Boletín.*)

lc *Rosa, Michele La. *Der Aether. Geschichte einer Hypothese.* Leipzig, 1912. (Italian tr in *Annuario della biblioteca filosofica, 1* (1912).)

lo Lodge, Oliver. "The density of the aether." *Philosophical magazine, 13* (1907), 488-506.

po Polak, L. S. "Iz istorii problemy efira." *Arkhiv istorii nauki i tekhniki, 9* (1936), 1-22.

pr Prokhovnik, S. J. "A note on relativistic phenomena in an ether theory." *BJPS, 18* (1967), 322-323.

sc Schaffner, K. F. *Nineteenth-century aether theories.* Oxford, 1972.

sg Shankland, Robert S., et al. "New analysis of interferometer observations of Dayton C. Miller." *Reviews of modern physics, 27* (1955), 167-178.

sj Shankland, Robert S. "Michelson and his interferometer." *PT, 27* (Apr. 1974), 36-43.

sv *Swenson, Lloyd S., Jr. *The ethereal aether: A descriptive history of the Michelson-Morley aether-drift experiments, 1880-1930.* Ph.D. thesis. Claremont Graduate School, 1962. (*DAI, 23,* 2102.)

sw Swenson, Lloyd S., Jr. "The Michelson-Morley-Miller experiments before and after 1905." *Journal for the history of astronomy, 1* (1970), 56-78.

sx Swenson, Lloyd S., Jr. *The ethereal aether: A history of the Michelson-Morley-Miller aether-drift experiments, 1880-1930.* Austin, Texas, 1962.

to *Tomaschek, R. "Die Entwicklung der Äthervorstellung." U.gg3.bk.

wh Whittaker, E. T. "The aether: Past and present." *Endeavour, 2* (Jul. 1943), 117-120.

See also: B.cb4.kc | dp1.kg, km | ro3.am; C.vm1.kl

The electron

ba1.ca   Casagrande, Federico. "L'introduzione del cronone nella teoria classica e quantistica dell'elettrone." *Scientia, 112* (1977), 401-415.

da   Darrow, Karl K. "Electron physics in America." *PT, 9* (May 1956), 23-27.

du   Dukov, V. M. "Ob istokakh elektronnoy teorii." *VIYeT, 9* (1960), 71-77.

fo   *Follett, David Henry. *The electron jubilee exhibition held at the Science Museum, London, September 1947-January 1948.* London, 1947. 48 p.

ga   Gaytner, D. B. "The electron." *PE, 6* (1971), 406-412.

lb   Laue, Max von. "Geschichte des Elektrons." *PB, 15* (1959), 105-111. (B.lf6.jl, *3,* 152-158.)

pa   Pais, Abraham. "The early history of the theory of the electron: 1897-1947." B.dk1.is, 79-93.

py   Pyenson, Lewis. "Physics in the shadow of mathematics: The Göttingen electron-theory seminar of 1905." *AHES, 21* (1974), 55-89.

ro   Rohrlich, Fritz. "The electron: development of the first elementary particle theory." A.ad1.me, 331-367.

rp   Rohrlich, Fritz. "A lesson in the construction of a physical theory." *Acta physica austriaca, 41* (1975), 375-383.

so   Sokolov, A. A. "Proshloye i budushcheye teorii 'svetyashchegosya' elektrona." *IMYeN: Fizika, 12* (1972), 191-196.

st   *Stark, Johannes. "Zur Geschichte der Vorstellung von der Struktur des Elektrons." Charlottenburg. Physikalisch-Technische Reichsanstalt. *Wissenschaftliche Abhandlungen, 22* (1938), 189- .

th   Thomson, George P. "The septuagenarian electron." *PT, 20* (May 1967), 55-61.

See also: B.eb1.ks

bb1.an   Anderson, David L. *The discovery of the electron: The development of the atomic concept of electricity.* Princeton, 1964.

bw   Bykov, G. V. "K istorii otkrytiya elektrona." *VIYeT, 15* (1963), 25-29.

by   Bykov, G. V. "K istorii otkrytiya elektrona: Otvet B. M. Kedrovu." *VIYeT, 28* (1969), 71-72.

ke   Kedrov, B. M. "K istorii otkrytiya elektrona." *VIYeT, 24* (1968), 75-77.

mo   Morrow, B. A. "On the discovery of the electron." *JCE, 46* (1969), 584-588.

oh   O'Hara, J. G. "George Johnstone Stoney, F.R.S., and the concept of the electron." RS. *Notes and records, 29* (1975), 265-276.

ow   Owen, G. E. "The discovery of the electron." *Annals of science, 11* (1955), 173-182.

th   Thomson, George P. "J. J. Thomson and the discovery of the electron." *PT, 9* (Aug. 1956), 14-23.

ti   Thomson, George P. "An unfortunate experiment: Hertz and the nature of cathode rays." RS. *Notes and records, 25* (1970), 237-242.

See also: F.bd1.go; I.dd1.sm; K.ab1.an

bc1.za   Zahar, Elie. "'Crucial' experiments: A case study." *BSPS, 58* (1978), 71-97.

bd1.du   Dukov, V. M. "Rol' ponyatiya konvektsionnogo toka v razvitii fiziki." IIYeT. *Trudy, 43* (1961), 112-139.

fi   Finn, Bernard S. "Electron theories of conduction in the 19th century: The problem of electrical-thermal interactions." ICHS, XI (1965). *Actes, 3* (1968), 398-401.

fr   Frankfurt, Usher I. "Ucheniye o termoelektrichestve s momenta vozniknoveniya elektronnoy teorii metallov (1900-1925)." *VIYeT, 13* (1962), 69-73.

je   Jensen, H. H., and Hans Niesen. "Metallernes elektronteori og den klassiske fysiks begraensing." *Fysisk tidsskrift, 60* (1962), 167-172.

mi   Miller, John David. "Rowland and the nature of electrical currents." *Isis, 63* (1972), 5-27.

sm   Smorodinskiy, Ya. A., and I. Ye. Tamm. "Raboty Ya. I. Frenkelya po teorii elektronov i atomnykh yader." B.fr1.jd, *2,* 455-459.

wh   Whyte, Lancelot Law. "The electric current: A study of the role of time in electron physics." *BJPS, 3* (1952), 242-255.

be1.an   Anderson, David L. "Resource letter ECAN-1." *Electronic charge and Avogadro's number: selected reprints.* NY, 1966. Pp. 1-7.

ba   Bader, Morris. "The Nobel Prize of 1923." *JCE, 55* (1978), 783.

di   Dirac, P. A. M. "Ehrenhaft, the subelectron and the quark." A.ad1.we, 290-293.

fr   Franklin, Allan. "Millikan's published and unpublished data on oil drops." *HSPS, 11* (1981), 185-201.

ho   Holton, Gerald. "Electron or subelectrons? Millikan, Ehrenhaft and the role of preconceptions." A.ad1.we, 266-289.

kl   Klein, Oskar. "Det elektriske elementarladning og kvanten-teorien." *Fysisk tidsskrift, 33* (1935), 102-109.

bf1.go   Goudsmit, Samuel A. "Die Entdeckung des Elektronenspins." *PB, 21* (1965), 445-453. (Also in *Journal de physique, 28* (1967), 123-128; *UFN, 93* (1967), 151-158.)

gp   Goudsmit, Samuel A. "It might as well be spin." *PT, 29* (Jun. 1976), 40-43.

kr   Kronig, R. de L. "The turning point." B.pd3.if, 5-39.

ku   Kusch, Polykarp. "The electron dipole moment: A case history." *PT, 19* (Feb. 1966), 23-35.

ri   Richter, Steffen. "Wolfgang Pauli und die Entstehung des Spin-Konzepts." *Gesnerus, 33* (1976), 253-270.

bg1.ca   Calbick, C. J. "The discovery of electron diffraction by Davisson and Germer." *PTeach, 1* (1963), 63-69.

fa   Fabrikant, V. A. "O nablyudenii difraktsii poocheredno let-yashchikh elektronov." *50 let kvantovy mekhaniki.* Ed. L. S. Po-lak. Moscow, 1979. Pp. 95-101.

gf   *Gehrenbeck, Richard Keith. *C. J. Davisson, L. H. Germer, and the discovery of electron-diffraction.* Ph.D. thesis. Univ. of Min-nesota, 1973. (*DAI, 1, 34,* 5595B.)

gg   Gehrenbeck, Richard K. "Electron diffraction fifty years ago." *PT, 31* (Jan. 1978), 34-41.

gh   Germer, Lester H. "Low-energy electron diffraction." *PT, 17* (Jul. 1964), 19-23.

mo   Möllenstedt, G. "Elektroneninterferenzen im konvergenten Bündel: Eine Entdeckung Walther Kossels." *PB, 4* (1948), 26-28.

th   Thomson, George P. "Early work in electron diffraction." *AJP, 29* (1961), 821-825.

ti   Thomson, George P. "The early history of electron diffraction." *CP, 9* (1968), 1-15.

bh1.br   Bromberg, Joan. "Remarks on the hole theory and Dirac's methodology." ICHS, XIV (1974). *Proceedings, 2* (1975), 233-236.

di   Dirac, P. A. M. "Sovremenoye sostoyaniye relyativistskoy teorii elektrona." IIYeT. *Trudy, 22* (1959), 32-33.

dj   Dirac, P. A. M. "Kvantovaya teoriya elektrona." IIYeT. *Trudy, 22* (1959), 34-68.

dk Dirac, P. A. M. "The relativistic electron wave equation." *SPU,* *22* (1979), 648-653.

gl Glebov, L. A. "K predystorii kvantovo-relyativistskoy teorii elektrona." IIYeT. *Trudy, 34* (1960), 157-171.

kr *Kragh, Helge. "The genesis of Dirac's relativity theory of electrons." *AHES* (1980).

wi Wightman, A. S. "The Dirac equation." B.dk1.is, 95-115.

bi1.be Becker, J. A. "Introduction [on thermionic phenomena]." B.ld3.jl, *3,* xvii- xxviii.

co *Cobine, J. D. "Introduction [on electrical discharge]." B.ld3.jl, *4,* xvii- .

ka *Kaptsov, N. A. "Fizika elektricheskikh razryadov v gazakh za 30 let v SSSR." *UFN, 35* (1948), 329-351.

ro Roginskiy, S. Z. "Introduction [on low pressure phenomena]." B.ld3.jl, *1,* lix-lxxv.

Magnetism

ma1.ak Akulov, N. S. "Rol' russkikh fizikov v razvitii ucheniya o magnetizme." *Rol' russkoy nauki v razvitii mirovoy nauki i kul'tury.* Moscow. University. *Uchenyye zapiski, 92* (1946), 58-62.

bb Bates, L. F. "A link between past and present in European magnetism." *CP, 13* (1972), 601-614.

bc Bauer, Edmund, and E. Herpin. "Magnetism." A.aa1.ta, 142-151.

do Dorfman, Ya. G. "L'evolution de la théorie du magnétisme au XXe siècle." ICHS, VIII (1956). *Actes, 1* (1958), 250-253.

ga Gans, Richard. "Ältere und neuere Theorien des Magnetismus." *Kultur der Gegenwart.* Ed. Paul Hinneberg. Vol. *3:3:1* (1915), 334-348.

ki Kirenskiy, L. B., et al. "Fizika magnetizma." C.vb1.pr, *2,* 76-99.

ko Kondorskiy, Ye. I. "Raboty uchenykh SSSR po ferromagnetizmu." *UFN, 33* (1947), 194-217.

kp Kondorskiy, Ye. I., and N. Z. Miryasov. "Istoriya razvitiya issledovaniy po magnetizmu." *IMYeN: Fizika, 6* (1968), 181-189.

me Meyenn, Karl von. "Die Geschichte des Magnetismus von Maxwell bis zur Entdeckung des Elektronenspins." *Journal of magnetism and magnetic materials, 9* (1978), 229-238.

vv Vleck, J. H. Van. "Landmarks in the theory of magnetism." *AJP, 18* (1950), 495-509.

See also: B.dp1.kc; P.ca1.he; U.bc1.pi

mb1.an Anderson, Philip W. "Van Vleck and magnetism." *PT, 21,* (Oct. 1968), 23-26.

    fr Frenkel', V. Ya. "On the history of the Einstein-de Haas effect." *SPU, 22* (1979), 580-587.

    ve Vebras, E. A. "Raboty D. A. Gol'dgammera po magnetizmu." A.ab1.vo, 360-368.

mc1.ch Chalmers, A. F. "Curie's principle." *BJPS, 21* (1970), 133-148.

    do Dorfman, Ya. G. "Vklad P'yera Kyuri v nauku o magnetizme." IIYeT. *Trudy, 19* (1957), 70-83.

mt1.po Povh, I. L., and A. D. Barinberg. "From the Einstein-Szilard patent to modern magnetohydrodynamics." *Impact of science on society, 29* (1979), 49-60.

    ry Rybaltovskiy, N. Yu. "Raboty A. N. Krylova po magnitnym kompasam i magnetizmu." B.kt1.as, 97-102.

Applications

ta1.ap Appleyard, Rollo. *Pioneers of electrical communication.* London, 1913.

    gr Grivet, Pierre. "Sixty years of electronics." *Advances in electronics and electron physics, 50* (1980), 89-174.

    lu Luk'yanov, S. Yu. "Sovetskaya elektronika za 30 let." *UFN, 33* (1947), 548-569.

    ma Marzin, P., and J. Le Mézec. "Electricity and electronics." A.aa1.ta, 152-202.

    mo Morgan, Brian Stanford. *Men and discoveries in electricity.* London, 1952.

    sa Sattelberg, Kurt. *Vom Elektron zur Elektronik: Eine Geschichte der Elektrizität.* Berlin, 1971.

tb1.cg Chernyshev, A. A. "Elektrofizika." C.vb4.an, 284-309.

    ch Chernyshev, A. A., and M. A. Shatelen. "Elektroenergetika." C.vb4.an, 263-283.

    da Damjanovič, Aleksandar. "Contribution à l'histoire de l'électrotechnique." B.te3.ap, A395-A402.

    ja Jarris, C. Mackechnie. "Nikola Tesla and the induction motor." *PE, 5* (1970), 280-287.

    jo Jovanovič, Dragomir. "Tesla Drehstrom-System, zwei Hauptepochen der Elektrotechnik." B.te3.ap, A151-A154.

    ra Rakić, Milivoje. "Fünfzig Jahre Drehstrom." B.te3.ap, A176-A181.

so   Sotin, B. S., and L. G. Davydova. "Russkiye elektrotekhnicheski-ye s'yezdy." IIYeT. *Trudy, 26* (1959), 3-59.

ta   Tank, F. "Die Hochfrequenztechnik und das Werk Nikola Teslas." B.te3.ap, A306-A310.

vi   Vidmar, Milan. "Nikola Tesla und die Geschichte der Elektrotechnik." B.te3.ap, A260-A268.

vo   Vologdin, V. "Tekhnicheskoye primeneniye tokov vysokoy chastoty dlya elektrotermii." C.vb4.an, 310-328.

wh   Wheeler, L. P. "Tesla's contribution to high frequency." B.te3.ap, A211-A214.

za   Žáček, August. "Nikola Tesla - Tvůrce vysokofrekventní techniky." B.te3.ap, A182-A187.

tc1.ai   Aitken, Hugh. *Syntony and spark: The origins of radio.* NY, 1976.

br   Brenev, Igor' Vasilyevich. *Izobreteniye radio A. S. Popovym.* Moscow, 1965.

fe   Fermi, Enrico. "Guglielmo Marconi e la propagaziona delle onde elettromagnetiche nell'alta atmosfera." B.fg1.jj, *1*, 1032-1036.

gu   Gulli, Luciano "Alcune considerazzioni sulla propagazione delle onde a frequenze elevate ed ultraelevate." ICHS, VIII (1956). *Actes, 1* (1958), 237-244.

gv   Gutton, Camille. "Sur la contribution de Tesla au developpement de la radiotélégraphie." B.te3.ap, A149-A150.

os   Ostroumov, B. A. "Radiotekhnika v Rossii posle A. S. Popova (1906-1912)." IIYeT. *Trudy, 44* (1962), 233-257.

po   Popov, A. S. *O besprovolochnoy telegrafii: Sbornik statey, dokladov, pisem i drugikh materialov.* Ed. A. I. Berg. Moscow, 1959.

ra   Ratcliffe, J. A. "Wireless and the upper atmosphere, 1900-1935." *CP, 19* (1978), 495-504.

ry   Rybkin, Petr Nikolayevich. *Desyat' let s izobretalem radio: Stranitsy vospominaniy.* Ed. A. I. Berg. Moscow, 1945.

su   Süsskind, Charles. *Popov and the beginnings of radiotelegraphy.* San Francisco, 1962.

ta   Tabarroni, Giorgio. *Bologna e la storia della radiazione.* Bologna, 1965.

td1.ak   *AN. *50 let radio, 1895-1945.* 2 vols. Moscow, 1945-48.

be   Belyakov, S. T. "V. I. Vernadskiy i radiyevaya promyshlennost'." *VIYeT, 23* (1968), 102-107.

da   Damjanovič, Aleksandar. "Einige Beiträge zur Geschichte der Radiotechnik." B.te3.ap, A269-A277.

fe   Feofilov, P. P., and I. A. Shlyakhter. "Neizvestnaya rabota S. I. Vavilova po radioobnaruzheniyu." *UFN, 49* (1953), 147-154.

go   Gorelik, G. S. "L. I. Mandel'shtam i ucheniye o rezonanse." B.me1.ia, 138-157.

ko   Kobylyanskiy, I. G. "Iskusstvennaya prelomlyayushchaya sreda dlya radiolinz." *UFN, 49* (1953), 473-476.

mg   Migulin, V. V. "L. I. Mandel'shtam and research in radiointerferometry." *SPU, 22* (1979), 640-647.

mi   Miljanič, Pavle. "Quarante-cinq ans de radiotechnique; un retour aux débuts de la radioélectricité." B.te3.ap, A172-A175.

pa   Papaleksi, N. D. "O deyatel'nosti akademika L. I. Mandel'shtama v oblasti radiofiziki i radiotekhniki." B.pb3.jp, 241-246.

po   *Popov, A. S. *Sbornik dokumentov k 50-letiyu izobreteniya radio.* Leningrad, 1945.

ry   Rytov, S. M. "L. I. Mandel'shtam i ucheniye o modulyatsii." B.me1.ia, 158-172.

se   Serdyukov, A. R. "Mikroradiopolya v trudakh P. N. Lebedeva i yego shkoly." *VIYeT, 9* (1960), 102-110.

vv   Vvedenskiy, B. A., and M. I. Ponomarev. "Sovetskaya radiofizika za 30 let." *UFN, 33* (1947), 318-334.

vw   Vvedenskiy, B. A. "Uspekhi sovetskoy radiofiziki." *Radio,* 1949: 5, 10-11.

te1.bo   Bowers, Brian. "Electricity." A.aa1.wi, *6,* 284-297.

du   Dunskaya, I. M. "Osnovnyye osobennosti razvitiya kvantovoy elektroniki." ICHS, XIII (1971). Section 6. *Actes* (1974), 129-132.

ka   Katayev, S. I. "Vklad sovetskikh uchenykh v razvitiye televideniya." *Radio,* 1948: 5, 14-17.

mc   McGee, J. D. "The contribution of A. A. Campbell Swinton, F.R.S, to television." RS. *Notes and records, 32* (1977), 91-105.

sc   Schröter, Fritz. "Vom Werden und Wachsen der Fernsehtechnik: Glücklich erlebte Jahre in der Fernsehenentwicklung." *PB, 24* (1968), 13-17.

to   Tovmasian, A. K. "The work of I. A. Adamian in the field of television and photo-telegraphy." ICHS, XI (1965). *Actes, 3* (1968), 381-382.

See also: T.ef1

tf1.ho Howeth, L. S. *History of communications-electronics in the United States Navy.* Washington, D.C., 1963.

jo Johnson, S. B. "More on the solid-state amplifier and Dr. Lilienfeld." *PT, 17* (May 1964), 60-62.

kr Kraus, Jerome. "The British electron-tube and semi-conductor industry, 1935-1962." *Technology and culture, 9* (1968), 544-561.

sp Spivak, G. V. "Gazovaya elektronika." C.vb1.pr, *2,* 99-117.

tu Tucker, D. G. "Electrical communication." A.aa1.wi, *7,* 1220-1267.

ty Tyne, Gerald, F. J. *Saga of the vacuum tube.* Indianapolis, Indiana, 1977.

tg1.bo Bose, D. M. "Jubilee of Sir J. C. Bose's investigations with centimeter radio waves." *Science and culture, 11* (1945), 286-290.

mi Miessner, Benjamin Franklin. *On the early history of radio guidance.* San Francisco, 1964.

su Süsskind, Charles. "Relative roles of science and technology in early radar." ICHS, XII (1968). *Actes, 106* (1971), 99-102.

th1.br Brillouin, Léon. "Les grandes machines mathématiques américaines." *Atomes,* no. 21 (1947), 400-404.

go Goldstine, Herman H. *The computer from Pascal to von Neumann.* Princeton, 1972.

hu Hughes, Thomas Parke. "ENIAC: Invention of a computer." *Technikgeschichte, 42* (1975), 148-165.

sh Shannon, Claude E. "Von Neumann's contributions to automata theory." American Mathematical Society. *Bulletin, 64:3:2* (1958), 123-129.

st *Stern, Nancy Furtgang. *Fron ENIAC to UNIVAC: A case study in the history of technology.* Ph.D. thesis. State Univ. of New York, Stony Brook, 1978. (*DAI, 39,* 3107A.)

tt1.bo Bojko, Evgenija S. "Über die Entwicklung der Methoden der Theorie nichtlinearer Schwingungen in der wissenschaftlichen Schule Mandel'štams und Andronovs (Am Beispiel des elektromagnetischen Unterbrechers)." *NTM, 13:2* (1976), 41-49.

br Brüche, Ernst. "Die Wandlung in der Oberflächenabbildung mit Elektronen." *PB, 25* (1969), 310-314.

je Jefferies, Zay. "Introduction [on incandescent lamps and tungsten]." B.ld3.jl, *2,* 161-175.

F. RELATIVITY

Surveys

aa1.bd   Bergmann, Peter G. "The development of the theory of relativity." B.ei4.ya, 1-16.

be   Bevilacqua, Fabio, and Pasquale Tucci. "Aspetti dello sviluppo dei concetti di spazio e di tempo dalla fisica prerelativistica alla relatività generale." *Sulla genesi storica e sul significato teorico della relatività di Einstein.* Pisa, 1973. Pp. 247-451. (Domus Galilaeana. *Quaderni di storia e critica della scienza,* 4.)

fr   Frankfurt, Usher I. *Spetsial'naya i obshchaya teoriya otnositel'nosti: Istoricheskiye ocherki.* Moscow, 1968.

ho   Horovitz, Karl. "Die geschichtliche Entwicklung des physikalischen Relativitätsgedanken." *Archiv für die Geschichte der Naturwissenschaften und Technik, 5* (1914), 251-265.

in   Infeld, Leopold. "Die Geschichte der Relativitätstheorie." *Nwn, 42* (1955), 431-436. (In Russian in B.ei6.cb, 183-196.)

ku   Kuznetsov, B. G. *Osnovy teorii otnositel'nosti i kvantovoy mekhaniki v ikh istoricheskom razvitii.* Moscow, 1957.

li   Lionnais, François Le. "La révolution relativiste." B.ei1.an, 107-160.

pa   Palatini, Attilio. "La teoria di relatività nel suo sviluppo storico." *Scientia, 26* (1919), 195-207, 277-289.

sp   *Spasskiy, B. I. "Ocherk vozniknoveniya i razvitiya teorii otnositel'nosti." *IMYeN: Fizika, 1* (1960), 5-60.

to   Tonnelat, M. A. "Relativity." A.aa1.ta, 89-106.

tp   Tonnelat, M. A. *Historie du principe de relativité.* Paris, 1971.

wh   *Whitrow, Gerald J. *Time, gravitation and the universe: The evolution of relativistic theories.* London, 1973.

wi   Williams, Leslie Pearce, ed. *Relativity theory: Its origins and impact on modern thought.* NY, 1968.

See also: B.ei6.jl

ab1.be   Bergmann, Peter G. "Fifty years of relativity." *Science, 123* (1956), 487-494.

bo   Born, Max. "Physics and relativity." F.ab1.me, 244-260.

la   Lazukin, V. N. "50-letiye teorii otnositel'nosti." AN. *Vestnik,* 1956:2, 106-110.

me Mercier, André, and Michel Kervaire. *Fünfzig Jahre Relativitätstheorie.* Basel, 1956. (*Helvetica physica acta,* supp. 4.)

st Straneo, Paolo. "La teoria della relatività a 40 anni dal suo avvento." *Scientia, 80* (1946), 8-18.

we Weyl, Hermann. "50 Jahre Relativitätstheorie." *Nwn, 38* (1950), 73-83.

ac1.gi *Giorgi, Giovanni. "Relativismo e assolutismo nel primo periodo di formazione della scienza fisica contemporanea." *Energia elettrica, 7* (1938), 453-458.

ad1.ba Baranov, A. G. "O nekotorykh eksperimentakh po proverke postulatov spetsial'noy teorii otnositel'nosti." *ES,* 1966, 284-297.

ch Chandrasekhar, S. "Verifying the theory of relativity." *BAS, 31* (1975), 17-22.

ci Chandrasekhar, S. "Verifying the theory of relativity." *RS. Notes and records, 30* (1976), 249-260.

di Dingle, Herbert. "Reason and experiment in relation to the special relativity theory." *BJPS, 15* (1964), 41-61.

dj Dingle, Herbert. "The relation of the special relativity theory to experiment." ICHS, XI (1965). *Actes, 1* (1968), 147-152.

ae1.cr Crelinsten, Jeffrey. "Physicists receive relativity: Revolution and reaction." *PTeach, 18* (1980), 187-193.

cs Crelinsten, Jeffrey. "Einstein, relativity, and the press: The myth of incomprehensibility." *PTeach, 18* (1980), 115-122.

go Goldberg, Stanley. "In defense of ether: The British response to Einstein's special theory of relativity, 1905-1911." *HSPS, 2* (1970), 89-125.

gp Goodstein, Judith R. "Levi-Città, Albert Einstein, and realtivity in Italy." Academia Nazionale dei Lincei. *Atti dei convegni,* 1975, 43-51. (Convegno Internazionale celebrativo del centenario della nascità di Tullio Levi-Città, 1973.)

ko Kolomý, Rudolf. "Ohlas vzniku teorie relativity ve fyzice v Československu " *Dějiny věd a techniky, 12* (1979), 209-225.

la *Lafuente-García, Antonio. "Apuentes sobre la relatividad en España." *Llull, 1* (1977). (Sociedad Española de Historia de las Ciencias, *Boletín.*)

px *Pyenson, Lewis. *The Goettingen reception of Einstein's general theory of relativity.* Ph.D. thesis. Johns Hopkins Univ., 1974. (*DAI, 35,* 2936B.)

py   Pyenson, Lewis. "La réception de la relativité généralisée: Disciplinarité et institutionalisation en physique." *RHS, 28* (1975), 61-73.

ra   Raman, V. V. "Relativity in the early twenties: Many-sided reactions to a great theory." *Indian journal of history of science, 7* (1972), 119-145.

See also: C.ga6.ri; E.ad1.do

Special theory

ba1.fr Frankfurt, U. I. *Ocherki po istorii spetsial'noy teorii otnositel'nosti.* Moscow, 1961.

ki   Kilmister, Clive W. *Special theory of relativity.* NY, 1970.

ku   Kuznetsov, B. G. "Osnovnyye idei spetsial'noy teorii otnositel'nosti." A.ab1.gr, 263-287.

mi   Miller, Arthur I. "On Einstein, light quanta, radiation and relativity in 1905." *AJP, 44* (1976), 912-923.

mj   Miller, Arthur I. "The physics of Einstein's relativity paper of 1905 and the electromagnetic world picture of 1905." *AJP, 45* (1977), 1040-1048.

mk   Miller, Arthur I. "On the history of the special relativity theory." B.ei4.ya, 89-108.

ml   Miller, Arthur I. *Albert Einstein's special theory of relativity. Emergence (1905) and early interpretation (1905-1911).* Reading, Mass., 1981.

pe   Petruccioli, Sandro, and Carlo Tarsitani. "L'approfondimento della conoscenza fisica dall'affermazione della concezioni maxwelliane alla relatività speciale (1890-1905)." *Sulla genesi storica e sul significato teorico della relatività di Einstein.* Pisa, 1973. Pp. 11-245. (Domus Galilaeana. *Quaderni di storia e critica della scienza,* 4.)

sc   Schaffner, Kenneth F. "Space and time in Lorentz, Poincaré, and Einstein: Divergent approaches to the discovery and development of the special theory of relativity." W.aa1.ma, 465-507.

sd   Schwartz, H. M. "Einstein's first paper on relativity." *AJP, 45* (1977), 18-25.

ty   Tyapkin, A. A. "K istorii spetsial'noy teorii otnositel'nosti." ICHS, XIII (1971). Section 6. *Actes* (1974), 63-67.

va   *Vasil'yev, M. B. "K istorii spetsial'noy teorii otnositel'nosti." Ulan-Ude. Buryatskiy zooveterinaryy institut. *Trudy,* no. 13 (1958), 329-341.

bb1.il Illy, József. "A speciáls relativitáselmélet megszületése." *Fizikai szemle, 25* (1975), 405-419.

ko Kottler, Friedrich. "Considérations de critique historique sur la théorie de la relativité. 1. De Fresnel à Lorentz." *Scientia, 36* (1924), 231-242.

to Tonnelat, M. A. "La relativité avant Einstein." *Organon, 2* (1965), 79-103.

tr Treder, Hans-Jürgen. *Über Prinzipien der Dynamik von Einstein, Hertz, Mach und Poincaré: Zur Geometrisierung der Relativität der Beschleunigung und der Trägheit.* Berlin, 1974. (Akademie der Wissenschaften, Berlin. Forschungsbereich Kosmische Physik. *Veröffentlichungen,* 4.)

See also: B.mb; E.aa1.wh

bc1.ch Chapman, Bryan R. "Special relativity and the Michelson-Morley experiment." *PE, 14* (1979), 217-220.

di Dingle, Herbert. "A re-examination of the Michelson-Morley experiment." *Vistas in astronomy, 9* (1967), 97-100.

la Laue, Max von, et al. "Diskussiya po dokladu E. Vudde 'K teorii opyta Maykel'sona' na 83-m sobranii nemetskikh yestestvoispytateley i vrachey v Karlsruye v sentyabre 1911 g." *ES,* 1971, 358-360.

sh Shankland, R. S. "Michelson-Morley experiment." *AJP, 32* (1964), 16-35.

si Shankland, R. S. "The Michelson-Morley experiment." *Scientific American, 211* (Nov. 1964), 107-114.

sj Shankland, R. S. "Michelson's role in the development of relativity." *Applied optics, 12* (1973), 2280-2287.

to *Tonnelat, M. A. "Vitesse de la lumière et relativité." *Roemer et la vitesse de la lumière.* Paris, 1978.

See also: E.az1

bd1.am Amaduzzi, Lavoro. "Le principe de relativité." *Scientia, 24* (1918), 239-243, 321-326.

bo Bork, Alfred M. "The 'Fitzgerald' contraction." *Isis, 57* (1966), 199-207.

br Brush, Stephen G. "Note on the history of the Fitzgerald-Lorentz contraction." *Isis, 58* (1967), 230-232.

go Goldberg, Stanley. "The Lorentz theory of electrons and Einstein's theory of relativity." *AJP, 37* (1969), 982-994.

gr Grieder, Alfons. "Protophysik der Zeit und Relativitätstheorie." *Dialectica, 30* (1976), 145-160.

hi Hirosige, Tetu. "Theory of relativity and the ether." *JSHS, 7* (1968), 37-53.

po Popper, Karl R. "A note on the difference between the Lorentz-Fitzgerald contraction and the Einstein contraction." *BJPS, 16* (1966), 332-333.

wh Whitrow, G. J. "The Fitzgerald-Lorentz contraction phenomenon and theories of the relativity of Galilean frames." Royal Dublin Society. *Scientific proceedings, 26* (1952), 37-44.

See also: E.ae1.sc

be1.cu Cuvaj, Camillo. "Henri Poincaré's mathematical contributions to relativity and the Poincaré stresses." *AJP 36* (1968), 1102-1113.

cv *Cuvaj, Camillo. *A history of relativity: The role of Henri Poincaré and Paul Langevin.* Ph.D. thesis. Yeshiva Univ., 1970. (*DAI, 31*, 7480B.)

cw Cuvaj, Camillo. "Note on Poincaré and relativity." *AJP, 38* (1970), 774-775.

gi Giannoni, Carlo. "Einstein and the Lorentz-Poincaré theory of relativity." *BSPS, 8* (1971), 575-589.

go Goldberg, Stanley. "Henri Poincaré and Einstein's theory of relativity." *AJP, 35* (1967), 934-944.

gp Goldberg, Stanley. "Poincaré's science and Einstein's relativity: The role of theory and experiment in Poincaré's physics." *BJHS, 5* (1970), 73-84. (In Russian in *ES*, 1972, 341-358.)

ho Holton, Gerald. "On the thematic analysis of science: The case of Poincaré and relativity." ICHS, X (1962). *Actes, 2* (1964), 797-800.

sc Schwartz, H. M. "A note on Poincaré's contribution to relativity." *AJP, 33* (1965), 170.

sd Schwartz, H. M. "Poincaré's *Rendiconti* paper on relativity." *AJP, 39* (1971), 1287-1294; *40* (1972), 862-872, 1282-1287.

se Scribner, Charles, Jr. "Henri Poincaré and the principle of relativity." *AJP, 32* (1964), 672-678.

st Starosel'skaya-Nikitina, O. A. "Rol' Anri Puankare v sozdanii teorii otnositel'nosti." *VIYeT, 5* (1957), 39-49.

sz *Szumilewicz, Irena. "Henri Poincaré a szczególna teoria wzglednośce." *Studia i materialy dziejów nauki polskiej*, Seria C, *20* (1975), 141-159.

See also: B.pm3

bf1.be Bergia, Silvio. "Einstein and the birth of special relativity." B.ei4.yf, 65-89.

fe Feuer, Lewis S. "The social roots of Einstein's theory of relativity." *Annals of science, 27* (1971), 277-298, 313-344.

gi Ginzburg, V. L. "Kak i kto sozdal teoriyu otnositel'nosti: Opyt retsenzii s predisloviyem i kommentariyami." *ES*, 1974, 351-384.

gr Grünbaum, Adolf. "The genesis of the special theory of relativity." W.aa1.fe, 43-53.

gu Gutting, Gary. "Einstein's discovery of special relativity." *PS, 39* (1972), 51-68.

hi Hirosige, Tetu. "A consideration concerning the origins of the theory of relativity." *JSHS, 4* (1965), 117-123.

ho Holton, Gerald. "Continuity and originality in Einstein's special relativity theory." ICHS, IX (1959). *Actes, 2* (1960), 499-502.

hp Holton, Gerald. "On the origins of the special theory of relativity." *AJP, 28* (1960), 627-636. (In Russian in *ES*, 1966, 177-194.)

hq Holton, Gerald. "Influences on Einstein's early work in relativity theory." *American scholar, 37* (1968), 59-79.

il Illy, József. "Einstein és a mozgó testek elektrodinamikája." *Magyar fizikai folyóirat, 24* (1976), 249-269.

it Itenberg, I Ya., and U. I. Frankfurt. "K istorii relyativistskoy mekhaniki tochki (1905-1913)." *ES*, 1971, 379-396.

ka Kahan, Théo. "Sur les origines de la théorie de la relativité restreinte." *RHS, 12* (1959), 159-165.

kc Keswani, G. H. "Origin and concept of relativity." *BJPS, 15* (1965), 286-306; *16* (1965), 19-32.

kf Keswani, G. H. "Origin and concept of relativity." *BJPS, 16* (1966), 273-294.

kr *Kragh, Helge. "Om relativitetsteoriens oprindelse." *Gamma*, no. 7 (1971), 3-20.

ku Kuznetsov, B. G. "K voprosy o genezlse i razvitii spetsial'noy teorii otnositel'nosti." IIYeT. *Trudy, 17* (1957), 363-388.

mi Miller, Arthur I. "Albert Einstein and Max Wertheimer: A gestalt psychologist's view of the genesis of special relativity theory." *History of science, 13* (1975), 75-103.

sp Spasskiy, B. I. "Ocherk vozniknoveniya i razvitiya teorii otnositel'nosti." *IMYeN: Fizika, 1* (1960), 5-60.

su Suvorov, S. G. "Einstein: The creation of the theory of relativity and some gnosiological lessons." *SPU, 22* (1979), 528-554.

bg1.bo Born, Max. *Einstein's theory of relativity.* Ed. Günther Leibfried and Walter Biem. NY, 1965.

la Laue, Max von. "Einstein und Relativitätstheorie." *Nwn, 43* (1956), 1-8. (Also in B.lf6.jl, *3*, 230-237.)

sc Schwartz, H. M. "Einstein's comprehensive 1907 essay on relativity." *AJP, 45* (1977), 512-517, 811-818, 899-902.

to Tonnelat, M. A. "Osnovleniye ponyatiya otnositel'nosti v fizike Eynshteyna." *VIYeT, 19* (1965), 35-45.

bh1.cu Cuvaj, Camillo. "Paul Langevin and the theory of relativity." *JSHS, 10* (1971), 113-142.

go Goldberg, Stanley. "Max Planck's philosophy of nature and his elaboration of the special theory of relativity." *HSPS, 7* (1976), 125-160.

it Itenberg, I. Ya., and U. I. Frankfurt. "Raboty M. Planka po spetsial'noy teorii otnositel'nosti." B.pl1.jp, 754-756.

lo Loris-Melikov, M. A. "Raboty A. A. Fridmana po teorii otnositel'nosti." Leningrad. Glavnaya geofizicheskaya observatoriya. *Geofizicheskiy sbornik, 5:1* (1927), 61-63.

py Pyenson, Lewis. "Hermann Minkowski and Einstein's special theory of relativity." *AHES, 17* (1977), 71-95.

See also: B.lc3.bs; D.be1.de; E.a; E.b

Space-time

ca1.eh Ehlers, Jürgen. "The nature and structure of spacetime." A.ad1.me, 71-91.

lo Lopes, J. Leite. "L'évolution des notions d'espace et de temps." *Scientia, 107* (1972), 411-433.

ma Malikova, M. A., and B. I. Spasskiy. "K istorii razvitiya predstavleniy o prostranstve i vremeni." A.ab1.vo, 425-429.

si Sida, D. W. "Einstein: The revolution in space-time." RAS of Canada. *Journal, 73* (1979), 133-145.

cb1.do Dorling, Jon. "Length contraction and clock synchronisation: The empirical equivalence of the Einsteinian and Lorentzian theories." *BJPS, 18* (1967), 67-69.

er Erlichson, Herman. "The rod contraction-clock retardation ether theory and the special theory of relativity." *AJP, 41* (1973), 1068-1077.

fo Fok, V. A. "Printsipi mekhaniki Galileya i teoria Eynshteyna." *UFN, 83* (1964), 577-582.

ne Newburgh, Ronald. "Fresnel drag and the principle of relativity." *Isis, 65* (1974), 379-386.

ro Rodichev, V. I. "Evolyutsiya ponyatiya sistemy otscheta i programma Eynshteyna." *ES,* 1974, 286-334.

to Tornebohm, Hakan. "The Lorentz-formulae and the metrical principle." *PS, 29* (1962), 269-278.

cc1.mo Molchanov, Yu. B. "O razlichnykh smyslakh otnosheniya odnovremennosti: K istorii voprosa." *ES,* 1968, 92-114.

ri Rindler, W. "Einstein's priority in recognizing time dilation physically." *AJP, 38* (1970), 1111-1115.

ul Ulegla, I. "Istoriya paradoksa chasov i kosmicheskiye puteshestviya." *VIYeT, 12* (1962), 184-189.

cd1.br Briginshaw, A. J. "The axiomatic geometry of space-time: An assessment of the work of A. A. Robb." *Centaurus, 22* (1979), 315-323.

me Menger, Karl. "The theory of relativity and geometry." B.ei4.zs, 459-474.

sm Smorodinskiy, Ya. A. "Geometriya Lobachevskogo i kinematika Eynshteyna." *ES,* 1971, 272-301.

General theory

da1.ei *Einstein-symposium, Berlin, 1965. *Entstehung, Entwicklung und Perspektiven der Einsteinschen Gravitationstheorie.* Berlin, 1966.

fr French, A. P. "The story of general relativity." B.ei4.yf, 91-112.

gi Ginzburg, V. L. "Geliotsentricheskaya sistema i obshchaya teoriya otnositel'nosti: Ot Kopernika do Eynshteyna." *ES,* 1973, 19-83.

gj Ginzburg, V. L. "Geliotsentricheckaya sistema i obshchaya teoriya otnositel'nosti (ot Kopernika do Eynshteyna)." B.ei7.ae, 301-371.

il Illy, József "Az általános relativitáselmélet megszületése." *Fizikai szemle, 26* (1976), 293-305.

iv Ivanenko, D. D. "Osnovnyye idei obshchey teorii otnositel'nosti." A.ab1.gr, 283-322.

iw Ivanenko, D. D. "Istoricheskiy ocherk razvitiya obshchey teorii otnositel'nosti." IIYeT. *Trudy, 17* (1957), 389-424.

pa Pakhner, Ya. "Printsip Makha v obshchey teorii otnositel'nosti." *ES,* 1968, 50-54.

vi   Vizgin, V. P., and Ya. A. Smorodinskiy. "From the equivalence principle to the equations of gravitation." *SPU, 22* (1979), 489-513.

za   Zahar, Elie G. "The mathematical origins of general relativity and of unified field theories." B.ei4.yn, 370-396.

db1.cg Chandrasekhar, S. "Einstein and general relativity: Historical perspectives." *AJP, 47* (1979), 212-217.

ch   Chandrasekhar, S. "Development of general relativity." *Nature, 252* (1974), 15-17.

st   Stachel, John. "The genesis of general relativity." B.ei4.yn, 428-442.

dc1.ea Earman, John, and Clark Glymour. "Einstein and Hilbert: Two months in the history of general relativity." *AHES, 19* (1978), 291-308.

le   Lenard, Philipp, et al. "Obshchaya diskussiya o teorii otnositel'nosti na 86-m sobranii nemetskikh yestestvoispytateley v Naugeyme v sentyabre 1920 g." *ES,* 1971, 374-378.

sy   Synge, J. L. "Whittaker's contributions to the theory of relativity." Edinburgh Mathematical Society. *Proceedings, 11* (1958), 39-55.

dd1.be Bergmann, Peter G. *The riddle of gravitation.* NY, 1968.

bo   Bondi, Hermann. "Relativity theory and gravitation." B.ei4.yf, 113-129.

ev   Everitt, C. W. F. "Gravitation, relativity, and precise experimentation." *Proceedings of the first Marcel Grossmann meeting on general relativity.* Ed. Remo Ruffini. Amsterdam, 1977. Pp. 545-615.

iv   Ivanenko, D. D. "Slavnyye periody issledovaniya gravitatsii." *VI-YeT, 47-48* (1974), 51-59.

iw   Ivanenko, D. D. "Sixty years of gravitational physics in the USSR." A.aa1.an, 11-28.

ku   Kursunoglu, Behram. "A non-technical history of the generalized theory of gravitation." B.ei4.yp, 15-37.

ta   Tangl, Károly. "Vizsgálatok a gravitációról." *Matematikai és physikai lapok, 27* (1918), 130-146.

tr   Trautman, Andrzej. "Theory of gravitation." A.ad1.me, 179-198.

we   Weber, Joseph. "Gravitational radiation." B.ei4.ya, 25-32.

wi   Will, Clifford M. "Gravitation theory." *Scientific American, 231* (May 1974), 24-33.

de1.di Dirac, P. A. M. "The excellence of Einstein's theory of gravitation." *Impact of science on society, 29* (1979), 11-14.

fo Fok, V. A. "Raboty A. A. Fridmana po teorii tyagoteniya Eynshteyna." *UFN, 80* (1963), 353-356. (Also in B.fs1.jf, 398-402.)

me Mehra, Jagdish. "Einstein, Hilbert, and the theory of gravitation." A.ad1.me, 92-178.

mf Mehra, Jagdish. *Einstein, Hilbert, and the theory of gravitation.* Dordrecht, 1974.

mi Mie, Gustav, et al. "Diskussiya po dokladu A. Eynshteyna 'K sovremennomu sostoyaniyu problemy gravitatsii' na 85-m sobranii nemetskikh yestestvoispytateley v Vene v 1913 g." *ES,* 1971, 361-370.

sc Schimming, Rainer. "Zur Geschichte der ebenen Gravitationswellen, einer Lösungsklasse der Einsteinschen Gleichungen." *NTM, 10:2* (1973), 21-31.

See also: U.bc1.cr

df1.ea Earman, John, and Clark Glymour. "Relativity and eclipses: The British eclipse expeditions of 1919 and their predecessors." *HSPS, 11* (1980), 49-85.

fo Forbes, Eric Gray. "A history of the solar red-shift problem." *Annals of science, 17* (1961), 129-164.

mi Mikhaylov, A. A. "Nablyudeniye effekta Eynshteyna vo vremya solnechnykh zatmeniy." B.ei6.cb, 140-159.

mo Moyer, Donald Franklin. "Revolution in science: The 1919 eclipse test of general relativity." B.ei6.yp, 55-101.

tr Trumpler, Robert. "Historical note on the problem of light deflection in the sun's gravitational field." *Science, 58* (1923), 161-163.

dg1.ge Gernet, M. M. "Nekotoryye epizody v razvitii geometrii mass." ICHS, XIII (1971). Section 5. *Actes* (1974), 304-306.

ki Kilchling, K. "Die Drehwaage von Eötvös." *PB, 4* (1918), 336-339.

la Laue, Max von. "Inertia and energy." B.ei4.zs, 503-533. (In German in B.lf6.jl, *3,* 120-144.)

li Linets, A. M. "K istorii issledovaniya proportsional'nosti mass." ICHS, XIII (1971). Section 6. *Actes* (1974), 178-182.

ro Roll, P. G., R. Krotov, and R. H. Dicke. "The equivalence of inertial and passive gravitational mass." *Annals of physics, 26* (1964), 442-517.

See also: I.ec1.gu

Philosophy

fa1.de   Delokarov, K. Kh. "Iz istorii filosofskogo analiza teorii otnositel'nosti (20-e gody)." ICHS, XIII (1971). Section 1. *Actes* (1974), 203-205.

ga   Gardner, Michael R. "Relationism and relativity." *BJPS, 28* (1977), 215-233.

gr   Grieder, Alfons. "Relativity, causality and the 'substratum'." *BJPS, 28* (1977), 35-48.

gs   *Grünbaum, Adolf. "The special theory of relativity as a case study of the importance of the philosophy of science for the history of science." Delaware. University, Newark. Delaware seminar in the philosophy of science. Ed. B. Baumrin. NY, 1963.

gu   Griese, Anneliese. "Philosophische Aspekte des Einsteinschen Programms zur Weiterentwicklung der Physik." B.ei7.ct, 59-153.

ho   Hörz, Herbert. "Philosophical concepts of space and time." B.ei4.yf, 229-242.

ku   Kuznetsov, B. G. "Dopolnitel'nost' i otnositel'nost'." *ES,* 1966, 121-176.

kv   Kuznetsov, B. G. "Relativität und Komplementarität." *Ideen des exakten Wissens,* 1969, 779-785.

la   Laue, Max von. "Erkenntnistheorie und Relativitätstheorie." B.lf6.jl,*3*,159-167.

mu   Müller, Aloys. *Die philosophischen Probleme der Einsteinschen Relativitätstheorie.* Braunschweig, 1922.

po   Polikarov, Asaria. "Overturn and continuity of the hypothesis in the framing of the theory of relativity." B.ei4.yn, 397-411.

to   Tonnelat, M. A. "L'apport epistemologique de soixante années de relativité." ICHS, XIII (1971). Colloquium preprint, 21 p.

wh   Wheeler, John A. "From relativity to mutability." A.ad1.me, 202-247.

fb1.gr   Graves, John Cowperthwaite. *The conceptual foundations of contemporary relativity theory.* Cambridge, Mass., 1971.

gs   Grünbaum, Adolf. "Logical and philosophical foundations of the special theory of relativity." *AJP, 23* (1955), 450-464.

ha   Harnack, A. "Die logischen Grundlagen der Relativitätstheorie." *Annalen der Natur- und Kulturphilosophie, 13* (1917), 46-51.

pr   Prokhovnik, S. J. *The logic of special relativity.* Cambridge, 1967.

sc   Schaffner, Kenneth F. "Outlines of a logic of comparative theory evaluation with special attention to pre- and post-relativistic electrodynamics." *MSPS, 5* (1970), 246-263.

fc1.ba   Balazes, N. L. "The acceptability of physical theories: Poincaré vs. Einstein." B.sy.io, 21-34.

po   Podlaha, M. F. "Some new aspects of relativity: Remarks on Zahar's paper." *BJPS, 27* (1976), 261-267.

pr   Prokhovnik, S. J. "Did Einstein's programme supersede Lorentz's ?" *BJPS, 25* (1974), 336-340.

sc   Schaffner, Kenneth F. "Einstein versus Lorentz: Research programmes and the logic of comparative theory evaluation." *BJPS, 25* (1974), 45-78.

sm   Smorodinskiy, Ya. A., and V. A. Ugarov. "Dva parodoksa spetsial'noy teorii otnositel'nosti." *ES,* 1972, 237-253.

st   Stiegler, Karl. "On errors and inconsistencies contained in Einstein's 1905 paper, 'Zur Elektrodynamik bewegter Körper.'" ICHS, XIII (1971). *Actes, 6* (1974), 53-63.

wi   Williamson, Robert B. "Logical economy in Einstein's 'On the electrodynamics of moving bodies.'" *SHPS, 8* (1977), 49-60.

wy   Wykstra, Steve. "On Einstein's second postulate." *BJPS, 27* (1976), 259-261.

za   Zahar, Elie."Why did Einstein's programme supersede Lorentz's ?" *BJHS, 24* (1973), 95-123, 223-262.

fd1.bl   Blokhintsev, D. I. "Za leninskoye ucheniye o dvizhenii." *Voprosy filosofii,* 1952:1, 181-183.

bu   Büchel, W. "Die Diskussion um die Relativitätstheorie in der Sowietunion." *PB, 17* (1961), 277-280.

de   *Delokarov, K. Kh. *Relativitätstheorie und Materialismus.* Berlin, 1978.

df   Delokarov, K. Kh. "Teoriya otnositel'nosti i sovetskaya filosofskaya nauka (istoriko-metodologicheskiy analiz)." B.ei7.ae, 520-566.

ko   Kol'man, E. "Ob odnoy leninskoy mysli." *VIYeT, 30* (1970), 54-57.

ku   Kuznetsov, B. G. "Lénine, Langevin et la préhistoire de la théorie de la rélativité." *La pensée,* no. 161 (1972), 41-45.

See also: W.bc1.mi

fe1.ca   Čapek, Milič. "Einstein and Meyerson on the status of becoming in relativity." ICHS, XI (1965). *Actes, 1* (1968), 129-139.

ed   Eddington, A. S. "A comparison of Whitehead's and Einstein's formulae." *Nature, 113* (1924), 192.

fo   Fowler, Dean R. "Whitehead's theory of relativity." *Process studies, 5* (1975), 159-174.

pe   Petzoldt, G. "Das Verhältnis der Machschen Gedankenwelt zur Relativitätstheorie." Ernst Mach. *Die Mechanik in ihrer Entwicklung historisch-kritisch dargestellt.* 8th edn. Leipzig, 1921. Pp. 490-517.

se   Seaman, Francis. "Whitehead and relativity." *PS, 22* (1955), 222-226.

us   Ushenko, A. P. "A note on Whitehead and relativity." *Journal of philosophy, 47* (1950), 100-102.

G. RADIATION

General

aa1.am   Amaduzzi, Lavoro. "La scienze della radiazione da Macedonio Melloni ad oggi." *Scientia, 45* (1929), 85-94.

pi   Picard, Emile. "L'évolution des idées sur la lumière et l'oeuvre d'Albert Michelson." *Revue scientifique, 74* (1936), 33-48. (Also in AS. *Mémoires, 62* (1935), 35 p.)

th   Thomson, George P. "Matter and radiation." A.aa1.ha, 43-105.

wi   Wiener, Otto. "Entwicklung der Wellentheorie des Lichtes." *Kultur der Gegenwart.* Ed. Paul Hinneberg. Vol. *3:3:1* (1915), 517-574.

ba1.fa   Fabrikant, V. "Raboty P. N. Lebedeva po svetovomu davleniyu." *UFN, 42* (1950), 282.

fe   Feofilov, P. P. "Vklad akademika S. I. Vavilova v ucheniye o svete." *UFN, 91* (1967), 3-9. (In English in *SPU, 10* (1967), 1-5.)

ht   Hughes, Thomas Parke. "A. A. Michelson and E. A. Sperry: The determination of the speed of light, 1924-26." ICHS, XIII (1971). *Actes, 11* (1974), 234-240.

hu   Hughes, Thomas Parke. *Science and the instrument maker: Michelson, Sperry, and the speed of light.* Washington, D.C., 1976.

ja   Jaffe, Bernard. *Michelson and the speed of light.* Garden City, NY, 1960.

ko   Koren', N. N., and U. I. Frankfurt. "Iz istorii fizicheskikh metodov opredeleniya skorosti sveta." *VIYeT, 10* (1960), 59-62.

kr   Kravets, T. P. "P. N. Lebedev i svetovoye davleniye." *UFN, 46* (1952), 306-320. (Also in IIYeT. *Trudy, 28* (1959), 45-65.)

le   Lerche, I. "The Fizeau effect: Theory, experiment, and Zeeman's measurements." *AJP, 45* (1977), 1154-1163.

sh   Shugaylin, A. V. "Ob otkrytii svetovogo davleniya P. N. Lebedevym." AN. Institut filosofii. *Filosofskiye voprosy.* Vol. 1 (1952), 332-357.

so   Sominskiy, M. S. *Ocherki po istorii vozzreniy na prirodu sveta.* Ed. T. P. Kravets. Moscow and Leningrad, 1950.

sp   Spasskiy, B. I., and Ye. I. Pogrebysskaya. "K istorii voprosa o prirode belogo sveta." *IMYeN, 8* (1970), 182-202.

ss   Stuewer, Roger H. "G. N. Lewis on detailed balancing, the symmetry of time, and the nature of light." *HSPS, 6* (1975), 469-511.

st   Stuewer, Roger H. "Bateman's constructive theory of radiation." ICHS, XIV (1974). *Proceedings, 2* (1975), 320-323.

wo   Wolf, Emil. "Einstein's researches on the nature of light." *Optics news, 5:1* (1979), 24-39.

See also: W.cg1.da

Optics

ca1.fm   Frank, I. M. "Einstein and optics." *SPU, 22* (1979), 975-986.

fr   Frankfurt, U. I., and A. M. Frank. "Ocherki razvitiya optiki dvizhushchikhsya tel." IIYeT. *Trudy, 43* (1961), 3-49.

iv   Ivanov, N. I., et al. "Razvitiye optiki na rubezhe XIX i XX stoletiy." C.vb1.pr, *1*, 339-353.

me   Meinel, Aden B. "[Twenty years of] optics." *PT, 21* (May 1968), 40-43.

ne   Newton, Roger G. "Optical theorem and beyond." *AJP, 44* (1976), 634-642.

rm   Ronchi, Vasco. "Ventiquattr' anni dopo." Fondazione Giorgio Ronchi. *Atti, 6* (1951), 164-169.

rn   Ronchi, Vasco. "L'ottica negli ultimi cinquant'anni." *Scientia, 91* (1956), 254-259. (Also in *Cinquant'anni di progress scientifico 1907-1956.* Milan, 1961. Pp. 44-49.)

ro   Ronchi, Vasco. "Optics." A.aa1.ta, 117-123.

rp   Ronchi, Vasco. "From 17th-century to 20th-century optics." *Organon, 9* (1973), 185-198.

ts   Tsuneishi, Kei-ichi. "Origin of information theory in optics." ICHS, XIII (1971). *Actes, 6* (1974), 27-32.

See also: B.rl3.kt; H.cc1.fr

ca2.ma   Landsberg, G. S. "Issledovaniya L. I. Mandel'shtama v oblasti optiki i molekulyarnoy fiziki." AN. *Izvestiya,* ser. fiz., *9* (1945), 21-29. (Also in B.me1.ia, 87-97.)

st   Strutt, Charles R. "The optical research of Robert John Strutt, fourth Baron Rayleigh." *Applied optics, 3* (1964), 1113-1115.

um   Gulo, D. D. "Raboty N. A. Umova po optike." IIYeT. *Trudy, 10* (1956), 269-298.

va   Levshin, V. L. "Trudy S. I. Vavilova v oblasti optiki." IIYeT. *Trudy, 17* (1957), 7-43.

ca4.ch   Chulamovskiy, V. M. "Sovetskaya optika za 20 let." *ZhETF, 7* (1937), 1209-1219.

ci   Chenakal, V. L. "Optika v dorevolyutsionnoy Rossii." AN. Institut istorii yestestvoznaniya. *Trudy, 1* (1947), 121-168.

fr   Frish, S. E. "The development of Soviet optics and spectroscopy during the past fifty years." *Applied optics, 6* (1967), 1783-1792.

ga   *Gal'pern, D. Yu. "Razvitiye vychislitel'noy optiki v SSSR." *Optiko-mekhanicheskaya promyshlennost'*, 1957, 21-23.

kr   Kravets, T. P. "Tridtsat' let sovetskoy optiki." *UFN, 33* (1947), 23-51.

ro   Rozhdestvenskiy, D. S. "Sud'by optiki v SSSR." B.ro7.jr, 312-324.

rp   Rozhdestvenskiy, D. S. "Optika vo vtoruyu pyatiletku." B.ro7.jr, 299-311.

ts   Tschulanovskiy, V. M. "Twenty years of Soviet optics." *Physikalische Zeitschrift der Sowjet Union, 12* (1937), 506-525.

va   Vavilov, S. I. "Optika v SSSR." C.vb4.an, 229-252.

See also: C.vl2.fr

ca6.ar   Ronchi, Vasco. "L'ottica pel colle di Arcetri." *Universo, 22:1* (1941), 181-191.

fi   G., I. S. "L'istituto d'ottica." *Universo, 10* (1929), 527-534.

mo   Korolev, F. A. "Razvitiye optiki v Moskovskom universitete." *IMYeN: Fizika, 6* (1968), 115-121.

we   Ivey, Henry F. "Optics at Westinghouse." *Applied optics, 11* (1972), 985-992.

Applied optics

da1.ba   *Bakhrakh, A. M. *Iz istorii opticheskogo priborostroyeniya: Ocherki.* Moscow, 1951.

bb   Bakhrakh, A. M. "Opticheskiye pribory A. N. Krylova." AN. B.ktl.as, 89-96.

ga   *Gal'pern, D. Yu. "Raboty akademika D. S. Rozhdestvenskogo po mikroskopii." Leningrad. Gosudarstvennyy opticheskiy institut. *Trudy, 23:138* (1953), 15-21.

gb   Gause, Hans. "The slit ultramicroscope after Siedentopf and Zsigmondy: An historical and optical study." *Jena review, 11* (1966), 327-333.

ha   Hauser, F. "Die Entwicklung mikroskopischer Apparate bei der Firma Zeiss in dem ersten Jahrhundert ihres Bestehens." *Jenaer Jahrbuch,* 1952, 1-64.

jo   Jobst, Rudolf. "120 years of scientific instrument manufacture in Jena." *Jena review, 11:* suppl. (1966), 24-31.

le   Lebedev, A. A. "Deyatel'nost' D. S. Rozhdestvenskogo v oblasti opticheskogo stekla." B.ro7.jr, 251.

li   Linnik, V. P. "Raboty akademika D. S. Rozhdestvenskogo v oblasti mikroskopii." AN. *Izvestiya,* ser. fiz., 5 (1941), 622-630.

lj   Linnik, V. P. "Raboty D. S. Rozhdestvenskogo v oblasti mikroskopii." B.ro7.jr, 230-231.

ma   Manek, Franz. "Pulfrich und der erste Stereoautograph Modell 1908." *Jenaer Jahrbuch,* 1958:2, 7-18.

mb   Manek, Franz. "Pulfrich und der Stereoautograph Modell 1909." *Jenaer Jahrbuch,* 1959:2, 7-23.

mc   Manek, Franz. "Pulfrich und die Stereoautographen Modell 1911 und Modell 1914." *Jenaer Jahrbuch,* 1960:2, 327-340.

rn   Ronchi, Vasco. "Ottica e construzione di strumenti astronomici." C.ia1.so, *1*, 523-534.

ro   Rozhdestvenskiy, D. S. "Nauchno-issledovatel'skaya rabota v opticheskoy promyshlennosti." B.ro7.jr, 288-298.

ta   Talanov, V. I. "Raboty L. I. Mandel'shtama po teorii opticheskogo izobrazheniya i sovremennaya kvazioptika." *UFN, 87* (1965), 23-28.

te   Teichmann, H. "Die Entwicklung der Photozelle." *Zeitschrift für die gesamte Naturwissenschaften, 4* (1938/9), 429-440.

ze   ** 75 Jahre Abteilung für Optische Messinstrumente [at Carl Zeiss].* Aalen/Württ., 1968.

da3.go   Gorokhovskiy, Yu. N. "O rabotakh shkoly T. P. Kravtsa po fotograficheskoy sensitometrii." B.kq4.jk, 333-337.

lo   Lobanov, A. N. "Razvitiye elektronnykh metodov v fotogrammetrii." IIYeT. *Trudy, 37* (1961), 302-310.

sa   Savost'yanova, M. V. "O rabotakh T. P. Kravtsa i yego uchenikov po skrytomu fotograficheskomu izobrazheniyu." B.kq4.jk, 320-332.

tu   Tudorovskiy, A. I. "Nauchno-tekhnicheskaya i issledovatel'skaya rabota v oblasti mikro-optiki i foto-optiki v SSSR." AN. *Izvestiya,* ser. mat. i yestest. nauk, 1937:6, 703-719.

da6.ga   Gabor, Dennis. "Holography, 1948-1971." *Science, 177* (1972), 299-313.

ze   Zernike, Frits. "Wie ich den Phasenkontrast entdeckte." *PB, 11* (1955), 159-165.

See also: T.eg1

Spectroscopy

ea1.de   DeKosky, Robert K. "Spectroscopy and the elements in the late 19th century: The work of Sir William Crookes." *BJHS, 6* (1973), 400-423.

di   Dingle, Herbert. "A hundred years of spectroscopy." *BJHS, 1* (1963), 199-216.

fr   Frish, S. E. "Raboty po atomnoy spektroskopii v SSSR." *UFN, 68* (1959), 3-12. (In English in *SPU, 2* (1959), 343-351.)

hi   Hindmarsh, W. R. *Atomic spectra.* Oxford, 1967.

ma   *Maier, Clifford Lawrence. *The role of spectroscopy in the acceptance of an internally structured atom* (1860-1920). Ph.D. thesis. Univ. of Wisconsin, 1964. (*DAI, 25,* 4109.)

mb   Mathieu, J. P. "Spectroscopy." A.aa1.ta, 124-133.

mc   McGucken, William. *Nineteenth-century spectroscopy.* Baltimore, 1969.

ro   Rozhdestvenskiy, D. S. "Evolyutsiya ucheniya o stroenii atomov i molekul." B.ro7.jr, 252-267.

See also: H.da1.bo | dc1.sp

ea2.fr   *Frish, S. E. "Razvitiye sovetskoy spektroskopii za 40 let." AN. *Izvestiya,* ser. fiz., *22* (1958), 650-653.

km   Koritskiy, V. G., et al. "Kratkiy ocherk razvitiya emissionnogo spektral'nogo analiza v SSSR." *UFN, 63* (1957), 435-454.

ko   Korolev, F. A. "Optika i spektroskopiya." C.vb1.pr, *2,* 25-52.

ne   Neporent, B. S. "Razvitiye molekulyarnoy spektroskopii v SSSR za posledniye gody." *UFN, 68* (1959), 13-29.

ra   *Rayevskiy, I. P. "Razvitiye spektral'noy tekhniki v pervom desyatiletii XX veka." C.vb1.vo, 131-136.

rb   Rayevskiy, I. P. "Vzaimosvyaz' teorii i eksperimenta v istorii spektroskopii." ICHS, XIII (1971). Section 6. *Actes* (1974), 168-170.

ro   Rozhdestvenskiy, D. S. "Analiz spektrov i spektral'nyy analiz." B.ro7.jr, 268-287.

st Stepanov, B. I. "Raboty belorusskikh uchenykh po spektroskopii i lyuminestsentsii." AN. *Vestnik,* 1959:1, 68-76.

ea4.ho Hoffmann, Fritz. "Strahlungsmessungen der PTR um die Jahrhundertwende." *PB, 4* (1948), 143-145.

me Meggers, William F. "A quarter-century of spectrochemical analysis at the National Bureau of Standards." Conference on Spectroscopy and its Applications, VII (1939). *Proceedings* (1940), 1-6.

na Yagi, Eri, and Tōsaku Kimura. "A statistical approach to Nagaoka's research in spectroscopy." *JSHS, 12* (1973), 93-97.

ro Ivanov, N. I. "Issledovaniya akademika D. S. Rozhdestvenskogo po spektram." Ulan-Ude. Buryatskiy pedagogicheskiy institut. *Uchenyye zapiski, 10* (1956), 52-53.

so Sommerfeld, Arnold. "Zwanzig Jahre spektroskopischer Theorie in München." *Scientia, 72* (1942), 123-130.

See also: C.gp1.sc; H.cf1.fo

fa1.fr Freymann, R. "Naissance et développement de la spectroscopie hertzienne." *Scientia, 97* (1962), 103-106.

fa2.ba Baeyer, Otto von. "Die Entdeckung der langwelligen Strahlung des Quecksilberdampfes durch Rubens." *Nwn, 10* (1922), 1027-1030.

bb Barnes, R. Bowling, and Lyman G. Bonner. "The early history and the methods of infrared spectroscopy." *AJP, 4* (1936), 181-189.

go Goubeau, J. "Raman- und Ultrarotspektrum." C.ga1.cl, 25-36.

jo Jones, R. Norman. "Coblentz' contribution to infrared spectroscopy." *Applied optics, 2* (1963), 1090-1097.

ka Kangro, Hans. "Das Paschen-Wiensche Strahlungsgesetz und seine Abänderung durch Max Planck." *PB, 25* (1969), 216-220.

kb Kangro, Hans. *Vorgeschichte des Planckschen Strahlungsgesetzes. Messungen und Theorien der spektralen Energieverteilung bis zur Begründung der Quantenhypothese.* Wiesbaden, 1970.

kc Kangro, Hans. *Early history of Planck's radiation law.* London, 1976.

kd Kangro, Hans. "Ultrarotstrahlung bis zur Grenze elektrisch erzeugter Wellen: Das Lebenswerk von Heinrich Rubens." *Annals of science, 26* (1970), 235-259.

ke   Kangro, Hans. "Ultrarotstrahlung bis zur Grenze elektrisch erzeugter Wellen, das Lebenswerk von Heinrich Rubens: Experimente zur Überberbrückung der Spektrumslücke zwischen optischen und elektrischen Wellen. Verknüpfund mit der Quantentheorie." *Annals of science, 27* (1971), 165-200.

kf   Kangro, Hans. "Heinrich Rubens' Ultrarotexperimente und die atomtheoretische Deutung der Rotationsspektren." ICHS, XIII (1971). *Actes, 6* (1974), 79-85.

ki   Kiselev, B. A. "Raboty P. N. Lebedeva po infrakrasnoy spektroskopii." *UFN, 40* (1950), 313-317.

sa   Sanderson, J. A. "The influence of W. W. Coblentz on radiometry." *Applied optics, 2* (1963), 1098-1100.

sc   Schaefer, Clemens. "Die Entwicklung der Strahlungsgesetze seit Kirchhoff." *Angewandte Chemie, 61* (1949), 119-123.

sh   *Schöpf, Hans-Georg. *Von Kirchhoff bis Planck: Theorie der Wärmestrahlung in historisch-kritischer Darstellung.* Braunschweig, 1978.

so   *Sokolov, V. A. "K istorii zakona chernogo izlucheniya." *UFN, 43* (1951), 275-283.

st   Steen, Lynn A. "Highlights in the history of spectral theory." *American mathematical monthly, 80* (1973), 359-381.

fa3.ba   Banet, Leo. "Evolution of the Balmer series." *AJP, 34* (1966), 496-503.

bb   Banet, Leo. "Balmer's manuscripts and the construction of his series." *AJP, 38* (1970), 821-828.

bo   Bohr, Niels. "Rydberg's discovery of the spectral laws." Lund. University. *Årsskrift, Avd. 2, 50:21* (1954), 15-21.

ni   Nisio, Sigeko. "From Balmer to the combination principle." *JSHS, 5* (1966), 50-74.

sh   Shenstone, A. G. "The influence of spectral series." Lund. University. *Årsskrift, Avd. 2, 50:21* (1954), 27-30.

fa6.ba   Bazhulin, P. A., et al. "Raboty G. S. Landsberga v oblasti molekulyarnoy spektroskopii." *Issledovaniya po eksperimental'noy i teoreticheskoy fizike.* Moscow, 1959. Pp. 17-26.

ga1.ru   Rüchardt, Eduard. "Die Geschichte der Entdeckung des Stark-Effektes." *PB, 9* (1953), 125-128.

st   Stark, Johannes, and P. S. Epstein. *Der Stark-Effekt.* Ed. A. Hermann. Stuttgart, 1965. (*Dokumente der Naturwissenschaften, 6.*)

Dispersion

ha1.bi   Billard, Jean. "Les études de la propagation des ondes lumineuses dans les milieux à la fois anisotropes et actifs." ICHS, XII (1968). *Actes, 5* (1971), 5-11.

fa   Fabelinskiy, I. L. "The discovery of combinational scattering of light (the Raman effect)." *SPU, 21* (1978), 780-797.

fr   Frish, S. E. "Sovremennoye razvitiye rabot D. S. Rozhdestvenskogo po anomal'noy dispersii." Leningrad. Gosudarstvennyy opticheskiy institut. *Trudy, 23:136* (1951), 19-24.

ka   Kastler, Alfred. "50 Jahre Hanle-Effekt." *PB, 30* (1974), 394-404.

kv   Kvater, G. S. "Raboty akademika D. S. Rozhdestvenskogo po anomal'noy dispersii." AN. *Izvestiya,* ser. fiz., *5* (1941), 611-621.

mo   Motulevich, G. P., et al. "Raboty G. S. Landsberga po klassicheskomu rasseyaniyu sveta." *Issledovaniya po eksperimental'noy i teoreticheskoy fizike.* Moscow, 1959. Pp. 5-16.

ne   Neporent, B. S. "O rabote T. P. Kravtsa 'Absorbtsiya sveta v rastvorakh okrashennykh veshchestv.'" B.kq4.jk, 308-319.

po   Pogrebysskaya, Ye. I. "Statisticheskiy analiz opticheskikh yavleniy v rabotakh Releya." ICHS, XIII (1971). Section 6. *Actes* (1974), 32-34.

te   *Terenin, A. N., and S. E. Frish. "Raboty D. S. Rozhdestvenskogo i yego shkoly po anomal'noy dispersii v parakh metallov." C.va2.an, *1,* 360-376.

tw   Twersky, Victor. "Rayleigh scattering." *Applied optics, 3* (1964), 1150-1162.

Instruments

ia1.ra   Rayevskiy, I. P. "Spektral'naya apparatura vo vtoroy polovine XIX v." IIYeT. *Trudy, 28* (1959), 377-404.

rb   Rayevskiy, I. P. "Evolyutsiya predstavleniya o roli pribora v spektral'nom razlozhenii." *VIYeT, 13* (1962), 73-75.

ro   Ronchi, Vasco. "Forty years of history of a grating interferometer." *Applied optics, 3* (1964), 437-451.

ia3.da   Danzer, Klaus. "Zur historischen Entwicklung der Emissionsspektralanalyse, insbesondere im Hinblick auf ihre Anwendung in der Praxis." *NTM, 6:2* (1969), 13-26; *7:1* (1970), 33-45.

pr   *Prokof'yev, V. K. "Emissionnyy spektral'nyy analiz i yego primeneniye v promyshlennosti." Leningrad. Gosudarstvennyy opticheskiy institut. *Trudy, 23:138* (1953), 3-14.

te   *Terenin, A. N. "Spektral'nyye zadachi problemy fotosinteza."
      Leningrad. Gosudarstvennyy Opticheskiy Institut. *Trudy, 23:142*
      (1954), 3-18.

X-rays, general

ka1.bl   Bleich, Alan Ralph, ed. *The story of x-rays from Roentgen to iso-*
          topes. NY, 1961.

bo   Broglie, Maurice de. "Die grundlegende Bedeutung der Rönt-
      genstrahlen in der Entwicklung der Physik der letzten vier
      Jahrzehnte." *Strahlentherapie, 56* (1936), 9-10.

br   Brown, Ronald A. "X-rays and after." *JCE, 56* (1979), 191-193.

cr   Crowther, J. A. "Röntgen centenary and fifty years of X-rays."
      Nature, 155 (1945), 351-353.

ge   Gerlach, Walther. "75 Jahre Röntgenstrahlen." *PB, 26* (1970),
      490-497.

gl   Glasser, Otto. "The genealogy of the Roentgen rays." *American*
      journal of roentgenology, 30 (1933), 180-200, 349-367.

ho   Holzknecht, G. "Abriss der historischen Entwicklung der
      wissenschaftlichen Anwendung der Röntgenstrahlen." *Festschrift*
      zur Feier seines 60. Geburtstages Max Neuburger gewidmet. Vien-
      na, 1928. Pp. 183-187.

kl   Klickstein, Herbert. *Wilhelm Conrad Röntgen on a new kind of*
      ray: A bibliographical study. Mallinckrodt Chemical Works, 1966.

mu   Muldawer, Leonard. "Resource letter XR-1 on x-rays." *AJP, 37*
      (1969), 123-134.

wh   Wheaton, Bruce R. *On the nature of x- and gamma-rays: Attitudes*
      toward localization of energy in the "new radiations," 1896-1922.
      Ph.D. thesis, Princeton, 1978. (*DAI, 39* (1978), 2496A.)

wi   Wheaton, Bruce R. "Impulse x-rays and radiant intensity: The
      double edge of analogy." *HSPS, 11* (1981), 367-390.

See also: H.cc1.ni

X-rays, discovery

la1.co   Cohen, I. Bernard. "The discovery of x-rays." *Isis, 47* (1956),
          419-420.

da   Dam, H. J. W. "The new marvel in photography." *McClure's*
      magazine, 6 (1896), 403-415.

de   Debye, Peter. "Röntgen und seine Entdeckung." Munich. Deutsches Museum. *Abhandlungen und Berichte, 6:4* (1934), 83-99.

dh   Dibner, Bern. *The new rays of Professor Röntgen.* Norwalk, Conn., 1963.

di   Dibner, Bern. *Wilhelm Conrad Röntgen and the discovery of x-rays.* NY, 1968.

ge   Gerlach, Walther. "Wilhelm Conrad Röntgen und die Röntgenstrahlen." *FF, 21/23* (1947), 51-53.

gl   Glasser, Otto. "What kind of tube did Röntgen use when he discovered the x-ray?" *Radiology, 27* (1936), 138-140.

gn   Glasser, Otto. "Strange repercussions of Röntgen's discovery of the x-rays." *Radiology, 45* (1945), 425-427.

io   Ioffe, A. F. "Istoricheskoye znacheniye otkrytiya Rentgena." B.io1.ji, *1,* 317-325.

ja   Jauncey, G. E. M. "The birth and early infancy of x-rays." *AJP, 13* (1945), 362-379.

kr   Kravets, T. P. "K istorii otkrytiya rentgenovykh luchey." AN. *Vestnik, 1946:3, 47-54.*

ku   Kuhn, Karl, and Ludwig Kuhn. "Aus der Entdeckungszeit von X-Strahlen und Radioaktivität." *PB, 27* (1971), 17-18.

le   Lebedev, P. N. "Ob otkrytykh Rentgenom x-luchakh." B.lh3.jl, 144-153.

li   Lenard, Philipp. "Zur Entdeckungsgeschichte der Hochfrequenzstrahlen." *Münchener medizinische Wochenschrift, 74* (1927), 817.

lo   Lodge, Oliver. "The surviving hypothesis concerning the x-rays." *Electrician, 37* (1896), 370-373.

ma   Manes, George I. "The discovery of x-ray[s]." *Isis, 47* (1956), 236-238.

mu   Müller, Alex. "The background of Röntgen's discovery. *Nature, 157* (1946), 119-121. (Also in RI. *Proceedings, 33* (1947), 515-522.)

re   Reynberg, S. A. "Zhizn' Vil'gel'ma Konrada Rentgena i istoriya otkrytiya rentgenovykh luchey." G.oa1.re, 10-25.

ri *Rizzoli, R. [Wilhelm Conrad Roentgen and the discovery of x-rays. (In Italian)] *Annali di radiologia diagnostica, 37* (1964), 1-25.

ro Rössler, Oskar. "Zur Entdeckung der nach Röntgen benannten Strahlen." *Münchener medizinische Wochenschrift, 82* (1935), 631.

sa Sarton, George. "The discovery of x-rays." *Isis, 26* (1937), 349-369.

sc Schmidt, F. Über die von einer Lenard-Fensterröhre mit Platinansatz ausgehenden Röntgen-Strahlen." *PZ, 36* (1935), 283-288.

sh Schreus, H. Th. "Zu Röntgens Entdeckung neuer Strahlen vor 70 Jahren." *Nwn, 52* (1965), 471-472.

st Stark, Johannes. "Zur Geschichte der Entdeckung der Röntgenstrahlen." *PZ, 36* (1935), 536-537.

th Thomas, W. K. "Iz istorii otkrytiya V. K. Rentgena." *VIYeT, 32* (1970), 57-59.

tu Thumm, Walter. "Röntgen's discovery of x rays." *PTeach, 13* (1975), 207-214.

wa Wagner, Siegfried. "Zur Entdeckung der Röntgenstrahlen." *Selecta, 45* (1979), 4152-4153

wf Watson, E. C. "The discovery of x-rays." *AJP, 13* (1945), 281-291.

wi Wien, Max. "Geschichte der Endeckung der Röntgen-Strahlen." *PZ, 36* (1935), 536.

See also: B.rk7.by

X-ray interference

ma1.bi Bijvoet, J. M., et al. "Forty years of x-ray diffraction." *Nature, 169* (1952), 949-951.

bo Born, Max. "Erinnerung an Max von Laues Entdeckung der Beugung von Röntgenstrahlen durch Kristalle." *Zeitschrift für Kristallographie, 112* (1959), 1-3.

br Bragg, W. L. *The history of x-ray analysis.* London, NY, and Toronto, 1943.

bs Bragg, W. L. "X-ray analysis: Past, present and future." RI. *Proceedings, 33* (1947), 393-400.

bt Bragg, W. L. "The discovery of x-ray diffraction by crystals." RI. *Proceedings, 35* (1954), 552-559.

bu   Bragg, W. L. "The diffraction of Röntgen rays by crystals." B.mk1.if, 147-151.

bv   Bragg, W. L. "The development of x-ray analysis." RS. *Proceedings, 262A* (1961), 145-158. (Also in RI. *Proceedings, 38* (1961), 526-543.)

bw   Bragg, W. L. "The history of x-ray analysis." *CP, 6* (1965), 161-171.

bx   Bragg, W. L. *The start of x-ray analysis.* London, 1967. (*Chemistry background books.*)

by   Bragg, W. L. "Half a century of x-ray analysis." *Arkiv för fysik, 40* (1971), 585-603.

bz   Bragg, W. L. *The development of x-ray analysis.* Ed. D. C. Phillips and H. Lipson. London and NY, 1975.

cb   Brüche, E. "40 Jahre Laue-Interferenzen." *PB, 8* (1952), 250-251.

ew   Ewald, Peter Paul. "Zur Entdeckung der Röntgeninterferenzen vor zwanzig Jahren und zu Sir W. Braggs siebzigsten Geburtstag." *Nwn, 20* (1932), 527-530.

ex   Ewald, Peter Paul. "Vor fünfzig Jahre." B.mk1.if, 145-146.

ey   Ewald, Peter Paul, ed. *Fifty years of x-ray diffraction.* Utrecht, 1962.

ez   Ewald, Peter Paul. "The myth of myths: Comments on Paul Forman's paper." *AHES, 6* (1969), 72-81.

fa   Faltheiner, Otmar. "Zur Frühgeschichte der Röntgenstrahlenanalyse; einige ausgewählte Briefe aus dem Nachlass von Paul von Groth." *Arithmos-Arrythmos. Skizzen aus der Wissenschaftsgeschichte.* Karin Figala and Ernst H. Berninger, ed. Munich, 1980. Pp. 49-70. (Deutsches Museum. Forschungs Institut. *Beiträge.)*

fn   Forman, Paul. "On the discovery of the diffraction of x-rays by crystals: Why Munich, which x-rays?" ICHS, XII (1968). *Actes, 5* (1971), 23-27.

fo   Forman, Paul. "The discovery of the diffraction of x-rays by crystals: A critique of the myths." *AHES, 6* (1969), 38-71.

fr   Friedrich, Walther. "Die Geschichte der Auffindung der Röntgenstrahlinterferenzen." *Nwn, 10* (1922), 363-366.

ga   Gasman, L. D. "Myths and x-rays." *BJPS, 26* (1975), 51-60.

hi   Hildebrandt, Gerhard. "62 Jahre Kristalloptik der Röntgen Strahlen." *PB, 35* (1979), 55-64, 103-118.

hu Hull, Albert W., and C. L. Burdick. "Early studies in x-ray crystallography." *PT, 11* (Oct. 1958), 18-20.

kn Knipping, Paul. "Zehn Jahre Röntgenspektroskopie." *Nwn, 10* (1922), 366-369.

ko Konobeyevskiy, S. T. "Rentgenovskiy strukturnyy analiz i rentgeno-spektroskopiya za 30 let." *UFN, 33* (1947), 533-548.

la Laue, Max von. "Bemerkung zur Geschichte der dynamischen Theorie der Röntgenstrahlinterferenzen." *Nwn, 19* (1931), 966.

lb Laue, Max von, et al. "Laue diagrams: 25 years of research on x-ray diffraction." *Current science, 5:* Special number (1937), 44 p.

lc Laue, Max von. "Zur Geschichte der Röntgenstrahlinterferenzen." B.lf6.jl, *3*, 110-117. (Also in *NR, 7* (1954), 1-8.)

li Lipson, H. "X-ray crystallography: A meeting place of the sciences." *CP, 1* (1960), 370-384.

ni Niggli, A. "Fünfzig Jahre Röntgeninterferenzen." *Nwn, 50* (1963), 461-462.

pl Planck, Max. "Zum 25-jährigen Jubiläum der Entdeckung von W. Friedrich, P. Knipping und M. Laue." DPG. *Verhandlungen, 18* (1937), 77-80.

th Thewlis, J. "Fortieth anniversary of the discovery of x-ray diffraction." *Nature, 171* (1953), 106-107.

See also: C.gm1.ge

X-ray effects

na1.ba Bartlett, Albert Allen. "Compton effect: Historical background." *AJP, 32* (1964), 120-127.

co Compton, Arthur Holly. "The scattering of x-rays." Franklin Institute. *Journal, 198* (1924), 57-72.

cp Compton, Arthur H. "The scattering of x-ray photons." *AJP, 14* (1946), 80-84.

cq Compton, Arthur Holly. "The scattering of x-rays as particles." *AJP, 29* (1961), 817-820.

he Heimann, P. M. "Moseley's interpretation of x-ray spectra." *Centaurus, 12* (1968), 261-274.

je   Jenkin, J. G., R. C. G. Leckey, and J. Liesegang. "The development of x-ray photoelectron spectroscopy: 1900-1960." *Journal of electron spectroscopy and related phenomena, 12* (1977), 1-35.

ru   Rutherford, Ernest. "Moseley's work on x-rays." *Nature, 116* (1925), 316-317.

ss   Stuewer, Roger H. *The history of the Compton effect.* Ph.D. thesis. Univ. of Wisconsin, 1968. (*DAI, 29:3,* 859A.)

st   Stuewer, Roger H. "Arthur Holly Compton and the discovery of the total reflection of x-rays." ICHS, XII (1968). *Actes, 5* (1971), 101-105.

su   Stuewer, Roger H. *The Compton effect: Turning point in physics.* NY, 1975.

sv   Stuewer, Roger H. "On Compton's research program." *Essays in memory of Imre Lakatos.* Ed. R. S. Cohen et al. Dordrecht, 1976. Pp. 617-633. *(BSPS, 39.)*

wi   Wilson, Richard. "From the Compton effect to quarks and asymptotic freedom." *AJP, 45* (1977), 1139-1147.

wy   Wynne, Brian. "C. G. Barkla and the J phenomenon: A case study in the treatment of deviance in physics." *SSS, 6* (1976), 307-347.

wz   Wynne, Brian. "C. G. Barkla and the J phenomenon." *PE, 14* (1979), 52-55.

See also: A.ab1.wi

Applied x-rays

oa1.br   Bragg, W. L. "First stages in the x-ray analysis of proteins." Institute of Physics and the Physical Society. *Reports on progress in physics, 28* (1965), 1-14.

go   *Gogoberidze, D. B. "Fiziki-pionery otechestvennoy rentgenologii." *Vestnik rentgenologii i radiologii,* 1952:4, 75-82.

gp   Gogoberidze, D. B. "Pionery russkoy rentgenografii." AN. *Izvestiya,* ser. fiz., *17* (1953), 177-185.

he   Hermann, Armin. "Röntgenstrahlen in Physik, Chemie und Biologie." B.rk7.at, 53-67.

hu   Hull, A. W. "Thirty years of x-ray research at the General Electric Research Laboratory." *AJP, 14* (1946), 71-79.

la   Law, John. "The development of specialties in science: The case of x-ray protein crystallography." *SSS, 3* (1973), 275-303.

ma   *Martinkevich, A. A. "Vklad russkikh uchenykh v rentgenologi-
     cheskuyu nauku v nachal'nom periode yeye razvitiya." *Vestnik
     rentgenologii i radiologii,* 1951:1, 87-91.

re   Reynberg, S. A. *Ocherki razvitiya meditsinskoy rentgenologii: 50 let
     rentgenovykh luchey v meditsine.* Moscow, 1948.

se   *Serwer, Daniel Paul. *The rise of radiation protection: Science,
     medicine and technology in society, 1896-1935.* Ph.D. thesis.
     Princeton Univ., 1977. (*DAI, 38,* 446A.)

sp   Spiers, F. W. "Radiation units and the measurement of ionizing
     radiation." *PE, 6* (1971), 257-262.

Other forms of radiation

pal.da   Danilycheva, M. N., and V. A. Fabrikant. "Stanovlenie so-
         vremennykh tsredstableniy o prirode fotolyuminestsentsii." ICHS,
         XIV (1974). *Proceedings, 2* (1975), 237-240.

fi   Firth, Ian. "N-rays: Ghost of scandal past." *New scientist, 44*
     (1969), 642-643.

fr   *Frank, I. M. *Izlucheniye Vavilova-Cherenkova.* Moscow, 1959.

kl   Klotz, Irving M. "The N-ray affair." *Scientific American, 242*
     (May 1980), 168-175.

ko   Kostantinova-Shlezinger, M. A. "Akademik S. I. Vavilov i yego
     rol' v razvitii lyuminestsentnogo analiza." *Zhurnal analiticheskoy
     khimii, 11* (1956), 115-119.

la   Lagemann, Robert T. "New light on old rays: N rays." *AJP, 45*
     (1977), 281-284.

ld   Levshin, V. L. "S. I. Vavilov—sozdatel' i glava sovetskoy shkoly
     lyuminestsentsii." AN. *Izvestiya,* ser. fiz., *15* (1951), 513-522.

le   Levshin, V. L. "Izucheniye yavleniy lyuminestsentsii i razvitiye
     yeye primeneniy v Sovetskom Soyuze." *UFN, 64* (1958), 55-92.

lf   Levshin, V. L. "Razvitiye idey S. I. Vavilova v oblasti lyu-
     minestsentsii." *UFN, 75* (1961), 241-250. (In English in *SPU, 4*
     (1962), 747-753.)

lg   Levshin, V. L. "Nauchnyye issledovaniya v oblasti lyuminest-
     sentsii." *IMYeN: Fizika, 6* (1968), 122-137.

lh   Levshin, V. L. "Lyuminestsentsiya." C.vb1.pr, *2,* 52-76.

li   Lindhard, Jens. "Ligedannethed i stød mellem ioner og atomer."
     Fysisk tidsskrift, 60 (1962), 147-166.

nx   Nye, Mary Jo. "Gustave LeBon's black light: A study in physics and philosophy in France at the turn of the century." *HSPS, 4* (1974), 163-195.

ny   Nye, Mary Jo. "N-rays: An episode in the history and psychology of science." *HSPS, 11* (1980), 125-156.

ro   Rosmorduc, Jean. "Une erreur scientifique au début du siècle: 'Les rayons N'." *RHS, 25* (1972), 13-25.

te   Terenin, A. N., and P. P. Feofilov. "Krupneyshiy sovetskiy uchenyy-optik (k 60-letiyu so dnya rozhdeniya S. I. Vavilova)." AN. *Vestnik,* 1951:3, 111-121.

Lightquantum

qa1.be   *Bergia, Silvio. "The light quantum and the wave-particle duality for radiation in Einstein's research, 1904-1905." [Einstein Symposium, Pueblo, Mexico, 25-27 July 1979.]

bo   Born, Max. "Albert Einstein und das Lichtquantum." *Nwn, 42* (1955), 425-431.

bp   Born, Max. "Al'bert Eynshteyn i svetovyye kvanty." B.ei6.cb, 172-182.

ca   Carruthers, P. "Resource letter QSL-1." *Quantum and statistical aspects of light: Selected reprints.* NY, 1963. Pp. 1-5.

co   Compton, A. H. "The corpuscular properties of light." *Nwn, 17* (1929), 507-515.

do   Dorling, Jon. "Einstein's introduction of photons: Argument by analogy or deduction from the phenomena?" *BJPS, 22* (1971), 1-8.

ei   Einstein, Albert. *Die Hypothese der Lichtquanten.* Ed. A. Hermann. Stuttgart, 1965. *(Dokumente der Naturwissenschaften, 7.)*

fr   Frank, A. M. "Teoriya izlucheniya Eynshteyna." *ES,* 1971, 192-225.

fu   Frankfurt, U. I., and A. M. Frank. "Istoki teorii izlucheniya Eynshteyna." *ES,* 1969-70, 270-300.

ma   Maximov, V. "The Sadovsky effect." ICHS, XI (1965). *Actes, 3* (1968), 369-371.

mc   McCormmach, Russell. "J. J. Thomson and the structure of light." *BJHS, 3* (1967), 362-387.

ni   Nikitenko, G. I. "Vozniknoveniye kvantovoy teorii sveta." IIYeT. *Trudy, 28* (1959), 405-420.

ns Nisio, Sigeko. "Sommerfeld's theory of the photoelectric effect." ICHS, XIV (1974). *Proceedings, 2* (1975), 302-304.

pe Petiau, Gérard. "La théorie du photon de Louis de Broglie." B.bw1.ag, 305-317.

sc Schweidler, Egon von. "Zur experimentellen Entscheidung der Frage nach der Natur des γ-Strahlen." *PZ, 11* (1910), 225-227, 614-619.

st Stuewer, Roger H. "Non-Einsteinian interpretations of the photoelectric effect." *MSPS, 5* (1970), 246-263.

su Stuewer, Roger H. "William H. Bragg's corpuscular theory of x-rays and γ-rays." *BJHS, 5* (1971), 258-281.

ta Tarsitani, Carlo. "La scoperta dell'effetto fotoelettrico e il suo ruolo nello sviluppo della teoria quantistica: Un caso storico di rapporto teoria-esperimento." *Physis, 20* (1978), 237-269.

ti *Timpanaro, Sebastiano. "Le ricerche del Righi sul fenomeno foto-elettrico." *Arduo, 2* (1922), 66-75. (See also *Arduo, 1*, July 1920.)

wh Wheaton, Bruce R. "Philipp Lenard and the photoelectric effect, 1889-1911." *HSPS, 9* (1978), 299-322.

H. ATOMIC PHYSICS

General

aa1.bo Boorse, Henry A., and Lloyd Motz, eds. *The world of the atom.* NY, 1966.

fe Feinberg, J. G. *The story of atomic theory and atomic energy.* NY, 1960.

ha Harig, Gerhard. "Klassische und moderne Atomistik." *NTM, 4:9* (1967), 1-23.

io Ioffe, A. F. "Die Entwicklung der atomistischen Anschauung im 20. Jahrhundert." *Unter dem Banner des Marxismus, 9:1* (1935), 81-101. (Also in *Pod znamenem marksizma,* 1934:4, 52-68.)

kr *Kragh, Helge. *Atomteoriens historie belyst ved kildeskrifter.* Copenhagen, 1973.

me Mellor, David P. *The evolution of the atomic theory.* NY, 1971.

ro Rosenfeld, Léon. "Men and ideas in the history of atomic theory." *AHES, 7* (1971), 69-90. (Also in *BSPS, 21* (1979), 266-296.)

sc Schonland, Basil. *The atomists, 1805-1933.* Oxford, 1968.

vi Virieux-Raymond, A. "Quelques remarques à propos de l'atomisme antique et des atomismes moderne et contemporain." ICHS, VII (1953). *Actes* (1953?), 620-624.

wh Whyte, Lancelot Law. *Essay on atomism: From Democritus to 1960.* NY, 1963.

ab1.cl Clark, Peter. "Atomism versus thermodynamics." W.ab1.ho, 41-105.

hi Hiebert, Erwin N. "The energetics controversy and the new thermodynamics." *Perspectives in the history of science and technology.* Ed. Duane H. D. Roller. Norman, Ok., 1971. Pp. 67-86.

ho Holt, Niles R. "A note on Wilhelm Ostwald's energism." *Isis, 61* (1970), 386-389.

jp Jost, Res. "Boltzmann und Planck: Die Krise des Atomismus um die Jahrhundertwende und ihre Überwindung durch Einstein." B.ei4.yn, 128-145.

ke Kerker, Milton. "The Svedberg and molecular reality." *Isis, 67* (1976), 190-216.

kr Krayevskiy, Vladislav. "Bor'ba Mariana Smolukhovskogo za nauchnuyu atomistiku." W.ac1.an, *2,* 191-221.

me Metz, André. "La notation atomique et la théorie atomique en France à la fin du XIXe siècle." *RHS, 16* (1963), 233-239.

ny Nye, Mary Jo. "The nineteenth-century atomic debates and the dilemma of an 'indifferent hypothesis'." *SHPS, 7* (1976), 235-268.

pp Post, H. R. "Atomism 1900." *PE, 3* (1968), 225-232, 307-312.

sc Schufle, J. A. "Comments on 'The Svedberg and molecular reality.'" *Isis, 68* (1977), 450-451.

si Silliman, Robert H. "William Thomson: Smoke rings and nineteenth-century atomism." *Isis, 54* (1963), 461-474.

th Thiele, Joachim. "Naturphilosophie und 'Monismus' um 1900." *Philosophia naturalis, 10* (1968), 295-315.

ac1.as Aston, F. W. "Forty years of atomic theory." A.aa1.ne, 93-142.

bi Birtwistle, George. *The quantum theory of the atom.* Cambridge, 1926.

cl Cline, Barbara L. *The questioners.* NY, 1965. (Also published as *Men who made a new physics.* NY, 1969.)

he *Heilbron, J. L. *A history of the problem of atomic structure from the discovery of the electron to the beginnings of quantum mechanics.* Ph.D. thesis. Univ. of California, Berkeley, 1964. (*DAI, 25,* 7216.)

hf Heilbron, J. L. "Lectures on the history of atomic physics, 1900-1922." A.ad1.we, 40-108.

hi Heilbron, J. L. *Historical studies in the theory of atomic structure.* NY, 1981.

io Ioffe, A. F. "Razvitiye atomisticheskikh vozzreniy v XX veke." *Front nauki i tekhniki,* 1934:9, 28-38. (Also in *Pod znamenem marksizma,* 1934:4, 52-68.)

ro Rozhdestvenskiy, D. S. "Evolyutsiya ucheniya o stroyenii atomov i molekul." *Arkhiv istorii nauki i tekhniki, 1* (1933), 1-20.

st Stroński, Ignacy. "Szkic historyczny polskich badań z zakresu nukleoniki w latach 1896-1939/45." Polska Akademia Nauk, Zaklad Historii Nauki I Techniki. *Studia* (1968), 86-132.

vi Vinokurov, B. Z. "Pervyye russkiye issledovaniya po elektronike i atomnoy fizike." *Voprosy istorii fiziko-matematicheskikh nauk.* Moscow, 1963. Pp. 345-350.

See also: C.ga2.fm; E.bd1.sm

ad1.br Branscomb, Lewis M. "[Twenty years of] atoms, molecules and electrons." *PT, 21* (May 1968), 36-39.

mb Margenau, Henry, and R. B. Setlow. "Atomic and molecular theory since Bohr." *AJP, 13* (1945), 73-95.

mc Margenau, Henry, and Arthur Wightman. "Atomic and molecular theory since Bohr." *AJP, 12* (1944), 119-130, 247-268.

st Stark, Johannes. "Experimentelle Fortschritte der Atomforschung." *ZGN, 4* (1938/9), 239-313.

Pre-Bohr models

ba1.be Behrens, C. "Atomic theory from 1904 to 1913." *AJP, 11* (1943), 60-66.

he *Hermann, Armin. "Die Entwicklung der Atomtheorie bis Niels Bohr." H.cb1.bo.

ro Robotti, Nadia. *I primi modelli dell'atomo dall'elettrone all'atomo di Bohr.* Turin, 1978.

bb1.he Heilbron, J. L. "J. J. Thomson and the Bohr atom." *PT, 30* (Apr. 1977), 23-30.

sn Snelders, H. A. M. "A. M. Mayer's experiments with floating magnets and their use in atomic theories of matter." *Annals of science, 33* (1976), 67-80.

wa Walton, Alan J. "The Kelvin-Thomson atom." *PE, 12* (1977), 326-328, 370-373.

za Zatkis, Henry. "Thomson atom." *AJP, 26* (1958), 635-638.

bc1.ya Yagi, Eri. "On Nagaoka's Saturnian atomic model (1903)." *JSHS, 3* (1964), 29-47.

yb Yagi, Eri. "The development of Nagaoka's Saturnian atomic model, I. Dispersion on light (1905)." *JSHS, 6* (1967), 19-25.

yc Yagi, Eri. "The development of Nagaoka's Saturnian atomic model." ICHS, XII (1968). *Actes, 5* (1971), 117-119.

yd Yagi, Eri. "The development of Nagaoka's Saturnian atomic model, II (1904-05). Nagaoka's theory of the structure of matter." *JSHS, 11* (1972), 73-89.

ye Yagi, Eri. "H. Nagaoka's theory of the structure of matter (1904-05)." ICHS, XIII (1971). *Actes, 6* (1974), 91-94.

bd1.mc McCormmach, Russell. "The atomic theory of John William Nicholson." *AHES, 3* (1966), 160-184.

be1.db Darwin, Charles G. "The discovery of atomic number." B.bo1.ip, 1-11. (Also in RS. *Proceedings, A236* (1956), 285-296.)

dc Darwin, Charles G. "Moseley and the atomic number of the elements." B.ru1.ad, 17-26.

hi Hirosige, Tetu. "The van den Broek hypothesis." *JSHS, 10* (1971), 143-162.

hj   Hirosige, Tetu. "On van den Broek's hypothesis." ICHS, XIII (1971). *Actes, 6* (1974), 97-101.

li   Lisnevskiy, Yu. I. "Vklad A. Van-der-Bruka v razvitiye fizicheskoy atomistiki." *VIYeT, 49* (1975), 53-57.

sq   Spronsen, Jan W. van. "Atomic number before Moseley." *JCE, 56* (1979), 106.

tu   Turner, Gerard L'E. "The discovery of atomic numbers." Institute of Physics (London). *Bulletin,* Feb. 1965, 54-55.

bf1.an   Andrade, E. N. da C. "The birth of the nuclear atom." *Scientific American, 195* (1956), 93-104.

co   Conn, K. T., and H. D. Turner. *The evolution of the nuclear atom.* London, 1965.

db   Darwin, Charles G. "The jubilee of the atomic nucleus." *New scientist, 11* (1961), 87-89.

de   Davis, William E. *Early history of the nuclear atom.* Dubuque, Iowa, 1974.

he   Heilbron, J. L. "The scattering of α and β particles and Rutherford's atom." *AHES, 4* (1968), 247-307.

hf   Heimann, P. M. "Rutherford, Nagaoka, and the nuclear atom." *Annals of science, 23* (1967), 299-303.

hg   Herron, J. Dudley. "Rutherford and the nuclear atom." *JCE, 54* (1977), 499.

tr   Trenn, Thaddeus J. "The Geiger-Marsden scattering results and Rutherford's atom, July 1912 to July 1913: The shifting significance of scientific evidence." *Isis, 65* (1974), 74-82.

wi   [Williams, Trevor I.] "The jubilee of the nuclear atom." *Endeavour, 21* (1962), 3-4.

See also: I.ra1.li

bg1.ha   Haas, Arthur Erich. *Der erste Quantenansatz für das Atom.* Ed. A. Hermann. Stuttgart, 1965. (*Dokumente der Naturwissenschaft,* 10.)

he   Hermann, Armin. "Arthur Erich Haas und der erste Quantenansatz für das Atom." *Sudhoffs Archiv, 49* (1965), 255-268.

hf   Hermann, Armin. "Arthur Erich Haas and the first quantum mechanical approach to atomic structure." ICHS, XI (1965). *Actes, 3* (1968), 424-429.

Old quantum theory

See also: L.a

ca1.be Behrens, C. "The early development of the Bohr theory." *AJP, 11* (1943), 135-147.

bf Behrens, C. "Further developments of Bohr's early atomic theory." *AJP, 11* (1943), 272-281.

bo Bohr, Niels. [Lecture after receiving Ørsted medal.] *Fysisk tidsskrift, 23* (1925), 10-17.

ge Gerlach, Walther. *Materie, Elektrizität, Energie. Die Entwicklung der Atomistik in den letzten zehn Jahren.* Dresden and Leipzig, 1923.

hp Hoyer, Ulrich. *Die Geschichte der Bohrschen Atomtheorie.* Weinheim, 1974.

kr Kramers, H. A. "Atom og kvanteteoriens udvikling i Aarene 1913-1925." *Fysisk tidsskrift, 33* (1935), 82-96.

pl Planck, Max. "Die Bohrsche Atomtheorie." *Nwn, 11* (1923), 535-537. (For reprintings see B.pl1.ju.)

po Polak, L. S. "Die Entstehung der Quantentheorie des Atoms." C.va2.ha, 226-242.

cb1.bo Bohr, Niels. *Das Bohrsche Atommodel.* Ed. A. Hermann. Stuttgart, 1965. (*Dokumente der Naturwissenschaft, 5.*)

he Heilbron, J. L., and Thomas S. Kuhn. "The genesis of the Bohr atom." *HSPS, 1* (1969), 211-290.

hj Hirosige, Tetu. "On the background of Bohr's theory of atomic constitution." ICHS, XI (1965). *Actes, 3* (1968), 430-434.

hk Hirosige, Tetu, and Sigeko Nisio. "Formation of Bohr's theory of atomic constitution." *JSHS, 3* (1964), 6-28.

hl Hirosige, Tetu, and Sigeko Nisio. "The genesis of the Bohr atom model and Planck's theory of radiation." *JSHS, 9* (1970), 35-47.

hp Hoyer, Ulrich. "Über die Rolle der Stabiltätsbetrachtungen in der Entwicklung der Bohrschen Atomtheorie." *AHES, 10* (1973), 177-206.

hu Hund, Friedrich. "Vor fünfzig Jahren: Der Schritt zur Quantentheorie des Atombaues und der Spektrallinien." *PB, 19* (1963), 494-502.

kr Kragh, Helge. "Chemical aspects of Bohr's 1913 theory." *JCE, 54* (1977), 208-210.

ni Nielsen, J. Rud. "Introduction." B.bo1.jb, *1*, 3-16, 93-129, 495.

nj Nisio, Sigeko. "The role of the chemical considerations in the development of Bohr atom model." *JSHS, 6* (1967), 26-40.

nk   Nisio, Sigeko. "The role of chemical considerations in the development of the Bohr atom model." ICHS, XII (1968). *Actes, 5* (1971), 71-73.

po   Polak, L. S. "Vozniknoveniye kvantovoy teorii atoma (model' atoma Rezerforda-Bora)." IIYeT. *Trudy, 19* (1957), 431-449.

ro   Robotti, Nadia. "La genesi del modello di Bohr sulla constituzione dell'atomo: Generalizzazione teorica e base empirica." *Physis, 18* (1976), 319-341.

rp   Rosenfeld, Léon. "Introduction." B.bo1.jc, xi-[lviii].

sq   Spencer, J. Brookes. "The origin and reception of the Bohr theory of the atom." ICHS, XII (1971). *Actes, 6* (1974), 86-90.

cc1.bo   Bohr, Niels. "Sommerfeld und die Atomtheorie." *Nwn, 16* (1928), 1036.

fr   Frankfurt, U. I., and A. N. Frank. "Voprosy optiki i atomnoy fiziki v perepiske mezhdu Eynshteynom i Zommerfel'dom." *ES,* 1969-1970, 301-330.

gl   Glaser, L. "Die Sommerfeldsche Feinstrukturkonstante als prinzipielle Frage der Physik. Beiträge zu den grundlegenden Werten der Atomphysik." *ZGN, 5* (1939), 289-331.

he   Heilbron, J. L. "The Kossel-Sommerfeld theory and the ring atom." *Isis, 58* (1967), 451-485.

ni   Nisio, Sigeko. "X-rays and atomic structure in the early stage of the old quantum theory." *JSHS, 8* (1969), 55-75.

cd1.kr   Kragh, Helge. "Niels Bohr's second atomic theory." *HSPS, 10* (1979), 123-86.

ni   Nielsen, J. Rud. "Introduction." B.bo1.jb, *3,* 3-46.

ce1.ch   Christiansen, J. A. "En kemikers møde med Niels Bohr." *Fysisk tidsskrift, 60* (1962), 31-46.

he   Heimann, P. M. "Moseley and celtium: The search for a missing element." *Annals of science, 23* (1967), 249-260.

hf   Hevesy, Georg von. "Historical notes on the discovery of hafnium." B.sj8.as, 681-686.

kr   Kragh, Helge, and Peter Robertson. "On the discovery of element 72." *JCE, 56* (1979), 456-459.

ks   Kragh, Helge. "Anatomy of a priority conflict: The case of element 72." *Centaurus, 23* (1980), 275-301.

cf1.an   Andrade, E. N. da C. *The structure of the atom.* London, 1923.

fo   Forman, Paul. "The doublet riddle and atomic physics circa 1924." *Isis, 59* (1968), 156-174.

fr   Frish, S. E. "Raboty D. S. Rozhdestvenskogo po stroyeniyu atoma." AN. *Izvestiya,* ser. fiz., *5* (1941), 631-634.

kr   Kramers, H. A., and Helge Holst. *The atom and the Bohr theory of its structure.* NY, 1923. (German ed., Berlin, 1925.)

lo   Loring, F. H. *Atomic theories.* London, 1921.

cg1.ca Caldirola, Piero. "Evoluzione storica del principio di esclusione nella fisica." *Scientia, 110* (1975), 51-67.

hu   Hutten, Ernest H. "On the Pauli principle." International Congress of the Philosophy of Science, II (1954). *Proceedings, 2* (1955), 12-18.

me   Meyenn, Karl von. "Paulis Weg zum Ausschliessungsprinzip." *PB, 36* (1980), 293-298; *37* (1981), 13-19.

pa   Pauli, Wolfgang. "Remarks on the history of the exclusion principle." *Science, 103* (1946), 213-215. (Also in B.pd3.jb, *2,* 1073-1075.)

pb   Pauli, Wolfgang. "Exclusion principle and quantum mechanics." B.pd3.jb, *2,* 1080-1096.

sh   Shpol'skiy, E. V. "Iz istorii printsipa isklyucheniya." *UFN, 32* (1947), 132-134.

wa   Waerden, B. L. van der. "Exclusion principle and spin." B.pd3.if, 199-244.

Zeeman effect

da1.bo Bohr, Niels. "Zeeman effect and theory of atomic constitution." B.ze1.ih, 131-134.

lo   Lodge, Oliver. "The history of Zeeman's discovery, and its reception in England." *Nature, 109* (1922), 66-69.

sp   *Spencer, J. Brookes. *An historical investigation of the Zeeman effect.* Ph.D. thesis. Univ. of Wisconsin, 1964. (*DAI, 25,* 3547.)

db1.en Endo, Shinji, and Sachie Saito. "Zeeman effect and the theory of electron of H. A. Lorentz." *JSHS, 6* (1967), 1-18.

ka   Onnes, Heike Kamerlingh. "Zeeman's ontdekking van het naar hem genoemde effect." *Physica, 1* (1921), 241-250.

ro   Romer, Alfred. "Zeeman's discovery of the electron." *AJP, 16* (1948), 216-223.

wa   Watson, E. C. "The discovery of the Zeeman effect." *AJP, 22* (1954), 633-635.

ze   Zeeman, Pieter. *Researches in magneto-optics.* London, 1913.

dc1.fo Forman, Paul. "Alfred Landé and the anomalous Zeeman effect, 1919-1921." *HSPS, 2* (1970), 153-261.

sp Spencer, J. Brookes. "The historical basis for interactions between the Bohr theory of the atom and investigations of the Zeeman effect: 1913-1925." ICHS, XII (1968). *Actes, 5* (1971), 95-100.

Quantum-mechanical atoms

ea1.hy Hylleraas, Egil. "Reminiscences from early quantum mechanics of two-electron atoms." *Reviews of modern physics, 35:3* (1963), 421-431.

tu Turner, J. E. "Minimum dipole moment required to bind an electron; molecular theorists rediscover phenomenon mentioned in Fermi-Teller paper 20 years earlier." *AJP, 45* (1977), 758-766.

Periodic system

ga1.pb Pauli, Wolfgang. "Die Geschichte des periodischen Systems der Elemente." Naturforschende Gesellschaft, Zürich. *Vierteljahrsschrift, 97* (1952), 137-139. (Also in B.pd3.jb, *2*, 1160-1162.)

se *Segrè, Emilio. "The completion and extension of the periodic system of the elements." Convegno mendeleeviano. *Atti* (1969), 49-71.

sp Spronsen, J. W. van. *The periodic system of chemical elements.* Amsterdam, 1969.

gb1.io *Ioffe, A. F. "Fizicheskiy smysl periodicheskoy sistemy." *Periodicheskiy zakon D. I. Mendeleyeva i yego filosofskoye znacheniye.* Moscow, 1947. Pp. 79-98. (Also in H.gb1.se, 97-114.)

se *Sem'desyat'pyat' let periodicheskogo zakona D. I. Mendeleyeva i Russkogo khimicheskogo obshchestva.* Moscow and Leningrad, 1947.

sf Semenchenko, V. K. "Rol' periodicheskogo zakona D. I. Mendeleyeva v razvitii atomnoy fiziki." *Rol' russkoy nauki v razvitii mirovoy nauki i kul'tury.* Moscow. University. *Uchenyye zapiski, 92* (1946), 38-45.

ye Yel'yashevich, M. A. "The Mendeleev periodic law, atomic spectra, and atomic structure." *SPU, 13* (1970), 1-23.

yf Yel'yashevich, M. A. "Periodicheskiy zakon D. I. Mendeleyeva spektry i stroyeniye atoma (K istorii fizicheskoy interpretatsii periodicheskoy sistemy)." *Periodicheskiy zakon i stroyeniye atoma.* Moscow, 1971. Pp. 41-106.

yg   Yel'yashevich, M. A. "Model' atoma Rezerforda i fizicheskaya interpretatsiya periodicheskogo zakona D. I. Mendeleyeva." ICHS, XIII (1971). Section 6. *Actes* (1974), 122-125.

gc1.pa   Pauli, Wolfgang. "Rydberg and the periodic system of the elements." Lund. University. *Årsskrift*, Avd. 2, *50:21* (1954), 22-26. (Also in B.pd3.jb, *2*, 1231-1235.)

I. NUCLEAR PHYSICS

Natural radioactivity

aal.br *Broglie, Louis de. "Les conséquences de la découverte des corps radioactifs pour le développement de nos connaissances en physique." *Atomes*, no. 58 (1951), 7- .

ch *Chalmers, Thomas Wightman. *A short history of radioactivity*. London, 1951.

cp Cotton, Eugénie. *Les Curie et la radioactivité*. Paris, 1963.

ga Gamow, George. *Atomic energy in cosmic and human life: Fifty years of radioactivity*. Cambridge, 1946.

gr Grégoire, Raymond. "Cinquante ans de physique nucléaire." *Atomes*, no. 58 (Jan. 1951), 12-15.

ha Haïssinky, M. "Pseudo-découvertes dans l'histoire de la radioactivité." ICHS, XIII (1971). Colloquium preprint, 15 p.

rn Romer, Alfred. "Concerning the true beginning of nuclear physics." *PT, 24* (1971), 43-44.

ro Rona, Elizabeth. *How it came about: Radioactivity, nuclear physics, atomic energy*. Oak Ridge Associated Universities, 1978.

sa Saukov, A. A. *Radioaktivnyye elementy zemli*. Moscow, 1961.

so Soddy, Frederick. *Radioactivity and atomic theory. Presenting facsimile reproductions of the annual progress reports on radioactivity, 1904-1920, to the Chemical Society*. Ed. Thaddeus J. Trenn. London, 1975.

st Starosel'skaya-Nikitina, O. A. *Istoriya radioaktivnosti i vozniknoveniya yadernoy fiziki*. Moscow, 1963.

za Zaytseva, L. L. "Nekotoryye neopublikovannyye materiali, otnosyshchiyesya k istorii ucheniya o radioaktivnosti." IIYeT. *Trudy, 35* (1961), 149-166.

See also: G.lal.ku

abl.fa Fajans, Kasimir. "Vospominaniya, svyazannyye s istoriyey nauki o radioaktivnosti." *Priroda*, 1973:10, 74-82.

go Gol'danskiy, V. I., and D. N. Trifonov. "75 let ucheniya o radioaktivnosti." *VIYeT, 34* (1971), 3-12.

hb Hahn, Otto. "30 Jahre Radiumforschung." *FF, 4* (1928), 279.

hc Hahn, Otto. "Einige persönliche Erinnerungen aus der Geschichte der natürlichen Radioaktivität." *Nwn, 35* (1948), 67-74.

jo   Joliot, Frédéric. "Les grandes découvertes de la radioactivité." *La pensée,* no. 74 (1957), 3-15.

ru   Rutherford, Ernest. "Early days in radio-activity." Franklin Institute. *Journal, 198* (1924), 281-289.

rv   Rutherford, Ernest. "Erinnerungen an die Frühzeit der Radioaktivität." *Zeitschrift für Elektrochemie und angewandte physikalische Chemie, 38* (1932), 476-480.

rw   Rutherford, Ernest. "Radioactivity: Old and new." *Nature, 135* (1935), 289-292.

See also: C.av2

ac1.fl   Flerov, G. N. "The study of radioactivity in the Soviet Union." ICHS, XIII (1971). Colloquium preprint, 15 p. (In Russian in *VIYeT, 36-37,* 136-141.)

yb   Yakoblev, K. P. "Raboty russkikh uchenykh po radioaktivnosti." C.vb1.pr, *1,* 380-386.

yc   *Yakobson, L. I. "Pervonachal'nyye radioaktivnyye issledovaniya v Rossii." AN Uzbeksoy SSR. Fiziko-tekhnicheskiy Institut. *Trudy, 5* (1953), 118-135.

za   Zaytseva, L. L. "V. A. Borodovskiy i yego raboty po radioaktivnosti." *VIYeT, 2* (1956), 124-237.

zc   Zaytseva, L. L., and N. A. Figurovskiy. *Issledovaniya yavleniy radioaktivnosti v dorevolyutsionnoy Rossii.* Moscow, 1961.

See also: B.bp4.cf

ad1.ba   *Badash, Lawrence. *The early developments in radioactivity, with emphasis on contributions from the United States.* Ph.D. thesis. Yale Univ., 1964. (*DAI, 25,* 4667.)

bb   Badash, Lawrence. *Radioactivity in America: Growth and decay of a science.* Baltimore and London, 1979.

ae1.st   Stroński, Ignacy. "Beginnings of the studies in radioactivity in Poland." ICHS, XI (1965). *Actes, 4* (1968), 126-129.

Early history of radioactivity

ba1.bs   Bruzzaniti, Giuseppe. *La radioattività da Becquerel a Rutherford.* Turin, 1980.

bv   Burke, John Butler. "The radio-activity of matter." *The monthly review, 13* (1903), 115-131.

el   Elster, Julius, and Hans Geitel. "Entdeckungsgeschichte und Grundtatsachen der Radioaktivität." *Kultur der Gegenwart.* Ed. Paul Hinneberg. Vol. *3:3:1* (1915), 478-494.

ja   Jauncey, G. E. M. "The early years of radioactivity." *AJP, 14* (1946), 226-241.

ki   Kirby, Harold W. *The early history of radiochemistry.* Miamisburg, Ohio, 1972. (Atomic Energy Commission. *Research and development report,* MLM-1960.)

ma   *Malley, Marjorie. *From hyperphosphorescence to nuclear decay: A history of the early years of radioactivity, 1896-1914.* Ph.D. thesis. Univ. of California, Berkeley, 1976. (*DAI, 37,* 6018A.)

pa   Pais, Abraham. "Radioactivity's two early puzzles." B.ra3.im, 116-136.

ro   Rogalya, A. M. "Osnovnyye etapy razvitiya eksperimental'nykh metodov issledovaniya radioaktivnosti." ICHS, XIII (1971). Section 6. *Actes* (1974), 119-122.

rp   Romer, Alfred. *The restless atom.* Garden City, NY, 1960.

si   *Sinclair, S. B. *Early history of radioactivity.* Ph.D. thesis. Univ. of London (Imperial College), 1976.

tr   Trifonov, D. N. "Kratkaya khronologiya osnovnykh sobytiy v razvitii ucheniya o radioaktivnosti." *VIYeT, 34* (1971), 13-19.

bb1.ba   Badash, Lawrence. "'Chance favors the prepared mind': Henri Becquerel and the discovery of radioactivity." *AIHS,* no. 70-71 (1965), 55-66.

bb   Badash, Lawrence. "Radioactivity before the Curies." *AJP, 33* (1965), 128-135.

bc   Badash, Lawrence. "Becquerel's 'unexposed' photographic plates." *Isis, 57* (1966), 267-269.

bd   Badash, Lawrence. "The discovery of thorium's radioactivity." *JCE, 43* (1966), 219-220.

bf   Bertrand, Gabriel. "Sur l'origine de la découverte de la radioactivité." AS. *Comptes rendus, 223* (1946), 698-700.

fa   Falkenberg, Dietrich. "Zur Entdeckungsgeschichte der natürlichen Radioaktivität." *NTM, 4:10* (1967), 53-62.

bc1.br   *Broglie, Louis de. "Le cinquantenaire de la découverte du radium." *Education nationale,* no. 23 (1950), 3-5.

ch   Christie, James. "The discovery of radium." Franklin Institute. *Journal, 167* (1909), 354-361.

da   Dabkowska, Michalina. "Le polonium et le radium dans le tableau de Mendéléev." Lublin. University. *Annales, 22AA* (1967), 61-69.

fa   Fajans, Kasimir. "Discovery of radium and the modern development of chemistry and physics." Polish Institute of Arts and Sciences in America. *Bulletin, 3* (1945), 222-245.

fo   Foley, Hamilton. "The sources of radium." Pan-American Union. *Bulletin* (Jul. 1921), 29-48.

jo   Joliot-Curie, Irène. "La découverte du radium par Pierre et Marie Curie." *Atomes,* no. 58 (Jan. 1951), 5-6.

jp   Joliot-Curie, Irène. "Les carnets du laboratoire de la découverte du radium." IIYeT. *Trudy, 19* (1957), 97-114. (In Russian, *ibid.*, 115-138.)

ku   Kuhn, Karl. "Entdeckungsgeschichte des Radiums." *PB, 17* (1961), 167-168.

te   Teske, Armin. "Les premières idées de Marie Sklodowska Curie sur le phénomène de la radioactivité." Lublin. University. *Annales, 22AA* (1967), 53-58.

vb   Vassails, Gérard. "Le cinquantenaire du radium." *La pensée,* no. 31 (1950), 8-18.

bd1.ba   Badash, Lawrence. "How the 'Newer Alchemy' was received." *Scientific American, 215* (1966), 88-95.

bb   Badash, Lawrence. "The suicidal success of radiochemistry." *BJHS, 12* (1979), 245-256.

fr   Freedman, Michael I. "Frederick Soddy and the practical significance of radioactive matter." *BJHS, 12* (1979), 257-260.

ma   Malley, Marjorie. "The discovery of atomic transmutation: Scientific styles and philosophies in France and Britain." *Isis, 70* (1979), 213-223.

rp   Romer, Alfred. "The transformation theory of radioactivity." *Isis, 49* (1958), 3-12.

rq   Romer, Alfred, ed. *The discovery of radioactivity and transmutation.* NY, 1964.

tr   *Trenn, Thaddeus J. *The rise and early development of the disintegration theory of radioactivity.* Ph.D. thesis. Univ. of Wisconsin, 1971. (*DAI, 32,* 7248B.)

ts   Trenn, Thaddeus J. "Rutherford and Soddy: From a search for radioactive constituents to the disintegration theory of radioactivity." *Rete, 1* (1971), 51-70.

tt   Trenn, Thaddeus J. *The self-splitting atom.* London, 1977.

tu   Trenn, Thaddeus J. "The justification of transmutation: Speculations of Ramsay and experiments of Rutherford." *Ambix, 21* (1974), 53-77.

See also: H.bf1.he

be1.ha   Hahn, Otto. "Die Auffindung des Radiothors und des Mesothors." *Chemiker-Zeitung, 61* (1937), 22.

hb   Hahn, Otto. "Einige Erinnerungen an das Radiothor und das Mesothor." *PB, 17* (1961), 570-576.

ki   Kirby, H. W. "The discovery of actinium." *Isis, 62* (1971), 290-308.

kr   Krätz, Otto. "Die Erstisolierung des Protoactiniums und seine Bedeutung für die Geschichte des Periodensystems." *Rete, 2* (1974), 269-283.

ku   Kuhn, F. K. "Zur Entdeckung der Thorium-Radioaktivität durch G. C. Schmidt." *PB, 4* (1948), 212.

tr   Trenn, Thaddeus J. "Thoruranium (U-236) as the extinct natural parent of thorium: The premature falsification of an essentially correct theory." *Annals of science, 35* (1978), 581-597.

vy   Vyal'tsev, A. N. "Ob otkrytii aktiniya-X." *VIYeT, 42* (1973), 40-43.

See also: C.gb5.me, zi

bf1.du   Dunskaya, I. M. "K istorii formulirovki usloviy obnaruzheniya indutsirovannogo izlucheniya." *VIYeT, 35* (1971), 48-50.

tr   Trenn, Thaddeus J. "Rutherford and recoil atoms: The metamorphosis and success of a once stillborn theory." *HSPS, 6* (1975), 513-547.

ts   Trenn, Thaddeus J. "The phenomenon of aggregate recoil: The premature acceptance of an essentially incorrect theory." *Annals of science, 37* (1980), 81-100.

See also: B.sn2.ah, ai; T.gb1.tq

bg1.an   Anders, Oswald U. "The place of isotopes in the periodic table: The 50th anniversary of the Fajans-Soddy displacement law." *JCE, 41* (1964), 522-525.

fe   Feather, Norman. "Isotopes, isomers and the fundamental law of radioactive change." *RS. Notes and records, 32* (1978), 225-231.

ke   Kent, Andrew, et al. "Isotopes, a fiftieth anniversary." *Chemical Society. Proceedings,* 1963, 325-331.

ne   Nemirovskiy, P. E. "K istorii obosnovaniya sistematiki izotopov." *VIYeT, 34* (1971), 20-30.

ro   Romer, Alfred. *Radiochemistry and the discovery of isotopes.* NY, 1970.

ta   Tanaka, Minoru. "The reception of Soddy's idea of isotope and the development of radioactivity studies in Japan." *JSHS, 16* (1977), 119-123.

Artificial radioactivity

ca1.be   Bernal, J. D., and D. K. Butt. "The technicial and social consequences of the discovery of artificial radioactivity in 1934." *Impact, 14* (1964), 89-100.

cp   Cotton, Eugénie. "Le vingtième anniversaire de la découverte de la radioactivité artificielle." *La pensée,* no. 56 (1954), 14-23.

fl   Fleischmann, Rudolf. "25 Jahre künstliche Kernanregung." *PB, 11* (1955), 395-399.

go   Gol'danskiy, V. I. "Plody velikogo otkrytiya: K 30-letiyu otkrytiya iskusstvennoy radioaktivnosti." AN. *Vestnik,* 1964:7, 31-35.

io   Ioffe, A. F. "Pervoye Mendeleyevskoye chteniye." AN. *Vestnik,* 1936:10, 43-45.

jo   Joliot, Frédéric, and Irène Joliot-Curie. "Otkrytiye iskusstvennoy radioaktivnosti." B.jj1.jn, 519-525.

jq   Joliot-Curie, Irène. "La découverte de la radioactivité artificielle." *Atomes,* no. 58 (Jan. 1951), 9-12.

jr   Joliot-Curie, Irène. "Die künstliche Radioactivität und die Entwicklung der Kernphysik." *NR, 6* (1953), 89-93.

se   Segrè, Emilio. "Zur Geschichte der künstlich hergestellten Elemente." *Angewandte Chemie: Nachrichten aus Chemie und Technik,* 1953, 135-136.

sh   Shushurin, S. F. "30-letiye otkrytiya radioaktivnykh izotopov Frederikom i Iren Zholio-Kyuri." *IMYeN, 8* (1970), 203-210.

sk   Skobel'tsyn, D. V. "La découverte de la radioactivité artificielle et son role dans le développement de la physique depuis vingt ans." *La pensée,* no. 56 (1954), 3-13.

tr   Trifonov, D. N., and G. A. Khakimbayeva. "Ob otkrytii iskusstvennogo prevrashchenyia elementov." *VIYeT, 60* (1978), 80-84.

va   Valadares, Manuel. "The discovery of artificial radioactivity." *Impact, 14* (1964), 83-88.

cb1.ab Abelson, Philip H. "A sport played by graduate students." *BAS, 30* (May 1974), 48-52.

bu   Burton, Milton. "Radiation chemistry: A brief history and forecast." *BAS, 3* (Dec. 1947), 366-369.

ha   Hahn, Otto. "Atomchemie." *25 Jahre Kaiser-Wilhelm-Gesellschaft zur Förderung der Wissenschaften.* 2 vols. Berlin, 1936. Vol. 2, 57-67.

hb   Hahn, Otto. "Über die Entwicklung der Kernchemie (aus meinen Erinnerungen)." *Zeitschrift für Elektrochimie, 58* (1954), 543-546.

me   Meitner, Lise. "Zur Entwicklung der Radiochemie: Otto Hahn zu 50 jährigen Doktor-Jubiläum." *Angewandte Chemie, 64* (1952), 1-4.

st   Stradyn', Ya. P. "Rikhard Svinne: Vidnyiy issledovatel' radioaktivnosti i periodicheskoy sistemy khimicheskikh elementov." *Iz istorii yestestvoznaniya i tekhniki pribaltiki, 3* (1971), 157-174.

See also: C.ba3.sp

ccl.dr Dragoni, Giorgio. "L'illusoria scoperta del primo elemento transuranico." *Physis, 15* (1973), 351-374.

fl   Flerov, G. N., and N. I. Tarantin. "Transuranovyye elementy i periodicheskaya sistema D. I. Mendeleyeva." *VIYeT, 29* (1969), 17-26.

gh   Ghiorso, Albert. "Discovery ،f element 101 — Mendelevium." *Adventures in experimental physics, 2* (1972), 245-254.

ha   Hahn, Otto. "Die 'falschen' Trans-Urane: Zur Geschichte eines wissenschaftlichen Irrtums." *NR, 15* (1962), 43-47.

sc   Seaborg, Glenn T. "Early radiochemical investigations of plutonium." B.mk1.if, 104-114.

sd   Seaborg, Glenn T. "Fortschritt über Plutonium hinaus· Die Entdeckungsgeschichte der Transurane bis 104." *PB, 23* (1967), 109-119.

se   Seaborg, Glenn T. "Some recollections of early nuclear age chemistry." *JCE, 45* (1968), 278-289.

sf   Seaborg, Glenn T. "The history of the transuranic elements and an outlook for their future." ICHS, XIII (1971). Plenary sessions. *Actes* (1974), 64-87. (In Russian in *VIYeT, 36-37* (1971), 126-136.)

sg   Seaborg, Glenn T. "From Mendeleev to Mendelevium—and beyond." A.aa1.nf, 267-296.

cd1.fr Frisch, Otto R. "The interest is focusing on the atomic nucleus." B.bo1.ar, 137-148.

fs   Frisch, Otto R., and John A. Wheeler. "The discovery of fission." *PT, 20* (Nov. 1967), 43-52.

ge   Gerlach, Walther. "Vor 25 Jahren 'Zerplatzte' der Urankern." *PB, 20* (1964), 11-14.

gr   Graetzer, Hans G. "Discovery of nuclear fission." *AJP, 32* (1964), 9-15.

gs   Graetzer, Hans, and David L. Anderson, eds. *The discovery of nuclear fission: A documentary history.* NY, 1971.

ha   Hahn, Otto. Über die Auffindung der 'Uranspaltung'." *Experientia, 4* (1948), 369-373.

hb   Hahn, Otto. "The discovery of fission." *Scientific American, 192* (Feb. 1958), 76-84.

hc   Hahn, Otto. "Zur Geschichte der Uranspaltung und den aus dieser Entwicklung entspringenden Konsequenzen." *Nwn, 46* (1959), 158-163.

hd   Hahn, Otto, and Fritz Strassmann. "Erinnerung an die Entdeckung der Uranspaltung." Max-Planck-Gesellschaft. *Mitteilungen,* 1957, 12-18.

he   Hahn, Otto. "Die Entwicklung der Radiochemie und die Spaltung des Urans." *NR, 6* (1953), 45-49.

hf   Hahn, Otto. "Zwanzig Jahre Uranspaltung." *Die Atomwirtschaft, 3* (1958), 485-487.

je   Jetter, U. "Die Gewinnung der Atomenergie." *PB, 2* (1946), 74-81.

ke   Keller, Cornelius. "Der Weg zur Kernspaltung." *NR, 31* (1978), 489-499.

la   Laue, Max von. "Erinnerung an die Entdeckung der Uranspaltung." Max-Plank-Gesellschaft. *Mitteilungen,* 1957, 9-12. (Also in B.lf6.jl, 243-246.)

sm   Smirenken, G. N. "Deleniye yader." C.vb1.pr, *2,* 334-359.

sp   Sparberg, Esther B. "A study of the discovery of fission." *AJP, 32* (1964), 2-8.

wo   Wohlfarth, Horst, ed. *40 Jahre Kernspaltung, eine Einführung in die Originalliteratur.* Darmstadt, 1979.

zi   Zimen, Karl Erik. "Otto Hahn, Lise Meitner und die Kernspaltung im Ausblick auf die Zukunft." *PB, 35* (1979), 200-210.

Nuclear, general

da1.be   Beyer, Robert T., ed. *Foundations of nuclear physics: Facsimiles of thirteen fundamental papers.* NY, 1949.

bl   Blackett, P. M. S. "The birth of nuclear science." *The listener, 51* (1954), 380-382, 424-425, 477-478.

br   Bromley, D. Allen. "[Twenty years of] the nucleus." *PT, 21* (May 1968), 29-36.

du   DuBridge, Lee A. "The large laboratory in nuclear research." *Physical science and human values.* Ed. Eugene P. Wigner. Princeton, 1947. Pp. 51-75.

fr   Frisch, Otto R. "Experimental work with nuclei: Hamburg, London, Copenhagen." I.dc1.st, 65-79.

ke   Kertesz, François. "Names for nuclear science." *Nature, 233* (1969), 21-23.

ko   Kolman, E. "Die Dialektik der Entwicklung der modernen Kernphysik." *NTM, 4:9* (1967), 42-45.

kp   Korsumsky, M. *The atomic nucleus.* Tr. G. Yankovsky. NY, 1963.

ma   Massey, Harrie. "Nuclear physics today and in Rutherford's day." RS. *Notes and records, 27* (1972), 25-44.

ro   Rosenfeld, Léon. "Nuclear physics, past and future." *Nuclear structure study with neutrons.* Ed. N. de Mévergnies, P. van Assche, and J. Verrier. Amsterdam, 1966. Pp. 483-487.

rp   Rosenfeld, Léon. "Nuclear reminiscences (in memory of George Gamow)." *BSPS, 21* (1979), 335-345.

st   Stulz, Percy. *Schlaglicht. Aus der Geschichte der Kernforschung.* Berlin [DDR], 1973.

we   Weiner, Charles, and Elspeth Hart, eds. *Exploring the history of nuclear physics.* NY, 1972. (American Institute of Physics. *Conference proceedings, 7.*)

db1.ad   Adams, J. B. "Four generations of nuclear physicists." RS. *Notes and records, 27* (1972), 75-94.

wg   Wheeler, John A. "Niels Bohr and nuclear physics." *PT,* (Oct. 1963), 36-45.

wh   Wheeler, John A. "Some men and moments in the history of nuclear physics: The interplay of colleagues and motivations." I.dc1.st, 217-322.

wj   Wilson, Jane. *All in our time: The reminiscences of twelve nuclear pioneers.* Chicago, 1975.

dc1.be   Bethe, Hans. "The happy thirties." I.dc1.st, 11-31.

ke   Kevles, Daniel J. "Towards the annus mirabilis: Nuclear physics before 1932." *PTeach, 10* (1972), 175-181.

la   Langevin, M. "Radioactivity and nuclear physics 1930-1940." A.aa1.ta, 213-221.

pu   Purcell, Edward M. "Nuclear physics without the neutron: Clues and contradictions." ICHS, X (1962). *Actes, 1* (1964), 121-133.

st   Stuewer, Roger H., ed. *Nuclear physics in retrospect: Proceedings of a symposium on the 1930's.* Minneapolis, 1979.

we   Weiner, Charles. "1932—moving into the new physics." *PT, 25* (May 1972), 40-49.

wf   Weiner, Charles. "Institutional settings for scientific change: Episodes from the history of nuclear physics." Arnold Thackray and Everett Mendelsohn, eds. *Science and values: Patterns of tradition and change.* NY, 1974. Pp. 187-212.

wi   Wheeler, John A. "Niels Bohr and nuclear physics." *PT, 16* (Oct. 1963), 36-45.

dd1.an   AN. Fiziko-tekhnicheskiy institut im. A. F. Ioffe, and Arkhiv AN, Leningradskoye otedeleniye. *Vklad akademika A. F. Ioffe v stanovleniye yadernoy fiziki v SSSR.* Leningrad, 1980.

ar   Artsimovich, L. A. "Fizika atomnogo yadra v SSSR k dvadtsatoy godovshchiye Oktyabrya." *ZhETF, 7* (1937), 1194-1202. (In English in *Physikalische Zeitschrift der Sowjetunion, 12* (1937), 526-541.)

da   Davydov, A. S. "Teoreticheskaya yadernaya fizika." C.vb1.pr, *2*, 243-256.

fr   Frank, I. M. "The beginnings of nuclear physics investigations at the physics institute of the Academy of Sciences and certain contemporary problems of nuclear structure." *SPU, 10:1* (1967), 6-16.

ft   Frenkel', Ya. I., et al. "Vystupleniye po dokladu I. Ye. Tamma." AN. *Izvestiya,* ser. fiz., *1* (1936), 324-345.

my   Mysovskiy, L. V. *Novye idei v fizike atomnogo yadra.* 3rd ed. Moscow, 1940.

sk   Skobel'tsyn, D. V. "Problema atomnogo yadra." C.vb4.an, 177-205.

sm   Smorodinskiy, Ya. A., and I. Ye. Tamm. "Raboty Ya. I. Frenkelya po teorii elektronov i tyazhelykh yadev." B.fr1.jd, 455-459.

tk   *Tkach, V. K. "Ocherk razvitiya radiofiziki na fiziko-matematicheskom fakul'tete." Kharkov. University. *Uchenyye zapiski, 60* (1955), 93-102.

de1.am   Amaldi, Edoardo. "Sulle ricerche di fisica nucleare eseguite a Roma nel quadriennio di guerra." *Ricerca scientifica, 16* (1946), 61-65.

dr   Dragoni, Giorgio. "Un momento della vita scientifica italiana delgi anni trenta: La scopertà dei neutroni lenti e la loro introduzione nella sperimentazione fisica." *Physis, 18* (1976), 131-164.

ho   Holton, Gerald. "Striking gold in science: Fermi's group and the recapture of Italy's place in physics." *Minerva, 12* (1974), 159-198.

se   Segrè, Emilio. "Nuclear physics in Rome." I.dc1.st, 35-62.

df1.bo   Bopp, Fritz, and Walther Bothe. "Elementarteilchen und Feldtheorie der Kernkräfte." C.ga1.bo, *1*, 1 20.

di   Dickel, G. "Inaktive Isotope, ihre Trennung und Anwendung." C.ga1.cl, 7-18.

fl   Flügge, S., et al. "Kernbau und Kernprozesse (ohne Spaltung)." C.ga1.bo, *1*, 107-170.

ha   Hahn, Otto, et al. "Physik der Kernspaltung." C.ga1.bo, *1*, 171-224.

hd   Heisenberg, Werner. "Die Entwicklung der jüngsten Zweige der Atomphysik in Deutschland." *FF, 15* (1939), 241-244.

he   Heisenberg, Werner, et al. "Kerntechknik." C.ga1.bo, *2*, 142-193.

st   Starke, K. "Physikalisch-chemische Effekte bei Kernumwandlungen." C.ga1.cl, 1-6.

su   Suess, H. "Isotopenaustauschgleichgewichte." C.ga1.cl, 19-24.

Nuclear structure

ea1.be   Berman, R. "S & U." *Progress in nuclear physics, 13* (1977), 28-38.

el   Elton, L. R. B., and Daphne F. Jackson. "Nuclear models." *PE, 3* (1968), 131-138.

fr   Friedman, F. L., and V. F. Weisskopf. "The compound nucleus."
        B.bo1.ip, 134-162.

je   Jensen, J. Hans D. "The history of the theory of structure of
        the atomic nucleus." *Science, 147* (1965), 1419-1422.

jo   Joliot-Curie, Irène, and Frédéric Joliot. "La mécanique ondula-
        toire et le noyau." B.bw1.ag, 205-214.

ra   Radvanyi, P., and R. Nataf. "Radioactivity and models of the nu-
        cleus." A.aa1.ta, 221-224.

wi   Wigner, Eugene P. "On the development of the compound nu-
        cleus model." *AJP, 23* (1055), 371-380.

eb1.br Bromberg, Joan. "The impact of the neutron: Bohr and Heisen-
        berg." *HSPS, 3* (1971), 307-341.

bs   Bromberg, Joan. "Heisenberg's papers on nuclear structure."
        ICHS, XII (1968). *Actes, 5* (1971), 13-16.

fl   Flammersfeld, A. "Zur Geschichte der Atomkernisomerie."
        B.mk1.if, 74-77.

sc   Schwartz, L. "La 'function' δ et les noyaux." B.dk1.is, 179-182.

za   Zacharias, Peter. "Zur Entstehung des Einteilchen-
        schalenmodells." *Annals of science, 28* (1972), 401-411.

ec1.al Alvarez, Luis W. "Discovery of muon-induced nuclear fusion."
        Adventures in experimental physics, 1 (1972), 72-74.

co   Condon, Edward U. "Tunneling—how it all started." *AJP, 46*
        (1978), 319-323.

go   Goldhaber, Maurice. "The nuclear photoelectric effect and re-
        marks on higher multiple transitions: A personal history."
        I.dc1,st, 83-110.

gu   Guggenheimer, W. H. "General relativity and nuclear reactions."
        Dialectica, 14 (1960), 183-187.

ma   Maruyama, Michio. "First measurement of nuclear reaction time
        using 'blocking effect'." *Adventures in experimental physics, 1*
        (1972), 52-57.

ra   Radvanyi, P. "Nuclear reactions." A.aa1.ta, 225-232.

si   Simons, Lennart. "Kompoundkärnan och den asymmetriska
        fissionen." *Fysisk tidsskrift, 60* (1962), 85-89.

st   Staub, Hans. "'Synthesizing' ^{8}Be and discovery of the effect of
        atomic electrons on nuclear resonances." *Adventures in experimen-
        tal physics, 3* (1973), 3-12.

te   Terwilliger, Kent M. "Early strong interaction counter experi-
        ments." T.ga1.da, 70-81.

we   Wertheim, G. K. "Resource letter ME-1." *Mössbauer effect: Selected reprints.* NY, 1963. Pp. 1-6.

wi   Wigner, E. P. "Resonance reactions." APS. *Proceedings, 90* (1946), 25-29.

ed1.na   Nataf, R. "Elementary interactions and nuclear forces." A.aa1.ta, 241-250.

pe   Peierls, Rudolf. "The development of our ideas on the nuclear forces." I.dc1,st, 183-211.

sc   Schwinger, Julian. "The Majorana formula." B.ra3.im, 170-184.

vy   *Vyal'tsev, A. N. *Istoriya problemy yadernykh sil.* Moscow, 1954. (Summary of thesis for Moscow University.)

ee1.bo   *Borovik-Romanov, A. S., et al. "Ob otkrytii paramagnitnogo rezonansa." *VIYeT,* 1980:2, 118-126.

go   Goudsmit, Samuel A. "Pauli and nuclear spin." *PT, 14* (Jun. 1961), 18-21.

ko   Kozyrev, B. M. "Raboty kazanskoy shkoly fizikov po paramagnitnomu rezonansu." AN. *Vestnik,* 1955:8, 13-19.

ef1.fr   Frisch, O. R. "Early steps towards the chain reaction." *Progress in nuclear physics, 13* (1977), 18-27.

we   Weart, Spencer R. "Scientists with a secret." *PT, 29* (Feb. 1976), 23-30.

wf   Weart, Spencer. "Secrecy, simultaneous discovery, and the theory of nuclear reactors." *AJP, 45* (1977), 1049-1060.

eg1.al   Alikhan'yan, A. I. "Searches for transition radiation at ultrarelativistic energies." *Adventures in experimental physics, 1* (1972), 117-119.

an   AN. Biblioteka. *Sovetskiye raboty po yadernoy spektroskopiy: Bibliograficheskiy ukazatel', 1917-1960 gg.* Leningrad, 1965.

go   Gorelik, G. S. "L. I. Mandel'shtam i ucheniye o rezonanse." AN. *Izvestiya,* ser. fiz., 9 (1945), 61-76.

ma   Mayer-Kuckuk, T. "Die Geburt des Mössbauer-Effekts: Kleine Geschichte einer grossen Entdeckung." *PB, 18* (1962), 9-13.

ml   Mladzhenovich, M. "K istorii issledovaniy vnutrenney konversii gamma-luchey." *VIYeT, 1980:3, 91-97.*

sh   Shipnel', V. S., and A. A. Sorokin. "Yadernaya spektroskopiya." C.vb1.pr, 2, 359-384.

Rays from radioactive substances

ra1.li   Lindhard, J. "On the passage through matter of swift charged particles." B.bo1.ip, 185-195.

tr   Trenn, Thaddeus J. "Rutherford on the alpha-beta-gamma classification of radioactive rays." *Isis, 67* (1976), 61-75.

rb1.ni   Nisio, Sigeko. "α-Rays and the atomic nucleus." *JSHS, 4* (1965), 91-116.

os   Osgood, Thomas H., and H. Sim Hirst. "Rutherford and his alpha particles." *AJP, 32* (1964), 681-686.

ro   Rosenblum, S. "Spectres magnétiques des particles alpha." B.mk1.if, 7-22.

tr   Trenn, Thaddeus J. "Rutherford's alpha-Teilchen." *Annals of science, 31* (1974), 49-72.

ts   Trenn, Thaddeus J. "Rutherford's *Radio-activity* and alpha ray research: The case of a misdated letter." *Ambix, 26* (1979), 134-136.

rc1.ba   Badash, Lawrence. "An Elster and Geitel failure: Magnetic deflection of beta rays." *Centarus, 11* (1966), 236-240.

ma   Malley, Marjorie. "The discovery of the beta particle." *AJP, 39* (1971), 1454-1461.

me   Meyer, Stefan. "Zur Geschichte der Entdeckung der Natur der Becquerel Strahlen." *Nwn, 36* (1949), 129-132.

rd1.ge   Gentner, W. "Einiges aus der frühen Geschichte der Gamma-Strahlen." B.mk1.if, 28-44.

Applications

sa1.be   Bethe, H. A. "Energy on earth and in the stars." A.aj1.fr, 9-20.

fa   Fabian, Hans-Georg. "Zur Geschichte der Kalium-Argon- und der Rubidium-Strontium-Methode für die geologische Altersbestimmung." *NTM, 11:2* (1974), 69-81.

il   Ilyina, T. "Pierwsze proby wykorzystania fizyki jadrowej w pracach poszukiwawczych nad kopalinami uzytecznymi. Zapomniane prace Leonarda Bogojawleńskiego i Kazimierza, Kalickiego." *KHNT, 22* (1977), 317-322.

ro   Rogalya, A. M. "K istorii razvitiya fizicheskikh metodov issledovaniya radioaktivnosti atmosfery." *VIYeT, 34* (1971), 31-41.

za   Zaytseva, L. L., and N. A. Figurovskiy. "Rol' Prof. P. P. Orlova v izuchenii radioaktivnosti prirodnykh ob'yektov Siviri i Altaya." *VIYeT, 4* (1957), 63-71.

Applications to 1950

ta1.ba Bankside, Lord Hinton of. "Atomic energy." A.aa1.wi, *1*, 223-267.

br Brown, Anthony Cave, and Charles B. MacDonald, eds. *The secret history of the atomic bomb.* NY, 1977.

go Goldschmidt, Bertrand. *The atomic adventure. Its political and technical aspects.* Tr. Peter Beer. Oxford, 1964.

gp Gómez Ortiz, Manuel. *Los padres de la bomba atómica.* Madrid, 1967.

gq *Gowing, Margaret, and Lorna Arnold. *The atomic bomb.* London, 1979.

gr Groueff, Stephane. *Manhattan project: The untold story of the making of the atomic bomb.* Boston, 1967.

gs Groves, Leslie R. *Now it can be told.* NY, 1962.

he *Herbig, Jost. *Kettenreaktion: Das Drama der Atomphysiker.* Munich, 1976.

hg Hewlett, Richard G., and O. E. Anderson, Jr. *A history of the United States Atomic Energy Commission.* Vol. 1: *The new world.* University Park, Pa., 1962.

ko *Koryakin, Yu. I. *Biografiya atoma.* Moscow, 1961.

ne Newley, E. F. "Development of the nuclear weapon." A.aa1.wi, *6*, 268-283.

ro Robinson, George O., Jr. *The Oak Ridge story.* Kingsport, Tenn., 1950.

sm Smyth, Henry D. *Atomic energy for military purposes.* Princeton, 1945.

sn Smyth, Henry D. "The 'Smyth Report.'" Princeton University Library. *Chronicle, 37* (1976), 173-189.

st Strauss, Lewis L. *Men and decisions.* NY, 1962.

th Thirring, Hans. *Die Geschichte der Atombombe.* Vienna, 1946.

va Vaucouleurs, C. de. *La conquête de l'energie atomique [1896-1945].* Paris, 1946.

wa Wattenberg, Albert. "Discorso per la celebrazione de Enrico Fermi." Accademia Nazionale dei Lincei, Rome. *Problemi attuali di scienza e di cultura. Quaderni,* no. 60 (1963), 3-6.

tb1.ba Badash, Lawrence, Joseph O. Hirschfelder, and Herbert P. Broida, eds. *Reminiscences of Los Alamos, 1943-1945.* Boston, 1980.

bb Badash, Lawrence. "Introduction." I.tb1.ba, xi-xxi.

bc   Baltá-Elías, José. "Enrico Fermi y el origen de la bomba atómica." *Atlantida, 5* (1967), 202-207.

br   Bradbury, Norris. "Los Alamos: The first 25 years." I.tb1.ba, 161-175.

bs   Brode, Bernice. "Tales of Los Alamos." LASL. *Community news, 2* (2, 30 Jun., 14, 28 Jul., 11, 25 Aug., 8, 22 Sep. 1960).

bt   Brode, Bernice. "Tales of Los Alamos." I.tb1.ba, 133-159.

ch   *Chambers, Marjorie Bell. *Technically sweet Los Alamos: The development of a federally sponsored scientific community.* Ph.D. thesis. Univ. of New Mexico, 1974. (*DAI, 35,* 6049A.)

du   Dudley, John H. "Ranch school to secret city." I.tb1.ba, 1-11.

ff   Feynman, Richard P. "Los Alamos from below." I.tb1.ba, 105-132.

hi   Hirschfelder, Joseph O. "The scientific and technological miracle at Los Alamos." I.tb1.ba, 67-88.

ki   Kistiakowsky, George B. "Reminiscences of wartime Los Alamos." I.tb1.ba, 49-65.

ku   Kunetka, James W. *City of fire: Los Alamos and the birth of the atomic age, 1943-1945.* Englewood Cliffs, N.J., 1978.

li   Libby, Leona Marshall. *The uranium people.* NY, 1979.

mc   McDaniel, Boyce. "A physicist at Los Alamos." *BAS, 30* (Dec. 1974), 39-43.

md   McMillan, Elsie. "Outside the inner fence." I.tb1.ba, 41-47.

me   McMillan, Edwin M. "Early days at Los Alamos." I.tb1.ba, 13-19.

mf   Manley, John H. "A new laboratory is born." I.tb1.ba, 21-40.

mi   Mitchell, Charles I. "Los Alamos: From weapons shop to scientific laboratory." *BAS, 26* (Nov. 1970), 24-27.

sm   Smith, Alice Kimball. "Los Alamos: Focus of an age." *BAS, 26* (Jun. 1970), 15-20. (Also in U.gk5.le, 33-46.)

we   Wiener, Norbert. "Moral reflections of a mathematician." *BAS, 12* (Feb. 1956), 53-57.

tc1.an Anderson, Herbert L. "Fermi, Szilard and Trinity." *BAS, 30* (Oct. 1974), 40-47.

ba   Bainbridge, Kenneth T. "Prelude to Trinity." *BAS, 31* (Apr. 1975), 42-46.

bb   Bainbridge, Kenneth T. "A foul and awesome display." *BAS, 31* (May 1975), 40-46.

fi   Fitch, Val L. "The view from the bottom." *BAS, 31* (Feb. 1975), 43-46.

fr   Frisch, Otto R. "The first nuclear explosion." *New scientist, 47* (1970), 274-276.

fs   Frisch, Otto R. "'Somebody turned the sun on with a switch'." *BAS, 30* (Apr. 1974), 12-18.

gr   Groves, Leslie R. "Some recollections of July 16, 1945." *BAS, 26* (Jun. 1970), 21-27. (Also in U.gk5.lc, 47-61.)

la   Lapp, Ralph. "Sunshine and darkness." *BAS, 15* (Jan. 1959), 27-29.

td1.al   Allred, John, and Louis Rosen. "Fast fusion neutrons from a thermonuclear weapon device." *Adventures in experimental physics, 5* (1976), 39-56.

be   Bertin, Leonard. *Atom harvest.* San Francisco, 1957.

cr   Creutz, Edward. "Nuclear power: Rise of an industry." U.gk5.le, 176-195.

fr   Frenkel', Ya. I. "Atomnaya energiya i yeye osvobozhdeniye." *Priroda,* 1946:5, 7-23. (Also in B.fr1.jf, 338-367.)

he   Hewlett, Richard G. "Pioneering on nuclear frontiers: Two early landmarks in reactor technology." *Technology and culture, 5* (1964), 512-522.

hf   Hewlett, Richard G., and Francis Duncan. *A history of the United States Atomic Energy Commission.* Vol. 2: *Atomic shield, 1947-1957.* [Oak Ridge, Tenn.], 1972.

hg   Hewlett, Richard G. "Beginnings of development in nuclear technology." *Technology and culture, 17* (1976), 465-478.

mc   McPhee, John. *The curve of binding energy.* NY, 1974.

ol   Oliphant, M. L. "The utilization of nuclear energy." RI. *Proceedings, 33* (1947), 506-514.

ra   Rabinowitch, Eugene. "Ten years that changed the world." *BAS, 12* (Jan. 1956), 2-6, 32.

sm   Smyth, Henry D., et al. "Symposium on atomic energy and its implications." APS. *Proceedings, 90* (1946), 1-79.

sn   Smyth, Henry D. "The development of nuclear power for peaceful purposes." *Electrical engineering, 73* (1954), 189-202.

See also: B.bo1.nb; C.la1.ro; H.aa1.fe; T.ei1

te1.gm   Gowing, Margaret. *Britain and atomic energy, 1939-1945.* NY, 1964.

gn   Gowing, Margaret *Reflections on atomic energy history.* Cambridge, 1978.

go   Gowing, Margaret. "Reflections on atomic energy history." *BAS, 35* (Mar. 1979), 51-54.

gp   Gowing, Margaret, and Lorna Arnold. *Independence and deterrence: Britain and atomic energy, 1945-1952.* 2 vols. NY, 1974.

gr   Gowing, Margaret, and Lorna Arnold. "The early politics of nuclear safety." *New scientist, 64* (1974), 741-743.

pe   Peierls, Rudolf E. "Britain in the atomic age." *BAS, 26* (Jun. 1970), 40-46. (Also in U.gk5.le, 91-105.)

See also: C.bh1.sp

tf1.be   Bergier, J., and P. de Latil. *Quinze hommes... un secret.* Paris, [1956].

sc   Scheinman, Lawrence. *Atomic energy policy in France under the Fourth Republic.* Princeton, 1965.

tg1.ba   *Bagge, Erich, Kurt Diebner, and Kenneth Jay. *Von der Uranspaltung bis Calder Hall.* Hamburg, 1957.

bc   Bar-Zohar, Michel. *The hunt for German scientists.* Tr. Len Ortzen. NY, 1967.

br   Brüche, Ernst. "Was wusste man 1943/44 in Deutschland von der Atombombe?" *PB, 20* (1964), 220-225.

go   Goudsmit, Samuel A. "How Germany lost the race: The German atomic energy project." *BAS, 1* (Mar. 1946), 4-5.

gp   Goudsmit, Samuel A. *Alsos.* NY, 1947.

he   Heisenberg, Werner. "The Third Reich and the atomic bomb." *BAS, 24* (Jun. 1968), 34-35.

ir   Irving, David. *The German atomic bomb: The history of nuclear research in Nazi Germany.* NY, 1967.

ra   Rabinowitch, Eugene. "The virus house: The German atomic bomb." *BAS, 24* (Jun. 1968), 32-34.

st   Starke, K., and G. Schubert. "Anwendungen der Kernphysik." C.ga1.bo, *2*, 127-141.

su   Suess, Hans E. "Virus House: Comments and reminiscences." *BAS, 24* (Jun. 1968), 36-39.

wi   Wirtz, K. "Historisches zu den Uranarbeiten in Deutschland in den Jahren 1940-1945." *PB, 3* (1947), 371-379.

th1.ba   Barwich, Heinz, and Elfi Barwich. *Das rote Atom.* Munich, 1967.

kr   Kramish, Arnold. *Atomic energy in the Soviet Union.* Stanford, Calif., 1959.

mo   Modelski, George A. *Atomic energy in the communist bloc.* [Melbourne], 1959.

See also: C.vb7.ig

tj1.do   Dower, J. W. "Science, society, and the Japanese atomic-bomb project during World War II." *Bulletin of concerned Asian scholars, 10:2* (1978), 41-54.

hu   Hughes, Phillip S. "Wartime fission research in Japan." *SSS, 10* (1980), 345-349.

sh   Shapley, Deborah. "Nuclear weapons history: Japan's wartime bomb projects revealed." *Science, 199* (1978), 152-157.

we   Weiner, Charles. "Retrospective saber rattling?" *BAS, 34* (Apr. 1978), 10-12.

K. PARTICLES AND BEAMS

Elementary particles

aa1.al Alvarez, Luis W. "Recent developments in particle physics." B.aj5.id, 1-49.

be Berestetskiy, V. B. "Issledovaniya v oblasti elementarnykh chastits." B.la8.il, 24-28.

fr Frenkel', V. Ya. "K istorii vozniknoveniya ponyatiya kvazichastits." ICHS, XIII (1971). Section 6. *Actes* (1974), 102-104.

iv Ivanenko, D. D. "Elementarnyye chastitsy." A.ab1.gr, 422-511.

ke Kemmer, N. "Some recollections from the early days of particle physics." *Hadronic interactions of electrons and photons.* Ed. J. Cummings and H. Osborn. London, 1971. Pp. 1-16.

li *Lifshits, Ye. M. "Kvazichastitsy v sovremennoy fizike." *V glub' atoma: Sbornik statey.* Ed. D. A. Frank-Kamenetskiy and B. N. Matsonashvili. Moscow, 1964.

me Meshcheryakov, M. G., and V. S. Barashenkov. "Progress fiziki vysokikh energiy." C.vb1.pr, *2*, 283-305.

pa Pais, Abraham. "[Twenty years of] particles." *PT, 21* (May 1968), 24-28.

pf Pfister, H. "Nobelpreis 1969 an Murray Gell-Mann für seine Arbeiten zur Elementarteilchenphysik." *PB, 26* (1970), 58-63.

re Rechenberg, Helmut. "Aus der Physik der Elementarteilchen, I. Abriss der Geschichte der Elementarteilchen." *PB, 19* (1963), 104-110.

wa Walker, Charles T., and Glen A. Slack. "Who named the -ons ?" *AJP, 38* (1970), 1380-1389.

wh Wheeler, J. A. "Problems and prospects in elementary particle research." APS. *Proceedings, 90* (1946), 36-47.

ab1.an Anderson, Carl David. "Early work on the positron and muon." *AJP, 29* (1961), 825-830.

de Deutsch, Martin. "Discovery of positronium." *Adventures in experimental physics, 4* (1974), 67-81.

ha Hanson, Norwood Russell. "Discovering the positron." *BJPS, 12* (1961), 194-214; *12* (1962), 299-313.

hb Hanson, Norwood Russell. *The concept of the positron: A philosophical analysis.* Cambridge, 1963.

ac1.am   Amaldi, Edoardo. "Personal notes on neutron work in Rome in the 30s and post-war European collaboration in high-energy physics." A.ad1.we, 294-351.

ba   Barshall, Henry H. "Three decades of fast-neutron experiments." *PT, 22* (Aug. 1969), 54-59.

ch   Chadwick, James. "Some personal notes on the search for the neutron." ICHS, X (1962). *Actes, 1* (1964), 159-162.

ci   Chadwick, James. "Search for the neutron." *Adventures in experimental physics, 1* (1972), 193-197.

es   Estulin, I. V. "Neytronnaya fizika." C.vb1.pr, *2*, 305-334.

fe   Feather, Norman. "A history of neutrons and nuclei." *CP, 1* (1960), 191-203, 257-266.

ff   Feather, Norman. "The experimental discovery of the neutron." ICHS, X (1962). *Actes, 1* (1964), 135-145.

se   Segrè, Emilio. "Fermi and neutron physics." *Reviews of modern physics, 27* (1955), 257-262.

sf   Segrè, Emilio. "The consequences of the discovery of the neutron." ICHS, X (1962). *Actes, 1* (1964), 149-158.

sh   Shebalin, S. F. "Otkrytiyu neytrona—30 let." *Priroda,* 1962:1, 83-84.

wi   Wigner, Eugene P. "The neutron: The impact of its discovery and its uses." I.dc1.st, 159-178.

ad1.br   Brown, Laurie M. "The idea of the neutrino." *PT, 31* (Sep. 1978), 23-28.

co   Cowan, Clyde L. "Anatomy of an experiment: An account of the discovery of the neutrino." Smithsonian Institution, Washington. *Report,* 1964, 409-430.

da   Dance, J. B. "The elusive neutrinos." *PE, 3* (1968), 298-306.

ga   Gamow, George. "Die Existenz des Neutrinos." *PB, 5* (1949), 108-114.

le   Lederman, Leon M. "Resource letter Neu-1: History of the neutrino." *AJP, 38* (1970), 129-136.

pa   Pauli, Wolfgang. "Zur älteren und neueren Geschichte des Neutrinos." B.pd3.jb, *2*, 1313-1337. (Also in B.pd3.jf, 156-180.)

re   Reines, Frederick. "The early days of experimental neutrino physics." *Science, 203* (1979), 11-16.

sc   Schwartz, Melvin. "Discovery of two kinds of neutrinos." *Adventures in experimental physics, 1* (1972), 82-85.

wi   Wilson, Fred L. "Fermi's theory of beta decay." *AJP, 36* (1968), 1150-1160.

wo   Wolfendale, Arnold W. *The search for the neutrino.* Durham, 1971.

wu   Wu, C. S. "History of beta decay." B.mk1.if, 45-65.

wx   Wu, C. S. "The neutrino." B.pd3.if, 249-300.

ae1.ab   Abashian, A. "The streamer chamber and K physics." T.ga1.da, 101-109.

an   Anderson, Herbert L. "Meson experiments with Enrico Fermi." *Reviews of modern physics, 27* (1955), 269-272.

go   Goldhaber, Gerson. "Discovery of massive neutral vector mesons." *Adventures in experimental physics, 5* (1976), 131-140.

gu   Gustavs, Arne. "Zur Entdeckung des Mesons: Paul Kunze zum 65. Geburtstag." *PB, 18* (1962), 503-506.

ja   Jaunlau, L. "From μ-mesons to τ-mesons." A.aa1.ta, 237-241.

ma   Maglich, Bogdan. "Discovery of omega meson, first neutral vector meson." *Adventures in experimental physics, 5* (1976), 79-105.

ri   Richter, Burton. "Discovery of massive neutral vector mesons." *Adventures in experimental physics, 5* (1976), 143-149.

ti   Ting, Samuel. "Discovery of massive neutral vector mesons." *Adventures in experimental physics, 5* (1976), 115-127.

See also: K.ab1.an

af1.ke   Kemmer, N. "The impact of Yukawa's meson theory on workers in Europe: A reminiscence." *Progress of theoretical physics,* 1965: Suppl., 602-608.

mu   Mukherji, Viśvapriya. "A short history of the meson theory from 1935 to 1943." *Indian journal of history of science, 6* (1971), 75-101, 117-134.

mv   Mukherji, Viśvapriya. "An historical note: The meson mass value in the history of the Yukawa theory." *Indian journal of history of science, 7* (1972), 146-152.

mw   Mukherji, Viśvapriya. "A history of the meson theory of nuclear forces from 1935 to 1952. *AHES, 13* (1974), 27-102.

op   Oppenheimer, J. Robert. "Thirty years of mesons." *PT, 19* (Nov. 1966), 51-58.

ro   Rosenfeld, Léon. "The conception of the meson field: Some reminiscences and epistemological comments." *Progress of theoretical physics, 41:* suppl. (1968), C1-C7. (Also in *BSPS, 21* (1979), 327-334.)

sa   Sakata, Shoichi. "On the establishment of the Yukawa theory." *Progress of theoretical physics, 41*: suppl. (1968), C8-C18.

sn   Snyder, James N. "On the changing status of mesons." *AJP, 18* (1950), 41-49.

yu   Yukawa, Hideki, and Chihiro Kikuchi. "The birth of the meson theory." *AJP, 18* (1950), 154-156.

ag1.le   Lederman, Leon. "Search for quarks using 'Fermi-motion' and discovery of the antideuteron." *Adventures in experimental physics, 2* (1972), 298-301.

Symmetries

ba1.te   Telegdi, V. L. "Crucial experiments on discrete symmetries." A.ad1.me, 454-478.

bb1.co   Cox, Richard. "Story of the experiment on double scattering of electrons: Was parity violation observed three decades before its actual discovery?" *Adventures in experimental physics, 3* (1973), 145-149.

fr   Franklin, Allan. "The discovery and nondiscovery of parity nonconservation." *SHPS, 10* (1979), 201-257.

ga   Garwin, Richard. "Discovery of parity violation in weak interactions." *Adventures in experimental physics, 3* (1973), 124-127.

te   Telegdi, V. L. "Discovery of parity violation in weak interactions." *Adventures in experimental physics, 3* (1973), 131-135.

wh   White, D. Hywell, Daniel Sullivan, and Edward J. Barboni. "The interdependence of theory and experiment in revolutionary science: The case of parity violation." *SSS, 9* (1979), 303-327.

wu   Wu, C. S. "Discovery of parity violation in weak interactions." *Adventures in experimental physics, 3* (1973), 101-118, 122-123.

bc1.ra   Rasche, G. "Zur Geschichte des Begriffes 'Isospin'." *AHES, 7* (1971), 257-276.

wi   Wilkinson, Denys Haigh. "Historical introduction to isospin." Wilkinson, ed , *Isospin in nuclear physics*. Amsterdam, 1969. Pp. 3-13.

Cosmic rays

ca1.an   AN. Fizicheskiy Institut. *Cosmic rays.* Ed. D. V. Skobel'tsyn. NY, 1965.

gr   Grigorov, N. L., and L. G. Mishchenko. "Kosmicheskiye luchi." C.vb1.pr, *2*, 256-283.

ja   Jauneau, L. "Cosmic rays and elementary particles." A.aa1.ta, 232-237.

ro   Rosen, Stephen, ed. *Selected papers on cosmic ray origin theories.* NY, 1969.

rp   Rossi, Bruno. *Cosmic rays.* NY, 1964.

st   Steinmaurer, Rudolf. "Fünfzig Jahre kosmische Strahlung: Rückblick auf Entdeckung und Erforschung." *PB, 18* (1962), 363-369.

sw   Swann, W. F. G. *The story of cosmic rays.* Cambridge, Mass., 1955.

sx   Swann, W. F. G. "The history of cosmic rays." *AJP, 29* (1961), 811-816.

cb1.al Alvarez, Luis W. "Search for hidden chambers in the pyramids using cosmic rays." *Adventures in experimental physics, 1* (1972), 159-166.

ba   Bagge, E., et al. "Kosmische Ultrastahlung." C.ga1.bo, Part 1, 21-106.

bl   Blau, Marietta. "Bericht über die Entdeckung der durch kosmische Strahlung erzeugten 'Sterne' in photographischen Emulsionen." C.av2.vi, 53-57.

mi   Millikan, R. A. "Bemerkungen zur Geschichte der kosmischen Strahlung." *PZ, 31* (1930), 241-247.

mj   Millikan, R. A. "History of research in cosmic rays." *Nature, 126* (1930), 14-16, 29-30.

my   *Mysovskiy, L. V. "Istoricheskoy obzor razvitiya ucheniya o kosmicheskikh luchakh v svyazi s issledovaniyem na bol'shikh vysotakh." Vsesoyuznaya konferentsiya po izucheniyu stratosfery. *Trudy.* Leningrad, 1935. Pp. 339-399, 445-449.

sk   Skobel'tsyn, D. V. "Vstupitel'noye slovo." AN. *Izvestiya,* ser. fiz., *17* (1953), 9-12.

ve   Vernov, S. N., et al. "Issledovaniye sostava pervichnogo kosmicheskogo izlucheniya." *UFN, 63* (1957), 131-148.

vf   Vernov, S. N., and N. A. Dobrotin. "Fiftieth anniversary of a fundamental discovery in cosmic-ray physics." *SPU, 20* (1977), 970-972.

Molecular beams

da1.er Estermann, Immanuel. "Molecular beam research in Hamburg, 1922-1923." B.sq3.ie, 1-7.

es   Estermann, Immanuel. "History of molecular beam research: Personal reminiscences of the important evolutionary period 1919-1933." *AJP, 43* (1975), 661-671.

mi   Millman, Sidney. "Recollections of a Rabi student of the early years in the molecular beam laboratory." B.ra3.im, 87-105.

ni   Nierenberg, W. A. "Molecular and atomic beams at Berkeley." B.sq3.ie, 9-42.

zo   Zorn, Jens C. "Resource letter MB-1." *Molecular beams: Selected reprints, 2,* NY, 1965. Pp. 4-15.

See also: B.sq3.ie

db1.fr   Franck, James, and Gustav Hertz. *Die Elektronenstossversuche.* Ed. A. Hermann. Stuttgart, 1965. (*Dokumente der Naturwissenschaften, 9.*)

dc1.as   Aston, F. W. "Kanalstrahlen und Atomphysik." *Nwn, 24* (1936), 467-469.

ru   Rüchardt, Eduard. "Zur Entdeckung der Kanalstrahlen vor fünfzig Jahren." *Nwn, 24* (1936), 465-467.

tr   Traubenberg, Heinrich Rausch von. "Die Bedeutung der Kanalstrahlen für die Entwicklung der Physik." *Nwn, 18* (1930), 773-776.

ts   Traubenberg, Heinrich Rausch von, et al. "Canal rays." *Current science, 6:* special number (Sep. 1937), 31p.

dd1.ge   Gerlach, Walther. "Zur Entdeckung des 'Stern-Gerlach-Effektes'." *PB, 25* (1969), 472.

sc   Schütz, Wilhelm. "Persönliche Erinnerungen an die Entdeckung des Stern-Gerlach Effektes." *PB, 25* (1969), 343-345.

de1.ni   Nikitin, Vladimir A., et al. "Collisions of high energy protons with supersonic stream of hydrogen." *Adventures in experimental physics, 2* (1972), 263-274.

pa   Parker, Everette F. "History of the polarized beam." T.ga1.da, 143-157.

ra   Ratner, Lazarus G. "The external proton beams and the proton-proton experiments." T.ga1.da, 90-100.

ro   Roberts, J. B. "The ZGS polarized beam program." T.ga1.da, 158-168.

Plasmas

ea1.al   Allis, W. P. "Development of plasma physics up to the last 10 years." *PTeach, 15* (Dec. 1962), 23-26.

co   Cobine, J. D. "Introduction [on plasma and oscillations]." B.ld3.jl, *5,* xvii-xx.

go   Gottlieb, Melvin B. "[Twenty years of] plasmas." *PT, 21* (May 1968), 46-49.

Philosophy and sociology

fa1.bo   Bopp, Fritz. "Die Entdeckung der Elementarteilchen als Beispiel für die Art naturwissenschaftlicher Wirklichkeitskenntnis." Akademie der Wissenschaften, Munich. Math.- Naturw. Klasse. *Sitzungsberichte,* 1967, 25-41.

br   Bromberg, Joan. "The concept of particle creation before and after quantum mechanics." *HSPS, 7* (1976), 161-191.

de   Destouches, Jean-Louis. "General mathematical physics and schemas, application to the theory of particles." *Dialectica, 19* (1965), 345-348.

dr   Drell, Sidney D. "The Richtmyer memorial lecture—when is a particle?" *AJP, 46* (1978), 597-606.

he   Heisenberg, Werner. "Bohrs Interpretation der Quantentheorie und die Physik der Elementarteilchen." *Fysisk tidsskrift, 60* (1962), 47-53.

pa   Park, David. "The idea of a particle in microphysics." *Dialectica, 19* (1965), 246-258.

tz   Tzara, Christophe. "Quelques réflexions à propos de particules récemment découvertes en physique." *La pensée,* no. 75 (1957), 123-126.

wa   Wallace, William A. "Elementarity and reality in particle physics." *BSPS, 3* (1967), 236-263.

fb1.bl   Blokhintsev, D. I. "Kniga V. I. Lenina *Materializm i empirokrititsizm* i sovremennyye predstavleniya o strukture elementarnykh chastits." *UFN, 69* (1959), 3-12.

ga   Gale, George. "Chew's monadology." *JHI, 35* (1974), 339-348.

ma   Maksakov, V. V., and Ts. S. Sarangov. "Metod analogiy v teorii sub'yadernykh chastits." *IMYeN: Fizika, 10* (1971), 63-76.

ne   Ne'eman, Yuval. "Concrete versus abstract theoretical models." W.aa1.el, 1-26.

wh   Whyte, L. L. "Fundamental physical theory: An interpretation of the present position of the theory of particles." *BJPS, 1* (1951), 303-327.

fc1.ba   *Barboni, Edward. *Functional differentiation and technological specialization in a specialty in high energy physics: The case of weak interactions of elementary particles.* Ph.D. thesis. Cornell Univ. 1976.

cr   Crane, Diana. "An exploratory study of Kuhnian paradigms in theoretical high energy physics." *SSS, 10* (1980), 23-54.

ka   Kaneseki, Yoshinori. "The elementary particle theory group." C.ja1.na, 221-252.

ta   Taketani, Mitsuo. "Methodological approaches in the development of the meson theory of Yukawa in Japan." C.ja1.na, 24-38.

See also: A.db1.su, sv; U.bc1.gb, pk, wh

L. QUANTUM PHYSICS

General

See also: H.c

aa1.ba *Bauer, Wolfram, et al., eds. *75 Jahre Quantentheorie: Festband zum 75. Jahrestag der Entdeckung der Planckschen Energiequanten.* Berlin, 1977. (Akademie der Wissenschaften, Berlin. *Abhandlungen, 1977:7.*)

bp Bopp, Fritz, and Oswald Riedel. *Die physikalische Entwicklung der Quantentheorie.* Stuttgart, 1950.

br Bopp, Fritz, and Arnold Sommerfeld. "Fifty years of quantum theory." *Science, 113* (1951), 85-92.

bt Broglie, Louis de. *The revolution in physics. A non-mathematical survey of quanta.* Tr. Ralph W. Niemeyer. NY, 1953.

cn Condon, Edward Uhler. "Evolution of the quantum theory." *Scientific monthly, 72* (1951), 217-222.

co Condon, Edward Uhler. "Sixty years of quantum physics." *PT, 15* (Oct. 1962), 37-49.

di Dirac, P. A. M. *The development of quantum theory: J. Robert Oppenheimer Memorial Prize acceptance speech.* NY, 1971.

gu Guillemin, Victor. *The story of quantum mechanics.* NY, 1968.

he Heisenberg, Werner. "50 Jahre Quantentheorie." *Nwn, 38* (1951), 49-55.

ho Hoffmann, Banesh *The strange story of the quantum.* NY, 1947.

ht Hund, Friedrich. *Geschichte der Quantentheorie.* Mannheim, 1967; 2nd ed., 1975. (English tr., London, 1974.)

ja Jammer, Max. *The conceptual development of quantum mechanics.* NY, 1966.

la Landau, L. D. "Teoriya kvant ot Maksa Planka do nashikh dney." B.pl1.ig, 94-108.

li Liebfried, Günther. "50 Jahre Quantentheorie." *PB, 6* (1950), 554-555.

pe Peierls, Rudolf. "The development of quantum theory." *CP, 6* (1964/5), 129-139, 192-205.

sc *Schmutzer, Ernst, ed. *75 Jahre Plancksches Wirkungsquantum— 50 Jahre Quantenmechanik.* Halle, 1976. (*Nova acta leopoldina, supplementum,* 8.)

See also: R.be1

ab1.fr Frank, A. M. "Dve tendentsii v razvitii kvantovoy teorii." ICHS, XIII (1971). Section 6. *Actes* (1974), 94-97.

he Heisenberg, Werner. "Development of concepts in the history of quantum theory." *AJP, 43* (1975), 389-394. (Also in A.ad1.me, 264-274.)

hf Hertz, Gustav. "Die Bedeutung der Planckschen Quantentheorie für die experimentelle Physik." *Nwn, 45* (1958), 401-405.

hu Hund, Friedrich. "Paths to quantum theory historically viewed." *PT, 19* (Aug. 1966), 23-29.

hv Hund, Friedrich. "Hätte die Geschichte der Quantentheorie auch anders ablaufen können?" *PB, 31* (1975), 29-35.

ro Rosenfeld, Léon. "Matter and force after fifty years of quantum theory." *BSPS, 21* (1979), 247-265.

we Weisskopf, Victor F. "The impact of quantum theory of modern physics." *Nwn, 60* (1973), 441-446. (Also in A.aa1.nf, 311-331.)

ac1.ga Garber, Elizabeth. "Some reactions to Planck's law, 1900-1914." *SHPS, 7* (1976), 89-126.

he Hermann, Armin. "Zur Frühgeschichte der Quantentheorie." ICHS, XII (1968). *Actes, 5* (1971), 35-39.

hf Hermann, Armin. *The genesis of quantum theory (1899-1913).* Tr. Claude W. Nash. Cambridge, Mass., 1971.

hg Hermann, Armin. *Frühgeschichte der Quantentheorie (1899-1913).* Mosbach in Baden, 1969.

ka Kallmann, H. "Von den Anfängen der Quantentheorie." *PB, 22* (1966), 489-500.

kl Klein, Martin J. "The beginnings of the quantum theory." A.ad1.we, 1-39.

ku Kuhn, Thomas S. *Black-body theory and the quantum discontinuity, 1894-1912.* Oxford and NY, 1978.

po Polak, L. S. "Pervyye shagi kvantovoy fiziki." *VIYeT, 6* (1958), 56-57.

pp Polak, L. S. "Kvantovaya fizika ot M. Planka do N. Bora (1900-1913 gg.)." B.pl1.ig, 143-220.

ro Rosenfeld, Léon. "La première phase de l'évolution de la théorie des quanta." *Osiris, 2* (1936), 149-196. (Also in *BSPS, 21* (1979), 193-234.)

ad1.ar *Arima, Katherine Sachiko. *Model and mechanism in quantum physics: A historical and philosophical analysis of systems represented by harmonic oscillators.* Ph.D. thesis. Univ. of Toronto, 1977.

bl   Bligh, Neville M. *The evolution and development of the quantum theory.* London, 1926.

cs   Cropper, William H. *The quantum physicists and an introduction to their physics.* NY, 1970.

ga   Gamow, George. *Thirty years that shook physics: The story of quantum theory.* Garden City, 1966.

gi   Giustini, Pietro A. *I trent' anni che rivoluzionarono la fisica (1900-1930): Origini e sviluppo della meccanica quantistica.* Rome, 1975.

ha   Haar, Dirk ter. *The old quantum theory.* Oxford, 1967.

he   *Hendry, J. *History of quantum conceptions, 1900-1927.* Ph.D. thesis. Univ. of London. (Imperial College), 1978.

la   Landé, Alfred. *Fortschritte der Quantentheorie.* Dresden and Leipzig, 1922.

pe   Persico, Enrico. "L'evoluzione della teoria dei quanti." *Scientia, 44* (1928), 373-386.

pl   Planck, Max. *Die Entstehung und bisherige Entwicklung der Quantentheorie.* Leipzig, 1920. (For reprintings and translations see B.pl1.ju.)

re   Reiche, Fritz. "Die Quantentheorie, ihre Ursprung und ihre Entwicklung." *Nwn, 6* (1918), 213-230.

rf   Reiche, Fritz. *Die Quantentheorie. Ihre Ursprung und ihre Entwicklung.* Berlin, 1921. (English tr., 2nd ed., London, 1924.)

ru   Rubinowicz, Adalbert. "Ursprung und Entwicklung der älteren Quantentheorie." *Handbuch der Physik.* 2nd ed. Ed. H. Geiger and K. Scheel. Vol. *24:1* (1933), 1-82.

ta   Tagliaferri, Guido. *Lineamenti di storia della fisica moderna, 1. La nascita della fisica quantistica.* Milan, 1977.

ye   Yel'yashevich, M. A. "From the origin of quantum concepts to the establishment of quantum mechanics." *SPU, 20* (1977), 656-682.

See also: C.ua2.se

ae1.jo Jordan, Pascual. "Fünfzig Jahre Quantenmechanik." *PB, 31* (1975), 597-602.

lu   Ludwig, Günther. *Wave mechanics.* Oxford, 1968.

me   Medicus, Heinrich A. "Fifty years of matter waves." *PT, 27* (Feb. 1974), 38-45.

po   Polak, L. S., ed. *50 let kvantovoy mekhaniki.* Moscow, 1979.

pr   Price, William C., et al., eds. *Wave mechanics: The first fifty years.* NY, 1973.

ye   Yel'yashevich, M. A. "Fifty years of quantum mechanics discovery." A.aa1.an, 1-10.

af1.bl   Bloch, Felix. "Heisenberg and the early days of quantum mechanics." *PT, 29* (Dec. 1976), 23-27.

fl   Flügge, S. "Die Entwicklung der Quantentheorie seit der Begründung der Quantenmechanik." *Angewandte Chemie, 61* (1949), 133-140.

he   Heisenberg, Werner. "Udviklingen af Kvantenteoriens principielle grundlag efter 1925." *Fysisk tidsskrift, 33* (1935), 96-101.

jo   Jordan, Pascual. "Die neuere Entwicklung der Quantenphysik." DPG. *Verhandlungen, 24* (1943), 3-12.

pe   Peierls, Rudolf. "The glorious days of physics." *Lepton and hadron structure.* Ed. A. Zichichi. NY, 1975. Pp. 917-931. (Subnuclear series, *12.)*

ro   Rosenfeld, Léon. "Quantum theory in 1929: Recollections from the first Copenhagen conference." *BSPS, 21* (1979), 302-312.

to   Tomonaga, Sin-itiro. "Development of quantum mechanics." A.ad1.me, 404-412.

ag1.fo   Fok, V. A. "Kvantovaya mekhanika." C.vb4.an, 165-176.

ah1.sl   Slater, John C. "Quantum physics in America between the wars." *PT, 21* (Jan. 1968), 43-51.

so   Sopka, Katherine R. *Quantum physics in America, 1920-1935.* NY, 1980. (Ph.D. diss., Harvard Univ., 1976.)

vv   Vleck, John H. Van. "Reminiscences of the first decade of quantum mechanics." *International journal of quantum chemistry, 5* (1971), 3-20.

Planck's discovery

See also: B.pl1

ha1.bl   Blackmore, John T. "Is Planck's 'principle' true?" *BJPS, 29* (1978), 347-349.

do   Dougal, R. C. "The presentation of the Planck radiation formula." *PE, 11* (1976), 438-443.

ne   *Needell, Allan A. *Irreversibility and the failure of classical dynamics: Max Planck's work on the quantum theory 1900-1915.* Ph.D. thesis. Yale Univ., 1980. (*DAI, 41:6,* 2742A.)

wi   Wien, Wilhelm. "Die Entwicklung von Max Plancks Strahlungstheorie." *Nwn, 6* (1918), 203-206.

bb1.de   Debye, Peter. "Die Geburt des Wirkungsquantums." *Zeitschrift für technische Physik, 19* (1938), 121-123.

ei   Einstein, Albert. "The advent of the quantum theory." *Science, 113* (1951), 82-84.

he   Hermann, Armin. "Die Geburt der Quantentheorie, eine wissenschaftshistorische Einführung." L.bb1.pn, 7-20.

pl   Planck, Max. "Zur Geschichte der Auffindung des physikalischen Wirkungsquantum." *Nwn, 31* (1943), 153-159.

pm   Planck, Max. *Die Entstehung der Wirkungsquantum.* Ed. A. Hermann. Stuttgart, 1969. (*Dokumente der Naturwissenschaft,* 11.)

pn   Planck, Max. *Die Quantenhypothese.* Ed. A. Hermann. Stuttgart, 1969. (*Dokumente der Naturwissenschaft,* 12.)

po   Polak, L. S. "Vozniknoveniye kvantovoy fiziki." A.ab1.gr, 323-389.

bc1.br   Broglie, Louis de. "Max Planck und das Wirkungsquantum." *PB, 4* (1948), 138-142.

gr   Grigor'yan, A. T. "Osnovatel' kvantovoy teorii." IIYeT. *Trudy, 22* (1959), 3-12.

he   Hertz, Gustav. "Osnovatel' kvantovoy teorii." B.pl1.ig, 134-142.

hu   Hund, Friedrich. "Max Planck und die Entdeckung des Wirkungsquantums." *FF, 21/23* (1947), 193-195.

kl   Klein, Martin J. "Max Planck and the beginnings of the quantum theory." *AHES, 1* (1962), 459-479.

lo   Lorentz, H. A. "Max Planck und die Quantentheorie." *Nwn, 13* (1925), 1077-1082. (In Russian in *UFN, 6* (1926), 80-92.)

po   Polak, L. S. "M. Plank i vozniknoveniye kvantovoy fiziki." B.pl1.jp, 635-734.

st   Strugalski, Z. "W 75-lecie wielkiego odkrycia Maxa Plancka." *KHNT, 21* (1976), 393-407.

bd1.ba   Baklayev, B. G. "L. Bol'tsman i gipoteza kvantov energii M. Planka." *VIYeT, 4* (1957), 167-169.

be   Bellone, Enrico. "L'energia molecolare e la velocità molecolare come parametri discreti in alcuni scritti di L. Boltzmann in relazione all'ipotesi di M. Planck ed alla teoria della radiazione di S. D. Poisson." *Physis, 10* (1969), 101-112.

kk   Klein, Martin J. "Planck, entropy, and quanta, 1901-1906." *Natural philosopher, 1* (1963), 83-108.

kl Klein, Martin J. "Thermodynamics and quanta in Planck's work." *PT, 19* (Nov. 1966), 23-32.

Early extensions

ca1.fr Franck, James, and Robert Pohl. "Rubens und die Quantentheorie." *Nwn, 10* (1922), 1030-1033.

he Hettner, G. "Die Bedeutung von Rubens Arbeiten für die Plancksche Stahlungsformel." *Nwn, 10* (1922), 1033-1040.

See also: F.aa1.ku

cb1.kk Klein, Martin J. "Einstein's first paper on quanta." *The natural philosopher, 2* (1963), 57-86.

kl Klein, Martin J. "Pervaya rabota Eynshteyna po kvantam." *ES,* 1966, 259-283.

km Klein, Martin J. "Einstein and the development of quantum physics." B.ei4.yf, 133-152.

le Lewis, Henry R. "Einstein's derivation of Planck's radiation law." *AJP, 41* (1973), 38-44.

pa Pais, Abraham. "Einstein and the quantum theory." *Reviews of modern physics, 51* (1979), 863-914.

pb Pauli, Wolfgang. "Einstein's contributions to quantum theory." B.ei4.zs, 149-160. (In German in B.pd3.jb, *1,* 1013-1022; in Russian in *UFN, 86* (1965), 413-420.)

ye Yel'yashevich, M. A. "Einstein's part in the development of quantum mechanics." *SPU, 22* (1979), 555-575.

See also: F.ba1.mi; G.qa1

cc1.mc McCormmach, Russell. "Henri Poincaré and the quantum theory." *Isis, 58* (1967), 37-55.

pl Planck, Max. "Henri Poincaré und die Quantentheorie." *Acta mathematica, 38* (1921), 387-397.

cd1.eh Ehrenfest, Paul. "Adiabatische Transformationen in der Quantentheorie und ihre Behandlung durch Niels Bohr." *Nwn, 11* (1923), 543-550.

gl Glebov, L. A. "K razvitiyu teorii adiabaticheskikh invariantov Erenfesta." *VIYeT, 11* (1961), 57-60.

kl Klein, Martin J. "The origins of Ehrenfest's adiabatic principle." ICHS, X (1962). *Actes, 2* (1964), 801-804.

ce1.he Hermann, Armin. "Die frühe Diskussion zwischen Stark und Sommerfeld über die Quantenhypothese." *Centaurus, 12* (1967), 38-59.

hf   Hermann, Armin. "Sommerfeld's role in the development of early quantum theory." B.so1.ib, 17-20.

ni   Nisio, Sigeko. "The formation of the Sommerfeld quantum theory of 1916." *JSHS, 12* (1973), 39-78.

nj   Nisio, Sigeko. "Sommerfeld's quantum theory of 1911." ICHS, XIV (1974). *Proceedings, 4* (1975), 232-235.

pa   Pauli, Wolfgang. "Sommerfelds Beiträge zur Quantentheorie." *Nwn, 35* (1948), 129-132.

so   Sommerfeld, Arnold. "Über die Anfänge der Quantentheorie von mehreren Freiheitsgraden." *Nwn, 17* (1929), 481-483.

wa   Waerden, B. L. van der. "The history of quantum theory in the light of the successive editions of Sommerfeld's *Atombau und Spektrallinien.*" B.so1.ib, 21-31.

Quantum mechanics

da1.bi   Birtwistle, George. *The new quantum mechanics.* Cambridge, 1928.

bo   Born, Max. "La grande synthèse." B.bw1.ag, 165-170.

fo   Fok, V. A. "Kvantovaya mekhanika." C.vb4.an, 165-176.

he   Heisenberg, Werner. "Die Entwicklung der Quantentheorie, 1918-1928." *Nwn, 17* (1929), 490-496.

ku   Kuznetsov, B. G. "Osnovnyye idei kvantovoy mekhaniki." A.ab1.gr, 390-421.

mi   Miller, Arthur I. "Visualization lost and regained: The genesis of the quantum theory in the period 1913-27." *On aesthetics in science.* Ed. Judith Wechsler. Cambridge, Mass., 1978. Pp. 73-102.

pa   Pauling, Linus. "The birth of quantum mechanics." Linus Pauling Institute of Science and Medicine. *Publications, 1* (1973-76), 469-470. (Reprinted from *Trends in biochemical sciences, 1* (1976).)

to   Tonietti, Tito. "La meccanica quantistica nel contesto matematico." U.aa1.fi, 35-91.

wa   Waerden, B. L. van der, ed. *Sources of quantum mechanics.* Amsterdam, 1967.

wb   Waerden, B. L. van der. "From matrix mechanics and wave mechanics." A.ad1.me, 276-293.

See also: C.ga2.fm, fn, fo, fp, fq | ga6.fo; U.ka1.bc

db1.ca *Cassidy, David Charles. *Werner Heisenberg and the crisis in quantum theory, 1920-1925.* Ph.D. thesis. Purdue University, 1976. (*DAI, 37,* 5313A.)

hu Hund, Friedrich. "Das Korrespondenzprinzip als Leitfaden zur Quantenmechanik von 1925." *PB, 32* (1976), 71-77.

ma MacKinnon, Edward. "Heisenberg, models, and the rise of matrix mechanics." *HSPS, 8* (1977), 137-188.

mb MacKinnon, Edward. "The discovery of a new quantum theory." *BSPS, 60* (1980), 261-272.

me Meyenn, Karl von, and Armin Hermann. "Wolfgang Paulis Beitrag zur Göttinger Quantenmechanik." *PB, 32* (1976), 145-150.

se Serwer, Daniel. "*Unmechanischer Zwang*: Pauli, Heisenberg, and the rejection of the mechanical atom, 1923-1925." *HSPS, 8* (1977), 189-256.

sl Slater, John C. "The development of quantum mechanics in the period 1924-1926." L.ae1.pr, 19-25.

sm *Small, Henry G. *The helium atom in the old quantum theory.* Ph.D. thesis. Univ. of Wisconsin, 1971. (*DAI, 32,* 3184A.)

ta Takabayasi, Takehiko. "Quantum transition, matter wave, and the formation of quantum mechanics." ICHS, XIV (1974). *Proceedings, 4* (1975), 208-222.

dc1.bo Bohr, Niels. "The genesis of quantum mechanics." B.bo1.je, 74-78. (In German in B.hh1.ib, ix-xii.)

bp Born, Max, Werner Heisenberg, and Pascual Jordan. *Zur Begründung der Matrizenmechanik.* Ed. A. Hermann. Stuttgart, 1962. (*Dokumente der Naturwissenschaft,* 2.)

br Briatore, Luigi. "Le origini della meccanica quantistica." *Cultura e scuola, 4:16* (1965), 206-211.

fu Fues, E. "Werner Heisenberg zum 60. Geburtstag: Die Erstgeburt der Quantenmechanik." *PB, 17* (1961), 560-569.

gl Globov, L. A. "Iz istorii sozdaniya kvantovoy mekhaniki." IIYeT. *Trudy, 28* (1959), 421-450.

he Heisenberg, Werner. "Erinnerungen an die Zeit der Entwicklung der Quantenmechanik." B.pd3.if, 40-47.

hu Hund, Friedrich. "Göttingen, Kopenhagen, Leipzig im Rückblick." B.hh1.ib, 1-7.

jo Jordan, Pascual. "Der Weg zur Quanten- und Wellenmechanik." *Angewandte Chemie, 61* (1949), 129-132.

jp   Jordan, Pascual. "Early years of quantum mechanics: Some reminiscences." A.ad1.me, 294-299. (In German in *PB, 31* (1975), 97-103.)

ro   Rosenfeld, Léon. "Early history of quantum mechanics." *Nature, 166* (1950), 883-884.

ru   Rumer, Yu. B. "Vozniknoveniye matrichnoy mekhaniki." L.ae1.po, 3-21.

ye   Yel'yashevich, M. A. "Pyat'desyat let otkrytiya kvantovoy mekhaniki." L.ae1.po, 71-77.

See also: B.jo1.bb

dd1.la   Lanczos, Cornelius. "The Poisson Bracket." B.dk1.is, 169-178.

Wave mechanics

ea1.fr   Frenkel', Ya. I. "Proiskhozhdeniye i razvitiye volnovoy mekhaniki." *Priroda,* 1930:1, 3-31.

ge   Gerber, Johannes. "Geschichte der Wellenmechanik." *AHES, 5* (1969), 349-416.

kr   Kragh, Helge. *On the history of early wave mechanics with special emphasis on the role of relativity.* Roskilde, 1979. (Roskilde. Universitetscenter. IMFUFA. *Tekster,* 23.)

ku   Kubli, Fritz. "A propos du 50e anniversaire de la mécanique ondulatoire." *RHS, 28* (1975), 97-112.

mo   Mott, N. F. "La mécanique ondulatoire. Qu'en avons-nous tiré?" B.bw1.ag, 175-184.

po   Polak, L. S. "Vozniknoveniye volnovogo aspekta kvantovoy mekhaniki." L.ae1.po, 22-70.

ps   Przibram, Karl, ed. *Briefe zur wellenmechanik.* Vienna, 1963.

pt   Przibram, Karl. *Letters on wave mechanics: Schrödinger, Planck, Einstein, Lorentz.* Tr. M. J. Klein. NY, 1967.

sc   Schrödinger, Erwin. *Die Wellenmechanik.* Ed. A. Hermann. Stuttgart, 1965. (*Dokumente der Naturwissenschaft,* 3.)

wi   Wilson, William. "The origin and nature of wave mechanics." *Science progress, 32* (Oct. 1937), 209-227.

See also: R.be1.le

eb1.br   Broglie, Louis de. "The beginnings of wave mechanics." L.ae1.pr, 12-18.

de   Destouches, Jean-Louis. "La genèse de la mécanique ondulatoire et les idées de Louis de Broglie." ICHS, XIII (1971). Colloquium preprint, 2 p.

ku   *Kubli, Fritz. *Louis de Broglie und die Entdeckung der Materiewelle.* Ph.D. thesis. ETH, Zurich, 1970

kv   Kubli, Fritz. "Louis de Broglie und die Entdeckung der Materiewellen." *AHES, 7* (1970), 26-68.

ma   MacKinnon, Edward. "De Broglie's thesis: A critical retrospective." *AJP, 44* (1976), 1047-1055.

mb   MacKinnon, Edward. "Reply to Richard Schlegel." *AJP, 45* (1977), 872-873.

sc   Schlegel, Richard. "Louis de Broglie's thesis." *AJP, 45* (1977), 871-872.

sh   Shushurin, S. F. "Sozdaniye osnov volnovoy mekhaniki L. de Broylem." L.ae1.po, 78-81.

to   Tonnelat, M. A. *Louis de Broglie et la mécanique ondulatoire.* Paris, 1966.

See also: B.bw1.bc

ec1.ha   Hanle, Paul A. "The Schrödinger-Einstein correspondence and the sources of wave mechanics." *AJP, 47* (1979), 644-648.

kr   Kragh, Helge. "Af Schrödingerligningens historie." *Fysisk tidsskrift, 73* (1975), 145-160.

po   Polak, L. S. "Optiko-mekhanicheskaya analogiya Shredingera." *Arkhiv istorii nauki i tekhniki, 8* (1936), 29-73.

ra   Raman, V. V., and Paul Forman. "Why was it Schrödinger who developed de Broglie's ideas?" *HSPS, 1* (1969), 291-314.

we   *Wessels, Linda. *Schroedinger's interpretations of wave mechanics.* Ph.D. thesis. Univ. of Indiana, 1975. (*DAI, 36,* 7481A.)

wf   Wessels, Linda. "Schrödinger's route to wave mechanics." *SHPS, 10* (1979), 311-340.

wg   *Wessels, Linda. "The intellectual sources of Schrödinger's interpretations." W.cb1.su.

ed1.ca   Carazza, B., and G. P. Guidetti. "La nascità dell'equazione di Klein Gordon." *AHES, 22* (1980), 373-383.

kr   Krajcik, R. A., and Michael M. Nieto. "Historical development of the Bhabha first-order relativistic wave equations for arbitrary spin." *AJP, 45* (1977), 818-822.

vv   Vleck, John H. Van. "Central fields in two vis-à-vis three dimensions: An historical divertissement." L.ae1.pr, 26-38.

Dirac equation *see* E.bh.1

Quantum statistics

fa1.bl   Blokhintsev, D. I. "Classical statistical physics and quantum mechanics." *SPU, 20* (1977), 683-690.

ca   Caldirola, P. "Teoria della misurazione e teoremi ergodici nella meccanica quantistica." *Scientia, 99* (1964), 219-231.

ko   Konovalov, V. M., and V. A. Dubchak. "O razvitii kvantovoy statistiki." *VIYeT, 10* (1960), 35-41.

ne   Nernst, Walther. "Quantentheorie und neuer Wärmesatz." *Nwn, 6* (1918), 206-207.

fb1.cl   Clusius, K. "Spez. Wärme und Wärmeinheit des Festkörpers." C.ga1.cl, 47-58.

di   Dickel, G. "Spez. Wärme von Gasen." C.ga1.cl, 43-46.

ei   Einstein, Albert, et al. *Zur spezifischen Wärme.* Ed. A. Hermann. Stuttgart, 1965. (*Dokumente der Naturwissenschaft,* 8.)

eu   Eucken, Arnold. "Rückblicke auf die Entwicklung unserer Kenntnis über die Molwärme der Gase." *Nwn, 31* (1943), 314-322.

he   Hermann, Armin. "Wissenschaftshistorische Einleitung." L.fb1.ei, 7-19.

kk   Klein, Martin J. "Einstein, specific heats, and the early quantum theory." *Science, 148* (1965), 173-180.

kl   Klein, Martin J. "Eynshteyn, udel'naya teployemkost' i rannaya kvantovaya teoriya." *ES,* 1974, 156-178.

ku   Kuhn, Thomas S. "The quantum theory of specific heats: A problem in professional recognition." ICHS, XIV (1974). *Proceedings, 1* (1974), 170-182.

fc1.be   *Bergia, Silvio, P. Luigi, and M. Zamboni. "Zero-point energy, Planck's law, and the history of stochastic electrodynamics. Einstein and Hopf's paper of 1910." Fondation Louis de Broglie. *Annales,* 1979.

bf   *Bergia, Silvio, P. Luigi, and M. Zamboni. "Zero-point energy, Planck's law, and Stern's paper of 1913." Fondation Louis de Broglie. *Annales,* 1979.

fd1.kl   Klein, Martin J. "Ehrenfest's contributions to the development of quantum statistics." Akademie van Wetenschappen, Amsterdam. *Proceedings, 62:B* (1959), 41-62.

fe1.ez   Ezawa, Hiroshi. "Einstein's contribution to statistical mechanics." B.ei4.ya, 69-88.

ha   Hanle, Paul A. "The coming of age of Erwin Schrödinger: His quantum statistics of ideal gases." *AHES, 17* (1977), 165-192.

tg   Theimer, O., and Budh Ram. "The beginning of quantum statistics." *AJP, 44* (1976), 1056-1057.

th   Theimer, O., and Budh Ram. "Bose's second paper: Conflict with Einstein." *AJP, 45* (1977), 242-246.

ff1.be   Belloni, Lanfranco. "A note on Fermi's route to Fermi-Dirac statistics." *Scientia, 113* (1978), 421-430.

pe   Peierls, Rudolf E. "Fermi-Dirac statistics." B.dk1.is, 117-127.

Quantum field theory

ha1.dy   Dyson, Freeman J. "Old and new fashions in field theory." *PT, 18* (Jun. 1965), 21-24.

ha   Haag, Rudolf. "Die Rolle der Quantenfeldtheorie in der Physik der letzten Jahrzehnte." *PB, 26* (1970), 529-535.

jo   Jost, Res. "Foundation of quantum field theory." B.dk1.is, 61-77.

lo   Low, Francis E. "Fifty years of quantum field theory." *Lepton and hadron structure.* Ed. A. Zichichi. NY, 1975. Pp. 935-938. (Subnuclear series, *12.*)

no   Novozhikov, Yu. V. "Presdisloviye." V. A. Fok. *Raboty po kvantovoy teorii polya.* Leningrad, 1957.

pe   Peierls, Rudolf E. "The development of quantum field theory." A.ad1.me, 370-378.

ro   Rosenfeld, Léon. "Some concluding remarks and reminiscences." *Fundamental problems in elementary particle physics.* NY, 1968. Pp. 231-234. (Instituts de Solvay.... Conseil de Physique. *Rapports et discussions,* 14.)

we   Weinberg, Stephen. "The search for unity: Notes for a history of quantum field theory." *Daedalus, 106* (1977), 17-35.

wf   Wentzel, Gregor. "Quantum theory of fields (until 1947)." B.pd3.if, 48-77. (Also in A.ad1.me, 380-403.)

See also: A.db1.su

hb1.ro   Rosenfeld, Léon. "Kvantenteori og feltfysik." *Fysisk tidsskrift, 33* (1935), 109-121.

ul   Uller, K. "Der Sturz der reinen und relativistischen Feldphysik durch die Wellenkinematik." *Zeitschrift für die gesamte Naturwissenschaft, 3* (1937/8), 399-414.

vi   Vizgin, V. P. "Yedinyye teorii polya i kvantovaya mekhanika." L.ae1.po, 82-94.

hc1.fe   Feynman, Richard P. "The development of the space-time view
            of quantum electrodynamics." *PT, 19* (Aug. 1966), 31-44. (Also
            in *Science, 153* (1966), 699-708.)

    ko   Kofink, W. "Nobelpreis 1965—Quantenelektrodynamik." *PB, 22*
            (1966), 201-209.

    ro   Rosenfeld, Léon. "On quantum electrodynamics." B.bo1.ip, 70-
            95. (*BSPS, 21* (1979), 413-441.)

    sc   Schwinger, Julian. "A report on quantum electrodynamics."
            A.ad1.me, 413-426.

    to   Tomonaga, Sin-itiro. "Development of quantum electrodynam-
            ics." *PT, 19* (Sep. 1966), 25-32.

hd1.br   Bromberg, Joan. "Dirac's quantum electrodynamics and the
            wave-particle equivalence." A.ad1.we, 147-157.

    he   Heisenberg, Werner. "Indefinite metric in state space." B.dk1.is,
            129-136.

    ta   *Talbot, Theodore R. *Bohr and Rosenfeld's foundations for quan-
            tum electrodynamics.* Ph.D. thesis. Columbia Univ., 1979. (*DAI,
            39*, 4985A.)

he1.sa   Salam, Abdus. "Progress in renormalization theory since 1949."
            A.ad1.me, 430-445.

hf1.ci   Cini, Marcello. "The history and ideology of dispersion relations.
            The pattern of internal and external factors in a paradigmatic
            shift." *Fundamenta scientiae, 1* (1980), 157-172.

hg1.la   Lamb, Willis E. "Feinstruktur des Wasserstoffatoms." *PB, 12*
            (1956), 249-256.

    lb   Lamb, Willis E. "Some history of the hydrogen fine structure
            experiment." B.ra3.im, 82-86.

Interpretation

ia1.bn   Born, Max. "The interpretation of quantum mechanics." *BJPS, 4*
            (1953), 95-106.

    bo   Born, Max. "Die statistische Deutung der Quantenmechanik."
            PB, 11 (1955), 193-202.

    bp   Born, Max. *Zur statistischen Deutung der Quantentheorie.* Ed. A.
            Hermann. Stuttgart, 1962. (*Dokumente der Naturwissenschaft, 1.*)

    br   Broglie, Louis de. "L'interprétation de la mécanique ondultoire."
            La pensée, no. 91 (1960), 16-45.

    bs   Broglie, Louis de. "The reinterpretation of wave mechanics."
            Foundations of physics, 1 (1970), 5-15.

bt   Broglie, Louis de. "K istorii vozniknoveniya i interpretatsii vol-novoy mekhaniki." *VIYeT, 47-48* (1974), 3-8.

df   Dewitt, Bryce S., and R. Neill Graham. "Resource letter IQM-1 on the interpretaion of quantum mechanics." *AJP, 39* (1971), 724-738.

fo   Fok, V. A. "Über die Deutung der Quantenmechanik." B.pl1.ik, 177-195. (Also in *P. N. Fedoseyev et al., eds., *Filosofskiye problemy sovremennogo yestestvoznaniya.* Moscow, 1959.)

he   Heisenberg, Werner. "The development of the interpretation of the quantum theory." B.bo1.ip, 12-29. (In German in *PB, 12* (1956), 289-304.)

hf   Heisenberg, Werner, and Niels Bohr. *Die Kopenhagener Deutung der Quantentheorie.* Ed. A. Hermann. Stuttgart, 1965. (*Dokumente der Naturwissenschaft,* 4.)

hg   Heisenberg, Werner. "Quantum theory and its interpretation." B.bo1.ar, 94-108.

ja   Jammer, Max. *The philosophy of quantum mechanics: The interpretations of quantum mechanics in historical perspective.* NY, 1974.

mb   *MacKinnon, Edward. "The rise and fall of the Schrödinger interpretation." W.cb1.su.

me   Mehra, Jagdish. "The quantum principle: Its interpretation and epistemology." *Dialectica, 27* (1973), 75-157.

pa   Pauli, Wolfgang. "Wahrscheinlichkeit und Physik." *Dialectica, 8* (1954), 112-118.

ib1.fo   Fok, V. A. "La physique quantique et les idéalisations classiques." *Dialectica, 19* (1965), 223-245.

kv   *Kuznetsov, I. V. *Printsip sootvetstviya v sovremennoy fizike i yego filosofskoye znacheniye.* Moscow and Leningrad, 1948.

me   Meyer-Abich, Klaus M. *Korrespondenz, Individualität, und Komplementarität: Eine Studie zur Geistesgeschichte der Quantentheorie in den Beiträgen Niels Bohrs.* Wiesbaden, 1965.

no   Nowak, Izabella, and Leszek Nowak. "W sprawie zasady korespondencji w fizyce." *KHNT, 18* (1973), 33-43.

ic1.br   Broglie, Louis de. "Le dualisme des ondes et des corpusules dans l'oeuvre de Albert Einstein." AS. *Notices et discours, 3* (1955), 599-633.

ha   Hanson, Norwood R. "Waves, particles, and Newton's 'fits'." *JHI, 21* (1960), 370-391.

he   Hendry, John. "The development of attitudes to the wave-particle duality of light and quantum theory, 1900-1920." *Annals of science, 37* (1980), 59-79.

kl   Klein, Martin J. "Einstein and the wave-particle duality." *The natural philosopher, 3* (1964), 1-49.

km   Klein, Martin J. "Eynshteyn i dualizm volny-chastitsy." *ES, 1966,* 212-258.

ro   Rosenfeld, Léon. "The wave-particle dilemma." A.ad1.me, 251-261. (Also in *BSPS, 21* (1979), 688-703.)

See also: F.fa1.ku

id1.bq   Bradley, R. D. "Determinism or indeterminism in microphysics." *BJPS, 13* (1962), 193-215.

br   Broglie, Louis de. "La physique quantique restera-t-elle indéterministe?" *RHS, 5* (1952), 289-311. (In German in *PB, 9* (1953), 488-497, 541-548.)

bs   Brush, Stephen G. "Irreversibility and indeterminism: Fourier to Heisenberg." *JHI, 37* (1976), 603-630.

ha   Hanle, Paul A. "Indeterminacy before Heisenberg: The case of Franz Exner and Erwin Schrödinger." *HSPS, 10* (1979), 225-269.

he   Heisenberg, Werner. "Der unanschauliche Quantensprung." *PB, 2* (1946), 4-6.

ho   Hoering, Walter. "Indeterminism in classical physics." *BJPS, 20* (1969), 247-255.

ja   Jauch, J. M. "Determinism in classical and quantal physics." *Dialectica, 27* (1973), 13-26.

la   Landé, Alfred. "Quantum indeterminacy, a consequence of cause-effect continuity." *Dialectica, 8* (1954), 199-209.

ie1.he   Heisenberg, Werner. "Remarks on the origin of the relations of uncertainty." L.ie1.pr, 3-6. (In German in *PB, 31* (1975), 193-196.)

ku   Kudryavtsev, P. S. "Aus der Geschichte der Unschärferelation." *NTM, 2:6* (1965), 20-22.

pr   Price, William C., and Seymour S. Chissick. *The uncertainty principle and foundations of quantum mechanics: A fifty years' survey.* NY, 1977.

if1.al   Alekseyev, I. S. "Razvitiye kontseptsii dopolnitel'nosti." L.ae1.po, 116-125.

fe   Feyerabend, Paul K. "Niels Bohr's interpretation of the quantum theory." W.aa1.fe, 371-390.

ho   Holton, Gerald. "The roots of complementarity." *Eranos Jahrbuch, 30* (1970), 45-90. (Also published in *Daedalus, 99* (1970), 1015-1055, and A.aa1.ho, 382-422.)

hp   *Howard, Don A. *Complementarity and ontology: Niels Bohr and the problem of scientific realism in quantum physics.* Ph.D. thesis. Boston Univ., 1979. (*DAI, 39,* 7379A.)

pa   *Pawlak, Adam. "Dzieje zasady komplementarności Nielsa H. D. Bohra." *Studia i materiały z dziejów nauki polskiej, ser. C, 23* (1979), 131-145.

ro   Rosenfeld, Léon. "Niels Bohr in the thirties. Consolidation and extension of the conception of complementarity." B.bo1.ar, 94-108.

See also: W

ig1.bl Blokhintsev, D. I. "Kritika filosofskikh vozzreniy tak nazy-vayemoy 'kopengagenskoy shkoly' v fizike." W.ac1.an, *1,* 358-395.

bo   Bohm, D. "On Bohr's views concerning the quantum theory." W.aa1.ba, 33-40.

bu   Bub, Jeffrey. "Hidden variables and the Copenhagen interpretation: A reconciliation." *BJPS, 19* (1968), 185-210.

ha   Hanson, Norwood R. "Copenhagen interpretation of quantum theory." *AJP, 27* (1959), 1-15.

pu   *Puligandla, Ramakrishna. *An examination of the Copenhagen interpretation of quantum theory.* Ph.D. thesis. Rice Univ., 1966. (*DAI, 27,* 1405A.)

su   Suvorov, S. G. "Problema 'fizicheskoy real'nosti' v Kopengagen-skoy shkole." *UFN, 62:2* (1957), 141-158.

we   Weizsäcker, C. F. von. "The Copenhagen interpretation." W.aa1.ba, 25-32.

See also: U.bc1.ha

ih1.bo Bohr, Niels "Discussion with Einstein on epistemological prob-lems in atomic physics." B.ei4.zs, 201-241. (Reprinted in Bohr, *Atomic physics and human knowledge.* NY, 1958. Pp. 32-66.)

bu   Bunge, Mario. "The Einstein-Bohr debate over quantum mechanics: Who was right about what?" B.ei4.yn, 204-219.

er   Erlichson, Herman. "The Einstein-Podolsky-Rosen paradox." *PS, 39* (1972), 83-85.

ja   Jammer, Max. "The history of the Einstein-Bohr controversy." ICHS, XIII (1971). *Actes, 6* (1974), 105-111.

kl   Klein, Martin J. "The first phase of the Bohr-Einstein dialogue." *HSPS, 2* (1970), 1-39.

km   Klein, Martin J. "Pervaya faza dialoga Bora i Eynshteyna." *ES,* 1974, 115-155.

my   Mykishev, G. Ya. "O 'paradokse' Eynshteyna, Podol'skogo i Rosena." A.ab1.vo, 429-438.

re   Reisler, Donald L. "The epistemological bases of Einstein's, Podolsky's and Rosen's objection to quantum theory." *AJP, 39* (1971), 821-831.

ro   Rosen, Nathan. "Can quantum-mechanical description of physical reality be considered complete?" B.ei4.ya, 57-68.

sh   Sharp, David H. "The Einstein-Podolsky-Rosen paradox re-examined." *PS, 28* (1961), 225-233.

ii1.ho   Hove, Léon van. "Von Neumann's contributions to quantum theory." American Mathematical Society. *Bulletin, 64:3:2* (1958), 95-99.

sn   Sneed, Joseph D. "Von Neumann's argument for the projection postulate." *PS, 33* (1966), 22-39.

ij1.be   Bergman, H. "The controversy concerning the law of causality in contemporary physics." *BSPS, 13* (1974), 395-462.

bo   Bohm, David. *Causality and chance in modern physics.* NY, 1957.

br   Briatore, Luigi. "Causalità e caso in meccanica quantistica." *Cultura e scuola, 5:18* (1966), 260-268.

ro   Rosenfeld, Léon. "Statistical causality in atomic theory." W.aa1.el, 469-480.

te   Terletskiy, Ya. P. "Le problème de la causalité en mécanique quantique." *La pensée,* no. 64 (1955), 14-20.

vi   Vigier, Jean-Pierre. "Remarques sur l'article du Professeur Terletski." *La pensée,* no. 64 (1955), 21-26.

we   Weinschenk, C. "Die moderne Physik und das Gesetz der Kausalität." *ZGN, 4* (1938/9), 422-428.

See also: W.c

O. SOLID STATE

General studies

aa1.ba Bardeen, John. "Reminiscences of early days in solid state physics." O.aa1.rs, 77-83.

be Bethe, Hans A. "Recollections of solid state theory, 1926-33." O.aa1.rs, 49-51.

br Braun, E. "The contribution of the Göttingen school to solid state physics: 1920-40." O.aa1.rs, 104-111.

ca Casimir, H. B. G. "Development of solid-state physics." A.ad1.we, 158-169.

fr Frölich, H. "Recollections of the development of solid state physics." O.aa1.rs, 102-103.

gu Guinier, A. "Solid state physics." A.aa1.ta, 107-116.

mo Mott, Nevill F. "Introduction." O.aa1.rs, 3-7.

mp Mott, Nevill F. "Memories of early days in solid state physics." O.aa1.rs, 56-66.

pe Peierls, Rudolf E. "Quantum theory of solids." B.pd3.if, 140-160.

pf Peierls, Rudolf E. "Recollections of early solid state physics." O.aa1.rs, 28-38.

rs RS. "The beginnings of solid state physics. A symposium...organized by Sir Nevill Mott." RS. *Proceedings. 371A*, (1980), 1-177.

sm Smoluchowski, R. "Random comments on the early days of solid state physics." O.aa1.rs, 100-101.

wi Wilson, Alan H. "Solid state physics 1925-33: Opportunities missed and opportunities seized." O.aa1.rs, 39-48.

zh Zhdanov, G. S. "Otdeleniye fiziki tverdogo tela." *IMYeN: Fizika, 6* (1968), 138-153.

zı Ziman, John M. "[Twenty years of] solid state." *PT, 21* (May 1968), 53-58.

ab1.ar Arkharov, V. I. "Razvitiye strukturnoy fiziki tverdogo tela na Urale." *Uchenyye Urala v bor'be za tekhnicheskiy progress.* Sverdlovsk, 1959. Pp. 95-125.

ho Hoddeson, Lillian Hartmann. "The roots of solid-state research at Bell Labs." *PT, 30* (Mar. 1977), 23-30.

kt   Kuznetsov, V. D. "Fizika tverdogo tela v Sovetskom Soyuze za 30 let." *Doklady, chitannyye na konferentsii "30 let sovetskoy nauki."* Tomsk, 1948. Pp. 91-132.

ku   *Kuznetsov, V. D. "25 let raboty otdela fiziki tverdogo tela Sibirskogo fiziko-tekhnicheskogo instituta." Tomsk. Sibirskiy fiziko-tekhnicheskiy institut. *Trudy,* no. 34 (1955), 3-21.

we   Welker, H. "Impact of Sommerfeld's work on solid-state research and technology." B.so1.ib, 32-43.

ac1.ak   AN. *Nekotoryye problemy prochnosti tverdogo tela: Sbornik statey, posvyashchennyy vos'midesyatiletiyu akademika AN SSSR N. N. Davidenkova.* Leningrad, 1959.

ar   Arkharov, V. I. "Dostizheniya i perspektivy issledovatel'skoy raboty nad problemami diffuzii veshchestva v tverdykh telakh." AN. Ural. filial. Institut fiziki metallov. *Trudy, 12* (1949), 94-120.

du   Dubchak, V. A. "Puti stanovleniya zonnoy teorii tverdykh tel i vklad sovetskikh uchenykh v yeye razvitiye." ICHS, XIII (1971). Section 6, *Actes* (1974), 146-148.

ko   Konobeyevskiy, S. T. "Rol' russkikh issledovateley v razvitii ucheniya o tverdom tele (Fedorov, Kurnakov, Chernov)." *Rol' russkoy nauki v razvitii mirovoy nauki i kul'tury.* Moscow. University. *Uchenyye zapiski, 92* (1946), 46-57.

zh   Zhdanov, G. S., et al. "Raboty po strukturnoy fizike tverdogo tela." *IMYeN: Fizika, 6* (1968), 154-157.

See also: C.vu2.ge

Properties of solids

ba1.bl   Blackman, Moses. "Heat capacity of crystals and the vibrational spectrum." RS. *Proceedings. 371A,* 116-119.

ch   Chaston, J. C. "Sir Willian Crookes. Investigations on indium crucibles and the volatility of the platinum metals." *Platinum metals review, 13* (1969), 68-72.

gr   Grube, G. "Die Forschungen G. Tammans über die Konstitution der Legierungen." *Zeitschrift für Metallkunde, 23* (1931), 137-138.

ka   Kawamiya, Nobuo. "Kotaro Honda: Founder of the science of metals in Japan." *JSHS, 15* (1976), 145-158.

ko   Körber, Fr. "Kristallisieren und Schmelzen." *Zeitschrift für Metallkunde, 23* (1931), 134-137.

ks   Köster, Werner. "Arbeiten von G. Tammann über die chemischen Eigenschaften von Metallen und Legierungen." *Zeitschrift für Metallkunde, 23* (1931), 142-146.

ma   Masing, G. "Tammanns Untersuchungen über Kaltreckung, Verfestigung und Rekristallisation." *Zeitschrift für Metallkunde, 23* (1931), 139-142.

pa   Parker, Earl R. "California's metallurgists prove the concept of dislocation." A.ad1.un, 113-123.

po   Portevin, A., ed. "La méthode d'analyse thermique et les travaux sur les alliages au laboratoire du Professeur Tallmann." *Revue de métallurgie, 4* (1907), 951-982; *5* (1908), 535-560; *6* (1909), 797-813.

ru   Rumpf, H. "Zur Entwicklungsgeschichte der Physik der Brucherscheinungen: A. Smekal zum Gedächtnis." *Chemie-Ingenieur-Technik, 31* (1959), 697-705.

sm   Smith, Cyril Stanley. "The prehistory of solid-state physics." *PT, 18* (1965), 18-22, 24-26, 29-30.

za   Zambonini, Ferruccio. "La mineralogia in Italia negli ultimi cinquant'anni." SIPS. *Atti, 5* (1911), 375-413.

bb1.io   Ioffe, A. F. "I. V. Kurchatov—issledovatel' dielektrikov." *UFN, 73* (1961), 611-614.

sk   Skanavi, G. I. "Fizika dielektrikov v Sovetskom Soyuze." *UFN, 33* (1947), 165-193.

so   Sokolov, V. A. "K istorii issledovaniy fizicheskikh svoystv dielektrikov." *VIYeT, 15* (1963), 96-101.

st   Starosel'skaya-Nikitina, O. A. "Raboty Polya Lanzhevena v oblasti p'yezoelektrichestva i ul'trazvuka." IIYeT. *Trudy, 19* (1957), 170-196.

vo   Vorob'yev, A. A. "Razvitiye predstavleniy ob udarnoy ionizatsii v tverdykh dielektrikakh i poluprovodnikakh." *VIYeT, 14* (1963), 37-48.

bc1.an   Ansel'm, A. I. "K voprosu o sostoyanii teorii poluprovodnikov." *UFN, 60* (1956), 179-189.

bo   Bottom, Virgil E. "Invention of the solid-state amplifier." *PT, 17* (Feb. 1964), 24-26.

bp   Brattain, Walter H. "Development of concepts in semiconductor research." *AJP, 24* (1956), 421-425.

bq   Brattain, Walter H. "Genesis of the transistor." *PTeach, 6* (1968), 109-114.

br   Brattain, Walter H. "Discovery of the transistor effect." *Adventures in experimental physics, 5* (1976), 3-13.

da   Davydov, B. I. "Sovetskiye issledovaniya po elektronnym poluprovodnikam." *UFN, 33* (1947), 157-164.

di   Dimarova, E. N. "K istorii izucheniya poluprovodnikovykh svoystv zakisi medi." IIYeT. *Trudy, 43* (1961), 165-181.

he   *Hempstead, C. *Semi-conductors, 1833-1919: An historical study of selenium and some related materials.* Ph.D. thesis. Univ. of Durham, 1977.

ih   *Ioffe, A. F. "Poluprovodniki v sovremennoy fizike i tekhnike." *Electrichestvo,* 1939:6, 5-10. (Also in *Priroda,* 1939:4, 13-19.)

ii   Ioffe, A. F. "Poluprovodniki v fizike i tekhnike." AN. *Vestnik,* 1940:10, 12-27. (Also in *Sovetskaya nauka, 11* (1940), 90-104.)

ik   Ioffe, A. F. "Poluprovodniki v sovremennoy fizike." *Priroda,* 1952:12, 16-24.

im   Ioffe, A. F. *Poluprovodniki i ikh primeneniye.* Moscow and Leningrad, 1956.

in   Ioffe, A. F. [History of semiconductors]. *Fizika poluprovodnikov.* Moscow, 1957. Pp. 3-10.

io   Ioffe, A. F. "Issledovaniye poluprovodnikov v Sovetskom Soyuze." *UFN, 63* (1957), 527-532.

ka   Kaiser, Walter. "Karl Bädekers Beitrag zur Halbleiter-forschung." *Centaurus, 22* (1978), 187-200.

ko   Konovalov, V. M., and V. A. Dubchak. "Ocherki po istorii fiziki poluprovodnikov." IIYeT. *Trudy, 34* (1960), 73-102.

ma   MacDonald, Stuart, and Ernest Braun. "The transistor and attitude to change." *AJP, 45* (1977), 1061-1065.

re   Renard, G. "La découverte et le perfectionnement des transistors." *RHS, 16* (1963), 323-358.

Electron theory of metals

da1.al Allen, Philip B., and William H. Butler. "Electrical conduction in metals." *PT, 31* (Dec. 1978), 44-49.

an   *Anon. "25 let metallovedeniya i fiziki metallov." *Problemy metallovedeniya i fiziki metallov, 5* (1958), 7-9.

bl   Bloch, Felix. "Memories of electrons in crystals." O.aa1.rs, 24-27.

du   Dukov, V. M. "Razvitiye klassicheskoy teorii metallicheskoy provodimosti." *VIYeT, 13* (1962), 64-69.

fr   Frenkel', Ya. I. "Nouveaux développements de la théorie électronique des metaux." *Scientia, 46* (1929), 1-12, 87-96.

he   Herring, William Conyers. "Recollections." O.aa1.rs, 67-76.

ho   Hoddeson, Lillian H., and G. Baym. "The development of the quantum mechanical electron theory of metals: 1900-28." O.aa1.rs, 8-23.

io   Ioffe, A. F. "Nasha rabota v oblasti izucheniya mekhanicheskikh i elektricheskikh svoystv tverdykh tel." C.vb4.an, 206-228.

ro   Rorschach, H. E., Jr. "The contributions of Felix Bloch and William V. Houston to the electron theory of metals." *AJP, 38* (1970), 897-904.

sh   Shur, Ya. S. "Rabota Instituta fiziki metallov UFAN v oblasti fiziki magnitnykh materialov." AN. Ural. filial. Institut fiziki metallov. *Trudy, 12* (1949), 62-73.

vo   Vonsovskiy, S. V. "Raboty Ya. I. Frenkelya po elektronnoy teorii tverdykh tel." B.fr1.jd, *2,* 21-27.

db1.ca   Coulson, C. A. "Interatomic forces: Maxwell to Schrödinger." *Nature, 195* (1962), 744-749.

de   Deryagin, B. V. "Idey P. N. Lebedeva o prirode molekulyarnykh sil." *UFN, 91* (1967), 341-346.

il   Il'in, B. V. "Problema molekulyarnykh sil v rabotakh P. N. Lebedeva i B. B. Golitsyna." *Rol' russkoy nauki v razvitii mirovoy nauki i kul'tury.* Moscow. University. *Uchenyye zapiski, 92* (1946), 63-68.

Crystallography

See also: G.ma1

fa1.an   Ansheles, O. M. "Ye S. Fedorov i sovremennaya kristallografiya." IIYeT. *Trudy, 10* (1956), 13-18.

bn   Bokiy, G. B., and I. I. Shafranovskiy. "Vyvod 230 prostranstvennykh grupp simmetrii." *Nauchnoye nasledstvo, 2* (1951), 297-313.

bo   Bokiy, G. B. "Ye. S. Fedorov i kristallokhimiya." IIYeT. *Trudy, 10* (1956), 19-27.

ko   Kopelevich, Y. Kh. "Communications between E. S. Fyodorov and British crystallographers." C.va4.an, 134-157.

pa   Päsler, Max. "Einiges aus der Geschichte der Kristallkunde: Zur 50sten Wiederkehr des Todestages von Woldemar Voigt." *PB, 25* (1969), 542-546.

sh   Shafranovskiy, I. I. "P'yer Kyuri—kristallograf." IIYeT. *Trudy, 19* (1957), 84-94.

su   Shubnikov, A. V. "O rabotakh P'yera Kyuri v oblasti simmetrii." *UFN, 59* (1956), 591-602.

wh   Whyte, Lancelot Law. "Pierre Curie's principle of one-way process." *Studium generale, 23* (1970), 525-532.

ye   Yeliseyev, N. A. "K shestidesyatiletiyu universal'nogo metoda Ye. S. Fedorova." IIYeT. *Trudy, 10* (1956), 66-84.

fb1.bo   Bokiy, G. B., and I. I. Shafranovskiy. "Russkiye kristallografy." IIYeT. *Trudy, 1* (1947), 81-120.

bp   Bragg, William Lawrence. "Forty years of crystal physics." A.aq1.ne, 77-89.

bq   Bragg, William Lawrence. *The history of x-ray analysis.* London, 1943.

br   Bragg, William Lawrence. "The history of x-ray analysis." *PTeach, 3* (1965), 295-300.

et   Ewald, P. P. "Historisches und Systematisches zum Gebrauch des 'Reziproken Gitters' in der Kristallstrukturlehre." *Zeitschrift für Kristallographie, 93* (1936), 396-398.

eu   Ewald, P. P. "Some personal experiences in the international coordination of crystal diffractometry." *PT, 6* (Dec. 1953), 12-17.

ev   Ewald, P. P. "William Henry Bragg and the new crystallography." *Nature, 195* (1962), 320-325.

ib   Ibers, James A. "[Twenty years of] structural crystallography." *PT, 21* (May 1968), 58-59.

la   Laue, Max von. "Die Entwicklung unserer Kenntnis von den Kristallstrukturen." *Angewandte Chemie, 62* (1950), 335.

te   Terpstra, P. "Jaeger als kristallograaf." *Chemisch weekblad, 31* (1934), 201-203.

fc1.bi   Birkhoff, Garrett. "Von Neumann and lattice theory." American Mathematical Society. *Bulletin, 64:3:2* (1958), 50-56.

bo   Born, Max. "Reminiscences of my work on the dynamics of crystal lattices." O.fc1.wb, 1-7.

br   Brandmüller, J., and R. Claus. "Raman und seine Theorie der Gitterschwingungen." *PB, 27* (1971), 295-301.

bu   Brush, Stephen G. "History of the Lenz-Ising model." *Reviews of modern physics, 39* (1967), 883-893.

de   Debye, Peter. "The early days of lattice dynamics." O.fc1.wb, 9-13.

gr   Gross, E. F. "Vazhnaya problema sovremennoy fiziki: Eksitony v kristallicheskoy reshetke." AN. *Vestnik*, 1958:10, 11-19.

wa   Waller, I. "Memories of my early work on lattice dynamics and x-ray diffraction." O.aa1.rs, 120-124.

wb   Wallis, R. F., ed. *Lattice dynamics*. Oxford, 1965.

fd1.bu   Burgers, W. G. "How my brother and I became interested in dislocations (With an addendum by J. M. Burgers)." O.aa1.rs, 125-130.

co   Cottrell, Alan H. "Dislocations in metals: The Birmingham school, 1945-55." O.aa1.rs, 144-148.

cr   Crussard, Charles. "Theory of dislocations: Pre-war nucleation, post-war crystallization and present growth." O.aa1.rs, 139-143.

fr   Frank, F. Charles. "The Frank-Read source." O.aa1.rs, 136-138.

hi   Hirsch, Peter B. "Direct observations of dislocations by transmission electron microscopy: Recollections of the period 1946-56." O.aa1.rs, 160-164.

jo   Jones, Harry. "Notes on work at the University of Bristol, 1930-7." O.aa1.rs, 52-55.

mi   Mitchell, J. W. "Dislocations in silver halides." O.aa1.rs, 149-159.

na   Nabarro, F. R. N. "Recollections of the early days of dislocation physics." O.aa1.rs, 131-135.

se   Seeger, Alfred Karl. "Some recollections of the radiation damage work of the 1950s." O.aa1.rs, 165-172.

sf   Seeger, Alfred Karl. "Early work on imperfections in crystals, and forerunners of dislocation theory." O.aa1.rs, 173-177.

Low temperature

ha1.ba   Bauer, Edmond, et al. *Les phénomènes cryomagnétiques*. Paris, 1948. (Hommage national à Paul Langevin et Jean Perrin.)

br   Brandt, N. B. "Fizika nizkikh temperatur." C.vb1.pr, *2*, 117-155.

cl   Clerke, Agnes M. "Low-temperature research at the Royal Institution." Royal Institution. *Proceedings, 16* (1901), 699-718.

ha   Hardin, W. L. *The rise and development of the liquefaction of gases*. NY, 1899.

ku   *Kurzyniec, E. "O pierszeństwie skroplenia wodoru w stanie dynamicznym." Polska Akademia Umiejętności. Komisja Historii Medycyny. *Prace, 3* (1953), 303-315.

lo   Lohmann, Hans-Dieter. "Über das historische Wechselverhältnis zwischen Produktion und kältephysikalischer Forschung. (Ein Beitrag zur Geschichte der Entwicklung der Wissenschaft zur Produktivkraft)." *NTM, 9:2* (1972), 1-22.

me   Mendelssohn, Kurt. *The quest for absolute zero.* London, 1966.

pi   Picard, Emile. "Les basses températures et l'oeuvre de M. Kamerlingh-Onnes." AS. *Mémoires, 63* (1939), 24 p.

sh   Shal'nikov, A. I. "Kafedra fiziki nizkikh temperatur." *IMYeN: Fizika, 6* (1968), 172-175.

wo   Wojtaszek, Zdzislaw. "The first years of cryogenics in the light of Olszewski's correspondence." ICHS, XIII (1971). *Actes, 7* (1974), 135-142.

hb1.ab   Abrikosov, A. A. "Problema sverkhprovodimosti." AN. *Vestnik,* 1958:4, 30-36.

an   Andronikashvili, E. L., and K. A. Tumanov. "Razvitiye v Sovetskom Soyuze ucheniya o sverkhprovodimosti." *UFN, 33* (1947), 469-532.

ba   Bardeen, John. "Development of concepts in superconductivity." *PT, 16* (Jan. 1963), 19-28.

bb   *Bardeen, John. "History of superconductivity research." Behram Kursunoglu and Arnold Perlmutter, eds. *Impact of basic research on technology.* NY, 1973. Pp. 15-59.

ca   Casimir, H. B. G. "Superconductivity." A.ad1.we, 170-181.

gi   Giaever, Ivar. "Discovery of electron tunneling into superconductors." *Adventures in experimental physics, 4* (1974), 133-142.

gm   Ginsberg, D. M. "Resource letter Scy-1 on superconductivity." *AJP, 32* (1964), 85-89. Also in *Superconductivity: Selected reprints.* NY, 1964. Pp. 1-5.

gz   *Ginzburg, V. L. "K istorii otkrytiya i izucheniya sverkhprovodimosti." *VIYeT,* 1980:1, 44-60.

la   Langenberg, Donald. "Observation of Josephson effect and measurement of e/h." *Adventures in experimental physics, 3* (1973), 68-75.

lc   Laue, Max von. "Geschichtliches über Supraleitung." *FF, 25* (1949), 278-280. (And B.lf6.jl, *3,* 58-100.)

le   Leprince, F. "1913-1973: Soixante ans de solénoides supraconducteurs." *Revue des questions scientifiques, 145* (1974), 233-254, 537-564.

sh   Shapiro, Sidney. "Observation of Josephson effect and measurement of e/h." *Adventures in experimental physics, 3* (1973), 55-61.

tu   *Tumanov, K. A., and Yu. V. Sharvin. *Sverkhprovodimost': O rabotakh laureata Stalinskoy premii A. I. Shal'nikova.* Moscow, 1949.

hc1.ca   Casimir, H. B. G. "Superconductivity and superfluidity." A.ad1.me, 481-498.

li   Lifshits, Ye. M. "Istoriya otkrytiya i ob'yasneniya sverkhtekuchesti." *Priroda*, 1968:1, 73-79.

lj   Lifshits, Ye. M. "Raboty P. L. Kapitsy i L. D. Landau po sverkhtekuchest' geliya." B.la8.il, 5-16.

vi   Vinen, W. F. "Discovery of quantized circulation in superfluids." *Adventures in experimental physics, 1* (1972), 22-23.

P. GEO-, ASTRO-, AND BIOPHYSICS

Geophysics

aa1.ba Bazilevich, V. V., and K. S. Shifrin. "Raboty Ya. I. Frenkelya po geofizike." B.fr1.jd, *2*, 515-519.

bu Büdel, Julius. "Die Erforschung der Erde im XX. Jahrhundert." A.aj1.sc, 260-278.

ca Caloi, P. "La geofisica [e la sismologia] nell' ultimo cinquantennio." *Scientia, 92* (1957), 95-102, 133-140.

fe Fekete, Jenö. "A földmágnességre vonatkozó vizsgálatokról." *Matematikai és physikai lapok, 27* (1918), 206-229.

iz *Izvekov, B. I. "Raboty A. A. Fridmana v oblasti geofiziki." *Zhurnal geofiziki i meteorologii, 1-2* (1926), 5-18.

ki Kimura, Tōsaku. "Nagaoka's geophysical studies and their role in his physical researches." *JSHS, 11* (1972), 91-98.

ma Magnitskiy, V. A., et al. "Fizika zemli." C.vb1.pr, *2*, 385-396.

me Medunin, A. Ye. "Geofizika na rubezhe XIX-XX vv." C.vb1.pr, *1*, 386-400.

sm *Smirnov, V. I. "Vydayushchiysya geofizik i matematik." *Zhurnal priroda, 11* (1963), 93-96.

st Stefani, Carlo de. "Fisica terrestre e geologia nell'ultimo cinquantennio, specialmente in Italia." SIPS. *Atti, 5* (1911), 155-215.

sv Stoneley, R. "Geophysics." A.aa1.ha, 106-122.

See also: B.bj1.af

Seismology and gravometrics

ba1.ag *Agamennone, Giovanni. "Inventore del sismografo a pendi." *Meteorologia pratica, 7* (1926).

al Alessandri, Camillo, and Giovanni Agamennone. "La sismologia a Roma e nel Lazio." Rome. Istituto di Studi Romani. *Le scienze* (1933), 327-350.

by Byerly, Perry. "The cradle of seismology in America." A.ad1.un, 42-52.

go Gorshkov, G. P. "Rol' B. B. Golitsyna v razvitii seysmologii." *Rol' russkoy nauki v razvitii mirovoy nauki i kul'tury.* Moscow. University. *Uchenyye zapiski, 92* (1946), 58-62.

kr   *Kravets, T. P., and P. M. Nikiforov. "Fizika i seysmologiya." *Akademiya nauk SSSR za desyat' let, 1917-1927.* Leningrad, 1927. Pp. 11-16.

ky   *Krylov, A. N. "O rabotakh kn. B. B. Golitsyna po seysmologii." *UFN, 1* (1918), 101-107.

me   Medunin, A. Ye. "Izucheniye v Rossii deformatsii zemli vyzvannykh lunno-solnechnym prityazheniyem (1892-1920)." IIYeT. *Trudy, 43* (1961), 151-164.

zy   Zyukov, P. I. "O pervykh rabotakh B. B. Golitsyna po seysmometrii." *VIYeT, 15* (1963), 101-103.

bg1.ba   Barton, Donald C. "Gravity measurements with the Eötvös torsion balance." National Research Council. *Bulletin, 78* (1931), 167-190.

ge   German, S. "Was ist 'Normal-Null'?" *PB, 14* (1958), 62-66.

ku   Kuzivanov, V. A., and M. U. Sagitov. "Razvitiye idey R. Ztvesha v SSSR v oblasti gravimetrii." Budapest. University. *Annales: sectio geologica, 7* (1964), 53-58.

me   Medunin, A. Ye. "Absolyutnyye opredeleniya sily tyazhesti metodom nesvobodnogo padeniya tel i s pomoshch'yu dlinnykh mayatnikov v Rossii (1892-1911)." *IMYeN: Fizika, 1* (1960), 195-200.

pe   Pekár, Dezsö. "Die geophysikalischen Messungen des Barons Roland v. Eötvös." *Nwn, 7* (1919), 149-159.

re   Reina, V. "Le misure gravimetriche italiane." SIPS. *Atti, 5* (1911), 355-374.

wo   Worzel, John Lamar. *Pendulum gravity measurements at sea 1936-1959.* NY, 1965. (Lamont Geological Observatory. *Contributions,* no. 807.)

Earth magnetism

ca1.ar   *Artemenko, D. T. "Raboty Umova po zemnomu magnetizmu." C.vb1.vo, 105-109.

fa   Farr, C. Coleridge, and Henry F. Skey. "The magnetic survey of New Zealand." *Terrestrial magnetism and atmospheric electricity, 37* (1932), 213-215.

gu   Gulo, D. D. "Raboty N. A. Umova po zemnomu magnetizmu." *IMYeN: Fizika, 10* (1971), 130-149.

ha   Haáz, I. B. "Roland Eötvös and paleomagnetism." Budapest. University. *Annales: sectio geologica, 7* (1964), 59-70.

he   Heck, N. H. "The magnetic survey and observatory-net of the United States." *Terrestrial magnetism and atmospheric electricity, 37* (1932), 219.

ja   Jackson, W. E. W. "The development of the magnetic survey of Canada." *Terrestrial magnetism and atmospheric electricity, 37* (1932), 215-216.

kr   Krzemin'ski, W. "Rola Stanislawa Kalinowskiego w badaniach magnetyzmu ziemskiego w Polsce." *KHNT, 21* (1976), 679-686.

ni   Nippolt, A. "Louis Agricola Bauer and terrestrial magnetism." *Terrestrial magnetism and atmospheric electricity, 37* (1932), 205-208.

ro   Romañá, A. "El estudio de las corrientes telúricas." *Scientia, 97* (1962), 150-156.

sv   Sverdrup, H. V. "Cooperative work of the Department of Terrestrial Magnetism under the directorship of Louis A. Bauer." *Terrestrial magnetism and atmospheric electricity, 37* (1932), 211-212.

Dating techniques

da1.ba   Badash, Lawrence. "Rutherford, Boltwood, and the age of the earth: The origin of radioactive dating techniques." APS. *Proceedings, 112* (1968), 157-169.

il   Ilyina, T. D. "New trends in the sciences of earth studies in connection with the radioactivity concept." ICHS, XIV (1974). *Proceedings, 3* (1975), 97-100.

See also: I.sa1.fa, za

Allied geological sciences

fa1.ba   Bascom, Willard. *A hole at the bottom of the sea. The story of the mohole project.* NY, 1961.

ko   Kopelevich, Y. Kh. "Geologists of Britain write to A. P. Karpinsky." C.va4.an, 158-176.

le   Levin, A. G. "Sozdatel' teorii proiskhozhdeniya Zemli." B.si9.ak, 64-84.

li   *Lipskiy, Yu. N. "Metod Umova i yego primeniye k issledovaniyu poverkhnostey planet." Moscow. University. Astronomicheskiy Institut. *Soobshcheniya,* no. 96 (1954), 23-35.

fb1.al   Aliverti, G. "I progressi della meteorologia nell'ultimo quantennio." *Scientia, 92* (1957), 191-196.

br   Brunt, D. "A hundred years of meteorology (1851-1951)." *Advancement of science, 8* (1951), 114-124.

hu   Hughes, S. "The Copernican legacy for meteorology." A.aa1.nf, 332-353.

ki   *Kibel', I. A. "Raboty akademika N. Ye. Kochina po dinamicheskoy meteorologii." AN. *Izvestiya,* ser. geogr. i geofiz., *9* (1945), 415-422.

ti   Tikhomirov, Ye. I. "Idei B'yerknesa i ikh rol' v sovremennoy meteorologii." *Klimat i pogoda,* 1927:5-6, 129-141.

fc1.ap   Appleton, Edward. "Sir Joseph Larmor and the ionosphere." Royal Irish Academy. *Proceedings, 61* (1961), 55-66.

bl   Blanchard, Duncan C. "Bentley and Lenard: Pioneers in cloud physics." *American scientist, 60* (1972), 746-749.

by   Byers, Horace. "Introduction [on cloud nucleation]." B.ld3.jl, *11,* xvii-xxii.

ch   Chapman, Sydney. "On the influence of the Fourth Baron Rayleigh on air glow and auroral research." B.st3.ji, 46-53.

gi   Gillmor, C. Stewart, and Douglas Gran. "Research in ionospheric physics." ICHS, XIII (1971). *Actes, 6* (1974), 160-164.

he   Hergesill, Hugo. "Die Physik des Erdkörpers und seiner Atmosphäre." C.ga1.ab, 329-342.

kh   Khrgian, A. A. "Fiziki atmosfery." C.vb1.pr, *2,* 429-443.

kv   Khvostikov, I. A. "Infrakrasnoye izlucheniye nochnogo neva i dissotsiatsiya azota v ionosfere." *UFN, 33* (1947), 570-600.

sc   Schaefer, V. J. "Introduction [on atmospheric phenomena]." B.ld3.jl, *10,* xvii-xxvi.

st   Scott, William T. "The personal character of the discovery of mechanisms in cloud physics." *BSPS, 60* (1980), 273-289.

fd1.bu   Buynitskiy, V. Kh. "Vydayushchiysya puteshestvennik i polyarnyy issledovatel'." B.si9.ak, 95-105.

ka   Kalashnikov, A. G. "O. Yu. Shmidt i geograficheskaya nauka." B.si9.ak, 115-126.

ri   Ricchievi, Giuseppe. "Il contributo degli italiani alla conoscenza della terra ed agli studi geografici nell'ultimo cinquantennio." SIPS. *Atti, 5* (1911), 325-354.

sh   Shcherbakov, D. I. "Na kryshe mira." B.si9.ak, 106-114.

Astrophysics

ha1.ch   Chandrasekhar, S. "The black hole in astrophysics: The origin of the concept and its role." *CP, 15* (1974), 1-24.

ci   Chandrasekhar, S. "A chapter in the astrophysicists' view of the universe." A.ad1.me, 34-44.

fr   Fracastoro, M. G. "Progressi dell' astrofisica nell'ultimo cinquantennio." *Scientia,* 91 (1956), 336-341.

go   Gorbatskiy, V. G. "Fizika zvezd." *Razvitiye astronomii v SSSR.* Moscow, 1967. Pp. 196-212.

he   Herrmann, Dieter B. "Zur Frühentwicklung der Astrophysik in Deutschland und in den USA." *NTM, 10:1* (1973), 38-44.

hf   Herrmann, Dieter B., and J. Hamel. "Zur Frühentwicklung der Astrophysik: Das internationale Forscherkollektiv 1865-1899." *NTM, 12:1* (1975), 25-30.

hu   Hufbauer, Karl. "Astronomers take up the stellar-energy problem." *HSPS, 11* (1981), 277-303.

sh   Shayn, G. A. "Lebedev i astrofizika." IIYeT. *Trudy, 28* (1959), 66-78.

st   Strong, John. "On the astrophysical work of W. W. Coblentz." *Applied optics, 2* (1963), 1101-1102.

tr   Treder, Hans-Jürgen. "Karl Schwarzschild und die Wechselbeziehungen zwischen Astronomie und Physik." *Sterne, 50* (1974), 13-19.

un   Unsöld, Albrecht. "Quantentheorie und Astronomie." *PB, 4* (1948), 188-189.

wo   Woltjer, Lodewyk. "[Twenty years of] astrophysics." *PT, 21* (May 1968), 63-66.

See also: C.gp1

hb1.de   *DeVorkin, D. H. *An astronomical symbiosis: Stellar evolution and spectral classification, 1860-1910.* Ph.D. thesis. Leicester Univ., 1978.

df   DeVorkin, D. H. "Steps toward the Hertzsprung-Russell diagram." *PT, 31* (Mar. 1978), 32-39.

ni   Nielsen, Axel V. "Contributions to the history of the Hertzsprung-Russell diagram." *Centaurus, 9* (1964), 219-253.

si   Sitterly, Bancroft W. "Changing interpretations of the Hertzsprung-Russell diagram, 1910-1940: A historical note." *Vistas in astronomy, 12* (1970), 357-366.

hd1.bd   Berendzen, Richard E., and Richard C. Hart. "Adriaan van Maanen's influence on the island universe theory." *Journal for the history of astronomy, 4* (1973), 46-56, 73-98.

be   Berendzen, Richard E., Richard C. Hart, and Daniel Seely. *Man discovers the galaxies.* NY, 1976.

go   Goldsmith, Donald W. "Edwin Hubble and the universe outside our galaxy." A.aa1.nf, 63-94.

ha   Hart, Richard C., and Richard Berendzen. "Hubble's classification of non-galactic nebulae, 1922-1926." *Journal for the history of astronomy, 2* (1971), 109-119.

he   Hetherington, Norriss. "The Shapley-Curtis debate." Astronomical Society of the Pacific. *Leaflet,* no. 490 (Apr. 1970), 8 p.

hi   Hirsh, Richard F. "The riddle of the gaseous nebulae." *Isis, 70* (1979), 197-212.

ho   Hoskin, Michael A. "The 'great debate': What really happened." *Journal for the history of astronomy, 7* (1976), 169-182.

hp   Hoskin, Michael A. "Ritchey, Curtis and the discovery of novae in spiral nebulae." *Journal for the history of astronomy, 7* (1976), 47-53.

sm   Smith, R. W. "The origins of the velocity-distance relation." *Journal for the history of astronomy, 10* (1979), 133-165.

hf1.co   Cocke, W. J., M. J. Disney, and D. J. Taylor. "The discovery of the first optical pulsar at Steward Observatory." *Adventures in experimental physics, 1* (1972), 7-10.

gi   Ginzburg, V. L. "N. D. Papaleksi i radioastronomiya." AN. *Izvestiya,* ser. fiz., *12* (1948), 34-37.

he   Hey, J. S. *The evolution of radio astronomy.* NY, 1973.

iv   Ivankov, A. G., and V. A. Dovgar'. "K voprosu o vozniknovenii radiospektroskopii." ICHS, XIII (1971). Section 6, *Actes* (1974), 126-129.

la   Landon, Jagdish Narain. "Radio astronomy." *Science and culture, 22* (1956), 4-11.

See also: C.bj1

Astronomy

ia1.am   Ambartsumyan, V. A. "Perspektivy razvitiya astronomii." *Problemy evolyutsii vselennoy.* Ed. Ambartsumyan. Yerevan, 1968. Pp. 232-235.

an   Ambartsumyan, V. A., and V. V. Kazyutyuskiy. "Revolyutsia v sovremmoy astronomii." *Priroda,* 1970:4, 16-26.

as   **Astronomiya v SSSR za 40 let, 1917-1957.* Moscow, 1960. (English trn V. Willis et al. St. Louis, 1964.)

ed   Eddington, A. S. "Forty years of astronomy." A.aa1.ne, 117-142.

st   Struve, Otto, and Velta Zebergs. *Astronomy of the 20th century.* NY, 1962.

ib1.bo   Born, Max. "Astronomical recollections." *Vistas in astronomy, 1* (1955), 41-44.

de   DeVorkin, David H. "Michelson and the problem of stellar diameters." *Journal for the history of astronomy, 6* (1975), 1-18.

id   Idel'son, N. I. "Raboty A. N. Krylova po astronomii." IIYeT. *Trudy, 15* (1956), 24-31. (Also in B.kt1.as, 47-52.)

ki   Kiro, S. N. "O neopublikovannoy rukopisi A. M. Lyapunova 'Compléments au mémoire: Recherches dans la théorie de la figure des corps célestes.'" D.ab1.ii, 67-85.

sz   Szafraniec, Rose. "Henry Norris Russell's contribution to the study of eclipsing variables." *Vistas in astronomy, 12* (1970), 7-20.

ye   Yefremov, Yu. N. "Fizicheskiye peremennyye zvezdy." *Razvitiye astronomii v SSSR.* Moscow, 1967. Pp. 173-189.

ic1.se   Seeley, D., and Richard Berendzen. "The development of research in interstellar absorption, c. 1900-1930." *Journal for the history of astronomy, 3* (1972), 52-64, 75-86.

st   Struve, Otto. "Trumpler discovers interstellar absorption." A.ad1.un, 28-41.

id1.ch   Chandrasekhar, Subrahmanyan. "Brownian motion, dynamical friction and stellar dynamics." *Dialectica, 3* (1949), 114-126.

he   Hetherington, Norriss. "The simultaneous 'discovery' of internal motions in spiral nebulae." *Journal for the history of astronomy, 4* (1975), 115-125.

ie1.ab   Abetti, Giorgio. "Histoire et problémes de la physique solaire." *Ciel et terre, 70* (1954), 161-174.

ac   Abetti, Giorgio. "Thirty years of solar work at Arcetri." *Vistas in astronomy, 1* (1955), 624-630.

ca   Cameron, A. G. W. "[Twenty years' study of] the solar system." *PT, 21* (May 1968), 61-63.

fe   Fesenkov, V. G. "Problema kosmogonii solnechnoy sistemy." *Priroda,* 1940:4, 7-15.

ho   Hoyt, William Graves. *Planets X and Pluto.* Tucson, 1980.

ku   Kuiper, Gerard P. *The sun.* Chicago. 1953.

st   Stenflo, Jan Olof. "Hale's attempts to determine the sun's general magnetic field." *Solar physics, 14* (1970), 263-273.

tu   Turkevich, Anthony. "First chemical analysis of the lunar surface, Rutherford scattering experiments on the moon." *Adventures in experimental physics, 4* (1974), 5-23.

Cosmology

ka1.be   Becker, Friedrich. "Die Erforschung des Weltalls im XX. Jahrhundert." A.aj1.sc, 207-223.

br   Brunner, William. *Pioniere der Weltallforschung.* Zurich, 1951.

bu   Burbidge, G., and M. Burbidge. "Modern riddles of cosmology." A.aa1.nf, 116-139.

ha   Haan, G. I. "Problemy i tendentsii relyativistskoy kosmologii." *ES,* 1966, 339-375.

he   Hetherington, Norriss S. "Observational cosmology in the twentieth century." ICHS, XV (1977). *Proceedings,* (1978), 567-575.

id   Idlis, G. M. "Printsip neopredelennosti i sovremennaya kosmologiya." L.ae1.po, 101-115.

ki   Kilmister, C. W. "Relativity and cosmology." A.aa1.ha, 14-42.

mc   McCrea, W. H. "Cosmology to-day. Inaugural lecture of the Chaire Georges Lemaître." *Revue des questions scientifiques, 31* (1970), 223-241.

mi   Mikulak, Maxim W. "Soviet philosophic-cosmological thought." *PS, 25* (1958), 35-50.

sc   Sciama, Dennis W. "The universe as a whole." A.ad1.me, 7-33.

sd   Sciama, Dennis W. "Cosmology." B.ci4.ya, 17-24.

wh   Whitrow, G. J. "Theoretical cosmology in the 20th century." ICHS, XV (1977). *Proceedings,* 1978, 576-593.

See also: B.ei6.gi, ns

kc1.br   Brush, Stephen G. "A geologist among astronomers: The rise and fall of the Chamberlin-Moulton cosmogony." *Journal for the history of astronomy, 9* (1978), 1-41, 77-104.

gn   Godart, O. "Les contributions de Lemaître au développement de la cosmologie actuelle." *Revue des questions scientifiques, 31* (1970), 221-222.

go   Godart, O., and M. Heller. "Einstein-Lemaître: Rencontre d'idées." *Revue des questions scientifiques, 150* (1979), 23-43.

gu   Gunter, P. A. Y. "Bergson's theory of matter and modern cosmology." *JHI, 32* (1971), 525-542.

he   Hetherington, Norriss. "Edwin Hubble and a relativistic, expanding model of the universe." Astronomical Society of the Pacific. *Leaflet,* no. 509 (Nov. 1971), 8 p.

sc   Schlegel, Richard. "Steady-state theory at Chicago." *AJP, 26* (1958), 601-604.

ze   Zel'dovich, Ya. B. "Teoriya rasshiryayushcheysya vselennoy, sozdannaya A. A. Fridmanom." *UFN, 80* (1963), 357-390.

Biophysics

ma1.ba   Baker, D. James, Jr. "Resource letter PB-1." *Physics and biology: Selected reprints.* NY, 1966. Pp. 1-10.

fl   Fleming, Donald. "Emigré physicists and the biological revolution." U.gb2.fl, 152-189.

mu   Mullins, Nicholas C. "The development of a scientific speciality: The phage group and the origins of molecular biology." *Minerva, 10* (1972), 51-82.

or   *Orbeli, L. A., ed. *Trudy soveshchaniya, posvyashchennogo 50-letiyu perekisnoy teorii medlennogo okisleniya i roli A. N. Bakha v razvitii otechestvennoy biokhimii.* Moscow, 1946.

pa   Pauling, Linus. "Fifty years of progress in structural chemistry and molecular biology." A.aa1.ho, 281-307.

wa   Watson, James D. *The double helix.* NY, 1968.

mb1.de   Deryagin, B. V. "O rabotakh P. P. Lazareva v oblasti biologicheskoy fiziki." *UFN, 32* (1947), 81-88. (Also in B.lgb.jl, *1,* 41-50; *Issledovaniya po adaptatsii,* ed. P. P. Lazarev (Moscow, 1947), 249-257.)

so   Sobotka, Harry. "Introduction [on protein structures]." B.ld3.jl, *7,* xvii-xlii.

st   Stone, Robert S. "Health protection activities of the plutonium project." APS. *Proceedings, 90* (1946), 11-19.

yo   Yoxen, E. J. "Where does Schroedinger's 'What is life?' belong in the history of molecular biology?" *History of science, 17* (1979), 17-52.

mc1.ko   Kohler, Robert E., Jr. "Rudolf Schoenheimer, isotopic tracers, and biochemistry in the 1930s." *HSPS, 8* (1977), 257-298.

lf   Levi, Hilde. "Isotoper og biologi på Bohrs Institut." *Fysisk tidsskrift, 60* (1962), 76-84.

lg   *Levi, Hilde.* "The development of the tracer method, 1935-1945." *International journal of applied radiation and isotopes, 16* (1965), 511-513.

See also: G.ia3.te | oa1.br, la

R. PHYSICAL CHEMISTRY

General

aa1.ar Armstrong, F. F., ed. *Chemistry in the twentieth century.* London, 1924.

be Bent, H. A. "Chemistry." A.aa1.ha, 123-138.

fi Findlay, Alexander. *A hundred years of chemistry.* London, 1948.

ha Haber, Fritz. "Chemie." C.ga1.ab, 343-350.

ih Ihde, Aaron J. *The development of modern chemistry.* NY, 1964.

pa Partington, J. R. *A history of chemistry.* Vol. 4, London, 1964.

sa Sachtleben, Rudolf. "Chemie im XX. Jahrhundert." A.aj1.sc, 103-128.

ti Tilden, William A., and S. Glasstone. *Chemical discovery and invention in the twentieth century.* NY, 1936.

we Weeks, Mary Elvira. *Discovery of the elements.* Easton, 1968.

See also: H.ce1.hf

ab1.bl *Bloch, Maks Abramovich. *Biograficheskiy spravochnik: Vydayush-chiyesya khimiki XIX i XX stoletiy.* Leningrad, 1929.

bu Bugge, G., ed. *Das Buch der grossen Chemiker.* 2 vols. Weinheim, 1929-30.

fa Farber, Eduard, ed. *Great chemists.* NY, 1961.

ha Harrow, Benjamin. *Eminent chemists of our time.* NY, 1920.

ti Tilden, William A. *Famous chemists: The men and their work.* London, 1921.

ac1.du Dubpernell, George, and J. H. Westbrook, eds. *Selected topics in the history of electrochemistry.* Princeton, N.J., 1978. (Electrochemical Society. *Proceedings, 78:6.*)

hu Hückel, Walter. "Die Entwicklung der Hypothese vom nichtklassischen Ion. Eine historisch-kritische Studie." Akademie der Wissenschaften, Heidelberg. Math.-Natur. Klasse. *Sitzungsberichte,* 1967/8, 291-341.

hw Hund, Friedrich. "Wie haben die Physiker die Chemie verstanden?" *PB, 29* (1973), 310-314.

la *The law of mass action: A centenary volume 1864-1964.* Oslo, 1964.

pr   Predvoditelev, A. S. "O problemakh, svyazannykh s prevras-hcheniyem veshchestva v gomogennykh i geterogennykh sistemakh." C.vb1.pr, *2*, 155-177.

ps   Predvoditelev, A. S. "K probleme zhidkogo sostoyaniya ve-shchestva." C.vb1.pr, *2*, 177-197.

ad1.ge   Gerasimova, Ya. I. *Razvitiye fizicheskoy khimi v SSSR.* Moscow, 1967.

so   Solov'yev, Yu. I. "Iz istorii fizicheskoy khimii." IIYeT. *Trudy, 35* (1961), 3-38.

sp   Solov'yev, Yu. I. *Ocherki po istorii fizicheskoy khimii.* Moscow, 1964.

sq   Sominskiy, M. S. "K istorii fizicheskogo otdeleniya Russkogo fiziko-khimicheskogo obshchestva." *Zhurnal tekhnicheskoy fiziki, 23* (1953), 553-574.

ae1.pa   Pauling, Linus. "Fifty years of physical chemistry in the Califor-nia Institute of Technology." *Annual review of physical chemistry, 16* (1965), 1-15.

se   *Servos, John W. *Physical chemistry in America, 1890-1933: Ori-gins, growth, and definition.* Ph.D. thesis. Johns Hopkins Univ., 1979. (*DAI, 40,* 426A.)

af1.ko   Kozawa, A., T. Takamura, and T. Ishikawa. "History of Japanese electrochemistry." R.ac1.du, 478-488.

ti   Tiselius, Arne, and Stig Claesson. "The Svedberg and fifty years of physical chemistry in Sweden." *Annual review of physical chemis-try, 18* (1967), 1-8.

ag1.er   Erbring, H. "Kolloidchemie." C.ga1.cl, 113-150.

he   Hevesy, Georg von, and Otto Stern. "Fritz Habers Arbeiten auf dem Gebiete der physikalischen Chemie und Elektrochemie." *Nwn, 16* (1928), 1062-1068.

ku   Kuznetsov, V. I. "O protivorechiyakh v otsenke roli V. Ostval'da v istorii kataliza." *VIYeT, 10* (1960), 79-85.

lu   Lund, Einar Wang, and Odd Hassel. "Guldberg and Waage and the law of mass action." R.ac1.la, 37-46.

sa   Sadron, Charles. "Jean Perrin et la chimie physique." *RHS, 24* (1971), 107-115.

sc   Schumacher, H. J. "Kinetik photochemischer Gasreaktionen." C.ga1.cl, 65-84.

th   Thiele, Joachim. "Franz Walds Kritik der theoretischen Chemie (nach Arbeiten aus den Jahren 1902-1906 und unveröffentlichten Briefen)." *Annals of science, 30* (1973), 417-433.

vo   Volkmann, H. "Flüssigkeitsstrukturen." C.ga1.cl, 151-182.

See also: B.ow1.bm | pl1.bs

ah1.ab   Adam, N. K. "Introduction [on evaporation, condensation, adsorption]." B.ld3.jl, *9*, xvii-xxi.

di   Dickel, G. "Adsorption und Desorption." C.ga1.cl, 199-204.

ve   Veil, Suzanne. "L'oeuvre de Langmuir dans le domaine de l'adsorption." *Revue scientifique, 76* (1938), 271-276.

vo   Volkmann, H. "Oberflächen- und Grenzflächen-spannung." C.ga1.cl, 205-226.

zi   Zisman, W. A. "Introduction [on mono-molecular films]." B.ld3.jl, *9*, 205-228.

at1.ew   Ewing, Galen W. "A letter from Heyrovsky." *JCE, 45* (1968), 154-155.

ko   Koelsch, W. "Physikalisch-chemische Messtechnik." C.ga1.cl, 227-256.

ro   Roth, W. A. "Methodik kalorimetrischer Messungen." C.ga1.cl, 59-64.

st   Stuart, H. A. "Physikalische Methoden zur Bestimmung der Form von Makromoleculen, insbesondere von Fadenmoleculen." C.ga1.cl, 183-198.

Molecular physics

ba1.br   Bresler, S. E. "Raboty Ya. I. Frenkelya po molekulyarnoy fizike." B.fr1.jd, *2*, 231-238.

kn   Knyazheskiy, P. N. "O nekotorykh rabotakh uchenykh MGU po molekulyarnoy fizike v pervyye gody posle revolyutsii." A.ab1.vo, 350-354.

pr   Predvoditelev, A. S. "Kafedra molekulyarnoy fiziki." *IMYeN: Fizika, 6* (1968), 39-85.

See also: G.ca2.ma

bb1.co   Condon, E. U. "The Franck-Condon principle and related topics." *AJP, 15* (1947), 365-374.

fr   Franck, James. "Fritz Habers Arbeiten über Anregung und Ionisierung durch chemische Reaktionen." *Nwn, 16* (1928), 1075-1078.

bc1.ba   Bantz, David A. "The structure of discovery: Evolution of structural accounts of chemical bonding." *BSPS, 60* (1980), 291-329.

bw   Bykov, G. V. "Ob evolyutsii kolichestvennykh teoriy elektronnogo stroyeniya organicheskikh molekul." IIYeT. *Trudy, 28* (1959), 477-521.

bx   Bykov, G. V. "Historical sketch of the electron theories of organic chemistry." *Chymia, 10* (1965), 199-253.

pa   Palmer, W. G. *A history of the concept of valency to 1930.* Cambridge, 1965.

ru   Russell, Colin Archibald. *The history of valency.* Leicester, 1971.

st   *Stranges, Anthony Nicholas. *The electron theory of valence: 1900-1925.* Ph.D. thesis. Univ. of Wisconsin, 1977. (*DAI, 38,* 3688A.)

bd1.kn   Kohler, Robert E., Jr. "The origin of G. N. Lewis's theory of the shared pair bond." *HSPS, 3* (1971), 343-376.

ko   Kohler, Robert E., Jr. "Irving Langmuir and the 'octet' theory of valence." *HSPS, 4* (1974), 39-87.

kp   Kohler, Robert E., Jr. "The Lewis-Langmuir theory of valence and the chemical community, 1920-1928." *HSPS, 6* (1975), 431-468.

kq   Kohler, Robert E., Jr. "G. N. Lewis's views on bond theory." *BJHS, 8* (1975), 233-239.

be1.da   Davies, D. W. "Quantum-mechanical theories of the electronic structure of molecules." *Scientia, 98* (1963), 127-136.

fo   Förster, Th. "Quantentheorie und chemische Bindung." *Angewandte Chemie, 61* (1949), 144-149.

gr   Groth, W. "Quantentheorie und Photochemie." *Angewandte Chemie, 61* (1949), 149-150.

le   Leroy, G. "Les apports de la mécanique ondulatoire au developpement de la chimie moderne." *Revue des questions scientifiques, 28* (1967), 57-70.

pa   Pauling, Linus. "Quantum theory and chemistry." *Science, 113* (1951), 92-94.

wi   Wirtz, K. "Quantentheorie und physikalische Chemie." *Angewandte Chemie, 61* (1949), 141-143.

See also: B.lg6.bv; H.cb1.kr

bf1.ku   *Kuz'minskiy, A. S. "Nauchnyye raboty po fizike i khimii kauchuka i reziny za 40 let." *Kauchuk i rezina,* 1957:10, 32-44.

ma   Mark, Herman F. "[Twenty years of] high-polymer physics." *PT,*
      21 (May 1968), 43-44.

Noble gases

ca1.he Hein, Hilde, and George E. Hein. "The chemistry of noble gases:
        A modern case history in experimental science." *JHI, 27* (1966),
        417-428.

   ri   Richardson, William Stobbart, and Julian Hall. *The discovery of*
        the inert gases. Harmondsworth, 1968.

   tr   Travers, Morris W. *The discovery of the rare gases.* London,
        1928.

cb1.da Day, John A. "The discovery of argon." *PTeach, 3* (1965), 103-
        110, 124-125.

   hi   Hiebert, Erwin N. "Historical remarks on the discovery of argon:
        The first noble gas." *Noble-gas compounds.* Ed. H. H. Hyman.
        Chicago, 1963. Pp. 3-20.

   tr   Travers, Morris W. "The discovery of argon." *Nature, 115*
        (1925), 121-122.

cc1.ga Gay, Hannah. "Noble gas compounds: A case study in scientific
        conservatism and opportunism." *SHPS, 8* (1977), 61-70.

   mo   Moore, R. B. "Helium: Its history, properties, and commercial
        development." Franklin Institute. *Journal, 191* (1921), 145-197.

Thermodynamics

See also: D.h

da1.al Allard, G. "Thermodynamics." A.aa1.ta, 134-141.

   ko   Kortüm, G. "Von der Thermodynamik zur Quantentheorie."
        Angewandte Chemie, 61 (1949), 123-129.

   ku   Kudryavtsev, P. S. "Razvitiye idey termodinamiki i atomistiki."
        A.ab1.gr, 229-235.

   la   Laue, Max von. "Thermodynamik und Kohärenz." *Nwn, 6*
        (1918), 207-213.

   mo   Møller, Christian. "Relativistic thermodynamics: A strange in-
        cident in the history of physics." Danske Videnskabernes Sel-
        skab. *Mat.-fys. meddelser, 36:1* (1967). (In Russian in *ES,*
        1969-70, 11-39.)

   ne   Nernst, Walther. "Zur neueren Entwicklung der Thermo-
        dynamik." Gesellschaft deutscher Naturforscher und Ärzte.
        Verhandlungen, 84:1 (1912), 100-116.

See also: H.ab1.cl

db1.go Gol'dberg, M. M., and N. P. Nazyuta. "Teoriya geterogennogo ravnovesiya Gibbsa, yeye istoki i razvitiye." *VIYeT, 26* (1969), 39-46.

he Hertz, Paul. "Gibbs theory, its foundations and applications." *Dialectica, 10* (1956), 368-383.

hi Hiromasa, Naohiko. "Formation of the concept of the Gibbs ensemble." ICHS, XIV (1974). *Proceedings, 2* (1975), 265-268.

kl Klein, Martin J. "Gibbs on Clausius." *HSPS, 1* (1969), 127-149.

dc1.fa Falkenhagen, H. "Die Elektrolytarbeiten von Max Planck und ihre weitere Entwicklung." B.pl1.ik, 11-34.

fr Frankfurt, U. I. "Termodinamicheskiye raboty M. Planka." B.pl1.jp, 737-744.

hi Hiebert, Erwin N. *The conception of thermodynamics in the scientific thought of Mach and Planck.* Freiburg/Br., 1968. (Ernst-Mach-Institut. *Wissenschaftlicher Bericht, 5/68.*)

dd1.kl Klein, Martin J. "Thermodynamics in Einstein's thought." *Science, 157* (1967), 509-516.

de1.hi Hiebert, Erwin N. "Nernst and electrochemistry." R.ac1.du, 180-200.

hj Hiebert, Erwin N. "Chemical thermodynamics and the third law: 1884-1914." ICHS, XV (1977). *Proceedings* (1978), 305-313.

su Suhling, Lothar. "Walther Nernst und der 3. Hauptsatz der Thermodynamik." *Rete, 1* (1972), 331-346.

df1.gu *Gumiński, K. "O pracach termodynamicznych Wladyslawa Natansona." *Postepy fizyki, 17* (1966), 101.

dh1.di Dickel, G. "Thermodiffusion und Diffusionsthermik." C.ga1.cl, 37-42.

ec Eckert, E. R. G. "Introduction [on transfer of heat]." B.ld3.jl, 2, xvii-xxviii.

pr Predvoditelev, A. S. "Teplota i molekulyarnaya fizika." C.vb1.pr, 1, 311-321.

si Šimek, A. "Het aandeel van Prof. F. M. Jaeger's laboratorium aan het exact physisch-chemisch onderzoek bij hooge temperaturen." *Chemisch weekblad, 31* (1934), 192-201.

T. TECHNIQUES AND APPARATUS

Mathematical methods

aa1.an   Andronov, A. A. "L. I. Mandel'shtam i teoriya nelineynykh kolebaniy." AN. *Izvestiya*, ser. fiz., *9* (1945), 30-55.

bo   Bochner, Salomon. "The significance of some basic mathematical conceptions for physics." *Isis, 54* (1963), 169-205.

br   Broglie, Louis de. "Le rôle des mathématiques dans le développement de la physique théorique contemporaine." F. Le Lionnais, ed. *Les grands courants de la pensée mathématique.* Paris, 1948. Pp. 398-412.

bu   Buchheim, Wolfgang. "William Rowan Hamilton und das Fortwirken seiner Gedanken in der modernen Physik." *NTM, 5:12* (1968), 19-30; *6:1* (1969), 43-60.

ha   Hawkins, Thomas. "The origins of the theory of group characters." *AHES, 7* (1971), 142-170.

hb   Hawkins, Thomas. "Hypercomplex numbers, Lie groups, and the creation of group representation theory." *AHES, 8* (1972), 243-287.

hr   Herbrand, Jacques. "Les bases de la logique hilbertienne." *Revue de métaphysique et de morale, 37* (1930), 243-255.

il   Illy, József. "On the birth of Minkowski's four dimensional world." ICHS, XIII (1971). *Actes, 6* (1974), 67-72.

ka   Kadison, Richard V. "Theory of operators, part II. Operator algebras." American Mathematical Society. *Bulletin, 64:3:2* (1958), 61-85.

lu   Lützen, Jesper. "Heaviside's operational calculus and the attempts to rigorise it." *AHES, 21* (1979), 161-200.

mc   McHugh, James A. M. "An historical survey of ordinary linear differential equations with a large parameter and turning points." *AHES, 7* (1971), 277-324.

mu   Murray, F. J. "Theory of operators, part I. Single operators." American Mathematical Society. *Bulletin, 64:3:2* (1958), 57-60.

pa   Pawlak, Adam. "Zasady wariacyjne a integracja teorii fizykalnych." *KHNT, 19* (1974), 45-58.

See also: C.gg1.py

Units and constants

da1.ba   Barrell, H. "The metre." *CP, 3* (1962), 415-434.

  br   Brouwer, Dirk. "The accurate measurement of time." *PT, 4* (Aug. 1951), 6-15.

  du   DuMond, Jesse W. M. "Pilgrims' progress in search of the fundamental constants." *PT, 18* (Oct. 1965), 26-43.

  eb   Ebert, Hermann. "Vom AEF—Ausschuss für Einheiten und Formalgrössen." *PB, 23* (1977), 73-78.

  ki   Kirchner, F. "Die atomaren Konstanten." *PB, 5* (1949), 308-319.

  kl   Klein, H. Arthur. *The world of measurements.* London, 1974.

Instruments

ea1.br   Brüche, Ernst. "Zur Entwicklung der instrumentellen Physik." *PB, 6* (1950), 360-363.

  de   Decker, Fred W. "Great originals of modern physics." *AJP, 40* (1972), 433-436.

  wh   *White, Frederick Andrew. *Significant contributions of American industrial research laboratories in the development of analytical instruments for the physical sciences, 1900-1950.* Ph.D. thesis. Univ. of Wisconsin, 1959. (*DAI, 20,* 4095.)

eb1.mi   Miller, A. H. "The theory and operation of the Eötvös torsion balance." Royal Astronomical Society of Canada. *Journal, 28* (1934), 1-31.

ec1.an   Andrade, E. N. da C. "The history of the vacuum pump." *Vacuum, 9* (1958), 41-47.

  ge   Gerlach, Walther. "Das Vakuum in Geistesgeschichte, Naturwissenschaft und Technik." *PB, 23* (1967), 97-106.

ee1.ge   *Gerlach, Walther. "Entwicklung der Röntgenröhre in ihrer Bedeutung für die Wissenschaft und Technik." *Chemie-Ingenieur-Technik, 6* (1933), 419-426.

  sh   Shiers, George. "The first electron tube." *Scientific American, 220* (Mar. 1969), 104-112.

  si   Shiers, George. "Ferdinand Braun and the cathode ray tube." *Scientific American, 230* (Mar. 1974), 92-101.

  wa   Watson, H. E. "The development of the neon glow lamp (1911-61)." *Nature, 191* (1961), 1040-1041.

  ze   Zenneck, J. "Zum 50. Jubiläum der Braunschen Röhre." *Nwn, 35* (1948), 33-38.

See also: E.ta1.lu

efl.br   Brüche, Ernst. "Gedanken zum 25-jährigen Bestehen des Elektronenmikroskops." *PB, 13* (1957), 493-500.

bs   Br[üche], Ernst. "20 Jahre Arbeitsgemeinschaft für Elektronenoptik." *PB, 27* (1971), 322-323.

fo   Föppl, Ludwig, and Ernst Mürch. "Die Spannungsoptik als Beispiel für die Zusammenarbeit von Physiker und Ingenieur." *PB, 12* (1956), 221-224.

gu   Gupta, N. N. Das, and M. L. De. "The electron microscope—its past and present." *Indian journal of history of science, 3* (1968), 25-41.

ma   Marton, Ladislaus L. *Early history of the electron microscope.* San Francisco, 1968.

ru   Ruska, E. *Die frühe Entwicklung der Elektronenlinsen und der Elektronenmikroskopie.* Leipzig, 1979. (*Acta historica leopoldina,* no. 12), 1979.

egl.ca   Carman, Robert L. "Lasers: Evolution and technological use." A.aal.nf, 508-525.

le   Lengyel, Bela A. "Evolution of masers and lasers." *AJP, 34* (1966), 903-913.

ot   Otten, E. W. "Der Physik-Nobelpreis 1966 für optisches Pumpen." *PB, 23* (1967), 120-124.

se   Sevin, J. "L'effet laser dans les solides." *RHS, 16* (1963), 359-372.

to   Torsiglieri, A. J., and W. O. Baker. "The origins of the laser." *Science, 199* (1978), 1022-1026.

eil.al   Allardice, Corbin, and Edward R. Trapnell. "The first pile." *BAS, 18* (Dec. 1962), 19-24.

am   Amaldi, Edoardo. "Vent'anni della prima reazione nucleare a catena controllata." Accademia Nazionale dei Lincei, Rome. *Problemi attuali di scienza e di cultura. Quaderni,* no. 60 (1963), 7-15.

an   Anderson, Herbert L. "Early days of the chain reaction." *BAS, 29* (Apr. 1973), 8-12.

br   Broglie, Maurice de. "La première pile atomique française." *Revue de deux mondes* (Feb. 1949), 385-389.

fe   Fermi, Enrico. "The development of the first chain reacting pile." APS. *Proceedings, 90* (1946), 20-24. (Also in B.fgl.jj, *2,* 542-549.)

jo   Joliot, Frédéric. "La première pile atomique française." *La pensée,* no. 23 (1949), 3-7. (Also in **Atomes,* no. 35 (1979), 39- , and in B.jjl.jn.)

ma   Maier-Leibnitz, H., et al. "Experimentelles Hilfsmittel der Kern-
     physik." C.ga1.bo, Part 2, 1-126.

sn   Snell, Arthur H., and Alvin M. Weinberg. "History and accom-
     plishments of the Oak Ridge graphite reactor." *PT, 17* (Aug.
     1964), 32-38.

wa   Wattenberg, Albert. "The building of the first chain reaction
     pile." *BAS, 30* (Jun. 1974), 51-57.

zi   Zinn, Walter H. "Fermi and atomic energy." *Reviews of modern
     physics, 27* (1955), 263-268.

eo1.br   Bragg, W. H. "The development of the vacuum flask." *Engineer-
     ing, 149* (1948), 42-43. (Also in *Nature, 145* (1940), 408-410.)

fi   Finlay, G. R. "Henri Moissan and the development of electric
     furnaces." R.ac1.du, 433-455.

Particle accelerators

ga1.ba   Baracca, Angelo, and Silvio Bergia. *La spirale delle alte energie.
     Aspetti politici e logica di sviluppo della fisica della particelle elemen-
     tari.* Milan, 1975.

bl   Blewett, John P. "Resource letter PA-1." *Particle accelerators:
     Selected reprints.* New York, 1966. Pp. 1-11.

da   Day, Joanne S., Alan D. Krisch, and Lazarus G. Ratner, ed.
     History of the ZGS. NY, 1980.

go   *Goldsmith, Maurice, and Edwin Shaw. *Europe's giant accelerator:
     The story of the CERN 400 GeV proton synchrotron.* London, 1977.

gp   Goldwasser, E. L. "The universities' role." T.ga1.da, 25-31.

gq   Grinberg, A. P. *Bibliografiya po uskoritelyam.* Leningrad, 1970.

gr   Grinberg, A. P. "History of the invention and development of ac-
     celerators (1922-1932)." *SPU, 18* (1975), 815-831.

ju   Jungk, Robert. *The big machine.* Tr. Grace M. Spruch and Traude
     Wess. NY, 1968.

ko   Kolomenskiy, A. A. "Razvitiye idey V. I. Veksler v oblasti uskor-
     iteley." *UFN, 93* (1967), 593-610.

kp   Kowarski, Lew. "The making of CERN: An experiment in co-
     operation." *BAS, 11* (Dec. 1955), 354-357, 381.

ku   Kustom, Robert L. "An engineer's view of the ZGS." T.ga1.da,
     181-189.

la   Lawrence, E. O. "High current accelerators." *Science, 122* (1955),
     1127-1132.

li   Livingston, M. Stanley. "History of the cyclotron, Part I." *PT, 12* (Oct. 1959), 18-23.

lj   Livingston, M. Stanley. "Early development of particle accelerators." *AJP, 27* (1959), 626-629.

lk   Livingston, M. Stanley. *The development of high energy accelerators.* NY, 1966.

lm   *Livingston, M. Stanley. *Early history of the 200 Gev accelerator.* Batavia, Ill., 1968. (National Accelerator Laboratory. *Report,* NAL-12, 0100.)

ln   Livingston, M. Stanley. *Particle accelerators: A brief history.* Cambridge, Mass., 1969.

lo   *Livingston, M. Stanley. *Origins and history of the Los Alamos meson facility.* Los Alamos, N.M., 1972. (Los Alamos Scientific Laboratory. *Report,* LA-5000.)

lp   Livingston, M. Stanley. "Early history of particle accelerators." *Advances in electronics and electron physics, 50* (1980), 1-88.

mc   McMillan, Edwin M. "History of the cyclotron, Part II." *PT, 12* (Oct. 1959), 24-34.

md   McMillan, Edwin M. "Early history of particle accelerators." I.dc1.st, 113-155.

ne   Nemenov, L. M. "Istoriya razvitiya tsiklotrona." *Atomnaya energiya, 4* (1958), 117-127.

we   Weiner, Charles. "Cyclotrons and internationalism: Japan, Denmark and the United States, 1935-1945." ICHS, XIV (1974). *Proceedings, 2* (1975), 353-365.

ga2.ho   Holm, Sven. "Tandem acceleratoren af Niels Bohr Institutets nye afdeling ved Risø." *Fysisk tidsskrift, 60* (1962), 120-146.

la   Lassen, N. D. "Lidt af historien om cyclotronen på Niels Bohr Institutet." *Fysisk tidsskrift, 60* (1962), 90-119.

ga6.vo   Vorob'yev, A. A. "Iz istorii razvitiya elektronnykh uskoriteley." *VIYeT, 8* (1959), 33-47.

ga7.ay   Ayres, D. "The effective mass spectrometer." T.ga1.da, 122-142.

hu   Hunt, S. E. "The development and application of the Van de Graaff accelerator." *PE, 2* (1967), 140-145.

pr   Prien, R. J. "A technician's view of high energy physics." T.ga1.da, 190-191.

ra   Ratner, L. G. "The life and death of a particle accelerator." T.ga1.da, 394-453.

te   Teng, L. C. "The ZGS - Conception to turn-on." T.ga1.da, 10-17.

yo   Yokosawa, A. "The polarized targets." T.ga1.da, 110-121.

Particle detectors

gb1.ri   Riedhammer, Johannes. "Das Geiger-Zählrohr." *PB, 6* (1950), 302-310.

tq   Trenn, Thaddeus J. "Rutherford's electrical method: Its significance for radioactivity and an expression of his metaphysics." ICHS, XIII (1971). *Actes, 6* (1974), 112-118.

tr   Trenn, Thaddeus J. "Die Erfindung des Geiger-Müller-Zählrohres." Munich. Deutsches Museum. *Abhandlungen und Berichte, 44:3* (1976), 54-64.

gb4.de   Derrick, M., L. G. Hyman, and E. G. Pewitt. "History of the superconducting magnet bubble chambers." T.ga1.da, 198-226.

wa   Walker, W. D. "The MURA−ANL−Fermilab 30" bubble chamber." T.ga1.da, 53-69.

U. PHYSICS AND SOCIETY

General

aa1.ba   Barber, Bernard. *Science and the social order.* Glencoe, 1952.

be   Bernal, J. D. *The social function of science.* NY, 1939.

co   Compton, K. T. "Science makes jobs." *Scientific monthly, 38* (1934), 297-300.

da   Daniels, George H. *Science in American society, a social history.* NY, 1971.

fi   *Fisica e società negli anni '20.* Milan, 1980.

hu   Huxley, Julian S. *Science and social needs.* NY, 1935.

ne   Newman, James R. *Science and sensibility.* 2 vols. London, 1961.

pi   Picone, Mauro. "L'analysi matematica al servizio del progresso civile." Accademia Nazionale dei Lincei, Rome. *Problemi attuali di scienza e di cultura. Quaderni,* no. 217 (1976), 13-16.

po   Powell, Cecil Frank. "The role of pure science in European civilization." *Old and new problems in elementary particles.* Ed. G. Puppi. NY, 1968. Pp. 262-271.

ra   Rabi, Isidor Isaac. *Science: The center of culture.* NY, 1970.

ri   Richter, Steffen. "Physik und Gesellschaft: Einige äussere Einflüsse auf die Entwicklung der Physik in Deutschland, 1850-1945." *PB, 33* (1977), 49-57.

sc   Schrödinger, Erwin. *Science, theory, and man.* NY, 1957. (Expanded ed. of *Science and the human temperament,* 1935.)

sn   Snow, C. P. *The two cultures and the scientific revolution.* NY, 1960.

we   Weisskopf, V. F. "La portée de la science: Aspects culturels et sociaux de la science et leurs relations avec la société." *Raison présente, 24* (1972), 41-63.

wi   Wigner, E. P. "The scientist and society." A.aj1.fr, 50-56.

ab1.ba   Baracca, Angelo, Stefano Ruffo, and Arturo Russo. *Scienza e industria 1848-1915.* Bari, 1979.

br   Braun, Ernest. "Science and technological innovation." *PE, 14* (1979), 353-358.

ca   Casimir, H. B. G. "The relations between science and technology." A.ad1.we, 447-457.

we   Weart, Spencer R. "The rise of 'prostituted' physics." *Nature, 262* (1976), 13-17.

Organization of physics

ba1.ba   Basalla, George. "Organizing science: The debate continues." *New scientist, 42:644* (1969), 76-77.

bc   Bastrakova, M. S. *Stanovleniye sovetskoy sistemy organizatsii nauki (1917-1922).* Moscow, 1973.

be   Belyayev, Ye. A., et al. *Organizatsiya nauchnoy deyatel'nosti.* Moscow, 1968.

by   Bykhovskiy, B. E., et al. *Organizatsiya sovetskoy nauki v 1926-1932 gg: Sbornik dokumentov.* Leningrad, 1974.

ca   Cardwell, D. S. L. *The organization of science in England.* 2nd ed. London, 1972.

cc   *Castro, Barry. *The scientific opportunities foregone because of the selective availability of federal support for university-based research in physics.* Ph.D. thesis. New York Univ., 1967. (*DAI, 28,* 4323A.)

fo   Fox, Robert, and George Weisz, eds. *The organization of science and technology in France 1808-1914.* Cambridge, 1980.

gv   Gvishyani, D. M., and S. R. Mikulinskiy. *Evolyutsiya form organizatsii nauki v razvitykh kapitalisticheskikh stranakh.* Moscow, 1972.

jo   Joliot, Frédéric. "Ob organizatsii nauki vo Frantsii." AN. *Vestnik,* 1950:3, 72-77. (Also in *Izvestiya,* ser. fiz., 1950:1, 64-69.)

kl   Kol'tsov, A. V. "V. I. Lenin i organizatsiya nauchnykh issledovaniy v pervyye gody Sovetskoy vlasti." *VIYeT, 30* (1970), 29-40.

ko   Kowarski, Lew. "New forms of organization in physical research after 1945." A.ad1.we, 370-401.

lu   Lundgreen, Peter. "The organization of science and technology in France: A German perspective." U.ba1.fo, 311-332.

os   Ostrovityanov, K. V., et al. *Organizatsiya nauki v pervyye gody sovetskoy vlasti (1917-1925): Sbornik dokumentov.* Leningrad, 1968.

pa   Parsons, Talcott. "National science legislation, part 1: An historical review." *BAS, 2* (Nov. 1946), 7-9.

pi   Piskotin, M. I., et al. *Organizatsionno-pravovyye voprosy rukovodstva naukoy v SSSR.* Moscow, 1973.

pr   Price, Derek J. de Solla. *Little science, big science.* NY, 1963.

sh   Shpol'skiy, E. V. "Organizatsiya sovetskoy fiziki." *UFN, 33* (1947), 3-22.

we   Weinberg, Alvin M. *Reflections on big science.* Cambridge, Mass., 1967.

See also: A.db1.su; T.ga1.ba

bc1.be   *Beaver, Donald de B. *The American scientific community, 1800-1860: A statistical-historical study.* NY, 1980. (Reprint of Ph.D. thesis. Yale Univ., 1966.)

bl   Blau, Judith R. "Sociometric structure of a scientific discipline." *Research in sociology of knowledge, science and art, 1* (1978), 191-206.

co   *Cole, Jonathan Richard. *The social structure of science: A study of the reward and communications systems of modern physics.* Ph.D. thesis. Columbia Univ., 1969. (*DAI, 30,* 2634A.)

cr   Collins, H. M. "Son of seven sexes: The social destruction of a physical phenomenon." *SSS, 11* (1981), 33-62.

ga   *Galinsky, M. David. *Personality development and vocational choice: A study of physicists and clinical psychologists.* Ph.D. thesis. Univ. of Michigan, 1961. (*DAI, 22,* 2464.)

gb   *Gaston, Jerry Collins. *Big science in Britain: A sociological study of the high energy physics community.* Ph.D. thesis. Yale Univ., 1969. (*DAI, 31,* 1383A.)

gu   Guralnick, Stanley M. "The American scientist in higher education, 1820-1910." C.ua1.re, 99-141.

ha   Harvey, Bill. "Plausibility and the evaluation of knowledge: A case-study of experimental quantum mechanics." *SSS, 11* (1981), 95-130.

hi   *Hildahl, Spencer Harlow. *The invisible-college phenomenon: An exploratory study of variables relating to informal communication among researchers in physics.* Ph.D. thesis. Cornell Univ., 1971. (*DAI, 32,* 5357A.)

ke   Kelle, V. Zh., and S. R. Mikulinskiy. *Sotsiologicheskiye problemy nauki.* Moscow, 1974.

me   *Merz, Louise Elizabeth. *The graduate school as a socializing agency: A pilot study of sociological aspects of graduate training in the physical sciences.* Ph.D. thesis. Cornell Univ., 1961. (*DAI, 22,* 2904.)

mu   Mulkay, Michael. "Conceptual displacement and migration in science: A prefatory paper." *SSS, 4* (1974), 205-234.

pi   Pickering, Andrew. "Constraints on controversy: The case of the magnetic monopole." *SSS, 11* (1981), 63-93.

pj   Pickering, Andrew. "The role of interests in high-energy physics: The choice between charm and colour." *The social process of scientific investigation.* Ed. K. D. Knorr, Roger Krahn, and Richard Whitley. Dordrecht, 1980. Pp. 107-138. (*Sociology of the sciences,* 4.)

pk   Pinch, Trevor J. "The sun-set: The presentation of certainty in scientific life." *SSS, 11* (1981), 131-158.

ro   Rossiter, Margaret W. "Women scientists in America before 1920." *American scientist,* 62 (1974), 312-323.

sn   *Snyder, Norman Conrad. *Socio-cultural background differences in the personnel of the social, biological, and physical sciences: A chapter in the institutionalization of the sciences.* Ph.D. thesis. Emory Univ., 1965. (*DAI, 26,* 1821.)

we   Weinberg, Alvin M. "Scientific teams and scientific laboratories." A.aa1.ho, 423-442.

wg   *Werskey, P. Gary. "British scientists and 'outsider' politics 1931-1945." *Sociology of science.* Ed. B. Barnes. London, 1972. Pp. 231-250.

wh   White, D. H., and D. Sullivan. "Social currents in the weak interactions." *PT, 32* (Apr. 1979), 40-47.

za   *Zaltman, Gerald. *Scientific recognition and communication in high energy physics.* Ph.D. thesis. Johns Hopkins Univ., 1968. (*DAI, 29,* 1969A.)

bd1.be   Bell, Raymond M. "Origins and ages of American physicists." *AJP, 14* (1946), 396-398.

bl   Blackwood, Oswald. "Undergraduate origins of American physicists." *AJP, 12* (1944), 149-150.

co   Cooper, John N. "Undergraduate origins of American physicists." *AJP, 20* (1952), 200-202.

cp   Cooper, John N. "American physicists and their graduate degrees." *AJP, 20* (1952), 484-487.

la   Lagemann, R. T., and Bruno E. K. Alter, Jr. "Publication records of certain American physicists." *AJP, 16* (1948), 96-99.

si   Siebring, B. Richard, and Duane H. Schwahn. "Baccalaureate origins of Ph.D. physicists." *AJP, 27* (1959), 647-648.

tr   Trytten, M. H. "The undergraduate origin of physics Ph.D.'s, 1936-45." *AJP, 15* (1947), 330-333.

be1.fi   *Fishman, Walda Katz. *Perspectives of the ethos of science: A comparative analysis of perceptions of the assumptions and moral norms of science among academic scientists in three fields.* Ph.D. thesis. Wayne State Univ., 1978. (*DAI, 39,* 1877A.)

go   *Goldsmith, Maurice. *Three scientists face social responsibility: Joseph Needham, J. D. Bernal, F. Joliot-Curie.* New Delhi, 1976.

ma   MacLeod, Roy M. "Of medals and men: A reward system in Victorian science, 1826-1914." RS. *Notes and records, 26* (1971), 81-105.

mc   McGucken, William. "On freedom and planning in science: The Society for Freedom in Science, 1940-46." *Minerva, 16* (1978), 42-72.

op   Oppenheimer, J. Robert. *The flying trapeze: Three crises for physicists.* London, 1964.

po   Polanyi, Michael. *Scientific thought and social reality.* Ed. Fred Schwartz. NY, 1974.

re   Reingold, Nathan. "The scientist as troubled American." American Industrial Hygiene Association. *Journal, 40* (1979), 1107-13.

si   Silvert, Kalman H., ed. *The social reality of scientific myth.* NY, 1969.

ul   Ulrich, Erich. "Über den Glauben der Naturwissenschaftler." *PB, 27* (1971), 49-54.

zu   Zuckerman, Harriet, and Robert K. Merton. "Patterns of evaluation in science: Institutionalization, structure and functions of the referee system." *Minerva, 9* (1971), 66-100.

Physics and other disciplines

ca1.cr   Crombie, A. C. "Die Naturwissenschaften im Mittelalter." *PB, 24* (1968), 49-56.

cc1.ca   Isada-Catalan, Gabriel. "Teilhard de Chardin and physical science and technology." *St. Louis University research journal, 3* (1972), 40-112.

ga   Garbasso, Antonio. *Scienza e poesia.* Ed. Jolanda de Blasi. Florence, 1934.

mi   Mindel, Joseph. "The uses of metaphor: Henry Adams and the symbols of science." *JHI, 26* (1965), 89-102.

se   Seeger, Raymond J. "On humanistic aspects of entropy." *Physis, 9* (1967), 215-234.

we   Welsh, Alexander. "Theories of science and romance, 1870-1920." *Victorican studies, 17* (1973), 135-154.

ce1.fr   Franz, Marie-Luise von. *Number and time: Reflections leading toward a unification of depth psychology and physics.* Tr. Adrea Dykes. Evanston, 1974.

pa   Pauli, Wolfgang. "Naturwissenschaftliche und erkenntnistheoretische Aspekte der Ideen vom Unbewussten." *Dialectica, 8* (1954), 283-301.

sc   Schultz, Julius August Heinrich. *Das Ich und die Physik.* Leipzig, 1935.

cg1.da   Davidson, M. "Modern cosmology and the theologians." *Vistas in astronony, 1* (1955), 166-172.

ja   Jaki, Stanley L. *The road of science and the ways to God.* Chicago and London, 1978.

Correspondence with scientists

da1.ba   Ball, Robert Stawell. *Reminiscences and letters.* Ed. W. Valentine Ball. Boston, 1915.

bo   Holdermann, Karl. *Im Banne der Chemie: Carl Bosch, Leben und Werk.* Düsseldorf, 1953.

br   Nevskaya, N. I. "Nauchnyye svyazi F. A. Bredikhina s krupneyshimi russkimi uchenymi posledney chetverti XIX v." *IIYeT. Trudy, 28* (1959), 464-476.

cl   Claude, Georges. *Ma vie et mes inventions.* Paris, 1957.

da   Rogers, C. A., et al. "Harold Davenport." RS. *BM, 17* (1971), 159-192.

du   Flechtner, Hans-Joachim. *Carl Duisberg; von Chemiker zum Wirtschaftsführer.* Düsseldorf, 1959.

ge   Struve, Otto. "About a Russian astronomer." *Sky and telescope, 16* (1957), 379-381. (Concerns B. P. Gerasimovich.)

gi   Sauermann, Lotte. "Eberhard Gieseler, Ingenieur und Physiker," *Annals of Science, 33* (1976), 81-103.

gr   Vasil'yev, O. F. "Nauchnoye naslediye I. S. Gromeki." *IIYeT. Trudy, 10* (1956), 245-268.

he   Herneck, Friedrich. "Emil Fischer als Mensch und Forscher." *Zeitschrift für Chemie, 10* (1970), 41-48.

ka   Gustavson, Torsten. "Gunnar Källen." Kungl. Fysiografiska Sällskapet. *Årsbok* (1969), 1-6.

ke   Teplyakov, G. M. "Nikolay Petrovich Kasterin." *IMYeN: Fizika, 10* (1971), 150-163.

ko   Koenigsberger, Leo. *Mein Leben.* Heidelberg, 1919.

li   Linde, Carl von. *Aus meinen Leben und von meiner Arbeit: Aufzeichnungen für meine Kinder und meine Mitarbeiter.* Munich, [1916].

ma   Margenau, Henry. *Physics and philosophy: Selected essays.* Dordrecht, 1978.

me   Mechnikov, I. I. *Stranitsy vospominaniy.* Moscow, 1946.

mo   Rozhkov, M. "N. A. Morozov—osnovopolozhnik." *UFN, 49* (1953), 180-181.

th   Abrahams, Harold J., and Marion B. Savin. *Selections from the scientific correspondence of Elihu Thomson.* Cambridge, Mass., 1971.

ti   Worthing, A. G. "Roland Roy Tileston, nominee for the 1943 Oersted Award." *AJP, 12* (1944), 93-95.

ul   Ulam, Stanislaw M. *Adventures of a mathematician.* NY, 1976.

va   Reznik, Semen Yefimovich. *Nikolay Vavilov.* Moscow, 1968.

wa   Walden, Paul. *Wege und Herbergen: Mein Leben.* Ed. Günter Kerstein. Wiesbaden, 1974. (*Beiträge zur Geschichte der Wissenschaft und der Technik, 13.*)

wb   Krebs, Hans, and Roswitha Schmid. *Otto Warburg: Zellphysiologe, Biochemiker, Mediziner, 1883-1970.* Stuttgart, 1979.

we   Paneth, Friedrich. "Zum 60 Geburtstag Auer von Welsbach." *Nwn, 16* (1928), 1037-1038.

wi   Willstätter, Richard. *Aus meinem Leben, von Arbeit, Musse und Freunden.* Ed. Arthur Stoll. Weinheim, 1949.

wj   Willstätter, Richard. *From my life: The memoirs of Richard Willstätter.* Tr. Lilli S. Hornig. NY, 1965.

ze   Lebedev, P. N. "Instruktsiya stud. Zernovy." *UFN, 46* (1952), 328-329.

Correspondence with nonscientists

ea1.la   Laporte, Paul M. "Cubism and relativity (with a letter from Albert Einstein)." *Art journal, 25* (1966), 246-248.

eb1.fl   Flexner, Abraham. *Abraham Flexner: An autobiography.* NY, 1940.

fm   Flexner, Simon, and James T. Flexner. *William Henry Welch and the heroic age of American medicine.* NY, 1941.

ed1.ne Nehru, Jawaharlal. *A bunch of old letters written mostly to Jawaharlal Nehru and some written by him.* Bombay, 1958.

ef1.bu Buber, Martin. *Briefwechsel aus sieben Jahrzehnten.* 3 vols. Heidelberg, 1972-1975.

he   Anon. *Dem Andenken Martin Heideggers.* Frankfurt am Main, 1977.

hg   Easton, Loyd D. *Hegel's first American followers: The Ohio Hegelians.* Athens, Ohio, 1966.

me   Kindinger, Rudolf. *Philosophenbriefe aus der wissenschaftliche Korrespondenz von Alexius Meinong.* Graz, 1965.

rt   Clark, Ronald W. *The life of Bertrand Russell.* NY, 1976.

ru   Russell, Bertrand. *Autobiography.* 3 vols. Boston, 1967-1969.

sp   Duncan, David. *Life and letters of Herbert Spencer,* vol. 2. NY, 1908.

eh1.fj Jones, Ernest. *The life and work of Sigmund Freud.* 3 vols. NY, 1953-1957.

fk   Jones, Ernest. *The life and work of Sigmund Freud.* Ed. Lionel Trilling and Steven Marcus. NY, 1961.

fr   Freud, Sigmund. *Gesammelte Werke,* vol. 16. London, 1950.

fs   Freud, Sigmund. *Letters of Sigmund Freud.* Ed. E. L. Freud. Tr. T. Stern and J. Stern. NY, 1960.

ft   Freud, Sigmund. *Briefe 1873-1939.* Ed. E. L. Freud. Frankfurt, 1960.

fu   Freud, Sigmund. *The standard edition of the complete psychological works of Sigmund Freud.* Vol. 22. Ed. James Strachey. London, 1964.

ju   Jung, Carl Gustav. *Briefe.* Ed. Aniela Jaffé and Gerhard Adler. 2 vols. Olten and Freiburg/Br., 1972.

jv   Jung, C. G. *Letters.* Ed. G. Adler and Aniela Jaffé. 2 vols. Princeton, N.J., 1973.

ek1.fo Forel, August. *Briefe, correspondance, 1864-1927.* Ed. H. H. Walser. Bern, 1968.

ma   Mann, Thomas. *Briefe.* 3 vols. Frankfurt-am-Main, 1961-65.

mb   Mann, Thomas. *Letters of Thomas Mann 1889-1955.* Ed. Richard and Clara Winston. NY, 1971.

eo1.pa   Merkulov, V. L. "I. P. Pavlov: Cooperation with British physiologists." C.va4.an, 94-115.

wr   Andronikov, Vladimir Mikhailovich. *Margarethe von Wrangel.* Munich, 1936.

Politics

ga1.bo   Born, Max. *Physik und Politik.* Göttingen, 1960.

bp   Born, Max. *Physics and politics.* NY, 1962.

ei   Einstein, Albert. *About zionism.* Ed. Leon Simon. NY, 1931.

gr   Greenberg, Daniel S. *The politics of pure science.* NY, 1967.

Politics: International

gb1.be   Beveridge, William Henry. *A defence of free learning.* London, 1959.

ek   Eklund, Sigvard. "The international atom." U.gk5.le, 126-139.

el   Eklund, Sigvard. "20 Jahre internationale Atomenergie-Organisation." *PB, 34* (1978), 101-105.

fe   Fermi, Laura. "After the fall of France: The Emergency Rescue Committee." *BAS, 24* (Feb. 1968), 9-13.

ge   Guéron, Jules. "Atomic energy in continental western Europe." U.gk5.le, 140-158.

go   Goldstein, W. "Science, politics and international affairs." A.ad1.we, 402-434.

ra   Radovskiy, M. I. *Iz istorii anglo-russkikh nauchnykh svyazey.* Moscow and Leningrad, 1961.

sc   Schroeder-Gudehus, Brigitte. "Challenge to transnational loyalties: International scientific organizations after the first world war." *SSS, 3* (1973), 93-118.

sd   Schroeder-Gudehus, Brigitte. "Tendances de centralisation dans l'organisation de la cooperation scientifique internationale, 1900-1945." ICHS, XV (1977). *Proceedings,* 1978, 150-162.

se   Schroeder-Gudehus, Brigitte. *Les scientifiques et la paix. La communauté scientifique internationale au cours des années 20.* Montreal, 1978.

sf   Schroeder-Gudehus, Brigitte. "Isolation und Kooperation der nationalen *scientific communities.*" B.ei4.yn, 517-536.

gb2.be   Bentwich, Norman. *The rescue and achievement of refugee scholars: The story of displaced scholars and scientists, 1933-1952.* The Hague, 1953.

du   Duggan, Stephen, and Betty Drury. *The rescue of science and learning: The story of the Emergency Committee in Aid of Displaced Foreign Scholars.* NY, 1948.

fe   Fermi, Laura. *Illustrious immigrants: The intellectual migration from Europe 1930-41.* Chicago, 1968.

fl   Fleming, Donald, and Bernard Bailyn, ed. *The intellectual migration: Europe and America, 1930-1960.* Cambridge, Mass., 1969.

we   *Wetzel, Charles John. *The American rescue of refugee scholars and scientists from Europe, 1933-1945.* Ph.D. thesis. Univ. of Wisconsin, 1964. (*DAI, 25,* 1180.)

wi   Weiner, Charles. "A new site for the seminar: The refugees and American physics in the thirties." U.gb2.fl, 190-234.

Politics: Austria

gc1.mo   Molisch, Paul. *Politische Geschichte der deutschen Hochschulen in Oesterreich von 1848 bis 1918.* Vienna and Leipzig, 1939.

Politics: Britain

gd1.fi   *Filner, Robert Earl. *Science and politics in England, 1930-1945: The social relations of science movement.* Ph.D. thesis. Cornell Univ., 1973. (*DAI, 34,* 6563A.)

fj   Filner, Robert E. "The roots of political activism in British science." *BAS, 32* (Jan. 1976), 25-29.

fo   *Forman, Charles William. *Britain's development of the empire through scientific research, 1895-1940.* Ph.D. thesis. University of Wisconsin, 1941.

ma   MacLeod, Roy, and Kay MacLeod. "The contradictions of professionalism: Scientists, trade unionism and the first world war." *SSS, 9* (1979), 1-32.

See also: C.ba1.we

Politics: France

ge1.gi   Gilpin, Robert. *France in the age of the scientific state.* Princeton, 1968.

See also: C. fa1.wf

Politics: Germany

gg1.bu   Burchardt, Lothar. *Wissenschaftspolitik in Wilhelmischen Deutschland.* Göttingen, 1975.

gr   *Grundmann, Siegfried. "Der deutsche Imperialismus, Einstein und die Relativitätstheorie (1914-1933)." B.ei7.ct.

kl   Kleinert, Andreas. "Nationalistische und antisemitische Ressentiments von Wissenschaftlern gegen Einstein." B.ei4.yn, 501-516.

pf   Pfetsch, Frank R. *Zur Entwicklung der Wissenschaftspolitik in Deutschland, 1750-1914.* Berlin, 1974.

pr   *Preston, David Lawrence. *Science, society, and the German Jews, 1870-1933.* Ph.D. thesis. Univ. of Illinois, 1971. (*DAI, 32,* 5911A.)

ri   Richter, Steffen. "Die Kämpfe innerhalb der Physik in Deutschland nach dem ersten Weltkrieg." *Sudhoffs Archiv, 59* (1973), 195-207.

sc   Schroeder-Gudehus, Brigitte. "The argument for the self-government and public support of science in Weimar Germany." *Minerva, 10* (1972), 537-570.

sd   Schroeder-Gudehus, Brigitte. *Deutsche Wissenschaft und internationale Zusammenarbeit 1914-1928.* Geneva, 1966.

sh   Shenck, Rudolf. "Arbeitsgemeinschaft und Gemeinschaftsarbeit in Naturwissenschaft und Technik." C.ga1.ab, 286-299.

See also: B.ei9.ct, hg; C.ga1.fn, fo, fq; C.ga2 | ga6.fo

gg3.an   Anon. "Eingabe an Rust." *PB, 3* (1947), 43-46.

be   Bechstedt, Martin. "'Gestalthafte Atomlehre'—Zur 'Deutschen Chemie' im NS-Staat." U.gg3.me, 142-165.

bk   Becker, August, ed. *Naturforschung in Aufbruch. Reden und Vorträge zur Einweihungsfeier des Philipp-Lenard-Instituts der Universität Heidelberg.* Munich, 1936.

by   Beyerchen, Alan. *Scientists under Hitler.* New Haven, 1977.

cb   Br[üche], Ernst. "'Deutsche Physik' und die deutschen Physiker." *PB, 2* (1946), 232-236.

ev   Evola, J. "Über das Problem der arischen Naturwissenschaft." *ZGN, 6* (1940), 161-172.

gl   Glaser, L. "Juden in der Physik: Jüdische Physik." *ZGN, 5* (1939), 272-275.

ha   Haberditzl, Werner. "Der Widerstand deutscher Naturforscher gegen die 'Deutsche Physik' und andere faschistische Zerrbilder." *Naturwissenschaft, Tradition, Fortschritt. NTM.* Beiheft, 1963. Pp. 320-326.

kl   Kleinert, Andreas. "Von der Science allemande zur Deutschen Physik: Nationalismus und moderne Naturwissenschaft in Frankreich und Deutschland zwischen 1914 und 1940." *Francia, 6* (1978), 509-525.

la Laue, Max von. "Bemerkung zu der vorstehenden Veröffentlichung von J. Stark." *PB, 3* (1947), 272-273. (See U.gg3.sv.)

lb Laue, Max von. "Gedenkworte für Friedrich Schmidt-Ott." B.lf6.jl, *3*, 238-242.

le Lenard, Philipp. *Idealle Kontinentalsperre.* Munich, 1940.

li Lindner, Helmut. "'Deutsche' und 'gegentypische' Mathematik. Zur Begrundung cincr 'arteigenen' Mathematik im 'Dritten Reich' durch Ludwig Bieberbach." U.gg3.me, 88-115.

me Mehrtens, Herbert, and Steffen Richter, ed. *Naturwissenschaft, Technik und NS-Ideologie. Beiträge zur Wissenschaftsgeschichte des Dritten Reiches.* Frankfurt a. M., 1980.

mf Mehrtens, Herbert. "Das 'Dritte Reich' in der Naturwissenschaftsgeschichte: Literatur und Problemskizze." U.gg3.me, 15-87.

mu Müller, Wilhelm. "Jüdischer Geist in der Physik." *ZGN, 5* (1939), 162-175.

mv Müller, Wilhelm. "Zur 'Krisis der Physik'." *ZGN, 6* (1940), 321-322.

pi Pinl, Maximillian, and Auguste Dick. "Kollegen in einer dunklen Zeit." Deutsche Mathematikervereinigung. *Jahresbericht, 75* (1973), 166-208.

pj Pinl, Maximillian, and Lux Furtmüller. "Mathematicians under Hitler." Leo Baeck Institute. *Yearbook, 18* (1973), 129-182.

pl Planck, Max. "Mein Besuch bei Adolf Hitler." *PB, 3* (1947), 143.

po *Polizkov, Léon, and Josef Wulf. *Das dritte Reich und seine Denker.* Berlin, 1959; Munich, 1978.

re Requard, Friedrich. "Physik und Erbcharakter." *ZGN, 6* (1940), 172-184.

ri Richter, Steffen. "Physiker im Dritten Reich." Technische Hochschule, Darmstadt. *Jahrbuch,* 1978/9, 103-113.

rj Richter, Steffen. "Die 'Deutsche Physik'." U.gg3.me, 116-141.

sc Scherzer, Otto. "Physik im totalitären Staat." Andreas Flitner, ed., *Deutsches Geistesleben und Nationalsozialismus.* Tübingen, 1965. Pp. 47-58.

st Stark, Johannes. *Adolf Hitler und die deutsche Forschung.* Berlin, [1934].

su *Stark, Johannes, and Wilhelm Müller. *Jüdische und deutsche Physik.* Leipzig, 1941.

sv   Stark, Johannes. "Zu den Kämpfen in der Physik während der Hitler-Zeit." *PB, 3* (1947), 271-272.

th   Thüring, B. "Physik und Astronomie in jüdischen Händen." *ZGN, 3* (1937/8), 55-70.

See also: B.ei9.dt; C.g

Politics: Italy

gi1.cr   Croce, Benedetto. *Scritti e discorsi politici,* vol. 2. Bari, 1963.

Politics: USA

gk1.au   Auerbach, Lewis E. "Scientists in the New Deal: A pre-war episode in the relations between science and government in the United States." *Minerva, 3* (1965), 457-482.

bu   Bush, Vannevar. *Modern arms and free men: A discussion of the role of science in preserving democracy.* NY, 1949.

bv   Bush, Vannevar. *Science, the endless frontier.* Washington, D.C., 1945, 1960.

du   Dupree, A. Hunter. *Science in the federal government.* Cambridge, Mass., 1957.

ke   Kevles, Daniel J. "Physicists and the revolt against science in the 1930's." *PT, 31* (Feb. 1978), 23-30.

ma   Maria, Michelangelo de, and Robert Seidel. "Lo scienziato e l'inventore. Inizio dell'integrazione sistematica fra scienza e industria in USA durante la prima guerra mondiale." *Testi e contesti,* no. 4 (1980), 5-32.

pe   Penick, James L., Jr., et al., ed. *The politics of American science: 1939 to the present.* Chicago, 1965.

to   Tobey, Ronald C. *The American ideology of national science, 1919-1930.* Pittsburgh, 1971.

gk5.bl   Blackett, P. M. S. *Military and political consequences of atomic energy.* London, 1948.

co   Condon, Edward Uhler. *Final report of the scientific study of unidentified flying objects.* Ed. Daniel S. Gillmor. NY, 1969.

fe   Fermi, Laura. "Bombs or reactors." U.gk5.le, 62-66.

gr   Green, Harold P. "Q-clearance: The development of a personnel security program." *BAS, 20* (May 1964), 9-15.

ki   Killian, James Rhyne. *Sputnik, scientists and Eisenhower: A memoir of the first special assistant to the President for science and technology.* Cambridge, Mass., 1977.

kl   Kliefoth, Werner. "Hearings zur Entstehung der H-Bombe, oder die Verantwortung der Physiker." *PB, 11* (1955), 549-554.

la   *Lasby, Clarence George. *German scientists in America: Their importatation, exploitation and assimilation, 1945-1952.* Ph.D. thesis. Univ. of California, Los Angeles, 1962.

le   Lewis, Richard S., Jane Wilson, and Eugene Rabinowitch, ed. *Alamogordo plus twenty-five years: The impact of atomic energy on science, technology, and world politics.* NY, 1971.

sa   Salomon, Jean-Jacques. "Science et pouvoir: Le tournant des premières bombes atomiques." *Fundamenta scientiae, 1* (1980), 183-198.

sa   Sapolsky, Harvey M. "Academic science and the military: The years since the second world war." C.ua1.re, 379-399.

sh   Shepley, J. R., and C. Blair. *The hydrogen bomb: The men, the menace, the mechanism.* NY, 1954.

wi   Wilson, Thomas W. *The great weapons heresy.* Boston, 1970.

ya   *Yavenditti, Michael John. *American reactions to the use of atomic bombs on Japan, 1945-1947.* Ph.D. thesis. Univ. of California, Berkeley, 1970. (*DAI, 31,* 3490A.)

yo   York, Herbert F. *The advisors: Oppenheimer, Teller and the super-bomb.* San Francisco, 1976.

yp   York, Herbert F., and G. Allen Greb. "Military research and development: A postwar history." *BAS, 33* (Jan. 1977), 13-26.

ys   Yoshiba, Kazuo. "A scientific-historical study on the social-cultural effect of the hydrogen-bomb experiment at Bikini Atoll in 1954." ICHS, XIII (1971). *Actes, 1* (1974), 130-135.

See also: B.ok1.sb; C.u

gll.ko   Kopp, Carolyn. "The origins of the American scientific debate over fallout hazards." *SSS, 9* (1979), 403-422.

ro   Rotblat, J. *Pugwash—the first ten years.* NY, 1968.

th   Thirring, Hans. "Die Pugwash Konferenzen." *PB, 18* (1962), 563-567.

See also: G.oa1.se

Politics: USSR

gm1.al   Alston, Patrick L. "Science, the Russian state and we." *History of education quarterly, 11* (1971), 435-441.

de   DeWitt, Nicholas. "The polity of Russian and Soviet science: A century of continuity and change." U.be1.si, 171-201.

pe   Pelseneer, Jean. *Les persécutions contre les savants et les intellectuels en U.R.S.S., 1917-1967. Syllabus.* Brussels, 1968.

War

ka1.ba   Badash, Lawrence. "British and American views of the German menace in World War I." RS. *Notes and records, 34* (1979), 91-121.

bc   Baracca, Angelo, Roberto Livi, and Stefano Ruffo. "Le tappe dello sviluppo della teoria dei quanti nel quadro della seconda rivoluzione industriale e della contraddizioni del capitalismo del primo dopoguerra." *Testi e contesti, 2* (1979), 7-51; *3* (1980), 51-80.

bk   Blackett, P. M. S. "The next war: Can it be avoided?" G. D. H. Cole, Arthur Salter, et al., eds. *What is ahead of us?* NY, 1937. Pp. 133-164.

bl   Blackett, P. M. S. *Fear, war and the bomb: Military and political consequences of atomic energy.* NY, 1949.

bm   Blackett, P. M. S. *Atomic weapons and East-West relations.* Cambridge, 1956.

bn   Blackett, P. M. S. *Studies of war, nuclear and conventional.* NY, 1962.

ei   Einstein, Albert. *The fight against war.* Ed. Alfred Lief. NY, 1933.

ej   Einstein, Albert, and Sigmund Freud. *Why war?* Tr. Stuart Gilbert. Paris, 1933.

ho   Hoffman, Frederic de. "Pure science in the service of wartime technology." *BAS, 31* (Jan. 1975), 41-44.

ke   Kevles, Daniel J. "'Into hostile political camps': The reorganization of international science in World War I." *Isis, 62* (1971), 47-60.

lo   Lovell, Bernard. "The effects of defence science on the advance of astronomy." *Journal for the history of astronomy, 8* (1977), 151-173.

kb1.bl   Blackett, P. M. S. "Tizard and the science of war." *Nature, 185* (1960), 647-653.

cl   Clark, Ronald W. *The rise of the boffins.* London, 1962.

gu   *Gusewelle, Jack Keeney. *The Board of Invention and Research: A case study in the relations between academic science and the Royal Navy in Great Britain during the first world war.* Ph.D. thesis. Univ. of California, Irvine, 1971. (*DAI, 33,* 6340A.)

jo   Jones, R. V. "Temptations and risks of the scientific adviser." *Minerva, 10* (1972), 441-451.

jp   Jones, R. V. *The wizard war: British scientific intelligence, 1939-1945.* NY, 1978. (Published in Britain as *Most Secret War.)*

jq   Jones, R. V. "Alfred Ewing and 'room 40'." RS. *Notes and records, 34* (1979), 65-90.

mc   McGucken, William. "The central organisation of scientific and technical advice in the United Kingdom during the second world war." *Minerva, 17* (1979), 33-69.

st   Strutt, Robert John, Fourth Baron Rayleigh. *Lord Balfour in his relation to science.* Cambridge, 1930.

See also: B.kil.ak; D.ktl.ha, kl

kd1.go   Goudsmit, S. A. "War physics in Germany." *Review of scientific instruments, 17* (1946), 49-52.

la   Lasby, Clarence G. *Project Paperclip: German scientists and the cold war.* NY, 1971.

kf1.am   Amrine, Michael. *The great decision: The secret of the atomic bomb.* Boston, 1950.

an   Anon. "Der Franck-Report." *PB, 20* (1964), 329-334.

ba   Baxter, James Phinney, III. *Scientists against time.* Boston, 1946.

be   Bernstein, Barton J. "Shatterer of worlds, Hiroshima and Nagasaki." *BAS, 31* (Dec. 1975), 12-22.

bl   Bohr, Aage. "The war years and the prospects raised by the atomic weapons." B.bol.ar, 191-214.

bo   Bohr, Niels. "Open letter to the United Nations." B.bol.ar, 340-352.

co   Cohen, I. Bernard. "American physicists at war." *AJP, 13* (1945), 223-235, 333-346.

cp   Compton, Karl T. "If the atomic bomb had not been used." *Atlantic monthly, 178* (Dec. 1946), 54-56.

du   DuBridge, Lee A. "The effects of world war II on the science of physics." *AJP, 17* (1949), 273-281.

dv   Dupree, A. Hunter. "The *Great Instauration* of 1940: The organization of scientific research for war." A.aal.ho, 443-467.

fe   Feis, Herbert. *The atomic bomb and the end of World War II.* Princeton, 1971. (Revision of *Japan subdued: The atomic bomb and the end of the war in the Pacific.* Princeton, 1961.)

fr   Frisch, David H. "Scientists and the decision to bomb Japan."
     BAS, 26 (Jun. 1970), 107-115. (Also in U.gk5.le, 249-270.)

gi   Gilpin, Robert. *American scientists and nuclear weapons policy.*
     Princeton, 1962.

gj   Giovanetti, L., and F. Freed. *The decision to drop the bomb.* NY,
     1965.

kn   Knebel, Fletcher, and Charles Bailey. "The fight over the A-
     bomb: Secret revealed after 18 years." *Look, 27* (13 Aug. 1963),
     22-23.

li   Lilienthal, David E. *Change, hope, and the bomb.* Princeton,
     1963.

ma   Manley, J. H. "Assembling wartime labs." *BAS, 30* (May 1974),
     42-48.

mo   Moorehead, Alan. *The traitors.* NY, 1952.

ne   *Nelson, William Richard. *Case study of a pressure group: The
     atomic scientists.* Ph.D. thesis. Univ. of Colorado, 1965. (*DAI,
     26,* 7424.)

pu   Pursell, Carroll. "Science agencies in World War II: The OSRD
     and its challengers." C.ua1.re, 359-378.

sc   Schoenberger, W. S. *Decision of destiny.* Athens, Ohio, 1969.

sh   *Sherwin, Martin J. *The atomic bomb, scientists and American di-
     plomacy during the second world war.* Ph.D. thesis. Univ. of Cali-
     fornia, Los Angeles, 1971. (*DAI, 33,* 1129A.)

si   Sherwin, Martin J. "The atomic bomb and the origins of the
     cold war: United States atomic-energy policy and diplomacy,
     1941-45." *American historical review, 78* (1973), 945-968.

sj   Sherwin, Martin J. *A world destroyed: The atomic bomb and the
     grand alliance.* NY, 1975.

sk   Sherwin, Martin J. "Niels Bohr and the atomic bomb: The
     scientific ideal and international politics, 1943-1944." A.ad1.we,
     352-369.

sm   Smith, Alice Kimball. "Behind the decision to use the atomic
     bomb: Chicago 1944-1945." *BAS, 14* (Oct. 1958), 288-312.

sn   Smith, Alice Kimball. *A peril and a hope: The atomic scientists'
     movement, 1945-1947.* Chicago, 1965.

st   Steiner, Arthur. "Baptism of the atomic scientists." *BAS, 31*
     (Feb. 1975), 21-28.

su   Steiner, Arthur. "Scientists, statesmen, and politicians: The competing influences on American atomic energy policy, 1945-46." *Minerva, 12* (1974), 469-509.

sw   Strickland, Donald A. *Scientists in politics: The atomic scientists movement, 1945-46.* Lafayette, Ind., 1968.

th   Thomas, Morgan. *Atomic energy and Congress.* Ann Arbor, 1956.

vi   Villa, Brian Loring. "A confusion of signals: James Franck, the Chicago scientists and early efforts to stop the bomb." *BAS, 31* (Dec. 1975), 36-43.

wh   White, Marsh W., and William H. Crew. "Physicists in and following world war II." *AJP, 18* (1950), 487-495.

yo   York, Herbert F. "Sounders of the alarm." *BAS, 31* (Dec. 1975), 43-45.

kh1.be   Beardsley, E. H. "Secrets between friends: Applied science exchange between the western Allies and the Soviet Union during World War II." *SSS, 7* (1977), 447-473.

er   Erickson, John. "Radio-location and the air defence problem: The design and development of Soviet radar, 1934-40." *SSS, 2* (1972), 241-268.

fe   Fedorov, N. G. "Raboty A. N. Krylova v oblasti teorii i proyektirovaniya minnogo oruzhiya." B.kt1.as, 117-123.

io   Ioffe, A. F. "Physics and war." *Science and society, 7* (1943), 193-204.

ka   Kapitsa, P. L. "Science and war." *Science, 95* (1942), 396-398.

ru   Ruggles, Melville J., and Arnold Kramish. *Soviet atomic policy.* Santa Monica, Ca., 1956.

W. PHILOSOPHY OF PHYSICS

See also: The various sections (B.___.k_) on the philosophical thoughts of individual physicists, especially B.ei7 (Einstein) and B.mb2 (Mach); F.f (relativity), K.f (nature of particle), and L.i (Copenhagen interpretation)

General

aa1.am Ambartsumyan, V. A. "Sovremennoye yestestvoznaniye i filosofii." *UFN, 96* (1968), 3-19.

ba Bastin, Ted E. W. *Quantum theory and beyond.* Cambridge, 1971.

ca Čapek, Milič. *The philosophical impact of contemporary physics.* NY, 1961.

cb Čapek, Milič. *Bergson and modern physics: A reinterpretation and re-evaluation.* Dordrecht, 1971. (*BSPS, 7*).

ce Centre International de Synthèse. *L'evolution de la physique et la philosophie.* Paris, 1935.

di Dingle, Herbert. "Philosophical aspects of cosmology." *Vistas in astronomy, 1* (1955), 162-166.

do Dorling, Jon. "Demonstrative induction: Its significant role in the history of physics." *PS, 40* (1973), 360-372.

el Elkana, Yehuda, ed. *The interaction between science and philosophy.* Atlantic Highlands, N. J., 1974.

fe Feigl, Herbert, and Grover Maxwell, eds. *Current issues in the philosophy of science.* NY, 1961. (American Association for the Advancement of Science. Section L. *Proceedings*, 1959.)

fp Frank, Philipp. *Between physics and philosophy.* Cambridge, Mass., 1941.

fr Frank, Philipp. *Modern science and its philosophy.* Cambridge, Mass., 1949.

gu Gunter, Peter A. Y., ed. *Bergson and the evolution of physics.* Knoxville, Tenn., 1969.

he Heidsieck, François. "Bergson et la physique contemporaine." *Revue de métaphysique et de morale, 80* (1975), 528-540.

ku Kuznetsov, B. G. *Razum i bytiye: Etyudy o klassicheskom ratsionalizme i neklassicheskoy nauke.* Moscow, 1972.

li Lindsay, Robert Bruce. *The nature of physics: A physicist's views on the history and philosophy of his science.* Providence, 1968.

ma   Machamer, Peter K., and Robert G. Turnbull, eds. *Motion and time, space and matter. Interactions in the history of philosophy and science.* Columbus, Ohio, 1976.

mi   Mikulinskiy, S. R., and M. G. Yaroshevskiy. *Nauchnoye otkrytiye i yego vospriyatiye.* Moscow, 1971.

se   Sesić, Bogdan. "O nekim epistemoloskim pitanjima fizike i filozofije." *Dijalektika, 1* (1966), 52-72.

so   Sommerfeld, Arnold. "Philosophie und Physik seit 1900." *NR, 1* (1948), 97-100.

ss   Stebbing, E. S. *Philosophy and the physicists.* NY, 1958.

st   Strauss, Martin. *Modern physics and its philosophy.* Dordrecht, 1972.

to   Torretti, Roberto. "Mathematical theories and philosophical insights in cosmology." B.ei4.yn, 320-335

wa   Wahl, J. "Physique et philosophie." *Revue de metaphysique et de morale, 66* (1961), 326-333.

we   Weizsäcker, C. F. von. "Physics and philosophy." A.ad1.me, 736-746.

See also: B.ei7.bt | mb2.ec

ab1.br   Bridgman, Percy W. *The logic of modern physics.* NY, 1927.

fe   Fertig, Hermann. "Die Modellmethode in der Physik." *PB, 30* (1974), 193-203.

go   Gordev, D. I., et al. *Problema razvitiya v sovremennom yestestvoznanii.* Moscow, 1968.

ha   Hanson, Norwood Russell. *Patterns of discovery: An inquiry into the conceptual foundations of science.* Cambridge, 1958.

ho   Howson, Colin, ed. *Method and appraisal in the physical sciences.* Cambridge, 1976.

ko   Kol'man, E. "Ponyatiye 'prostoty' v fiziko - matematicheskikh nauk." ICHS, XIII (1971). Section 1. *Actes* (1974), 80-84.

ma   Margenau, Henry. "Methodology of modern physics." *PS, 2* (1935), 48-72, 164-187. (Also in Margenau. *Physics and philosophy: Selected essays.* Dordrecht, 1978. Pp. 52-89.)

po   Popper, Karl R. *The logic of scientific discovery.* NY, 1961.

sa   Sarangov, Ts. S., and B. I. Spasskiy. "O metode analogiy kak za-
      konomernosti razvitiya fizicheskoy nauki." *IMYeN: Fizika, 10*
      (1971), 15-28.

sh   Shushurin, S. F. "Fizika i kibernetika: K voprosu o gnoseologi-
      cheskom analize metodologii chastnykh nauk." *IMYeN: Fizika, 12*
      (1972), 45-58.

sp   Spasskiy, Boris I., and Ts. S. Sarangov. "Analogii v fizike."
      IMYeN: Fizika, 6 (1968), 231-255.

sq   Spasskiy, Boris I. "Le développement du concept de modèle en
      physique." ICHS, XII (1968). *Actes, 5* (1971), 91-94.

ac1.an AN. Institut filosofii. *Filosofskiye voprosy sovremennoy fiziki.* 2
      vols. Moscow, 1952-58.

fr   Frank, Philipp. *Das Ende der mechanistischen Physik.* Vienna,
      1935. (*Einheitswissenschaft,* 5.)

hu   Hujer, Karel. "Problems in the philosophy of modern physics."
      Physis, 6 (1964), 5-14.

ju   Juhos, Béla. *Die erkenntnislogischen Grundlagen der modernen Phy-
      sik.* Berlin, 1967.

ob   Obchinnikov, N. F. "Ponyatiya massy i energii v sovremennoy
      fizike i ikh filosofskoye znacheniye." W.ac1.an, *1,* 445-488.

pi   Pietschmann, Herbert. "Moderne Physik und Naturphilosophie."
      Philosophia naturalis, 12 (1970), 80-86.

sz   Szumilewicz, Irena. "Postulat mikroredukeji od Lukrecjusza do
      Boltzmanna i Brillouina." *KHNT,* 14 (1969), 15-29.

ad1.bn Born, Max. "Der Realitätsbegriff in der Physik." *Universitas, 13*
      (1958), 927-945.

bo   Born, Max. "Symbol and reality." *Dialectica, 20* (1966), 143-157.

bu   Bunge, Mario. "Physics and reality." *Dialectica, 19* (1965), 195-
      222; *20* (1966), 174-195.

du   Dubarle, D. "Objectivité et réalité dans le cas de la physique pro-
      babiliste." *Dialectica, 20* (1966), 158-173.

ei   Einstein, Albert. "Quanten-Mechanik und Wirklichkeit." *Dialecti-
      ca, 2* (1948), 320-324.

ma   Margenau, Henry. *The nature of physical reality.* NY, 1950.

pa   Palacios, Julio. "Ficción matemática y realidad física." *Atlantida, 1*
      (1963), 642-649.

pc   Pauli, Wolfgang. "Phänomen und physikalische Realität." *Dialec-
      tica, 11* (1957), 36-48. (Also in B.pd3.jb, *2,* 1350-1161.)

pe   Pelseneer, Jean. *L'évolution de la notion de phénomène physique des primitifs à Bohr et Louis de Broglie.* Brussels, 1947.

sc   Schatzman, Evry. "Physique quantique et réalité." *La pensée*, nos. 42-43 (1952), 107-122.

su   Suvorov, S. G. "On the roles of experiment and theory in cognition (comment on the article by Max Born)." *SPU, 1* (1958), 179-190.

sv   Suvorov, S. G. "Opyt i fizicheskaya teoriya." *ES*, 1972, 359-388.

to   Toulmin, Stephen, ed. *Physical reality: Philosophical essays on 20th-century physics.* NY, 1970.

ae1.an   Andelić, Tatomir. "Plank, Ajnstajn i De Brolji o kauzalnosti i determinizmu." *Dijalektika, 1:4* (1966), 81-90.

bo   Born, Max. *Natural philosophy of cause and chance.* Oxford, 1949.

ro   Rosenfeld, Léon. "The evolution of the idea of causality." *BSPS, 21* (1979), 446-464. (In French in Liège. Société Royale des Sciences. *Mémoires, 6* (1945), 57-87.)

Marxist

ba1.ci   Ciccotti, Giovanni, et al. *L'ape e l'architetto. Paradigmi scientifici e materialismo.* Milan, 1976.

gr   Graham, Loren R. *Science and philosophy in the Soviet Union.* NY, 1972.

jo   *Joravsky, David. *Soviet Marxism and the philosophy of natural science, 1922-1929: The rejection of positivism.* Ph.D. thesis. Columbia Univ., 1958. (*DAI, 19*, 125.)

jp   Joravsky, David. *Soviet marxism and natural science, 1917-1932.* London, 1961.

ku   Kuznetsov, I. V., and N. F. Ovchinnikov. "Za posledovatel'noye dialektiko- materialisticheskoye osveshcheniye dostizheniy sovremennoy fiziki." *UFN, 45* (1951), 113-140.

om   *Omel'yanovskiy, M., et al. *L'interpretazione materialistica della meccanica quantistica.* Ed. Silvano Tagliagambe. Milan, 1972.

bb1.bi   Bitsakis, E. I. "Lénine, le matérialisme dialectique et la physique contemporaine." *La pensée*, no. 157 (1971), 43-56; no. 158 (1971), 78-96.

do   Dorfman, Ya. G. "Leninskiy filosovskiy analiz i razvitiye fiziki v XX stoletii." *VIYeT, 30* (1970), 10-19.

ke   *Kedrov, B. M. *Lenin i revolyutsii v yestestvoznanii XX veka.* Moscow, 1969.

ki   Kedrov, B. M. "Prognozy Lenina w dziedzinie przyro-
     doznawstwa." *KHNT, 16* (1971), 287-299.

la   Langevin, Luce. "*Matérialisme et empiriocriticisme* et
     l'enseignement de la physique." *La pensée*, no. 85 (1959), 23-32.

le   Lenin, V. I. *Materialism and empirio-criticism.* [1908]. Lenin. *Col-
     lected works*, 14. Moscow, 1968.

vb   Vavilov, S. I. "Lénine et la physique moderne." *La pensée*, no. 23
     (1949), 27-34.

vc   Vavilov, S. I. "*Materializm i empiriokrititsizm* V. I. Lenina i
     filosofskiye problemy sovremennoy fiziki." AN. *Vestnik*, 1949:6,
     30-39.

vd   Vavilov, S. I. "Lenin i filosofskiye problemy sovremennoy fiziki."
     Velikaya sila idey leninizma. Ed. Ts. A. Stepanyan. Moscow, 1950.
     Pp. 171-186.

ve   *Vavilov, S. I. *Lenin i fizika: Sbornik statey.* Moscow, 1960.

vf   Vavilov, S. I. *Lenin i sovremennaya fizika.* Moscow, 1970. (Ear-
     lier edn tr. as *Lenin and philosophical problems of modern physics.
     Moscow, 1953.)

vi   Vigier, Jean-Pierre. "Quelques problèmes physiques posés par les
     thèses de Lénine." *La pensée*, no. 57 (1954), 60-66.

vn   *Vizgin, V. P. "V. I. Lenin o sostoyanii fiziki na rubezhe XIX i
     XX vv." *VIYeT*, 1980:2, 19-40.

bc1.gr Graham, Loren R. "Quantum mechanics and dialectical material-
     ism." *Slavic review, 25* (1966), 381-410.

la   Labérenne, Paul. "La contribution des savants roumaines à l'
     interprétation matérialiste de la physique moderne." *La pensée*,
     no. 80 (1958), 128-129.

mi   *Mikulak, Maxim William. *Relativity theory and Soviet communist
     philosophy (1922-1960).* Ph.D. thesis. Columbia Univ., 1965.
     (*DAI, 25*, 6002.)

Quantum

ca1.bo Bohr, Niels. "Wirkungsquantum und Naturbeschreibung." *Nwn,
     17* (1929), 483-486.

bp   Bohr, Niels. "Über Erkenntnisfragen der Quantenphysik."
     B.pl1.ik, 169-175.

de   Destouches, J. L. "Über den Begriff der Quantisierung." B.pl1.ik,
     371-384.

fn   Fok, V. A. "Critique épistémologique de théories récentes." *La pensée*, no. 91 (1960), 8-15.

fo   Fok, V. A. "Quantum physics and philosophical problems." *Foundations of physics, 1* (1971), 293-306. (In Russian in **Voprosy filosofii, 4* (1970), 65- .)

fp   Folse, Henry J., Jr. "The Copenhagen interpretation of quantum theory and Whitehead's philosophy of organism." *Tulane studies in philosophy, 23* (1974), 32-47.

hd   Heisenberg, Werner. *Das Plancksche Wirkungsquantum.* Berlin, 1945. (Akademie der Wissenschaften, Berlin. *Vorträge und Schriften*, 21.)

he   Heisenberg, Werner. "Die Plancksche Entdeckung und die philosophischen Grundfragen der Atomlehre." *Nwn, 45* (1958), 227-234. (Also in Max-Planck-Gesellschaft. *Mitteilungen*, 1958, 140-161; in Russian in *UFN, 66* (1958), 163-175.)

jo   Jordan, Pascual. "Die Erfahrungsgrundlagen der Quantentheorie." *Nwn, 17* (1929), 498-507.

pe   Petersen, Aage. *Quantum physics and the philosophical tradition.* Cambridge, Mass., 1968.

sh   Shimoney, Abner. "Quantum physics and the philosophy of Whitehead." *BSPS, 2* (1965), 307-330.

te   Terletskiy, Ya. P. "Problemy razvitiya kvantovoy teorii." W.ac1.an, *1*, 432-444.

we   Weizsäcker, C. F. von. "Classical and quantum descriptions." A.ad1.me, 635-667.

cb1.ha   Hanson, Norwood Russell. "Are wave mechanics and matrix mechanics equivalent theories?" W.aa1.fe, 401-425.

hi   Hill, E. L. "Quantum physics and the relativity theory." W.aa1.fe, 429-441.

lb   Landé, Alfred. *Foundations of quantum theory: A study in continuity and symmetry.* London, 1955.

lc   Landé, Alfred. "Non-quantal foundations of quantum mechanics." *Dialectica, 19* (1965), 349-357.

ld   Landé, Alfred. "Why do quantum theorists ignore the quantum theory?" *BJPS, 15* (1965), 307-313.

le   Landé, Alfred. *New foundations of quantum mechanics.* Cambridge, 1965.

ma   Malisoff, William Marius. "An examination of the quantum theories." *PS, 1* (1934), 71-77, 170-175, 398-408.

mb Margenau, Henry. "Conceptual foundations of the quantum theory." *Science, 113* (1951), 95-101.

su Suppes, Patrick, ed. *Studies in the foundations of quantum mechanics.* East Lansing, Mich., 1980.

cc1.bo Bohr, Niels. "On the notions of causality and complementarity." *Dialectica, 2* (1948), 312-319.

br Broglie, Louis de. "Sur la complémentarité des idées d'individu et de système." *Dialectica, 2* (1948), 325-330.

df Destouches, P. "Manifestation et sens de la notion de complémentarité." *Dialectica, 2* (1948), 383-412.

ff Feyerabend, Paul K. "On a recent critique of complementarity." *PS, 35* (1968), 309-331; *36* (1969), 82-105.

fo Fok, V. A. "Comments." *Slavic review, 25* (1966), 411-413.

go Gonseth, F. "Remarque sur l'idée de complémentarité." *Dialectica, 2* (1948), 413-420.

ro Rosenfeld, Léon. "L'évidence de la complémentarité." B.bw1.ag, 43-65.

rp Rosenfeld, Léon. "Foundations of quantum theory and complementarity." *Nature, 190* (1961), 384-388.

cd1.lb Landé, Alfred. "From dualism to unity in quantum mechanics." *BJPS, 10* (1959), 16-24.

lc Landé, Alfred. *From dualism to unity in quantum physics.* Cambridge, 1960.

ld Landé, Alfred. "Unitary interpretation of quantum theory." *AJP, 29* (1961), 503-507.

le Landé, Alfred. "From duality to unity in quantum mechanics." W.aa1.fe, 350-360.

lf Landé, Alfred. "Dualismus in der Quantentheorie: Eine Entgegung." *Philosophia naturalis, 11* (1969), 395-397.

lg Landé, Alfred. "Einheit in der Quantenwelt (gegen den Bohr-Heisenberg'schen Positivismus)." *Dialectica, 30* (1972), 115-130.

ce1.em Emch, Gérard, and Josef Maria Jauch. "Structures logiques et mathématiques en physique quantique." *Dialectica, 19* (1965), 259-279.

es Espagnat, Bernard d'. "Quantum logic and non-separability." A.ad1.me, 714-735.

fr Frank, Philipp. "The place of logic and metaphysics in the advancement of modern science." *PS, 15* (1948), 275-286.

ga   Gardner, Michael R. "Two deviant logics for quantum theory: Bohr and Reichenbach." *BJPS, 23* (1972), 89-109.

ku   Kuznetsov, B. G. "Puti razvitiya kvantovorelyativistskoy logiki." IIYeT, *Trudy,* 22 (1959), 69-105.

lo   Losee, John. "The use of philosophical arguments in quantum physics." *PS, 31* (1964), 10-17.

we   Weizsäcker, C. F. von. "Komplementarität und Logik: Niels Bohr zum 70. Geburtstag am 7.10.1955 gewidmet." *Nwn, 42* (1955), 521-529, 545-555.

cf1.ba   Balibar, Françoise. "Formalism and interpretation in quantum physics." *Fundamenta scientiae, 1* (1980), 173-181.

bu   Bunge, Mario. "Analogy in quantum theory: From insight to nonsense." *BJPS, 18* (1967), 265-286.

de   Destouches, Jean-Louis. "Aspect dialectique de la notion de système physique." *Dialectica, 11* (1957), 57-69.

fo   Folse, Henry J. "The formal objectivity of quantum mechanical systems." *Dialectica, 29* (1975), 127-145.

re   Reichenbach, Hans. "The principle of anomaly in quantum mechanics." *Dialectica, 2* (1948), 337-350.

cg1.da   Dambska, Izydora. "L'instrument et l'objet de recherche à la lumière de la théorie physique d'après Duhem, Bridgman, et Bohr." ICHS, XII (1968). *Actes, 2* (1970), 25-28.

fr   Frisch, O. R. "The conceptual problem of quantum theory from the experimentalist's point of view." W.aa1.ba, 13-22.

go   Goto, Kunio. "A historical investigation of macroscopic variables in quantum mechanics." ICHS, XIV (1974). *Proceedings, 2* (1975), 253-256.

ma   Margenau, Henry. "Philosophical problems concerning the meaning of measurement in physics." *PS, 25* (1958), 23-33.

cz1.ca   Capra, Fritjof. *The tao of physics. An exploration of the parallels between modern physics and Eastern mysticism.* Berkeley, 1975.

re   Restivo, Sal P. "Parallels and paradoxes in modern physics and Eastern mysticism, I. A critical reconnaissance." *SSS, 8* (1978) 143-181.

Author index

The index notices all authors and editors cited in the bibliography except editors mentioned in entries of the following form:

> Weller, Samuel. "Pickwick and the Hampstead Ponds." *A chrestomathy of Mudfog transactions.* Ed. S. Pecksniff. London, 1850.

Weller would appear in the index, Pecksniff would not. Our computer program is responsible for this discrimination.

Brüche, Ernst: A.bp1.br | bp1.gh |
  ei2.db | lf6.sb | lj3.sb | rb3.cd, cb, gb |
  ru1.bc | sc7.cb, cc | wh3.gb; C.ga3.bq,
  br | ga4.bq, br | ga7.br | gb1.br | gd1.br |
  gj2.bq, br; E.tt1.br; G.ma1.cb;
  I.tg1.br; T.ea1.br | ef1.br, bs;
  U.gg3.cb
Bruggencate, Paul ten: B.se8.bb
Brunner, William: P.ka1.br
Brunt, D: P.fb1.br
Brush, Stephen G: A.bh1.br | cb1.br,
  bs; B.mb2.cc; D.ha1.br | hg1.br, bs,
  bt, bu, bv, bw | hh1.br; F.bd1.br;
  L.id1.bs; O.fc1.bu; P.kc1.br
Bruzzaniti, Giuseppe: I.ba1.bs
Bryksin, V. V: C.va3.br
Bub, Jeffrey: L.ig1.bu
Buber, Martin: U.ef1.bu
Buchdahl, Gerd: B.cb4.kc
Buchheim, Wolfgang: T.aa1.bu
Buchwald, Eberhard: A.bb1.bu;
  B.ko1.gb | lt3.cb | so1.gc; C.ga4.bu
Buck, Barbara R: C.ia1.bu
Buckel, Werner: A.pe1.bu
Buckley, Oliver F: B.iv1.eb
Buckley, Paul: A.aj1.bu
Büchel, W: F.fd1.bu
Büdel, Julius: P.aa1.bu
Bühler, Karl: B.ei7.qb
Bugge, G: R.ab1.bu
Buhl, A: B.ap1.ed, gd
Bullard, Edward: B.ew3.eb
Bunge, Mario: B.ru1.ae; L.ih1.bu;
  W.ad1.bu | cf1.bu
Burbidge, Geoffrey: P.ka1.bu
Burbidge, Margret: P.ka1.bu
Burcham, W. E: B.ru1.bd
Burchardt, Lothar: C.gb4.bu; U.gg1.bu
Burckhardt, Carl J: B.hh1.ib
Burckhardt, J. J: B.ff1.jf
Burdick, C. L: G.ma1.hu
Burdowicz-Nowicka, Maria: B.cv1.cg
Burgers, W. G: O.fd1.bu
Burke, John Butler: I.ba1.bv
Burrill, E. Alfred: B.gr1.bd
Burton, E. F: B.ru1.eb
Burton, Milton: I.cb1.bu
Busemann, A: B.pr1.eb
Bush, Vannevar: B.by4.ac; U.gk1.bu,
  bv

Butler, William H: O.da1.al
Butt, D. K: I.ca1.be
Buynitskiy, V. Kh: P.fd1.bu
Byerly, Perry: P.ba1.by
Byers, Horace: P.fc1.by
Bykhovskiy, B. E: U.ba1.by
Bykov, G. V: E.bb1.bw, by; R.bc1.bw,
  bx
Bykova-Orlova, Ye. G: C.vb2.by

Cabannes, Jean: B.pf3.ec
Cafiero, Luca: B.mb1.jd
Cajori, Florian: A.ab1.ca
Calbick, C. J: E.bg1.ca
Caldirola, Piero: A.ah1.ca; D.hb1.ca;
  H.cg1.ca; L.fa1.ca
California. University of, Berkeley:
  A.ad1.un
Caloi, P: P.aa1.ca
Calvo-Hernando, Manuel: B.ok1.sf
Cameron, Alastair G. W: P.ie1.ca
Cameron, Frank: C.ua5.ca
Cameron, Neil: A.ae1.ca
Campbell, Norman Robert: C.bc1.ca
Cap, Ferdinand: B.mf1.ec
Čapek, Milič: B.mb2.mc; F.fe1.ca;
  W.aa1.ca, cb
Capra, Fritjof: W.cz1.ca
Carathéodory, C: B.hm1.eo
Carazza, B: L.ed1.ca
Cardani, Pietro: B.rh7.ee
Cardwell, D. S. L: C.bm2.ca; U.ba1.ca
Carelli, Antonio: A.af1.ca
Carman, Robert L: T.eg1.ca
Caroe, Gwendolyn N: B.bs1.ac, cc, jk
Carrington, A: B.ae8.ec
Carruthers, P: G.qa1.ca
Cartan, Elie: B.ei6.fc
Carter, Luther J: C.uw2.ca
Cartwright, D. E: B.pt1.ec
Carus, Paul: B.mb1.jf
Casagrande, Federico: E.ba1.ca
Casals, Pablo: B.ei4.ps
Casimir, Hendrik Bruygt Gerhart:
  A.af1.cb; B.cc1.cc, ce | kq1.bc | lp8.cc;
  O.aa1.ca | hb1.ca | hc1.ca; U.ab1.ca
Cassidy, David C: B.ei6.as | hh1.bc,
  bd; C.gb3.cb; L.db1.ca
Castro, Barry: U.ba1.cc

Davydova, L. G: E.tb1.so
Day, C. R: C.fa1.da
Day, Joanne S: T.ga1.da
Day, John A: R.cb1.da
De, M. L: T.ef1.gu
Deacon, G. E. R: B.pg2.ed
Debye, Peter: A.af1.de; B.df1.jd |
  fd1.gd | so1.id; D.be1.de; G.la1.de;
  L.bb1.de; O.fc1.de
Decker, Fred W: T.ea1.de
Dee, P. I: B.ru1.cn | wr3.jd
Dehn, M: B.hm1.be
Dejean, Maurice: B.cv3.cf
DeKosky, Robert Keith: B.cu1.bd;
  G.ea1.de
Delokarov, K. Kh: F.fa1.de | fd1.de, df
Delone, B. N: B.ff1.bd | mr5.ce
Delorme, Albert: B.ei2.fd
Dennison, David M: B.dh1.cd | le3.ec
Derenzini, Tullio: B.fg1.jg
Derrick, M: T.gb4.de
Deryagin, B. V: B.lg6.cc, cd; O.db1.de;
  P.mb1.de
Derzhavin, A. N: B.lh3.ci
Derzhavin, N: A.cd1.de
Destouches, Jean-Louis: B.bw1.ch;
  K.fa1.de; L.eb1.de; W.ca1.de | cf1.de
Destouches, P: W.cc1.df
Deutsch, Martin: B.di9.cd; K.ab1.de
Devik, Olaf: B.bj1.cb, ed | su9.ed
Devons, Samuel: B.ru1.bf
DeVorkin, David H: P.hb1.de, df |
  ib1.de
Dewitt, Bryce S: L.ia1.df
DeWitt, Nicholas: U.gm1.de
Dibner, Bern: G.la1.dh, di
Dick, Auguste: U.gg3.pi
Dicke, Robert Henry: D.bg1.di;
  F.dg1.ro
Dickel, G: I.df1.di; L.fb1.di; R.ah1.di |
  dh1.di
Diebner, Kurt: I.tg1.ba
Dieke, Gerhart Heinrich: B.wt3.ed
Dieminger, Walter: B.zf8.ed
Diepert, Randall R: B.mb2.od
Dijkstra, D. W: B.jc1.bd
Dikarev, A. V: C.vr2.ko
Dillon, Ya. G: B.rk7.cf
Dimarova, E. N: O.bc1.di
Dingle, Herbert: B.dj7.jd | eb1.ke |

ei5.ls | fo1.ed; E.az1.di; F.ad1.di, dj |
  bc1.di; G.ea1.di; W.aa1.di
Dingler, Hugo: A.af1.df, dg | ah1.di;
  B.mb1.ee | mb2.kg | wf3.bd | ze4.bd
Dingwall, E. J: B.cu1.af
Dinze, O. V: B.kt1.jm
Dirac, Paul Adrian Maurice: A.ah1.dj |
  ba1.di, dj; B.bo1.bd | dk1.cd, ce |
  li6.bd; E.be1.di | bh1.di, dj, dk;
  F.de1.di; L.aa1.di
Disney, M. J: P.hf1.co
Ditchburn, R. W: B.to3.ed
Dobiash, A. A: B.kg8.gd
Dobretsov, L. N: B.ls3.ed
Dobronravin, P. P: B.si6.ed, ee, jm
Dobrotin, Nikolay Alexeyevich:
  B.vf4.gd; K.cb1.vf
Dobrotin, R. B: B.hp1.ad
Dobrovol'skiy, O. V: B.um1.ad
Dodge, Homer Levi: B.dk9.pd
Dolch, Heimo: B.hh1.cd
Donini, Elisabetta: C.ga2.do, dp |
  ua2.do, dp
Donnan, Frederick George: B.cj1.ed |
  gh1.bd | hp1.ed | of1.ed
Doran, Barbara Jean Giusti: E.ad1.do
Dorfman, Yakov Grigor'yevich:
  A.bc1.do | ca1.do | da1.do; B.fr1.eg |
  lc3.cg; C.vs2.do; E.ma1.do | mc1.do;
  W.bb1.do
Dorling, Jon: F.cb1.do; G.qa1.do;
  W.aa1.do
Dorodnitsyn, A. A: B.kl8.jm
Dorozynski, Alexander: B.la8.ak
Dorsay, N. Ernst: B.all.eg
Dougal, R. C: L.ba1.do
Douglas, Allie Vibert: B.eb1.ad, bd |
  ei4.kv
Dovgar', V. A: P.hf1.iv
Dower, J. W: I.tj1.do
Dragoni, Giorgio: I.cc1.dr | de1.dr
Draper, Wanetta W: B.te3.ah
Drell, Sidney D: K.fa1.dr
Dresden, Max: A.pe1.dr
Drury, Betty: U.gb2.du
Druyveteyn, M. J: B.dm1.ed
Dryden, Hugh L: B.kd1.bd, be, ed, ee
Drysdale, N: C.gh1.dr
Dubarle, D: W.ad1.du
Dubchak, V. A: L.fa1.ko; O.ac1.du |
  bc1.ko

Evers, G. A: B.rk7.ch
Evladov, V: C.ve2.ev
Evola, J: U.gg3.ev
Ewald, Peter Paul: B.es1.ce | lf6.ce, ee | so1.ce; C.gm1.ew; G.ma1.ew, ex, ey, ez; O.fb1.et, eu, ev
Ewing, Galen W: R.at1.ew
Ewing, James Alfred: B.hs1.ce | pb7.ee
Exner, Franz: B.mb1.ei
Eykhenval'd, Aleksandr Aleksandrovich: B.ey1.je
Eyring, Dean Henry: D.da1.ey
Ezawa, Hiroshi: L.fe1.ez

Fabelinskiy, I. L: B.lb6.en; G.ha1.fa
Fabian, Hans-Georg: I.sa1.fa
Fabrikant, Valentin Aleksandrovich: B.lb6.pf; E.bg1.fa; G.ba1.fa | pa1.da
Fabry, Charles: B.pe7.ef
Fagen, Mortimer D: C.ua3.fa, fb
Fainbaum, Iosif: B.kc1.gf | ru1.pf
Fajans, Kasimir: B.hb1.cf; I.ab1.fa | bc1.fa
Falkenberg, Dietrich: I.bb1.fa
Falkenhagen, H: R.dc1.fa
Faltheiner, Otmar: G.ma1.fa
Farber, Eduard: A.pd1.fa; B.mt1.kf; R.ab1.fa
Farr, C. Coleridge: B.ru1.ef; P.ca1.fa
Farren, W. S: B.tn3.ef
Favrholdt, David: B.bo1.ke
Fayerman, G. P: B.kq4.cf
Faynboym, I. V: B.jj1.af
Feather, Norman: A.ad1.fe; B.cd1.em | ru1.ak, cp, cq, jo | wk3.ef; I.bg1.fe; K.ac1.fe, ff
Fedorov, N. G: U.kh1.fe
Feigl, Herbert: W.aa1.fe
Feinberg, Gerald: B.ei2.he
Feinberg, J. G: H.aa1.fe
Feis, Herbert: U.kf1.fe
Fekete, Jenö: D.bg1.pf; P.aa1.fe
Feld, Bernard T: B.ei9.cb
Feofilov, Petr Petrovich: B.va4.bd, bf, bt, ce; E.td1.fe; G.ba1.fe | pa1.te
Fereira, Ricardo: B.mw1.ff
Ferguson, Allan: B.lo8.eg | pl1.kf
Fermi, Enrico: B.cm4.ef | fg1.jj, jk; C.un1.fe; E.tc1.fe; T.ei1.fe

Fermi, Laura: B.fg1.af, nf; U.gb1.fe | gb2.fe | gk5.fe
Fernandez, Carlos Graef: B.ei5.mv
Fernbach, Sidney: B.tc3.im
Ferraz, J. de Sampaio: C.la1.fe
Fertig, Hermann: W.ab1.fe
Fesenkov, Vasiliy Grigor'yevich: C.vr2.fe; P.ie1.fe
Feshbach, H: B.we6.is
Fessenden, Helen May: B.fh1.af
Feuer, Lewis S: B.ei1.ef | mb1.df; F.bf1.fe
Feyerabend, Paul K: B.ei7.gm; L.if1.fe; W.cc1.ff
Feynberg, Yevgeniy L'vovich: B.ta3.cf, gg, gh, pg | va4.nf
Feynman, Richard P: I.tb1.ff; L.hc1.fe
Fierz, Markus: B.pd3.if
Figurovskiy, N. A: A.cb1.iv; B.at1.as | jj1.cf, ek; C.va1.fi | va2.fh; I.ac1.zc | sa1.za; P.da1.za
Filatova, L. A: C.va2.gr
Filner, Robert Earl: U.gd1.fi, fj
Finashnaya, G. N: B.an1.ap
Findlay, Alexander: B.dj1.cf; R.aa1.fi
Fine, Arthur: B.ei2.hf
Finetti, Bruno de: B.ei2.if
Finis, Francesco de: B.ei4.yd
Finlay, G. R: T.eo1.fi
Finlay-Freundlich, Erwin: B.ei9.mf
Finn, Bernard S: E.bd1.fi
Finzi, B: A.ah1.fi
Fiodorov, Aleksandr S: C.va2.fi | va3.fi
Firsov, G. A: D.tc1.fi
Firth, Ian: G.pa1.fi
Fisher, M. E: B.og1.el
Fishman, Walda Katz: U.be1.fi
Fitch, Val L: I.tc1.fi
FitzGerald, George F: B.fi1.jf
Flamm, D: B.bo4.ch
Flamm, Ludwig: B.bo4.cf, cg, gf | mc1.ef | se1.ef | sl6.ef | tf3.gf
Flammersfeld, A: I.eb1.fl
Flechtner, Hans-Joachim: U.da1.du
Fleck, Alexander: B.sn2.ef
Fleischmann, Rudolf: B.br1.ef; I.ca1.fl
Fleming, Arthur P. M: B.te3.bf, cf
Fleming, C. A: B.mf7.ef
Fleming, Donald: P.ma1.fl; U.gb2.fl
Fleming, John Ambrose: B.fj4.af, ag |

Friedman, Robert Marc: B.bj1.af
Friedrich, A: C.ga2.ft
Friedrich, Walther: B.rk7.ef; G.ma1.fr
Friesen, Sten von: C.su1.fr
Frisch, David H: U.kf1.fr
Frisch, Otto R: B.fu1.af | mk1.ef, if;
 I.cd1.fr, fs | da1.fr | ef1.fr | tc1.fr, fs;
 W.cg1.fr
Frish, Sergey Eduardovich: B.ro7.af,
 ag, cf, cg; C.vl2.fr; G.ca4.fr | ea1.fr |
 ea2.fr | ha1.fr, te; H.cf1.fr
Frölich, Herbert: O.aa1.fr
Frost, E. B: B.sd1.ef
Fuchs, Franz: C.gm2.fu
Fünfer, E: B.ah1.bf
Fues, Erwin: B.bp1.ge; L.dc1.fu
Fueter, Rudolf: B.ri3.ef
Fukushima, Y: C.ja1.fu
Furtmüller, Lux: U.gg3.pj

G., I. S: G.ca6.fi
Gabor, Dennis: B.bw1.ck | jb1.eg |
 mk9.eh; G.da6.ga
Gaede, Hannah: B.gb1.ag
Gale, George: K.fb1.ga
Galinsky, M. David: U.bc1.ga
Galison, Peter Louis: B.mr5.bg
Gal'pern, D. Yu: G.ca4.ga | da1.ga
Gamow, George: A.ad1.ga; B.bo1.ch |
 ei4.ea | gc1.ag; I.aa1.ga; K.ad1.ga |
 ad1.ga
Gans, Richard: E.ma1.ga
Gaponov-Grekhov, A. V: D.cd1.ga
Garbasso, Antonio: U.cc1.ga
Garbedian, H. Gordon: B.ei1.gd
Garber, Elizabeth: L.ac1.ga
Gardner, Michael R: F.fa1.ga;
 W.ce1.ga
Garin, G: B.rk7.cj
Garvy, George: B.ei9.cm
Garwin, Richard: K.bb1.ga
Gasman, L. D: G.ma1.ga
Gaston, Jerry Collins: A.bb1.ga;
 U.bc1.gb
Gauld, Alan: B.lo8.ag
Gause, Hans: G.da1.gb
Gavin, William: B.st2.ag
Gavrilov, A. F: B.fs1.jg
Gay, Hannah: R.cc1.ga

Gayduk, Yu. M: C.vu3.ga
Gaysinskaya, L. I: A.ce1.ga
Gaysinskiy, M: B.cv3.bf
Gaytner, D. B: E.ba1.ga
Geake, J. E: B.ru1.bg
Geddes, Patrick: B.bq1.ag
Geguzin, Ya. Ye: C.vu2.ge
Geheniau, Jules: B.ei2.lg
Gehlhoff, Georg: B.wa6.pg
Gehrcke, Ernst: B.lt3.cg | wa6.cg
Gehrenbeck, Richard Keith: E.bg1.gf,
 gg
Geiger, Hans: B.ru1.cr, eg, eh
Geitel, Hans: I.ba1.el
Gentile, Giovanni, Jr: B.gf4.jg
Gentner, W: I.rd1.ge
George, André: B.bw1.ag, cn | pl1.ci
George, J: B.wc3.eg
Gerasimova, Ya. I: R.ad1.ge
Gerber, Johannes: L.ea1.ge
Gerding, H: B.sm5.gg
Gerhards, Karl: B.mb2.ng
Gerlach, Walther: B.ei4.eg | hb1.eg, ei,
 ek, em, gc | hi1.gg | mm1.gg | pc3.gg |
 pl1.ad, ck | rd3.eg | rk7.bg, cl | sq3.eg;
 C.gm1.ge; G.ka1.ge | la1.ge; H.ca1.ge;
 I.cd1.ge; K.dd1.ge; T.ec1.ge | ee1.ge
German, S: P.bg1.ge
Germany. Reichstudentenführer:
 B.lj3.sr
Germer, Lester H: E.bg1.gh
Gernet, M. M: F.dg1.ge
Gershtein, S. S: B.zf3.gg
Getman, F. D: B.lg6.cg
Geyvish, Yu. G: B.lc3.ag, kg, kh
Ghimesan, S: B.lc3.ah
Ghiorso, Albert: I.cc1.gh
Giaever, Ivar: O.hb1.gi
Giannarás, Anastasios: B.ho1.gg
Giannoni, Carlo: F.be1.gi
Giauque, William Francis: B.ll8.cg
Giazanov, V. N: B.te3.ch
Gibbs, J. Willard: B.gh1.jg, ji
Gibson, A. H: D.ec1.gi
Giedgmin, Jerzy: B.pm3.kg
Gill, F: B.hg1.eg
Gillespie, E. S: B.re7.cg
Gillmor, C. Stewart: P.fc1.gi
Gilpin, Robert: U.ge1.gi | kf1.gi
Ginsberg, D. M: O.hb1.gm, gn

Schimank, Hans: B.hn1.cs│nk1.bt│
rk7.do
Schimming, Rainer: F.de1.sc
Schinz, H. R: B.rk7.dp
Schlapp, R: B.bp1.ek
Schlegel, Richard: L.eb1.sc; P.kc1.sc
Schlesinger, G: B.bt7.ks
Schlicker, Wolfgang: C.ga6.sc
Schlüter, A: B.ah1.bf
Schmid, Roswitha: U.da1.wb
Schmidt, Egon: A.ac1.sc
Schmidt, F: C.gh1.sc; G.la1.sc
Schmidt, Gerhardt Karl: B.hn1.as, ct
Schmutzer, Ernst: A.ba1.sc; L.aa1.sc
Schneider, Erich: A.pd1.sc
Schneider, Friedrich: B.pu3.cs
Schönbeck, Charlotte: B.lj3.jk;
C.gk5.sc
Schoenberg, D: B.lp2.es
Schoenberger, W. S: U.kf1.sc
Schöpf, Hans-Georg: B.ei4.rv;
G.fa2.sh
Schofield, Roy: A.bg1.sc; B.ei3.ks
Scholz, G: C.gp1.sc
Schonland, Basil F. J: B.bi3.es;
H.aa1.sc
Schopper, H: B.hq1.cs
Schreus, Hans Theo: B.rk7.as;
G.la1.sh
Schroeder-Gudehus, Brigitte:
U.gb1.sc, sd, se, sf│ggl.sc, sd
Schrödinger, Erwin: B.se1.ks; L.ea1.sc;
U.aa1.sc
Schröter, Fritz: E.te1.sc
Schubert, G: I.tg1.st
Schück, H: A.pc1.sc
Schütz, Wilhelm: K.dd1.sc
Schufle, J. A: H.ab1.sc
Schultz, Betty: B.bo1.js
Schultz, Julius August Heinrich:
U.ce1.sc
Schultze, G. R: B.bp1.gh
Schulz-DuBois, E. O: A.pe1.kl
Schumacher, H. J: R.ag1.sc
Schurmann, Paul F: B.ei5.tk
Schuster, Arthur: A.ae1.sc; B.go1.es│
ln8.es│qu1.es│se4.as│st2.es
Schwahn, Duane H: U.bd1.si
Schwartz, H. M: F.ba1.sd│be1.sc, sd│
bg1.sc

Schwartz, L: I.eb1.sc
Schwartz, Melvin: K.ad1.sc
Schweidler, Egon von: B.ex1.es;
G.qa1.sc
Schwerte, Hans: A.aj1.sc
Schwinger, Julian: B.sf5.js; I.ed1.sc;
L.hc1.sc
Sciama, Dennis W: P.ka1.sc, sd
Sciascia, Leonardo: B.md4.as
Scislowski, W: B.bil.es
Scott, O. C. A: B.gr7.el
Scott, William Taussig: B.se1.as;
P.fc1.st
Scotts, Linda F: B.ei6.yp
Scribner, Charles, Jr: F.be1.se
Seaborg, Glenn T: B.ei3.mc│ok1.br,
bs│sf9.js; I.cc1.sc, sd, se, sf, sg
Seabrook, William B: B.wt3.as, at
Seaman, Francis: B.mb2.cs, os;
F.fe1.se
Seamans, Robert C., Jr: B.dn5.eh
Seares, F. H: B.hc1.ss
Sechenov, I. M: B.sg5.as, js
Séclet-Riou, Mme. F: B.lc3.pr
Sedov, L. I: B.lm3.es
Seeger, Alfred Karl: O.fd1.se, sf
Seeger, Raymond J: B.mb2.ae, fs;
U.cc1.se
Seeley, D: P.icl.se
Seelig, Carl: B.ei1.ps, pt, pu, pw│
ei4.ns
Seely, Daniel: P.hd1.be
Segrè, Emilio: A.ad1.se, sf│ag1.se, sf;
B.aj5.gs│fg1.au, bs, cu│sq3.es;
C.ia1.se; H.ga1.se; I.ca1.se│de1.se;
K.ac1.se, sf
Seidel, Robert W: C.ua2.se│ucl.he,
se, sf; U.gk1.ma
Seitz, Frederick: B.rj7.eg│sh3.se│
wp3.gs
Selby, F. J: B.gj1.es
Semenchenko, V. K: B.bn1.cs│gh1.bs;
H.gb1.sf
Semenov, N. N: B.sh5.js
Semenova, N. M: B.zh3.js
Sen, Samarendra Nath: B.sb2.at
Serber, Robert: B.ok1.br, bs
Serdyukov, A. R: B.lh3.bp, js;
C.vm3.se; E.td1.se
Servos, John W: C.uc2.se; R.ae1.se